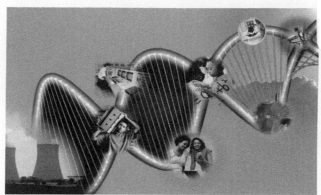

# TECHNOLOGY & SOCIETY

*Making Connections between Social Systems
and Interpersonal Relationships*

4th Edition

DANIELLE JACKSON

MARCELLA GEMELLI

Mc
Graw
Hill
Education

2 3 4 5 6 7 8 9 0 SCI SCI 18 17 16

ISBN-13: 978-1-259-88926-4
ISBN-10: 1-259-88926-2

*Solutions Program Manager: Joyce Berendes*
*Project Manager: Tina Bower*
*Cover Photo Credits: © Hemera Technologies*

# Contents

# Introduction

Technology plays a significant role in our everyday lives. Individually, we use technological inventions to clothe, feed, and shelter us; we use technology to keep us warm and cool. We use technological innovation to transport us from our homes to work and to various countries and cities around the world; we can even "visit" a new country via our computers without ever leaving our home. We use technologies to stay connected to our communities and for entertainment. Undeniably, technology is embedded in our everyday lives defining who we are and how we see the world.

Yet, technologies are more than specific inventions influencing individual identity and behavior. Technological innovation, development, and application are embedded in our social systems, which is why we must consider the social relationships, social practices, norms, and values of a society. Technology and society are intertwined composing a complex relationship that spans history to our future.

This book was created to enlighten the reader on the many ways technology is built into our individual lives and social systems. The composition and arrangement of the sections demonstrate a variety of relevant issues that illustrate our connections with technology. Certainly, the topics covered in this book are by no means exhaustive, as the relationship between technology and society encompasses much more than can be captured in one book. However, the compiled readings were deliberately chosen to elucidate how technology is embedded in our personal relationships with one another, with our work, our health, our political and educational systems, our national security, individual privacy, and our future. We believe these topics are representative of an interdisciplinary focus designed specifically for students who take Technology and Society courses. Students and other readers are invited to critically examine the issues set forth here, as well as to extrapolate learned knowledge into other areas shaping our technological lives.

# Theories of Technology and Society

Since the beginning of time, individuals have modified their lives through the use of technology as a way to find viable solutions to everyday problems. The history of technology involves the development and accomplishments of scientific endeavors, corresponding with the evolutionary process of human progress. As our needs have seemingly become more complex, so have our technologies. The evolution of technology has given us artifacts such as the printing press, the pencil, a door hinge, a bicycle, while also providing us with access to knowledge and information with smartphones and Google. From fire to Facebook, technological innovation is dependent on human needs and desires. Furthermore, throughout history, technology has been informed by such social systems as politics and business. Would the steam engine or the computer have become a reality had it not been for the capacity of human imagination or the economic investment of an idea? The history of technology informs us of where we have been and what is possible moving forward.

Broadly, theory helps us understand our complex world by evaluating social realities, relationships, and systems. Technological theories provide foundational explanations that explore the role of technology in our everyday lives. They help us understand how and why technological development takes place and the impact it has on our relationships, institutions, industry, and politics. Does society shape technology or does technology shape society? In other words, do we as society and individuals dictate what technology is developed, or does technology drive our behavior? Is the development of technology driven by social and political forces, does it cause unalterable social changes, or do we as humans guide the conception and use of technology? The theories of technology and society presented in this section attempt to answer these complex questions.

## Learning Objectives

1. Distinguish among the different theories of technological development such as technological momentum, social constructionism, and technological determinism.
2. Identify positive and negative attributes of the different theories of technological development.
3. Through the various theories, analyze how technological change impacts our everyday lives.

# Do Machines Make History?

The hand-mill gives you society with the feudal lord; the steam-mill, society with the industrial capitalist.

**Marx, *The Poverty of Philosophy***

That machines make history in some sense—that the level of technology has a direct bearing on the human drama—is of course obvious. That they do not make all of history, however that word be defined, is equally clear. The challenge, then, is to see if one can say something systematic about the matter, to see whether one can order the problem so that it becomes intellectually manageable.

To do so calls at the very beginning for a careful specification of our task. There are a number of important ways in which machines make history that will not concern us here. For example, one can study the impact of technology on the political course of history, evidenced most strikingly by the central role played by the technology of war. Or one can study the effect of machines on the social attitudes that underlie historical evolution: one thinks of the effect of ratio or television on political behavior. Or one can study technology as one of the factors shaping the changeful content of life from one epoch to another: when we speak of "life" in the Middle Ages or today we define an existence much of whose texture and substance is intimately connected with the prevailing technological order.

None of these problems will form the focus of this essay. Instead, I propose to examine the impact of technology on history in another area—an area defined by the famous quotation from Marx that stands beneath our title. The question we are interested in, then, concerns the effect of technology in determining the nature of the socioeconomic order. In its simplest terms the question is: did medieval technology bring about feudalism? Is industrial technology the necessary and sufficient condition for capitalism? Or, by extension, will the technology of the computer and the atom constitute the ineluctable cause of a new social order?

Prof. Heilbroner, of the New School for Social Research, is the author of *The Worldly Philosophers, The Limits of American Capitalism*, and other books dealing with economic theory and development.

Even in this restricted sense, our inquiry promises to be broad and sprawling. Hence, I shall not try to attach it head-on, but to examine it in two stages:

1. If we make the assumption that the hand-mill does "give" us feudalism and the steam-mill capitalism, this places technological change in the position of a prime mover of social history. Can we then explain the "laws of motion" of technology itself? Or to put the question less grandly, can we explain why technology evolves in the sequence it does?
2. Again, taking the Marxian paradigm at face value, exactly what do we mean when we assert that the hand-mill "gives us" society with the feudal lord? Precisely how does the mode of production affect the superstructure of social relationships?

These questions will enable us to text the empirical content—or at least to see if there is an empirical content—in the idea of technological determinism. I do not think it will come as a surprise if I announce now that we will find *some* content, and a great deal of missing evidence, in our investigation. What will remain then will be to see if we can place the salvageable elements of the theory in historical perspective—to see, in a word, if we can explain technological determinism historically as well as explain history by technological determinism.

## I

We begin with a very difficult question hardly rendered easier by the fact that there exist, to the best of my knowledge, no empirical studies on which to base our speculations. It is the question of whether there is a fixed sequence to technological development and therefore a necessitous path over which technologically developing societies must travel.

I believe there is such a sequence—that the steam-mill follows the hand-mill not by chance but because it is the next "stage" in a technical conquest of nature that follows one and only one grand avenue of advance. To put it differently, I believe that it is impossible to proceed to the age of the steam-mill until one has passed through the age of the hand-mill, and that in turn one cannot move to the age of the hydroelectric plant before one has mastered the steam-mill, nor to the nuclear power age until one has lived through that of electricity.

Before I attempt to justify so sweeping an assertion, let me make a few reservations. To begin with, I am fully conscious that not all societies are interested in developing a technology of production or in channeling to it the same quota of social energy. I am very much aware of the different pressures that different societies exert on the direction in which technology unfolds. Lastly, I am not unmindful of the difference between the discovery of a given machine and its application as a technology—for example, the invention of a steam engine (the aeolipile) by Hero of Alexandria long before its incorporation into a steam-mill. All these problems, to which we will return in our last section, refer however to the way in which technology makes its peace with the social, political, and economic institutions of the society in which it appears. They do not directly affect the contention that there exists a determinate sequence of productive technology for those societies that are interested in originating and applying such a technology.

What evidence do we have for such a view? I would put forward three suggestive pieces of evidence:

## 1. The Simultaneity of Invention

The phenomenon of simultaneous discovery is well known.[1] From our view, it argues that the process of discovery takes place along a well-defined frontier of knowledge rather than in grab-bag fashion. Admittedly, the concept of "simultaneity" is impressionistic,[2] but the related phenomenon of technological "clustering" again suggests that technical evolution follows a sequential and determinate rather than random course.[3]

## 2. The Absence of Technological Leaps

All inventions and innovations, by definition, represent an advance of the art beyond existing base lines. Yet, most advances, particularly in retrospect, appear essentially incremental, evolutionary. If nature makes no sudden leaps, neither, it would appear, does technology. To makes my point by exaggeration, we do do not find experiments in electricity in the year 1500, or attempts to extract power from the atom in the year 1700. On the whole, the development of the technology of production presents a fairly smooth and continuous profile rather than one of jagged peaks and discontinuities.

## 3. The Predictability of Technology

There is a long history of technological prediction, some of it ludicrous and some not.[4] What is interesting is that the development of technical progress has always seemed *intrinsically* predictable. This does not mean that we can lay down future timetables of technical discovery, nor does it rule out the possibility of surprises. Yet I venture to state that many scientists would be willing to make *general* predictions as to the nature of technological capability twenty-five or even fifty years ahead. This too suggests that technology follows a developmental sequence rather than arriving in a more chancy fashion.

I am aware, needless to say, that these bits of evidence do not constitute anything like a "proof" of my hypothesis. At best they establish the grounds on which a prima facie case of plausibility may be rested. But I should like now to strengthen these grounds by suggesting two deeper-seated reasons why technology *should* display a "structured" history.

The first of these is that a major constraint always operates on the technological capacity of an age, the constraint of its accumulated stock of available knowledge. The application of this knowledge may lag behind its reach; the technology of the hand-mill, for example, was by no means at the frontier of medieval technical knowledge, but technical realization can hardly precede what men generally know (although experiment may incrementally advance both technology and knowledge concurrently). Particularly from the mid-nineteenth century to the present do we sense the loosening constraints on technology stemming from successively yielding barriers of scientific knowledge—loosening constraints that result in the successive arrival of the electrical, chemical, aeronautical, electronic, nuclear, and space stages of technology.[5]

---

[1] See Robert K. Merton, "Singletons and Multiples in Scientific Discovery: A Chapter in the Sociology of Science," *Proceedings* of the American Philosophical Society, CV (October 1961), 470–86.

[2] See John Jewkes, David Sawers, and Richard Stillerman, *The Sources of Invention* (New York, 1960 [paperback edition]), p. 227, for a skeptical view.

[3] "One can count 21 basically different means of flying, at least eight basic methods of geophysical prospecting; four ways to make uranium explosive: ... 20 or 30 ways to control birth. ... If each of these separate inventions were autonomous, i.e., without cause, how could one account for their arriving in these functional groups?" S. C. Gilfillan, "Social Implications of Technological Advance," *Current Sociology*, I (1952), 197. See also Jacob Schmookler, "Economic Sources of Inventive Activity," *Journal of Economic History* (March 1962), pp. 1–20; and Richard Nelson. "The Economics of Invention: A Survey of the Literature," *Journal of Business*, XXXII (April 1959), 101–19.

[4] Jewkes et al. (see n. 2) present a catalogue of chastening mistakes (p. 230 f.). On the other hand, for a sober predictive effort, see Francis Bello, "The 1960s: A Forecast of Technology," *Fortune*, LIX (January 1959), 74–78: and Daniel Bell, "The Study of the Future," *Public Interest*, I (Fall 1965), 119–30. Modern attempts at prediction project likely avenues of scientific advance or technological function rather than the feasibility of specific machines.

[5] To be sure, the inquiry now regresses one step and forces us to ask whether there are inherent stages for the expansion of knowledge, at least insofar as it applies to nature. This is very uncertain question. But having already risked so much, I will hazard the suggestion that the roughly parallel sequential development of scientific understanding in those few cultures that have cultivated it (mainly classical Greece, China, the high Arabian culture, and the West since the Renaissance) makes such a hypothesis possible, provided that one looks to broad outlines and not to inner detail.

The gradual expansion of knowledge is not, however, the only order-bestowing constraint on the development of technology. A second controlling factor is the material competence of the age, its level of technical expertise. To make a steam engine, for example, requires not only some knowledge of the elastic properties of steam but the ability to cast iron cylinders of considerable dimensions with tolerable accuracy. It is one thing to produce a single steam-machine as an expensive toy, such as the machine depicted by Hero, and another to produce a machine that will perienced power economically and effectively. The difficulties experienced by Watt and Boulton in achieving a fit of piston to cylinder illustrate the problems of creating a technology, in contrast with a single machine.

Yet until a metal-working technology was established–indeed, until an embryonic machine-tool industry had taken root–an industrial technology was impossible to create. Furthermore, the competence required to create such a technology does not reside alone in the ability or inability to make a particular machine (one thinks of Babbage's ill-fated calculator as an example of a machine born too soon), but in the ability of many industries to change their products or processes to "fit" a change in one key product or process.

This necessary requirement of technological congruence[6] given us an additional cause of sequencing. For the ability of many industries to co-operate in producing the equipment needed for a "higher" stage of technology depends not alone on knowledge or sheer skill but on the division of labor and the specialization of industry. And this in turn hinges to a considerable degree on the sheer size of the stock of capital itself. Thus the slow and painful accumulation of capital, from which springs the gradual diversification in industrial function, becomes an independent regulator of the reach of technical capability.

In making this general case for a determinate pattern of technological evolution-at least insofar as that technology is concerned with production–I do not want to claim too much. I am well aware that reasoning about technical sequences is easily faulted as post hoc ergo propter hoc. Hence, let me leave this phase of my inquiry by suggesting no more than that the idea of a roughly ordered progression of productive technology seems logical enough to warrant further empirical investigation. To put it as concretely as possible, I do not think it is just by happenstance that the steam-mill follows, and does not precede, the hand-mill, nor is it mere fantasy in our own day when we speak of the coming of the automatic factory. In the future as in the past, the development of the technology of production seems bounded by the constraints of knowledge and capability and thus, in principle at least, open to prediction as a determinable force of the historic process.

## II

The second proposition to be investigated is no less difficult than the first. It relaters, we will recall, to the explicit statement that a given technology imposes certain social and political characteristics upon the society in which it is found. Is it true that, as Marx wrote in *The German Ideology*, "A certain mode of production, or industrial stage, is always combined with a certain mode of cooperation, or social stage,"[7] or as he put it in the sentence immediately preceding our hand-mail, steam-mil paradigm, "In acquiring new productive forces men change their mode of production, and in changing their mode of production they change their way of living–they change all their social relation"?

As before, we must set aside for the moment certain "cultural" aspects of the question. But if we restrict ourselves to the functional relationships directly connected with the process of production itself, I think we can indeed state that the technology of a society imposes a determinate pattern of social relations on that society.

We can, as a matter of fact, distinguish at least two such modes of influence:

### 1. The Composition of the Labor Force

In order to function, a given technology must be attended by a labor force of a particular kind. Thus, the hand-mill (if we may take this as referring to late medieval technology in general) required a work force composed of skilled or semiskilled craftsmen, who were free to practice their occupations at home or in a small atelier, at times and seasons that varied considerably. By way of contrast, the steam-mill-that is, the technology of the nineteenth century–required a work force composed of semiskilled or unskilled operatives who could work only at the factory site and only at the strict time schedule enforced by turning the machinery on or off. Again, the technology of the electronic age has steadily required a higher proportion of skilled attendants; and the coming technology of automation will still further change the needed mix of skills and the locale of work, and may as well drastically lessen the requirements of labor time itself.

### 2. The Hierarchical Organization of Work

Different technological apparatuses not only require different labor forces but different orders of supervision and co-ordination. The internal organization of the eighteenth-century handicraft unit, with its typical man-master relationship, presents a social

---

[6] The phrase is Richard LaPiere's in *Social Change* (New York, 1965), p.263 f.
[7] Karl Marx and Friedrich Engels, *The German Idecology* (London, 1942), p.18

configuration of a wholly different kind from that of the nineteenth-century factory with its men-manager confrontation, and this in turn differs from the internal social structure of the continuous-flow, semi-automated plant of the present. As the intricacy of the production process increases, a much more complex system of internal controls is required to maintain the system in working order.

Does this add up to the proposition that the steam-mill gives us society with the industrial capitalist? Certainly the class characteristics of a particular society are strongly implied in its functional organization. Yet it would seem wise to be very cautious before relating political effects exclusively to functional economic causes. The Soviet Union, for example, proclaims itself to be a socialist society although its technical base resembles that of old-fashioned capitalism. Had Marx written that the steam-mill gives you society with the industrial *manager*, he would have been closer to the truth.

What is less easy to decide is the degree to which the technological infrastructure is responsible for some of the sociological features of society. Is anomic, for instance, a disease of capitalism or of all industrial societies? Is the organization man a creature of monopoly capital or of all bureaucratic industry wherever found? These questions tempt us to look into the problem of the impact of technology on the existential quality of life, an area we have ruled out of bounds for this paper. Suffice it to say that superficial evidence seems to imply that the similar technologies of Russia and America are indeed giving rise to similar social phenomena of this sort.

As with the first portion of our inquiry, it seems advisable to end this section on a note of caution. There is a danger, in discussing the structure of the labor force or the nature of intrafirm organization, of assigning the sole causal efficacy to the visible presence of machinery and of overlooking the invisible influence of other factors at work. Gilfillan, for instance, writes, "engineers have committed such blunders as saying the typewriter brought women to work in offices, and with the type setting machine made possible the great modern newspaper, forgetting that in Japan there are women office workers and great modern newspapers getting practically no help from typewriters and typesetting machines."[8] In addition, even where technology seems unquestionably to play the critical role, as independent "social" element unavoidably enters the scene in the design of technology, which must take into account such facts as the level of education of the work force or its relative price. In this way the machine will reflect, as much as mould, the social relationships of work.

These caveats urge us to practice what William James called a "soft determinism" with regard to the influence of the machine on social relations. Nevertheless, I would say that our cautions qualify rather than invalidate the thesis that the prevailing level of technology imposes itself powerfully on the structural organization of the productive side of society. A foreknowledge of the shape of the technical core of society fifty years hence may not allow us to describe the political attributes of that society, and may perhaps only hint at its sociological character, but assuredly it presents us with a profile of requirements, both in labor skills and in supervisory needs, that differ considerably from those of today. We cannot say whether the society of the computer will give us the latte-day capitalist or the commissar, but it seems beyond question that it will give us the technician and the bureaucrat.

# III

Frequently, during our efforts thus far to demonstrate what it valid and useful in the concept of technological determinism, we have been forces to defer certain aspects of the problem until later. It is time now to turn up the rug and to examine what has been swept under it. Let us try to systematize our qualifications and objections to the basic Marxian paradigm:

## 1. Technological Progress Is Itself a Social Activity

A theory of technological determinism must contend with the fact that the very activity of invention and innovation is an attribute of some societies and not of others. The Kalahari bushmen or the tribesmen of New Guinea, for instance, have persisted in a neolithic technology to the present day; the Arabs reached a high degree of technical proficiency in the past and have since suffered a decline; the classical Chinese developed technical expertise in some fields while unaccountably neglecting it in the area of production. What factors serve to encourage or discourage this technical thrust s a problem about which we know extremely little at the present moment.[9]

## 2. The Course of Technological Advance Is Responsive to Social Direction

Whether technology advances in the area of war, the arts, agriculture, or industry depends in part on the rewards, inducements, and incentives offered by society. In this way the direction of technological advance is partially the result of social policy. For example, the system of interchangeable parts, first introduced into France and then independently into England failed to take root in either country for lack of government interest or market stimulus. Its success in America is attributable mainly to government support

---

[8] Gilfillan (see n.3), p. 202.
[9] An interesting attempt to find a line of social causation is found in E. Hagen, *The Theory of Social Change* (Homewood, Ill, 1962).

and to its appeal in society without guild traditions and with high labor costs.[10] The general level of technology may follow an independently determined sequential path, but its areas of application certainly reflect social influences.

## 3. Technological Change Must Be Compatible with Existing Social Conditions

An advance in technology not only must be congruent with the surrounding technology but must also be compatible with the existing economic and other institutions of society. For example, labor-saving machinery will not find ready acceptance in a society where labor is abundant and cheap as a factor of production. Nor would a mass production technique recommend itself to a society that did not have a mass market. Indeed, the presence of slave labor seems generally to inhibit the use of machinery and the presence of expensive labor to accelerate it.[11]

These reflections on the social forces bearing on technical progress tempt us to throw aside the whole notion of technological determinism as false or misleading.[12] Yet, to relegate technology from an undeserved position of *primum mobile* in history to that of a mediating factor, both acted upon by and acting on the body of society, is not to write off its influence but only to specify its mode of operation with greater precision. Similarly, to admit we understand very little of the cultural factors that give rise to technology does not depreciate its role but focuses our attention on that period of history when technology is clearly a major historic force, namely Western society since 1700.

# IV

What is the mediating role played by technology within modern Western society? When we ask this much more modest question, the interaction of society and technology begins to clarify itself for us:

## 1. The Rise of Capitalism Provided a Major Stimulus for the Development of a Technology of Production

Not until the emergence of a market system organized around the principle of private property did there also emerge an institution capable of systematically guiding the inventive and innovative abilities of society to the problem of facilitating production. Hence the environment of the eighteenth and nineteenth centuries provided both a novel and an extremely effective encouragement for the development of an *industrial* technology. In addition, the slowly opening political and social framework of late mercantilist society gave rise to social aspirations. for which the new technology offered the best chance of realization. It was not only the steam-mill that gave us the industrial capitalist but the rising inventor-manufacturer who gave us the steam-mill.

## 2 The Expansion of Technology within the Market System Took on a New "Automatic" Aspect

Under the burgeoning market system not alone the initiation of technical improvement but its subsequent adoption and repercussion through the economy was largely governed by market considerations. As a result, both the rise and the proliferation of technology assumed the attributes of an impersonal diffuse "force" bearing on social and economic life. This was all the more pronounced because the political control needed to buffer its disruptive consequences was seriously inhibited by the prevailing laissez-faire ideology.

## 3. The Rise of Science Gave a New Impetus to Technology

The period of early capitalism roughly coincided with and provided a congenial setting for the development of an independent source of technological encouragement–the rise of the self-conscious activity of science. The steady expansion of scientific research, dedicated to the exploration of nature's secrets and to their harnessing for social use, provided an increasingly important stimulus for technological advance from the middle of the nineteenth century. Indeed, as the twentieth century has progressed, science has become a major historical force in its own right and is now the indispensable precondition for an effective technology.

It is for these reasons that technology takes on a special significance in the context of capitalism–or, for that matter, of a socialism based on maximizing production or minimizing costs. For in these societies, both the continuous appearance of technical advance and its diffusion throughout the society assume the attributes of autonomous process, "mysteriously" generated by society and thrust upon its members in a manner as indifferent as it is imperious. This is why, I think, the problem of technological

---

[10] See K.R. Gilbert, "Machine-Tools," in Charles Singer, E. J. Holmyard, A.R. Hall, and Trevor I. Williams (eds.), *A History of Technology* (Oxford, 1958). IV, chap. xiv.

[11] See LaPiere (see n.6), p.284; also H.J. Habbakuk, *British and American Technology in the 19th Century* (Cambridge, 1962), passim.

[12] As, for example, in A. Hansen, "The Technological Determination of History," *Quarterly Journal of Economics* (1921), pp.76-83.)

determinism–of how machines make history–comes to us with such insistence despite the case with which we can disprove its more extreme contentions.

*Technological determinism is thus peculiarly a problem of a certain historic epoch*–specifically that of high capitalism and low socialism–in which the *forces of technical change have been unleased, but when the agencies for the control or guidance of technology are still rudimentary.*

The point has relevance for the future. The surrender of society to the free play of market forces is now on the wane, but its subservience to the impetus of the scientific ethos is on the rise. The prospect before us is assuredly that of an undiminished and very likely accelerated pace of technical change. From what we can foretell about the direction of this technological advance and the structural alterations it implies, the pressures in the future will be toward a society marked by a much greater degree of organization and deliberate control. What other political, social, and existential changes the age of the computer will also bring we do not know. What seems certain, however, is that the problem of technological determinism–that is, of the impact of machines on history–will remain germane until there is forged a degree of public control over technology far greater than anything that now exists.

# Article 2

## Technological Momentum

*In 1969 Thomas Hughes published an article about hydrogenation in post-World War I Germany in which he coined the phrase "technological momentum" to explain how that nation's leading chemical manufacturer subsequently became linked with Adolf Hitler's Nazi regime. Ever since, historians have debated the relationship of technological momentum to technological determinism—particularly, whether they are synonymous in meaning and, if they are not, how they differ.*

*In the essay that follows, Hughes provides a useful clarification by locating the concept of technological momentum "somewhere between the poles of technological determinism and social constructivism." Through a series of examples drawn from his extensive research on the emergence of technological systems, he shows that younger developing systems tend to be more open to sociocultural influences while older, more mature systems prove to be more independent of outside influences and therefore more deterministic in nature. Hughes views technological momentum as an alternative to technological determinism and contends that it is a more valuable interpretative concept than either technological determinism or social constructivism because it is time dependent yet sensitive to the messy complexities of society and culture. To some critics, however, Hughes's systems-oriented explanation of the past remains essentially deterministic because it places technology at the center of the historical process and links everything else to it. Hughes naturally denies this charge, emphasizing that technological momentum is an integrative concept that gives equal weight to social and technical forces. Whether or not one agrees with Hughes's interpretative framework, his emphasis on the momentum of technological systems has helped to define more precisely the differences between the technological and social determinants of change.*

The concepts of technological determinism and social construction provide agendas for fruitful discussion among historians, sociologists, and engineers interested in the nature of technology and technological change. Specialists can engage in a general discourse that subsumes their areas of specialization. In this essay I shall offer an additional concept—technological momentum—that will, I hope, enrich the discussion. Technological momentum offers an alternative to technological determinism and social construction. Those who in the past espoused a technological determinist approach to history offered a needed corrective to the conventional interpretation of history that virtually ignored the role of technology in effecting social change. Those who more recently advocated a social construction approach provided an invaluable corrective to an interpretation of history that encouraged a passive attitude toward an overwhelming technology. Yet both approaches suffer from a failure to encompass the complexity of technological change.

All three concepts present problems of definition. Technological determinism I define simply as the belief that technical forces determine social and cultural changes. Social construction presumes that social and cultural forces determine technical change. A more complex concept than determinism and social construction, technological momentum infers that social development shapes and is shaped by technology. Momentum also is time dependent. Because the focus of this essay is technological momentum, I shall define it in detail by resorting to examples.

"Technology" and "technical" also need working definitions. Proponents of technological determinism and of social construction often use "technology" in a narrow sense to include only physical artifacts and software. By contrast, I use "technical" in referring to physical artifacts and software. By "technology" I usually mean technological or sociotechnical systems, which I shall also define by examples.

Discourses about technological determinism and social construction usually refer to society, a concept exceedingly abstract. Historians are wary of defining society other than by example because they have found that twentieth-century societies seem quite different from twelfth-century ones and that societies differ not only over time but over space as well. Facing these ambiguities, I define the social as the world that is not technical, or that is not hardware or technical software. This world is made up of institutions, values, interest groups, social classes, and political and economic forces. As the reader will learn, I see the social and the technical as interacting within technological systems. Technological system, as I shall explain, includes both the technical and the social. I name the world outside of technological systems that shapes them or is shaped by them the "environment." Even though it may interact with the technological system, the environment is not a part of the system because it is not under the control of the system as are the system's interacting components.

In the course of this essay the reader will discover that I am no technological determinist. I cannot associate myself with such distinguished technological determinists as Karl Marx, Lynn White, and Jacques Ellul. Marx, in moments of simplification, argued that water-wheels ushered in manorialism and that steam engines gave birth to bourgeois factories and society. Lenin added that electrification was the bearer of socialism. White elegantly portrayed the stirrup as the prime mover in a train of cause and effect culminating in the establishment of feudalism. Ellul finds the human-made environment structured by technical systems, as determining in their effects as the natural environment of Charles Darwin. Ellul sees the human-made as steadily displacing the natural—the world becoming a system of artifacts, with humankind, not God, as the artificer.[1]

Nor can I agree entirely with the social constructivists. Wiebe Bijker and Trevor Pinch have made an influential case for social construction in their essay "The Social Construction of Facts and Artifacts."[2] They argue that social, or interest, groups define and give meaning to artifacts. In defining them, the social groups determine the designs of artifacts. They do this by selecting for survival the designs that solve the problems they want solved by the artifacts and that fulfill desires they want fulfilled by the artifacts. Bijker and Pinch emphasize the interpretive flexibility discernible in the evolution of artifacts: they believe that the various meanings given by social groups to, say, the bicycle result in a number of alternative designs of that machine.

The various bicycle designs are not fixed; closure does not occur until social groups believe that the problems and desires they associate with the bicycle are solved or fulfilled.

In summary, I find the Bijker-Pinch interpretation tends toward social determinism, and I must reject it on these grounds. The concept of technological momentum avoids the extremism of both technological determinism and social construction by presenting a more complex, flexible, time-dependent, and persuasive explanation of technological change.

## Technological Systems

Electric light and power systems provide an instructive example of technological systems. By 1920 they had taken on a messy complexity because of the heterogeneity of their components. In their diversity, their complexity, and their large scale, such mature technological systems resemble the megamachines that Lewis Mumford described in *The Pentagon of Power*.[3] The actor networks of Bruno Latour and Michel Callon[4] also share essential characteristics with technological systems. An electric power system consists of inanimate electrons and animate regulatory boards, both of which, as Latour and Callon suggest, can be intractable if not brought in line or into the actor network.

The Electric Bond and Share Company (EBASCO), an American electric utility holding company of the 1920s, provides an example of a mature technological system. Established in 1905 by the General Electric Company, EBASCO controlled through stock ownership a number of electric utility companies, and through them a number of technical subsystems—namely electric light and power networks, or grids.[5] EBASCO provided financial, management, and engineering construction services for the utility companies. The inventors, engineers, and managers who were the system builders of EBASCO saw to it that the services related synergistically. EBASCO management recommended construction that EBASCO engineering carried out and for which EBASCO arranged financing through sale of stocks or bonds. If the utilities lay in geographical proximity, then EBASCO often physically interconnected them through high-voltage power grids. The General Electric Company founded EBASCO and, while not owning a majority of stock in it, substantially influenced its policies. Through EBASCO General Electric learned of equipment needs in the utility industry and then provided them in accord with specifications defined by EBASCO for the various utilities with which it interacted. Because it interacted with EBASCO, General Electric was a part of the EBASCO system. Even though I have labeled this the EBASCO system, it is not clear that EBASCO solely controlled the system. Control of the complex systems seems to have resulted from a consensus among EBASCO, General Electric, and the utilities in the systems.

---

[1] Lynn White, Jr., Medieval Technology and Social Change (Clarendon, 1962); Jacques Ellul, The Technological System (Continuum, 1980); Karl Marx, *Capital: A Critique of Political Economy*, ed. F. Engels; *Electric Power Development in the U.S.S.R.*, ed. B. I. Weitz (Moscow: INRA, 1936).

[2] The essay is found in *The Social Construction of Technological Systems: New Directions in the Sociology and History of Technology*, ed. W. E. Bijker et al. (MIT Press, 1987).

[3] Lewis Mumford, *The Myth of the Machine: II. The Pentagon of Power* (Harcourt Brace Jovanovich, 1970).

[4] Bruno Latour, *Science in Action: How to Follow Scientists and Engineers through Society* (Harvard University Press, 1987); Michel Callon, "Society in the Making: The Study of Technology as a Tool for Sociological Analysis," in The Social Construction of Technological Systems.

[5] Before 1905, General Electric used the United Electric Securities Company to hold its utility securities and to fund its utility customers who purchased GE equipment. See Thomas P. Hughes, *Networks of Power: Electrification in Western Society, 1880–1930* (Johns Hopkins University Press, 1983), pp. 395–396.

Other institutions can also be considered parts of the EBASCO system, but because the interconnections were loose rather than tight[6] these institutions are usually not recognized as such. I refer to the electrical engineering departments in engineering colleges, whose faculty and graduate students conducted research or consulted for EBASCO. I am also inclined to include a few of the various state regulatory authorities as parts of the EBASCO system, if their members were greatly influenced by it. If the regulatory authorities were free of this control, then they should be considered a part of the EBASCO environment, not of the system.

Because it had social institutions as components, the EBASCO system could be labeled a sociotechnical system. Since, however, the system had a technical (hardware and software) core, I prefer to name it a technological system, to distinguish it from social systems without technical cores. This privileging of the technical in a technological system is justified in part by the prominent roles played by engineers, scientists, workers, and technical-minded managers in solving the problems arising during the creation and early history of a system. As a system matures, a bureaucracy of managers and white-collar employees usually plays an increasingly prominent role in maintaining and expanding the system, so that it then becomes more social and less technical.

## EBASCO as a Cause and an Effect

From the point of view of technological—better, technical—determinists, the determined is the world beyond the technical. Technical determinists considering EBASCO as a historical actor would focus on its technical core as a cause with many effects. Instead of seeing EBASCO as a technological system with interacting technical and social components, they would see the technical core as causing change in the social components of EBASCO and in society in general. Determinists would focus on the way in which EBASCO's generators, by energizing electric motors on individual production machines, made possible the reorganization of the factory floor in a manner commonly associated with Fordism. Such persons would see street, workplace, and home lighting changing working and leisure hours and affecting the nature of work and play. Determinists would also cite electrical appliances in the home as bringing less—and more—work for women,[7] and the layout of EBASCO's power lines as causing demographic changes. Electrical grids such as those presided over by EBASCO brought a new decentralized regionalism, which contrasted with the industrial, urban-centered society of the steam age.[8] One could extend the list of the effects of electrification enormously.

Yet, contrary to the view of the technological determinists, the social constructivists would find exogenous technical, economic, political, and geographical forces, as well as values, shaping with varying intensity the EBASCO system during its evolution. Social constructivists see the technical core of EBASCO as an effect rather than a cause. They could cite a number of instances of social construction. The spread of alternating (polyphase) current after 1900, for instance, greatly affected, even determined, the history of the early utilities that had used direct current, for these had to change their generators and related equipment to alternating current or fail in the face of competition. Not only did such external technical forces shape the technical core of the utilities; economic forces did so as well. With the rapid increase in the United States' population and the concentration of industry in cities, the price of real estate increased. Needing to expand their generating capacity, EBASCO and other electric utilities chose to build new turbine-driven power plants outside city centers and to transmit electricity by high-voltage lines back into the cities and throughout the area of supply. Small urban utilities became regional ones and then faced new political or regulatory forces as state governments took over jurisdiction from the cities. Regulations also caused technical changes. As the regional utilities of the EBASCO system expanded, they conformed to geographical realities as they sought cooling water, hydroelectric sites, and mine-mouth locations. Values, too, shaped the history of EBASCO. During the Great Depression, the Roosevelt administration singled out utility holding-company magnates for criticism, blaming the huge losses experienced by stock and bond holders on the irresponsible, even illegal, machinations of some of the holding companies. Partly as a result of this attack, the attitudes of the public toward large-scale private enterprise shifted so that it was relatively easy for the administration to push through Congress the Holding Company Act of 1935, which denied holding companies the right to incorporate utilities that were not physically contiguous.[9]

## Gathering Technological Momentum

Neither the proponents of technical determinism nor those of social construction can alone comprehend the complexity of an evolving technological system such as EBASCO. On some occasions EBASCO was a cause; on others it was an effect. The system both shaped and was shaped by society. Furthermore, EBASCO's shaping society is not an example of purely technical determinism, for EBASCO, as we have observed, contained social components. Similarly, social constructivists must acknowledge that social forces in the environment were not shaping simply a technical system, but a technological system, including—as systems invariably do—social components.

---

[6] The concept of loosely and tightly coupled components in systems is found in Charles Perrow's *Normal Accidents: Living with High Risk Technology* (Basic Books, 1984).

[7] Ruth Schwartz Cowan, "The 'Industrial Revolution' in the Home," *Technology and Culture* 17 (1976): 1–23.

[8] Lewis Mumford, *The Culture of Cities* (Harcourt Brace Jovanovich, 1970), p. 378.

[9] More on EBASCO's history can be found on pp. 392–399 of *Networks of Power*.

The interaction of technological systems and society is not symmetrical over time. Evolving technological systems are time dependent. As the EBASCO system became larger and more complex, thereby gathering momentum, the system became less shaped by and more the shaper of its environment. By the 1920s the EBASCO system rivaled a large railroad company in its level of capital investment, in its number of customers, and in its influence upon local, state, and federal governments. Hosts of electrical engineers, their professional organizations, and the engineering schools that trained them were committed by economic interests and their special knowledge and skills to the maintenance and growth of the EBASCO system. Countless industries and communities interacted with EBASCO utilities because of shared economic interests. These various human and institutional components added substantial momentum to the EBASCO system. Only a historical event of large proportions could deflect or break the momentum of an EBASCO, the Great Depression being a case in point.

## Characteristics of Momentum

Other technological systems reveal further characteristics of technological momentum, such as acquired skill and knowledge, special-purpose machines and processes, enormous physical structures, and organizational bureaucracy. During the late nineteenth century, for instance, mainline railroad engineers in the United States transferred their acquired skill and knowledge to the field of intra-urban transit. Institutions with specific characteristics also contributed to this momentum. Professors in the recently founded engineering schools and engineers who had designed and built the railroads organized and rationalized the experience that had been gathered in preparing roadbeds, laying tracks, building bridges, and digging tunnels for mainline railroads earlier in the century. This engineering science found a place in engineering texts and in the curricula of the engineering schools, thus informing a new generation of engineers who would seek new applications for it.

Late in the nineteenth century, when street congestion in rapidly expanding industrial and commercial cities such as Chicago, Baltimore, New York, and Boston threatened to choke the flow of traffic, extensive subway and elevated railway building began as an antidote. The skill and the knowledge formerly expended on railroad bridges were now applied to elevated railway structures; the know-how once invested in tunnels now found application in subways. A remarkably active period of intra-urban transport construction began about the time when the building of mainline railways reached a plateau, thus facilitating the movement of know-how from one field to the other. Many of the engineers who played leading roles in intra-urban transit between 1890 and 1910 had been mainline railroad builders.[10]

The role of the physical plant in the buildup of technological momentum is revealed in the interwar history of the Badische Anilin und Soda Fabrik (BASF), one of Germany's leading chemical manufacturers and a member of the I.G. Farben group. During World War I, BASF rapidly developed large-scale production facilities to utilize the recently introduced Haber-Bosch technique of nitrogen fixation. It produced the nitrogen compounds for fertilizers and explosives so desperately needed by a blockaded Germany. The high-technology process involved the use of high-temperature, high-pressure, complex catalytic action. Engineers had to design and manufacture extremely costly and complex instrumentation and apparatus. When the blockade and the war were over, the market demand for synthetic nitrogen compounds did not match the large capacity of the high-technology plants built by BASF and other companies during the war. Numerous engineers, scientists, and skilled craftsmen who had designed, constructed, and operated these plants found their research and development knowledge and their construction skills underutilized. Carl Bosch, chairman of the managing board of BASF and one of the inventors of the Haber-Bosch process, had a personal and professional interest in further development and application of high-temperature, high-pressure, catalytic processes. He and other managers, scientists, and engineers at BASF sought additional ways of using the plant and the knowledge created during the war years. They first introduced a high-temperature, high-pressure catalytic process for manufacturing synthetic methanol in the early 1920s. The momentum of the now-generalized process next showed itself in management's decision in the mid 1920s to invest in research and development aimed at using high-temperature, high-pressure catalytic chemistry for the production of synthetic gasoline from coal. This project became the largest investment in research and development by BASF during the Weimar era. When the National Socialists took power, the government contracted for large amounts of the synthetic product. Momentum swept BASF and I.G. Farben into the Nazi system of economic autarky.[11]

When managers pursue economies of scope, they are taking into account the momentum embodied in large physical structures. Muscle Shoals Dam, an artifact of considerable size, offers another example of this aspect of technological momentum. As the loss of merchant ships to submarines accelerated during World War I, the United States also attempted to increase its indigenous supply of nitrogen compounds. Having selected a process requiring copious amounts of electricity, the government had to construct a hydroelectric dam and power station. This was located at Muscle Shoals, Alabama, on the Tennessee River. Before the nitrogen-fixation facilities being built near the dam were completed, the war ended. As in Germany, the supply of synthetic nitrogen compounds then exceeded the demand. The U.S. government was left not only with process facilities but also with a very large dam and power plant.

---

[10] Thomas Parke Hughes, "A Technological Frontier: The Railway," in *The Railroad and the Space Program*, ed. B. Mazlish (MIT Press, 1965).
[11] Thomas Parke Hughes, "Technological Momentum: Hydrogenation in Germany 1900–1933," *Past and Present* (August 1969): 106–132.

Muscle Shoals Dam (later named Wilson Dam), like the engineers and managers we have considered, became a solution looking for a problem. How should the power from the dam be used? A number of technological enthusiasts and planners envisioned the dam as the first of a series of hydroelectric projects along the Tennessee River and its tributaries. The poverty of the region spurred them on in an era when electrification was seen as a prime mover of economic development. The problem looking for a solution attracted the attention of an experienced problem solver, Henry Ford, who proposed that an industrial complex based on hydroelectric power be located along 75 miles of the waterway that included the Muscle Shoals site. An alliance of public power and private interests with their own plans for the region frustrated his plan. In 1933, however, Muscle Shoals became the original component in a hydroelectric, flood-control, soil-reclamation, and regional development project of enormous scope sponsored by Senator George Norris and the Roosevelt administration and presided over by the Tennessee Valley Authority. The technological momentum of the Muscle Shoals Dam had carried over from World War I to the New Deal. This durable artifact acted over time like a magnetic field, attracting plans and projects suited to its characteristics. Systems of artifacts are not neutral forces; they tend to shape the environment in particular ways.[12]

## Using Momentum

System builders today are aware that technological momentum—or whatever they may call it—provides the durability and the propensity for growth that were associated more commonly in the past with the spread of bureaucracy. Immediately after World War II, General Leslie Groves displayed his system-building instincts and his awareness of the critical importance of technological momentum as a means of ensuring the survival of the system for the production of atomic weapons embodied in the wartime Manhattan Project. Between 1945 and 1947, when others were anticipating disarmament, Groves expanded the gaseous-diffusion facilities for separating fissionable uranium at Oak Ridge, Tennessee; persuaded the General Electric Company to operate the reactors for producing plutonium at Hanford, Washington; funded the new Knolls Atomic Power Laboratory at Schenectady, New York; established the Argonne and Brookhaven National Laboratories for fundamental research in nuclear science; and provided research funds for a number of universities. Under his guiding hand, a large-scale production system with great momentum took on new life in peacetime. Some of the leading scientists of the wartime project had confidently expected production to end after the making of a few bombs and the coming of peace.[13]

More recently, proponents of the Strategic Defense Initiative (SDI), organized by the Reagan administration in 1983, have made use of momentum. The political and economic interests and the organizational bureaucracy vested in this system were substantial—as its makers intended. Many of the same industrial contractors, research universities, national laboratories, and government agencies that took part in the construction of intercontinental ballistic missile systems, National Air and Space Administration projects, and atomic weapon systems have been deeply involved in SDI. The names are familiar: Lockheed, General Motors, Boeing, TRW, McDonnell Douglas, General Electric, Rockwell, Teledyn, MIT, Stanford, the University of California's Lawrence Livermore Laboratory, Los Alamos, Hanford, Brookhaven, Argonne, Oak Ridge, NASA, the U.S. Air Force, the U.S. Navy, the CIA, the U.S. Army, and others. Political interests reinforced the institutional momentum. A number of congressmen represent districts that receive SDI contracts, and lobbyists speak for various institutions drawn into the SDI network.[14] Only the demise of the Soviet Union as a military threat allowed counter forces to build up sufficient momentum to blunt the cutting edge of SDI.

## Conclusion

A technological system can be both a cause and an effect; it can shape or be shaped by society. As they grow larger and more complex, systems tend to be more shaping of society and less shaped by it. Therefore, the momentum of technological systems is a concept that can be located somewhere between the poles of technical determinism and social constructivism. The social constructivists have a key to understanding the behavior of young systems; technical determinists come into their own with the mature ones. Technological momentum, however, provides a more flexible mode of interpretation and one that is in accord with the history of large systems.

What does this interpretation of the history of technological systems offer to those who design and manage systems or to the public that might wish to shape them through a democratic process? It suggests that shaping is easiest before the system has acquired political, economic, and value components. It also follows that a system with great technological momentum can be made to change direction if a variety of its components are subjected to the forces of change.

For instance, the changeover since 1970 by U.S. automobile manufacturers from large to more compact automobiles and to more fuel-efficient and less polluting ones came about as a result of pressure brought on a number of components in the huge

[12] On Muscle Shoals and the TVA, see Preston J. Hubbard's *Origins of the TVA: The Muscle Shoals Controversy, 1920–1932* (Norton, 1961).

[13] Richard G. Hewlett and Oscar E. Anderson, Jr., *The New World, 1939–1946* (Pennsylvania State University Press, 1962), pp. 624–638.

[14] Charlene Mires, "The Strategic Defense Initiative" (unpublished essay, History and Sociology of Science Department, University of Pennsylvania, 1990).

[15] Max Weber, *The Protestant Ethic and the Spirit of Capitalism*, tr. T. Parsons (Unwin–Hyman, 1990), p. 155.

automobile production and use system. As a result of the oil embargo of 1973 and the rise of gasoline prices, American consumers turned to imported compact automobiles; this, in turn, brought competitive economic pressure to bear on the Detroit manufacturers. Environmentalists helped persuade the public to support, and politicians to enact, legislation that promoted both anti-pollution technology and gas-mileage standards formerly opposed by American manufacturers. Engineers and designers responded with technical inventions and developments.

On the other hand, the technological momentum of the system of automobile production and use can be observed in recent reactions against major environmental initiatives in the Los Angeles region. The host of institutions and persons dependent politically, economically, and ideologically on the system (including gasoline refiners, automobile manufacturers, trade unions, manufacturers of appliances and small equipment using internal-combustion engines, and devotees of unrestricted automobile usage) rallied to frustrate change.

Because social and technical components interact so thoroughly in technological systems and because the inertia of these systems is so large, they bring to mind the iron-cage metaphor that Max Weber used in describing the organizational bureaucracies that proliferated at the beginning of the twentieth century.[15] Technological systems, however, are bureaucracies reinforced by technical, or physical, infrastructures which give them even greater rigidity and mass than the social bureaucracies that were the subject of Weber's attention. Nevertheless, we must remind ourselves that technological momentum, like physical momentum, is not irresistible

# Article 3 ↵

Trevor J. Pinch and Wiebe E. Bijker

## The Social Construction of Facts and Artefacts: Or How the Sociology of Science and the Sociology of Technology Might Benefit Each Other

**O**ne of the most striking features of the growth of 'science studies' in recent years has been the separation of science from technology. Sociological studies of new knowledge in science abound, as do studies of technological innovation, but thus far there has been little attempt to bring such bodies of work together.[1] It may well be the case that science and technology are essentially different and that different approaches to their study are warranted. However, until the attempt to treat them within the same analytical endeavour has been undertaken we cannot be sure of this.

**Social Studies of Science (SAGE, London, Beverly Hills and New Delhi), Vol. 14 (1984), 399–441**

It is the contention of this paper that the study of science and the study of technology should, and indeed can, benefit from each other. In particular we will argue that the social constructivist view prevalent within the sociology of science, and which is also emerging within the sociology of technology, provides a useful starting point. We will set out the constitutive questions which such a unified social constructivist approach must address analytically and empirically. But our intention is not just to make a programmatic appeal: empirical examples, drawn from our own work on science and technology, will be used to illustrate the potential of our programme.[2]

The paper falls into three main sections. In the first part, we will outline various strands of argumentation and review bodies of literature which we consider to be relevant to our goals. We will then go on to discuss the two specific approaches from which our integrated viewpoint has developed: the Empirical Programme of Relativism[3] and a social constructivist approach to the study of technology.[4] In the third part, we will bring these two approaches together and give some empirical examples. We will conclude by summarizing our provisional findings, and indicate the directions in which we believe the programme can most usefully be pursued.

## Some Relevant Literature

In this section we draw attention to three bodies of literature in science and technology studies. The three areas discussed are the sociology of science, the science-technology relationship, and technology studies. We will take each in turn.

### Sociology of Science

It is not our intention to review in any depth developments in this field as a whole.[5] We are concerned here only with the recent emergence of the sociology of scientific *knowledge*.[6] Studies in this area take the actual content of scientific ideas, theories, and experiments as the subject of analysis. This contrasts with earlier work in the sociology of science which was concerned with science as an institution and the study of scientists' norms, career patterns, and reward structures.[7] One major — if not *the* major — development in the field in the last decade has been the extension of the sociology of knowledge into the arena of the 'hard science'. The need for such a 'strong programme' has been outlined by Bloor:[8] its central tenets are that, in investigating the causes of beliefs, sociologists should be impartial to the truth or falsity of the beliefs, and that such beliefs should be explained symmetrically. In other words, differing explanations should not be sought for what is taken to be a scientific 'truth' (for example, the existence of X-Rays) and a scientific 'falsehood' (for example, the existence of N-Rays). Within such a programme all knowledge and all knowledge-claims are to be treated as being socially constructed: that is to say, explanations for the genesis, acceptance and rejection of knowledge-claims are sought in the domain of the Social World rather than in the Natural World.[9]

This approach has generated a vigorous programme of empirical research and it now possible to understand the processes of the construction of scientific knowledge in a variety of locations and contexts. For instance, on group of researchers has concentrated their attention on the study of the laboratory bench.[10] Another has chosen the scientific controversy as the location for their research and have thereby focussed on the social construction of scientific knowledge amongst a wider community of scientists.[11] As well as in 'hard' sciences, such as physics and biology, the approach has been shown to be fruitful in the study of fringe science,[12] and in the study of public-science debates, such as lead pollution.[13]

Although there are the usual differences of opinion among researchers as to the best place to locate such research (for instance, the laboratory, the controversy or the scientific paper), and there are differences as to the most appropriate methodological strategy to pursue,[14] there is widespread agreement that scientific knowledge can be, and indeed has been, shown to be thoroughly socially constituted. These approaches, which we shall refer to as 'social constructivist', mark an important new development in the sociology of science. The treatment of scientific knowledge as a social construction implies that there is nothing epistemologically special about the nature of scientific knowledge: it is merely one in a whole series of knowledge cultures (including, for instance, the knowledge systems pertaining to 'primitive' tribes).[15] Of course, the successes and failures of certain knowledge cultures still need to be explained, but this is to be seen as a sociological rather than an epistemological task.

The sociology of scientific knowledge promises much for other areas of 'science studies'. For example, it has been argued that the new work has relevance for the history of science,[16] philosophy of science,[17] and science policy.[18] The social constructivist view seems not only to be gaining ground as an important body of work in its own right: it also shows every potential of wider application. It is this body of work which forms one of the pillars of our own approach towards the study of science and technology.

## Science-Technology Relationship

The literature on the relationship between science and technology, unlike that referred to above, is rather heterogeneous and includes contributions from a variety of disciplinary perspectives. We do not claim to present anything other than a very partial review, reflecting our own particular interests.

One theme which has been pursued by philosophers is the attempt to separate technology from science on analytical grounds. In doing so, philosophers tend to posit over-idealized distinctions, such as, for example, that science is about the discovery of truth whilst technology is about the application of truth. Indeed, the literature on the philosophy of technology is rather disappointing.[19] We prefer to suspend judgement on it until philosophers propose more realistic models of both science and technology.

Another line of investigation into the nature of the science-technology relationship has been carried out by innovation researchers. They have attempted to investigate empirically the degree to which technological innovation incorporates, or originates from, basic science. A corollary of this approach has been the work of some scholars who have looked for relationships in the other direction — that is, they have argued that pure science is indebted to developments in technology.[20] The results of the empirical investigations of the dependence of technology on science have been rather frustrating. It has been difficult to specify the interdependence. For example, Project Hindsight, funded by the US Defense Department, found that most technological growth came from mission-oriented projects and engineering R & D, rather than from pure science.[21] These results were to some extent supported by a later British study.[22] On the other hand, Project TRACES, funded by the NSF in response to Project Hindsight, found that most technological development stemmed from basic research.[23] All these studies have been criticized for lack of methodological rigour and one must be cautious in drawing any firm conclusions form such work.[24] Most researchers today seem willing to agree that technological innovation takes place in a wide range of circumstances and historical epochs and that the import which can be attached to basic science therefore probably varies considerably.[25] Certainly the view prevalent in the 'bad old days'[26] that science discovers and technology applies will no longer suffice. Simplistic models and generalizations have been abandoned. As Layton has remarked in a recent review:

> Science and technology have become intermixed. Modern technology involves scientists who 'do' technology and technologists who function as scientists . . . The old view that basic sciences generate all the knowledge which technologists then apply will simply not help in understanding contemporary technology.[27]

Researchers concerned to measure the exact interdependence of science and technology seem to have asked the wrong question because they have assumed science and technology to be well-defined monolithic structures. In short, they have not grasped that science and technology are themselves socially produced in a variety of social circumstances.[28] It does seem, however, that there is now a move towards a more sociological conception of the science-technology relationship. For instance, Layton writes:

> The divisions between science and technology are not between the abstract functions of knowing and doing. Rather they are social. . .[29]

Barnes has recently described this change of thinking as follows:

> I start with the major reorientation in our thinking about the science-technology relationship which has occurred in recent years . . . We recognize science and technology to be on a par with each other. Both sets of practitioners creatively

extend and develop their existing culture; but both also take up and exploit some part of the culture of the other . . . they are in fact enmeshed in a symbiotic relationship.[30]

Although Barnes may be overly optimistic in claiming that a 'major reorientation' has occurred, it can be seen that a social constructivist view of science and technology fits well with his conception of the science-technology relationship. Scientists and technologists can be regarded as constructing their respective bodies of knowledge and techniques with each drawing upon the resources of the other when and where such resources can profitably be exploited. In other words, science and technology are both socially constructed cultures and bring to bear whatever cultural resources are appropriate for the purposes at hand. In this view the boundary between science and technology is, in particular instances, a matter for social negotiation, and represents no underlying distinction: it then makes little sense to treat the science-technology relationship in a general unidirectional way. Although we will not pursue this issue further in this paper, the social construction of the science-technology relationship is clearly a matter deserving further empirical investigation.

## Technology Studies

Our discussion of work under this heading is even more schematic. There is a very large amount of writing which falls under the rubric of 'technology studies'. It is convenient to divide the literature into three parts — innovation studies, history of technology, and sociology of technology. We will discuss each in turn.

Most innovation studies have been carried out by economists looking for the conditions for success in innovation. Factors researched include various aspects of the innovating firm (for example, size of R & D effort, management strength and marketing capability (along with macro-economic factors pertaining to the economy as a whole. This literature is in some ways reminiscent of the early days in the sociology of science, when scientific knowledge was treated like a 'black box'[31] and, for the purpose of such studies, scientists might as well have produced meat pies. Similarly, in the economic analysis of technological innovation everything is included that might be expected to influence innovation, expect any discussion of the technology itself. As Layton notes:

What is needed is an understanding of technology from inside, both as a body of knowledge and as a social system. Instead, technology is often treated as a 'black box' whose contents and behaviour may be assumed to be common knowledge.[32]

Only recently have economists started to look into this black box.[33]

The failure to take into account the content of technological innovations results in the widespread use of simple linear models to describe the process of innovation. The number of developmental steps assumed in these models seem to be rather arbitrary (for an example of a six-stage process see Figure 1).[34] Although such studies have undoubtedly contributed much to our understanding of the conditions for economic success in technological innovation,[35] because they ignore the technological content they cannot be used as the basis for a social constructivist view of technology.

This criticism cannot be levelled at the history of technology, where there are many finely crafted studies of the development of particular technologies. However, for the purposes of a sociology of technology, this work presents two kinds of problem. The first is that descriptive historiography is endemic in this field. Very few scholars (but there are some notable exceptions — see below) seem concerned to generalize beyond historical instances, and it is difficult to discern any overall patterns upon which to build a theory of technology.[36] This is not to say that such studies might not be useful building bricks for a social constructivist view of technology — merely that these historians have not yet demonstrated that they are doing sociology of knowledge in a different guise.[37]

The second problem concerns the asymmetrical focus of the analysis. For example, it has been claimed that in 25 volumes of *Technology and Culture* only 9 articles were devoted to the study of failed technological innovations.[38] This contributes to the implicit adoption of a linear structure of technological development, which suggests that

. . . the whole history of technological development had followed an orderly or rational path, as though today's world was the precise goal toward which all decisions, made since the beginning of history, were consciously directed.[39]

This preference for successful innovations seems to lead scholars to assume that the success of an artefact is an explanation of its subsequent development. Historians of technology often seem content to rely on the manifest success of the artefact as evidence that there is no further explanatory work to be done. For example, many histories of synthetic plastic start by describing the 'technically sweet' characteristics of Bakelite: these features are then used implicitly to position Bakelite at the starting point of the glorious development of the field:

God said: 'let Baekeland be' and all was plastics![40]

However, a more detailed study of the developments of plastic and varnish chemistry following the publication of the Bakelite process in 1909[41] shows that Bakelite was at first hardly recognized as the marvellous synthesis resin which it later proved to be.[42] And this situation did not change very much for some ten years. During the first world war the market prospects for synthetic plastics actually grew worse. However, the dumping of war supplies of phenol (used in the manufacture of Bakelite) in 1918 changed all

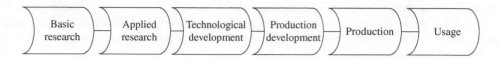

**Fig. 1.** A Six-Stage Linear Model of the Innovation Process

this,[43] and made it possible to keep the price sufficiently low to compete with (semi-)natural resins, such as celluloid. One can speculate over whether Bakelite would have acquired its prominence if it had not profited from the phenol dumping. In any case it is clear that a historical account founded upon the retrospective success of the artefact leaves much untold.

Given our intention of building a sociology of technology which treats technological knowledge in the same symmetrical, impartial manner that scientific facts are treated within the sociology of scientific knowledge, it would seem that much of the historical material does not go far enough. The success of an artefact is precisely what needs to be explained. For a sociological theory of technology it should be the *explanandum*, not the *explanans*.

Our account would not be complete, however, without mentioning some recent developments, especially in the American history of technology. These show the emergence of a growing number of theoretical themes upon which research is focussed.[44] For example, the systems approach towards technology,[45] and consideration of the effect of labour relations on technological development,[46] seem to herald departures from the 'old' history of technology. Such work promises to be very valuable for a sociological analysis of technology, and we shall return to some of it below.

The final body of work we wish to discuss is what might be described as 'sociology of technology'.[47] There have been some limited attempts in recent years to launch such a sociology, using ideas developed in the history and sociology of science — studies by, for example, Johnston[48] and Dosi,[49] who advocate the description of technological knowledge in terms of Kuhnian paradigms.[50] Such approaches certainly appear to be more promising than standard descriptive historiography, but it is not clear whether these authors share our understanding of technological artefacts as social constructs. For example, neither Johnston nor Dosi consider explicitly the need for a symmetrical sociological explanation which treats successful and failed artefacts in an equivalent way. Indeed, by locating their discussion at the level of technological paradigms it is not clear how the artefacts themselves are to be approached. As neither author has yet produced an empirical study using Kuhnian ideas, it is difficult to evaluate how the Kuhnian terms may be operationalized.[51] Certainly this has been a pressing problem in the sociology of science, where it has not always been possible to give Kuhn's terms a clear empirical reference.[52]

The possibilities of a more radical social constructivist view of technology have recently been touched upon by Mulkay.[53] He argues that the success and efficacy of technology could pose a special problem for the social constructivist view of scientific knowledge. The argument Mulkay wishes to counter is that the practical effectiveness of technology somehow demonstrates the privileged epistemology of science, and thereby exempts it from sociological explanation. Mulkay opposes this view, rightly in our opinion, by pointing out the problem of the 'science discovers, technology applies' notion implicit in such claims. In a second argument against this position, Mulkay notes (following Mario Bunge)[54] that it is possible for a false, or partly-false, theory to be used as the basis for successful practical application: the success of the technology would not then have anything to say about the 'truth' of the scientific knowledge upon which it was based. We find this second point not entirely satisfactory. We would rather stress that the truth or falsity of scientific knowledge are irrelevant to sociological analysis of belief: to retreat to the argument that science may be wrong but good technology can still be based upon it is to miss this point. Furthermore, the success of technology is still left unexplained within such an argument. The only effective way to deal with these difficulties is to adopt a perspective which attempts to show that technology, as well as science, can be understood as a social construct.

Mulkay seems to 'be reluctant to take this step because, as he points out, 'there are very few studies . . . which consider how the technical meaning of hard technology is socially constructed'.[55] This situation however, is starting to change: a number of such studies have recently emerged. For example, Michel Callon, in a pioneering study, has shown the effectiveness of focussing upon technological controversies. He draws upon an extensive case-study of the electric vehicle in France (1960-75) to demonstrate that almost everything is negotiable: what is certain and what is not; who is a scientist and who is a technologist; what is technological and what is social; and who can participate in the controversy.[56] David Noble's study of the introduction of numerically-controlled machine tools can also be regarded as an important contribution to a social constructivist view of technology.[57] Noble's explanatory goals come from a rather different (Marxist) tradition,[58] and his study has much to recommend it: he considers the development of both a successful and failed technology, and gives a symmetrical account of both developments. Another intriguing study in this tradition is Lazonick's account of the introduction of the self-acting mule:[59] he shows that aspects of this technical development can be understood in terms of the relations of production rather than any inner logic of technological development. The work undertaken by Bijker, Bönig and Van Oost is another attempt to show how the socially constructed character of the content of some technological artefacts might be approached empirically:[60] six case studies were carried out, using historical sources.

In summary, then, we can say that the predominant traditions in technology studies — innovation studies and the history of technology — do not yet provide much encouragement for our programme. However, there are exceptions, and some very recent studies in the sociology of technology form promising starts upon which a unified approach could be built. We will now give a more extensive account of how these ideas may be synthesized.

# EPOR and SCOT

In this part of the paper we outline in more detail the concepts and methods which we wish to employ. We start by describing the Empirical Programme of Relativism as it has been developed in the sociology of scientific knowledge. We then go on to discuss in more detail one approach taken in the sociology of technology.

## The Empirical Programme of Relativism (EPOR)

The EPOR is an approach which has produced several studies demonstrating the social construction of scientific knowledge in the 'hard' science. This tradition of research has emerged from recent sociology of scientific knowledge. Its main characteristics, which distinguish it from other approaches in the same area, are the focus upon the empirical study of contemporary scientific developments, and the study, in particular, of scientific controversies.[61]

Three stages in the explanatory aims of the EPOR can be identified. In the *first stage* the interpretative flexibility of scientific findings is displayed — in other words, it is shown that scientific findings are open to more than one interpretation. This shifts the focus for the explanation of scientific developments from the Natural World to the Social World. However, although this interpretative flexibility can be recovered in certain circumstances, it remains the case that such flexibility soon disappears in science — that is to say, a scientific consensus will usually emerge as to what the 'truth' is in any particular instance. Social mechanisms which limit interpretative flexibility, and thus allow scientific controversies to be terminated, are described in the *second stage*. A *third stage*, which has not yet been carried through in any study of contemporary science, is to relate such 'closure mechanisms' to the wider social-cultural milieu. If all three stages were to be addressed in a single study, as Collins writes, 'The impact of society on knowledge "produced" at the laboratory bench would then have been followed through in the hardest possible case'.[62]

The EPOR represents a continuing effort by sociologist to understand the content of the natural sciences in terms of social construction. Various parts of the programme are better researched than others. The third stage of the programme has not yet even been addressed: but there are many excellent studies exploring the first stage. Most current research is aimed at elucidating the 'closure mechanisms' whereby consensus emerges (the second stage). Many studies within the EPOR have been most fruitfully located in the area of scientific controversy. Controversies offer a methodological advantage in the comparative ease with which they reveal the interpretative flexibility of scientific results. Interviews conducted with scientists engaged in a controversy usually reveal strong and differing opinions over scientific findings. As such flexibility soon vanishes from science, it is difficult to recover from the textual sources with which historians usually work. Collins has highlighted the importance of the 'controversy group' in science by his use of the term 'Core-Set'.[63] These are the scientists most intimately involved in a controversial research topic. Because the 'Core-Set' is defined in relation to knowledge production in science (the 'Core-Set' constructs scientific knowledge) some of the empirical problems encountered in the identification of groups in science by purely sociometric means can be overcome. And studying the Core-Set has another methodological advantage, in that the resulting consensus can be monitored. In other words, the group of scientists who experiment and theorize at the research frontiers, and who become embroiled in scientific controversy, will also reflect the growing consensus as to the outcome of that controversy. The same group of 'Core-Set' scientists can then be studied in both the first and second stages of the EPOR.[64]

## Social Construction of Technology (SCOT)

Before outlining some of the concepts found to be fruitful by Bijker and his collaborators in their studies in the sociology of technology, we should point out an imbalance between the two approaches (EPOR and SCOT) we are considering. The EPOR is part of a flourishing tradition in the sociology of scientific knowledge: it is a well-established programme supported by much empirical research. In contrast, the sociology of technology is an embryonic field with no well-established traditions of research: and the approach we draw upon specifically (SCOT) is only in its early empirical stages. Most readers, whilst having some familiarity with the EPOR, will probably be unaware of the concepts employed in SCOT. In bringing together a mature research tradition and an embryonic one, there is a danger that the reader with interpret the imbalance to the detriment of the 'younger' partner. In an attempt to engender a more sympathetic reading, we will devote considerable space to outlining some of the concepts and empirical material used in SCOT. Of course, the feeling of imbalance will persist, since it is a real imbalance. However, by being honest about the status of our studies we hope it will be seen more clearly what has and what has not been achieved.

In SCOT, the developmental process of a technological artefact is described as an alternation of variation and selection.[65] This results in a 'multi-directional' model, in contrast with the linear models used explicitly in many innovation studies, and implicitly in much history of technology. Such a multi-directional view is essential to any social constructivist account of technology. Of course, with historical hindsight, it is possible to collapse the multi-directional model onto a simpler linear model; but this misses the thrust of our argument that the 'successful' stages in the development are not the only possible ones.

Let us consider the development of the bicycle.[66] Applied to the level of artefacts in this development, this multi-directional view results in the description summarized in Figure 2. Here we see the artefact 'Ordinary' (or, as it was nicknamed after becoming less ordinary, the 'Penny-farthing'), and a range of possible variations. It is important to recognize that, in the view of the actors of those days, these variants were at the same time very different from each other and equally were serious rivals. It is only by retrospective distortion that a quasi-linear development emerges, as depicted in Figure 3. In this representation the so-called 'safety ordinaries' ('Xtraordinary' [1878], 'Facile' [1879], and 'Club Safety' [1885]) only figure as amusing aberrations which need not be taken seriously. Such a retrospective description can be challenged by looking at the actual situation in the 1880s. Some of the 'safety ordinaries' were produced commercially, whilst Lawson's 'Bicyclette', which seems to play an important role in the linear model, proved to be a commercial failure.[67]

However, if a multi-directional model is adopted, it is possible to ask why some of the variants 'die', whereas others 'survive'. To illuminate this 'selection' part of the developmental processes, let us consider the problems and solutions presented by each artefact at particular moments. The rationale for this move is the same as that for focussing upon scientific controversies within EPOR — in this way, one can expect to bring out more clearly the interpretative flexibility of technological artefacts.

successful development _____

failed development – – – – – – – – – – – – – – –

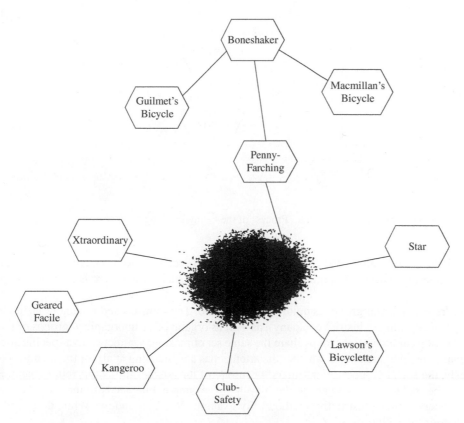

*Note:* the grey area has been filled in and magnified in Figure 7.

**Fig. 2.** A Multi-Directional View of the Developmental Process of the Penny-Farthing Bicycle.

**Key for Figures 2-7**

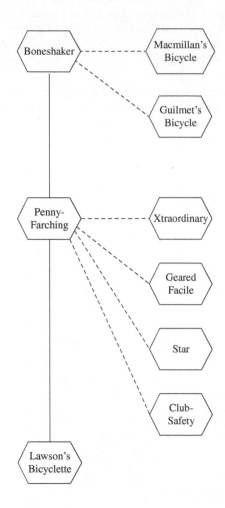

**Fig. 3.** The Traditional Quasi-Linear View of the Developmental Process of the Penny-Farthing Bicycle

In deciding which problems are relevant, a crucial role is played by the social groups concerned with the artefact, and by the meanings which those groups give to the artefact: a problem is only defined as such, when there is a social group for which it constitutes a 'problem'.

The use of the concept 'relevant social group' is quite straightforward. The term is used to denote institutions and organizations (such as the military or some specific industrial company), as well as organized or unorganized groups of individuals. The key requirement is that all members of a certain social groups share the same set of meanings, attached to a specific artefact.[68] In deciding which social groups are relevant, the first question is whether the artefact has any meaning at all for the members of the social group under investigation. Obviously, the social group of 'consumers' or 'users' of the artefact fulfils this requirement. But also less obvious social groups may need to be included. In the case of the bicycle, for example, one needs to mention the 'anti-cyclists'. Their actions ranged from derisive cheers to more destructive methods. For example, Rev L. Meadows White described such resistance to the bicycle in his book, *A Photographic Tour on Wheels*:

> . . . but when to words are added deeds, and stones are thrown, sticks thrust into the wheels, or caps hurled into the machinery, the picture has a different aspect. All the above in certain districts are of common occurrence, and have all happened to me, especially when passing through a village just after school is closed.[69]

Clearly, for the anti-cyclists the artefact 'bicycle' had taken on meaning!

Another question we need to address, is whether a provisionally defined social group is homogeneous with respect to the meanings given to the artefact — or is it more effective to describe the developmental process by dividing a rather heterogeneous group into several different social groups? Thus, within the group of cycle-users, we discern a separate social group? Thus, within the group of cycle-users, we discern a separate social group of women cyclists. During the days of the high-wheeled 'Ordinary', women were not supposed to mount a bicycle. For instance, in a magazine advice column (1885) it is proclaimed, in reply to a letter from a young lady:

> The mere fact of riding a bicycle is not in itself sinful, and if it is the only means of reaching the church on a Sunday, it may be excusable.[70]

Tricycles were the permitted machines for women. But engineers and producers anticipated the importance of women as potential bicyclists. In a review of the annual Stanley Exhibition of Cycles in 1890, the author observes:

> From the number of safeties adapted for the use of ladies, it seems as if bicycling was becoming popular with the weaker sex, and we are not surprised at it, considering the saving of power derived from the use of a machine having only one slack.[71]

Thus some parts of the bicycle's development can be better explained by including a separate social group of feminine cycle-users. This need not, of course, be so in other cases: for instance, we do not expect it would be useful to consider a separate social group of women user of, say, fluorescent lamps.[72]

Once the relevant social groups have been identified, they are described in more detail. Although the only defining property is some homogeneous meaning given to a certain artefact, the intention is not just to retreat to worn-out, general statements about 'consumers' and 'producers'. We need to have a detailed description of the relevant social groups in order better to define the function of the artefact with respect to each group. Without this, one could not hope to be able to give any explanation of the developmental process. For example, the social group of cyclists riding the high-wheeled Ordinary consisted of 'young men of means and nerve: they might be professional men, clerks, schoolmasters or dons'.[73] For this social group, the function of the bicycle was primarily for sport. The following comment in the Daily Telegraph emphasizes sport, rather than transport:

> Bicycling is a healthy and manly pursuit with much to recommend it, and, unlike other foolish crazes, it has not died out.[74]

Let us now return to the exposition of the model. Having identified the relevant social groups for a certain artefact (Figure 4), we are especially interested in the problems each group has with respect to that artefact (Figure 5). Around each problem, several variants of solution can be identified (Figure 6). In the case of the bicycle, some relevant problems and solutions are shown in Figure 7, in which the grey area of Figure 2 has been filled. This way of describing the developmental process brings out clearly all kinds of conflicts: conflicting technical requirements by different social groups (for example, the 'speed' requirement and the 'safety' requirement); conflicting solutions to the same problem (for example, the Safety Low Wheelers and the Safety Ordinaries — this type of conflict often results in patent litigation); and moral conflicts (for example, women wearing skirts or trousers on a High Wheeler). Within this scheme, various solutions for these conflicts and problems are possible — not only technological, but also judicial, or even moral (for example, changing attitudes towards women wearing trousers).

Following the developmental process in this way, we see growing and diminishing degrees of stabilization[75] of the different artefacts. In principle, the degree of stabilization is different in different social groups. By using the concept of stabilization, the 'invention' of the Safety Bicycle is seen not as an isolated event (1884), but as a nineteen-year process (1879-98). For example, at the beginning of this period the relevant groups did not see the 'safety bicycle', but a wide range of bi- and tricycles — and, among those, a rather ugly crocodile-like bicycle with a relatively low front wheel and rear chain drive (Lawson's Bicyclette). By the end of the period, the word 'safety bicycle' denoted a low-wheeled bicycle with rear chain drive, diamond frame, and air tyres. As a result of the stabilization of the artefact after 1898, one did not need to specify these details: they were taken for granted as the essential 'ingredients' of the safety bicycle.

We want to stress that our model is not used as a mould, into which the empirical data have to be forced, coûte que coûte. The model has been developed from a series of case studies, and not from purely philosophical or theoretical analysis. Its function is primarily heuristic — to bring out all the aspects relevant for our purposes. This is not to say that there are no explanatory and theoretical aims, analogous to the different stages of the EPOR.[76] And indeed, as we have shown, this model already does more than merely describe technological development: it highlights its multidirectional character. Also, as will be indicated below, it brings out the interpretative flexibility of technological artefacts and the role which different closure mechanisms may play in the stabilization of artefacts.

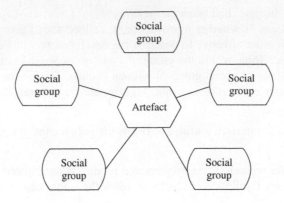

**Fig. 4.** The Relationship between an Artefact and the Relevant Social Groups

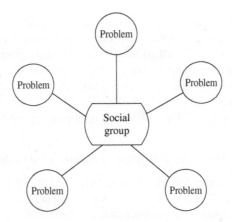

**Fig. 5.** The Relationship between One Social Group and the Perceived Problems

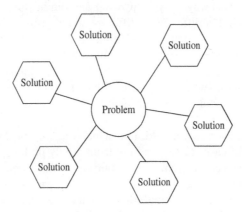

**Fig. 6.** The Relationship between One Problem and its Possible Solutions

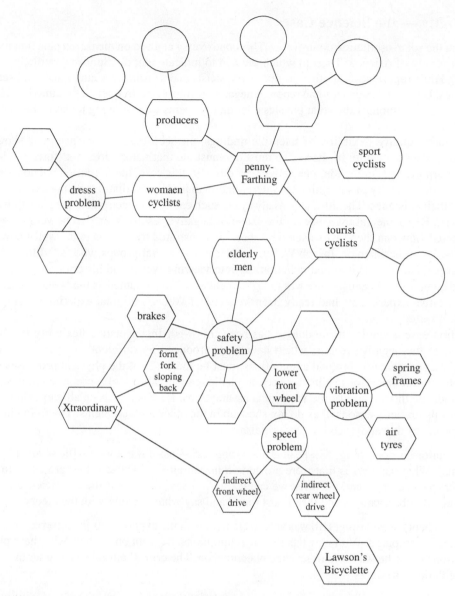

*Note:* because of lack of space, not all relevant social groups, problems and solutions are shown

**Fig. 7.** Some Relevant Social Groups, Problems and Solutions in the Developmental Process of the Penny-Farthing Bicycle

# The Social Construction of Facts and Artefacts

Having described the two approaches to the study of science and technology we wish to draw upon, we will now discuss in more detail the parallels between them. As a way of putting some flesh on our discussion we will, where appropriate, give empirical illustrations drawn from our own research.

The first stage of the EPOR involves the demonstration of the interpretative flexibility of scientific findings. To illustrate in more detail what we mean here, we will give a brief example.

## Interpretative Flexibility — the Science Case

Our example is drawn from the solar-oscillation controversy. This controversy centred on measurements first made in 1975 by Henry Hill (a physicist at the University of Arizona, Tucson) which seemed to indicate that the Sun was oscillating at a number of different frequencies. Following Hill's report, several other groups of physicists and astronomers attempted to observe these oscillations, using a variety of techniques. By 1978, six groups had reported negative results at the frequencies claimed by Hill, thus casting doubt upon Hill's claims. The consensus amongst the solar physics community seems to be moving towards the view that the oscillations claimed by Hill do not exist.

To demonstrate the interpretative flexibility of scientific findings, the sociologist of science must show that differing interpretations of the natural world are available: in short, s/he must demonstrate that nature does not 'force the issue' of the existence or non-existence of some purported phenomenon, one way or the other. In this case, the purported phenomenon is the existence of solar oscillations. There is little difficulty in sustaining the interpretation that these oscillations do not exist, since most experimental results have not confirmed their existence. The difficulty, as always in such cases, is in recovering the plausibility of the rejected view that the oscillations do exist. Experimental evidence, in the shape of negative results, seems to be very compelling. The way that the plausibility of the rejected view can then be recovered has been demonstrated by Collins in his well-known study of the gravity wave episode.[77] In that case, an experimenter, Joseph Weber, was faced by several groups who failed to confirm his experimental claims to have detected large fluxes of gravitational radiation. By interviewing Weber and his critics, Collins was able to show that the negative results lacked compulsion because there was no agreement as to what counted as the 'same' experiment. It was possible to question whether the negative experiments had really been 'repeats' of Weber's original experiment. The thrust of the negative experiments could thus be diverted.

In the solar-oscillation case a similar methodology has been followed. Interpretative flexibility has been demonstrated by monitoring Hill's response to the negative results, which have been produced by different techniques to those used by Hill. To compare the differing techniques, some theoretical assumptions must be made about the physical processes occurring in the solar photosphere. Hill's response to the negative results has been to challenge the validity of these assumptions, and to claim that the different results actually indicate the poverty of the theoretical assumptions. He has thus been able to maintain that his oscillations are real but that, for various theoretical reasons, they do not show up in the other measurements. The following comment by Hill (in interview) illustrates the power of this approach towards criticism:

> My attitude is that Stanford is not wrong, Kitt Peak is not wrong, Eric Fossat is not wrong [these are all groups reporting negative experiments]. What happens is that there are certain measurements whose values are taken to be correct, and you take our numbers to be correct and ask what we can learn . . . I say look this is the way science is supposed to be, you look at Nature and do observations and then I turn round and say what's wrong with the theory.

By suggesting that the theory was wrong, Hill was able to claim that all the experiments gave correct results, but that the results could not be straightforwardly compared. With new theoretical assumptions, he went on to show why these other techniques would not be sensitive to oscillations. Thus he was able to save the phenomenon. The critics' attitude was rather different. As one observer, who had failed to find oscillations, said:

> You should just take what we are observing, and using very straightforward assumptions . . . , you would have a big oscillation in our data but you don't.

For the critics, their negative results could straightforwardly be used to cast doubt upon Hill's measurements, implying that solar oscillations did not exist.

Of course, this example is merely illustrative, and to make a convincing case all the technical arguments over the reality of the oscillations, and the veracity of the various theoretical analyses, must be examined. However, we think this example will suffice for demonstrating how interpretative flexibility is to be shown in the science case.

## Interpretative Flexibility — the Technology Case

In SCOT, the equivalent of the first stage of the EPOR would seem to be the demonstration that technological artefacts are culturally constructed and interpreted — in other words, the interpretative flexibility of a technological artefact must be shown. By this we mean, not only that there is flexibility in how people think of, or interpret, artefacts, but also that there is flexibility in how artefacts are designed. There is not just one possible way, or one best way, of designing an artefact. In principle this could be demonstrated in the same way as for the science case — that is, by interviews with technologists who are engaged in a contemporary technological controversy. For example, we can imagine that if interviews had been carried out in 1890 with the cycle engineers, we would have been able to show the interpretative flexibility of the artefact 'air tyre'. For some, this artefact was a solution to the vibration problem of small-wheeled vehicles:

[The air tyre was] devised with a view to afford increased facilities for the passage of wheeled vehicles — chiefly of the lighter class such for instance as velocipedes, invalid chairs, ambulances — over roadways and paths, especially when these latter are of rough or uneven character.[78]

For others, the air tyre was a way of going faster (this will be outlined in more detail below). For yet another group of engineers, it was an ugly looking way of making the low-wheeler yet more unsafe (because of side-slipping) than it already was. For instance, the following comment describing The Stanley Exhibition of Cycles, is revealing:

The most conspicuous innovation in the cycle construction is the use of pneumatic tires. These tires are hollow, about 2 in. diameter, and are inflated by the use of a small air pump. They are said to afford most luxurious riding, the roughest macadam and cobbles being reduced to the smoothest asphalte. Not having had the opportunity of testing these tires, we are unable to speak of them from practical experience; but looking at them from a theoretical point of view, we opine that considerable difficulty will be experienced in keeping the tires thoroughly inflated. Air under pressure is a troublesome thing to deal with. From the reports of those who have used these tires, it seems that they are prone to slip on muddy roads. If this is so, we fear their use on rear-driving safeties — which are all more or less addicted to side-slipping — is out of the question, as any improvement in this line should be to prevent side slip and not to increase it. Apart from these defects, the appearance of the tires destroys the symmetry and graceful appearance of a cycle, and this alone is, we think, sufficient to prevent their coming into general use.[79]

And indeed, other artefacts were seen as providing a solution for the vibration problem, as the following comment reveals:

With the introduction of the rear-driving safety bicycle has arisen a demand for anti-vibration devices, as the small wheels of these machines are conducive to considerable vibration, even on the best roads. Nearly every exhibitor of this type of machine has some appliance to suppress vibration.[80]

Most solutions used various spring constructions in the frame, the saddle, and the steering-bar. In 1896, even after the safety bicycle (and the air tyre with it) achieved a high degree of stabilization, 'spring frames' were still being marketed.

It is important to realize that this demonstration of interpretative flexibility, by interviews and historical sources, is only one of a set of possible methods. At least in the study of technology, another method is applicable, and has actually been used. It can be shown that different social groups have radically different interpretations of one technological artefact. We call these differences 'radical' because the content of the artefact seems to be involved. It is something more than what Mulkay rightly claims to be rather easy — 'to show that the social meaning of television varies with and depends upon the social context in which it is employed'. As Mulkay notes, 'it is much more difficult to show what is to count as a "working television set" is similarly context-dependent in any significant respect'.[81]

We think that our account — in which the different interpretations by social groups of the content of artefacts lead via different chains of problems and solutions to different further developments — involves the content of the artefact itself. Our earlier example of the development of the safety bicycle is of this kind. Another example is variations within the high-wheeler. The high-wheeler's meaning as a virile, high-speed bicycle led to the development of larger front wheels — for, with a fixed angular velocity, the only way of getting a higher translational velocity over the ground was by enlarging the radius. One of the last bicycles resulting from this strand of development was the Rudge Ordinary of 1892, which had a 56-inch wheel and air tyre. But groups of women and of elderly men gave quite another meaning to the high-wheeler. For them, its most important characteristic was its lack of safety:

Owing to the disparity in wheel diameters and the small weight of the backbone and trailing wheel, also to the rider's position practically over the centre of the wheel, if the large front wheel hit a brick or large stone on the road, and the rider was unprepared, the sudden check to the wheel usually threw him over the handlebar. For this reason the machine was regarded as dangerous, and however enthusiastic one may have been about the ordinary — and I was an enthusiastic rider of it once — there is no denying that it was only possible for comparatively young and athletic men.[82]

This meaning gave rise to lowering the front wheel, moving back the saddle, and giving the front fork a less upright position. Via another chain of problems and solutions (see Figure 7), this resulted in artefacts such as Lawson's Bicyclette (1879) and the Xtraordinary (1878). Thus, there was not one high-wheeler — there was the macho machine, leading to new designs of bicycles with even higher front wheels, and there was the unsafe machine, leading to new designs of bicycle with lower front wheels, saddles moved backwards, or reversed order of small and high wheel.[83] Thus the interpretative flexibility of the artefact 'Penny-farthing' is materialized in quite different design lines.

## Closure and Stabilization

The second stage of the EPOR concerns the mapping of mechanisms for the closure of debate — or, in SCOT, for the stabilization of an artefact. We have already noted that the stabilization of an artefact is always a matter of degree: it seems that consensus in science can be described in similar terms. For example, Latour and Woolgar have shown that in the social construction of scientific facts modalities are attached or withdrawn from statements about facts in order to connote the degree of stabilization of the fact.84 Thus the statements: The experiments claim to show the existence of X', 'The experiments show the existence of X', and 'X exists', not only exhibit progressively fewer modalities but also progressively greater degrees of stabilization of X.85 In technological cases, we have also found varieties in the number of definitions, specifications, and elucidations attached to statements about the artefact. We can use this as a measure of the degree of stabilization which the artefact has achieved. However, there is a methodological problem in using language in this way. The need to add definitions and elucidations in order to be able to communicate about an artefact depends on more than just the degree of stabilization of that artefact in that social group; it will at least also depend on the context in which the statement is used (for example, a research paper, a patent, or a handbook).86

In considering the emergence of consensus and stabilization, one difference between science and technology arises. In the case of science, consensus formation can often be studied by focussing upon one group — the Core-Set — although the wider scientific community plays a specific role, especially in the case of a rhetorical closure (see below). But in the case of technology, it is typically necessary to analyze the stabilization of an artefact amongst more than one group, as we have shown above; and, since a variety of social groups must then be identified, it is impossible to carry out quite such neat case studies as can be achieved in science. This is partly a matter of strategy, for, in the study of science, it is sometimes necessary to follow more than one social group. For instance, in her study of a scientific laboratory, Knorr-Cetina argues that stabilization occurs amongst a variety of groups which she refers to as 'trans-scientific fields'.87

It seems that a variety of closure mechanisms play a part in bringing about both scientific agreement and the stabilization of an artefact. In some cases one particular mechanism may predominate; other cases may be resolved by other mechanisms or combinations of mechanisms. We will now illustrate what we mean by a closure mechanism by giving examples of two types which seem to have played a role in cases with which we are familiar. We refer to the particular mechanisms upon which we focus as 'rhetorical closure', and 'closure by redefinition of problem'. Firstly, we will discuss rhetorical closure in the science and technology cases. We will then go on to illustrate 'closure by redefinition of problem' for the technology case.

## Rhetorical Closure — the Science Case

What we have in mind here is some 'crucial' experimental result, 'definitive' proof, or 'knockdown' argument which has the effect of closing the debate on some controversial issue. The character of such experimental results, proofs or arguments is that they are not convincing to the scientists most concerned with the debate — those scientists who form the Core-Set. Indeed, such scientists will usually be aware of the inadequacies of such 'crucial' experiments, 'definitive' proofs and 'knockdown' arguments, which usually have more influence in persuading the wider community than the Core-Set itself.

An example of an experiment which played this role was that carried out by one of the scientists involved in the gravity-wave dispute. This experiment (performed by 'Quest') did not have the requisite sensitivity to challenge Weber's results, but it played a significant role in their demise.88 Another example might be the ritualistic recitation of von Neumann's hidden variable impossibility proof as a means of closing down the debate over David Bohm's 1952 hidden variable interpretation of quantum mechanics. This proof continued to be cited with little attempt being made to investigate its veracity. A third example of rhetorical argument serving as a closure mechanism is documented by Pickering in his study of the reception of Price's magnetic monopole claim. A talk by Louis Alvarez which was full of rhetorical arguments (that is, not convincing to specialists) played an important role in the demise of the monopole claim amongst the high-energy physics community.90

To illustrate this type of mechanism further, we will turn to an example drawn from the solar-oblateness controversy.91 This controversy began in 1967, and centred on Princeton physicist Robert Dicke's claims to have observed that the Sun was oblate — that is to say, he found the solar equatorial diameter to be larger than the solar polar diameter. This result was very important because it suggested an alternative explanation for the well-known anomaly in the perihelion advance of Mercury's orbit. This anomaly was widely believed to be explained by Einstein's general theory of relativity — and this was, indeed, one of the major successes claimed for Einstein's theory. However, a quadrupole moment from an oblate Sun (assuming the oblateness was produced by a rapidly rotating core) could account for enough of Mercury's perihelion to suggest that rival theories of gravity, such as the Brans-Dicke scalar-tensor theory, might provide the correct explanation.

When Dicke's oblateness results were published they immediately produced a storm of controversy. By 1974, eighteen major theoretical papers had been published challenging the results. Soon an experimental challenge also emerged. A new measurement of the oblateness was carried out by Henry Hill (who was also involved in the solar oscillation controversy). Hill's measurements contradicted Dicke's and furthermore suggested that Einstein's theory was largely correct. Hill's results received wide attention in the scientific press and in effect closed down the controversy. Whenever the oblateness issue threatened to raise its head again, Hill's result was ritually cited as having shown that Dicke was wrong. As is typical with rhetorical closure, none of the possible interpretative loopholes in Hill's experiment were explored (in contrast to his work on solar oscillations), and Hill's results were of more significance to the whole community than to the Core-Set.

## Rhetorical Closure — the Technology Case

Closure in technology involves the stabilization of an artefact and the 'disappearance' of problems. To close a technological 'controversy' the problems need not be solved in the common sense of that word. The key point is whether the relevant social groups see the problem as being solved. In technology, advertising can play an important role in shaping the meaning which a social group gives to an artefact.[92] Thus, for instance, an attempt was made to 'close' the 'safety controversy' around the high-wheeler by simply claiming that the artefact was perfectly safe. An advertisement of the 'Facile' Bicycle (sic!) reads:

> Bicyclists! Why risk your limbs and lives on high Machines when for road work a 40 inch or 42 inch 'Facile' gives all the advantages of the other, together with almost absolute safety.[93]

This claim of 'almost absolute safety' was a rhetorical move, considering the height of the bicycle and the forward position of the rider, which were well known to engineers at the time to present problems of safety.

## Closure by Redefinition of Problem — the Technology Case

We have already mentioned the controversy around the air tyre: for most of the engineers it was a theoretical and practical monstrosity. For the general public, in the beginning it meant an aesthetically awful accessory:

> . . . messenger boys guffawed at the sausage tyre, factory ladies squirmed with merriment, while even sober citizens were sadly moved to mirth at a comicality obviously designed solely to lighten the gloom of their daily routine.[94]

For Dunlop and the other protagonists of the air tyre, originally it meant a solution to the vibration problem. However, the group of sporting cyclists riding their high-wheelers did not accept that to be a problem at all. Vibration only presented a problem to the (potential) users of the low-wheeled bicycle. Three important social groups were therefore opposed to the air tyre. But then the air tyre was mounted on a racing bicycle. When, for the first time, the tyre was used at the racing track, its entry was hailed with derisive laughter. This was, however, quickly silenced by the high speed achieved, and there was only astonishment left when it outpaced all rivals.[95] Very soon handicappers had to give racing cyclists on high-wheelers a considerable start if riders on air-tyred low-wheelers were entered. After a short period no racer of any pretensions troubled to compete on anything else.[96]

What had happened? With respect to two important groups, the sporting cyclists and the general public, closure had been reached — but not by convincing those two groups of the feasibility of the air tyre in its meaning as an antivibration device. One can say, we think, that the meaning of the air tyre was translated[97] to constitute a solution to quite another problem: the problem of 'how to go as fast as possible'. And thus, by redefining the key problem with respect to which the artefact should have the meaning of a solution, closure was reached for two of the relevant social groups. How the third group, the engineers, came to accept the air tyre is another story, and need not be told here. Of course, there is nothing 'natural' or logically necessary about this form of closure. It could be argued that speed is not the most important characteristic of the bicycle, or that existing cycle races were not appropriate tests of a cycle's 'real' speed (after all, the idealized world of the race track may not match everyday road conditions, anymore than the formula-one racing car bears upon the performance requirements of the average family saloon). Still, bicycle races have played an important role in the development of the bicycle, and since racing can be viewed as a specific form of testing, this observation is very much in line with Constant's recent plea to pay more attention to testing procedures in studying technology.[98]

## The Wider Context

Finally, we come to the third stage of our research programme. The task here in the area of technology would seem to be the same as for science — to relate the content of a technological artefact to the wider sociopolitical milieu. This aspect has not yet been demonstrated for the science case,[99] at least not in contemporaneous sociological studies.[100] However, the SCOT method of describing technological artefacts by focussing upon the meanings given to them by relevant social groups seems to suggest a way forward. Obviously, the sociocultural and political situation of a social group shapes its norms and values, which in turn influence the meaning given to an artefact. Since we have shown above how different meanings can constitute different lines of development, SCOT's descriptive model seems to offer an operationalization of the relationship between the wider milieu and the actual content of technology.[101]

## Concluding Summary and Implications for Further Research

In this paper we have been concerned to outline an integrated social constructivist approach towards the empirical study of science and technology. We first reviewed several relevant bodies of literature and strands of argument. We indicated that the social constructivist approach is a flourishing tradition within the sociology of science, and that it shows every promise of wider application. We reviewed the literature on the science-technology relationship, and showed that here, too, the social constructivist approach is starting to bear fruit. And we reviewed some of the main traditions in technology studies. We argued that innovation studies, and much of the history of technology, were unsuitable for our sociological purposes. We discussed some recent work in the sociology of technology, and noted encouraging signs that a 'new wave' of social constructivist case studies was beginning to emerge.

We then outlined in more detail the two approaches — one in the sociology of scientific knowledge (EPOR), and one in the field of sociology of technology (SCOT) — upon which we base our integrated perspective. Finally, we indicated the similarity of the explanatory goals of the two approaches, and illustrated these goals with some examples drawn from science and technology.

Despite the imbalance between the two approaches — an imbalance largely due to the underdeveloped state of the sociology of technology — a number of important points of comparison have already emerged. Particularly, we have seen that the concepts of 'interpretative flexibility' and 'closure mechanism', and the notion of 'social group', can be given empirical reference in both the science and technology cases. A number of remarks stemming from our comparison are, however, appropriate.[102]

We have already indicated that the way in which interpretative flexibility has been demonstrated in the technology case, with the use of the descriptive model, is one of several possible methods. It would be fruitful to apply the 'controversy method', which has proved its success in the science case, and carry out a study of a contemporary controversy in technology.

More systematic studies of closure mechanisms in science and technology are also needed. We have looked at only two types of closure mechanism: others must be researched. It is possible that the type of closure mechanism predominant in science and the type predominant in technology are different. For example, we were not able to find a close analogue of 'closure by redefinition of problem' in the solar physics material. However, it would seem that phenomena such as 'ignoring a problem' or 'moving on', which are encountered in other areas of science, are related to 'closure by redefinition'. It can be speculated that the differences in types of closure mechanisms are linked to differences in the number of relevant groups involved in the developmental process. In science (at least in those parts of physics and biology which have so far been researched) it does seem to be the case that the social construction of scientific knowledge can be followed through by monitoring the activities of one dominant social group — the Core-Set. In technology it seems that there is no equivalent group, and that a number of social groups must be studied. Perhaps with more groups involved, 'redefinition of problem' is likely to be a more effective closure mechanism in technology than in science. The study of technology should thus give rise to a better analysis of closure mechanisms. This, in turn, should lead to a more systematic study of the functioning of various social groups, in science as well as technology. For instance, the role which rhetoric plays in the relation between the Core-Set and the wider scientific community seems to be analogous to the role played by advertising in the relation between the social group of producers and various groups of (potential) users.

The difference in the number of relevant social groups perhaps sheds some light on the different paths which sociology of science and technology studies have taken. The large number of social groups relevant to the technology case does present problems for the micro-study approach which has proved to be so fruitful in the sociology of scientific knowledge. As there does not appear to be any one key social group in technology, researchers may have been reluctant to look in too fine detail, afraid to miss key developments associated with unresearched social groups. The solution to this problem does not seem to us to be to go to the opposite extreme and use techniques of aggregation, because one then runs into the difficulty (which we have already noted) of ignoring the technological content of the artefact. We believe that the approach we have outlined — of identifying the relevant social groups — does provide a means of researching technology, but in such a way as not to lose sensitivity to the content of the artefact; in that way, it enables us to sail between the Scylla of the isolated artefact and the Charybdis of a mass aggregation.[103]

An alternative location for micro-studies of science — the ethnographic study of the scientific laboratory — has recently been advocated. Such a location has proved to be particularly useful for showing the interpretative flexibility of scientific knowledge.[104] However, the laboratory location is a rather poor place in which to study the formation of scientific consensus. This is because the processes of consensus formation are not usually to be found in a single laboratory. Unless one is prepared to use other data than purely ethnographic sources, it is difficult to study processes of consensus formation in individual laboratories.[105] The problem is even worse in the case of the study of the stabilization of technological artefacts. This is because there is *an even larger number of social groups* to study, and one is likely to obtain even less relevant data from the individual laboratory. It is important that an ethnographic study — say of an R & D lab — be carried out, but such a study will, it seems, be more useful for showing the interpretative flexibility of technological artefacts than for the study of closure mechanisms.

Studies of the influence of the wider cultural and social milieu are still few and far between, in both science and technology. The notion of 'relevant social group', as it is employed in SCOT, may, as we have indicated, provide a fruitful approach. Such studies are the most daunting to carry out, but we can only hope that they will be forthcoming, as they are an integral part of our social constructivist programme.

As we have noted throughout this paper, the sociology of technology is still underdeveloped, in comparison with the sociology of scientific knowledge. It would be a shame if the advances made in the latter field could not be used to throw light on the study of technology. On the other hand, in our studies of technology it appeared to be fruitful to include several social groups in the analysis, and there are some indications that this method may also bear fruit in studies of science. Thus our integrated approach to the social study of science and technology indicates how the sociology of science and the sociology of technology might benefit each other.

But there is another reason, and perhaps an even more important one, to argue for such an integrated approach. And this brings us to a question which some readers might have expected to be dealt with in the very first paragraph of this article — namely, the question of how to demarcate between science and technology. We think that it is rather unfruitful to make such an a priori distinction, using elaborate definitions. Instead, it seems worth while to start with commonsensical notions of science and technology, and to study them in an integrated way, as we have proposed. Whatever interesting differences may exist, will gain contrast within such a programme. This would constitute another concrete result of the integrated study of the social construction of facts and artefacts.

## • NOTES

We are grateful to Henk van den Belt, Ernst Homburg, Donald Mackenzie and Steve Woolgar for comments on an earlier draft of this paper. We would like to thank the Stiftung Volkswagen, Federal Republic of Germany, the University of Technology Twente, The Netherlands, and the UK SSRC (G/00/23/0072/1), for financial support.

1. The science-technology divorce seems to have resulted not so much from the lack of overall analytical goals within 'science studies', but more from the contingent demands of carrying out empirical work in these areas. To give an example: the new sociology of scientific knowledge, which attempts to take account of the actual content of scientific knowledge, can best be carried out by researchers who have some training in the science they study, or at least who are familiar with an extensive body of technical literature (indeed, many researchers are ex-natural scientists). Once having gained such expertise, there is a tendency to stay within the domain where that expertise can best be deployed. Similarly, R&D studies and innovation studies, in which the analysis centres on the 'firm' and 'market place', have tended to demand the specialist competences of economists. Such disparate bodies of work do not easily lead towards a more integrated conception of science and technology. One notable exception is J. R. Ravetz, *Scientific Knowledge and its Social Problems* (Oxford: Oxford University Press, 1971). This is one of the few works of recent science studies in which both science and technology and their differences are explored within a common framework.

2. The studies of science have been carried out by Pinch. The examples we draw upon in this paper come from his recent comparative study of four episodes of scientific controversy. For some of the provisional findings of this study, see T. J. Pinch, 'Towards an Analysis of Scientific Observation: The Externality and Evidential Significance of Observation Reports in Physics', *Social Studies of Science*, forthcoming. In this paper we will use examples connected with the work of one scientist — Henry Hill.

    The studies of technology have been carried out by Bijker. In all, six technological innovations were studied. See W. E. Bijker, J. Bönig and E. C. J. van Oost, The Social Construction of Technological Artefacts', paper presented to the EASST Conference (Deutschlandsberg, Austria: 24-26 September 1982). In this paper we mostly use examples drawn from the case-study of the bicycle.

3. H. M. Collins, 'Stages in the Empirical Programme of Relativism', *Social Studies of Science*, Vol. 11 (1981), 3-10.

4. Bijker et al., op. cit. note 2.

5. A comprehensive review can be found in M. J. Mulkay and V. Milić, The Sociology of Science in East and West', *Current Sociology*, Vol. 28 (Winter 1980), 1-342.

6. For a recent review of the sociology of scientific knowledge, see H. M. Collins The Sociology of Scientific Knowledge: Studies of Contemporary Science', *Annual Review of Sociology*, Vol. 9 (1983), 265-85.

7. For discussion of the earlier work (largely associated with Robert Merton and his students), see R. D. Whitley, 'Black Boxism and the Sociology of Science: A Discussion of the Major Developments in the Field', in P. Halmos (ed.), *The Sociology of Science, Sociological Review Monograph* No. 18 (Keele: University of Keele, 1972), 61-92.

8. D. Bloor, 'Wittgenstein and Mannheim on the Sociology of Mathematics', *Studies in History and Philosophy of Science*, Vol. 4 (1973), 173-91.

9. For more discussion, see B. Barnes, *Scientific Knowledge and Sociological Theory* (London: Routledge and Kegan Paul, 1974); M. Mulkay, *Science and the Sociology of Knowledge* (London: Allen and Unwin, 1979); Collins, op. cit. note 6; and B. Barnes and D. Edge (eds), *Science in Context* (Milton Keynes, Bucks.: The Open University Press, 1982). The origins of this approach can be found in L. Fleck, *Entstehung und Entwicklung einer wissenschaftlichen Tatsache: Einführung in die Lehre vom Denkstil und Denkkollektiv* (Basel: Benno Schwabe & Co., 1935; Frankfurt am Main: Suhrkamp, 1980); English edition: L. Fleck, *The Genesis and Development of a Scientific Fact* (Chicago: The University of Chicago Press, 1979).

10. See, for example, B. Latour and S. Woolgar, Laboratory Life (London and Beverly Hills, Calif.: Sage, 1979); K. D. Knorr-Cetina, The Manufacture of Knowledge: An Essay on the Constructivist and Contextual Nature of Science (Oxford: Pergamon, 1981); M. Lynch, Art and Artefact in Laboratory Science: A Study of Shop Work and Shop Talk in a Research Laboratory (London: Routledge and Kegan Paul, forthcoming, 1984); and S. Woolgar, 'Laboratory Studies: A Comment on the State of the Art', Social Studies of Science, Vol. 12 (1982), 481-98.

11. See, for example, H. M. Collins, 'The Seven Sexes: A Study in the Sociology of a Phenomenon, Or the Replication of Experiments in Physics', *Sociology*, Vol. 9 (1975), 205-24; B. Wynne, 'C. G. Barkla and the J Phenomenon: A Case Study of the Treatment of Deviance in Physics', *Social Studies of Science*, Vol. 6 (1976), 307-47; T. J. Pinch, 'What Does a Proof Do if it Does not Prove? A Study of the Social Conditions and Metaphysical Divisions leading to David Bohm and John von Neumann Failing

to Communicate in Quantum Physics', in E. Mendelsohn, P. Weingart and R. Whitley (eds), *The Social Production of Scientific Knowledge* (Dordrecht and Boston, Mass.: Reidel, 1977), 171-215; and the studies by A. Pickering, B. Harvey, H. M. Collins, G. D. L. Travis and T. J. Pinch collected together in Collins (ed.), *Knowledge and Controversy, Social Studies of Science*, Vol. 11 (1981), 3-158.

12. H. M. Collins and T. J. Pinch, The Construction of the Paranormal: Nothing Unscientific is Happening', in R. Wallis (ed.), On the Margins of Science: *The Social Construction of Rejected Knowledge, Sociological Review Monograph* No. 27 (Keele: University of Keele, 1979), 237-70; and Collins and Pinch, *Frames of Meaning: The Social Construction of Extraordinary Science* (London: Routledge and Kegan Paul, 1982).

13. D. Robbins and R. Johnston, The Role of Cognitive and Occupational Differentiation in Scientific Controversies', Social Studies of Science, Vol. 6 (1976), 349-68. For a similar analysis of public science controversies, see B. Gillespie, D. Eva and R. Johnston, 'Carcinogenic Risk Assessment in The United States and Great Britain: The Case of Aldrin/Dieldrin', *Social Studies of Science*, Vol. 9 (1979), 265-301; and F. B. McCrea and G. E. Markle, The Estrogen Replacement Controversy in the USA and UK: Different Answers to the Same Question?', Social Studies of Science, Vol. 14 (1984), 1-26.

14. Some of the most recent debates can be found in K. D. Knorr-Cetina and M.J. Mulkay (eds), *Science Observed — Perspectives on the Social Study of Science* (London and Beverly Hills, Calif.: Sage, 1983).

15. As, for instance, argued by Barnes, op. cit. note 9, and Collins and Pinch, op. cit. note 12.

16. S. Shapin, 'History of Science and its Sociological Reconstructions', *History of Science*, Vol. 20 (1982), 157-211.

17. T. Nickles, 'ERISS and International Sociology of Science', presented to the Sixth Annual Meeting of the Society for Social Studies of Science (Atlanta: 5-7 November 1981), and Nickles, 'How Discovery is Important to Cognitive Studies of Science', paper presented to the Philosophy of Science Association Meeting (Philadelphia: 30 October 1982).

18. F. Healey, The Research Funding Organization As a Focus for Science Studies', paper presented to the Science Studies Conference (Oxford: 27-28 September 1982), and H. M. Collins, 'Scientific Knowledge and Science Policy: Some Foreseeable Implications', *EASST Newsletter*, Vol. 2 (November 1983), 5-8.

19. For a recent review of some of this literature, see Ron Johnston, 'Controlling Technology: An Issue for the *Social Studies of Science*', *Social Studies of Science*, Vol. 14 (1984), 97-112.

20. The *locus classicus* is the study by B. Hessen, 'The Social and Economic Roots of Newton's Principia', in N. I. Bukharin, A. F. Joffe, M. Rubinstein, B. Zavadovsky, E. Colman, N. I. Vavilov, W. Th. Mitkewich and B. Hessen, *Science at the Crossroads* (London: Frank Cass, 1931), 147-212.

21. C. W. Sherwin and R. S. Isenson, *First Interim Report on Project Hindsight: Summary* (Washington, DC: Office of the Director of Defense Research and Engineering, 1966); Sherwin and Isenson, 'Project Hindsight: A Defense Department Study of the Utility of Research', Science, Vol. 156 (23 June 1967), 1571-77.

22. J. Langrish, M. Gibbons, W. G. Evans and F. R. Jevons, *Wealth from Knowledge* (London: Macmillan, 1972).

23. Illinois Institute of Technology, *Technology in Retrospect and Critical Events in Science (TRACES)* (Chicago: IIT Research Institute, 1968).

24. See K. Kreilkamp, '*Hindsight and the Real World of Science Policy*', *Science Studies*, Vol. 1 (1971), 43-66, and D. C. Mowery and N. Rosenberg, The Influence of Market Demand upon Innovation: A Critical Review of Some Recent Empirical Studies', *Research Policy*, Vol. 8 (1979), 103-53.

25. See, for example, Derek J. deSolla Price, The Structure of Publication in Science and Technology', in W. H. Gruber and D. G. Marquis (eds), *Factors in the Transfer of Technology* (Cambridge, Mass.: MIT Press, 1969), 91-104; F. R. Jevons, The Interaction of Science and Technology Today, or, is Science the Mother of Invention?', *Technology and Culture*, Vol. 17 (1976), 729-42; and O. Mayr, The Science-Technology Relationship as a Historiographic Problem', Technology and Culture, Vol. 17 (1976), 663-73.

26. B. Barnes, The Science-Technology Relationship: A Model and a Query', *Social Studies of Science*, Vol. 12 (1982), 166-72.

27. E. Layton, 'Conditions of Technological Development', in I. Spiegel-Rösing and D.J. deSolla Price (eds), *Science, Technology, and Society* (London and Beverly Hills, Calif.: Sage, 1977), 210.

28. Mayr, op. cit. note 25.

29. Layton, op. cit. note 27, 209.

30. Barnes, op. cit. note 26, 166.

31. See Whitley, op. cit. note 7.

32. Layton, op. cit. note 27, 198.

33. See, for example, N. Rosenberg, *Inside the Black Box: Technology and Economics* (Cambridge: Cambridge University Press, 1982).

34. Adapted from L. Uhlmann, *Der Innovationsprozess in westeuropäischen Industrieländern. Band 2: Den Ablauf industriellen Innovationsprozesse* (Berlin and München: Duncker and Humblot, 1978), 45.

35. See, for example, C. Freeman, *The Economics of Industrial Innovation* (Harmondsworth, Middx: Penguin, 1974), and Freeman, 'Economics of Research and Development', in Spiegel-Rösing and deSolla Price (eds), op. cit. note 27, 223-75.

36. John M. Staudenmaier, SJ, 'What SHOT Hath Wrought and what SHOT Hath Not: Reflections on 25 Years of the History of Technology', paper presented to the 25th Annual Meeting of SHOT, 1983. See, for a more extensive account, Staudenmaier, *Technology's Storytellers: Recovering the Human Fabric* (Cambridge, Mass.: MIT Press, forthcoming), based on his *Design and Ambience: Historians and Technology, 1958-1977* (unpublished PhD thesis, University of Pennsylvania, Philadelphia, 1980).

37. Shapin writes that 'A proper perspective of the uses of science might reveal that sociology of knowledge and the history of technology have more in common than is usually thought': S. Shapin, 'Social Uses of Science', in G. S. Rousseau and R. Porter (eds), *The Ferment of Knowledge* (Cambridge: Cambridge University Press, 1980), 93-139, at 132. Whilst we are sympathetic to Shapin's argument we think the time is now ripe for asking more searching questions of historical studies.

38. Staudenmaier, op. cit. note 36.

39. Eugene Ferguson, 'Toward a Discipline of the History of Technology', *Technology and Culture*, Vol. 15 (1974), 13-30, 19.

40. M. Kaufman, *The First Century of Plastics; Celluloid and its Sequel* (London: Plastics Institute, 1963), 61.

41. L. H. Baekeland, 'The Synthesis, Constitution, and Uses of Bakelite', *Industrial and Engineering Chemistry*, Vol. 1 (1909), 149-61; and Baekeland, 'On Soluble, Fusible, Resinous Condensation Products of Phenols and Formaldehyde', *Journal of Industrial and Engineering Chemistry*, Vol. 1 (1909), 545-49.

42. Manuals describing resinous materials do mention Bakelite, but not with the amount of attention which, retrospectively, we would think to be justified. Professor Max Bottler, for example, devotes only one page to Bakelite in his 228-page book on resins and the resin industry: Bottler, *Harze und Harzindustrie* (Leipzig: Max Jänecke, 1924). Even when Bottler concentrates, in another book, on the *synthetic* resinous materials, Bakelite does not receive an indisputable 'first place'. Only half of the book is devoted to phenol/formaldehyde condensation products, and roughly half of the latter is devoted to Bakelite: Bottler, *Uber Herstellung und Eigenschaften von Kunstharzen und deren Verwendung in der Lack- und Firnisindustrie und zu elektrotechnischen und industriellen Zwecken* (München: J. F. Lehmanns Verlag, 1919). See also A. R. Matthis, *Insulating Varnishes in Electrotechnics* (London: John Heywood, approximately 1920).

43. W. Haynes, *American Chemical Industry*, Vol. 2 (New York: Van Nostrand, 1954), esp. 137-38.

44. Staudenmaier, op. cit. note 36. See also Thomas P. Hughes, 'Emerging Themes in the History of Technology', *Technology and Culture*, Vol. 20 (1979), 697–711.

45. See, for example, Edward W. Constant, II, *The Origins of the Turbojet Revolution* (Baltimore, Md.: Johns Hopkins University Press, 1980); Thomas P. Hughes, *Networks of Power: Electrification in Western Society*: 1880-1930 (Baltimore, Md.: Johns Hopkins University Press, 1983); and John F. Hanieski, 'The Airplane as an Economic Variable: Aspects of Technological Change in Aeronautics, 1903-1955', *Technology and Culture*, Vol. 14 (1973), 535-52.

46. See, for example, David F. Noble, 'Social Choice in Machine Design: The Case of Automatically Controlled Machine Tools', in A. Zimbalist (ed.), *Case Studies on the Labor Process* (New York: Monthly Review Press, 1979), 18-50; Merritt Roe Smith, *Harpers Ferry Armory and the New Technology: The Challenge of Change* (Ithaca, NY and London: Cornell University Press, 1977); and W. Lazonick, 'Industrial Relations and Technical Change: the Case of the Self-Acting Mule', *Cambridge Journal of Economics*, Vol. 3 (1979), 231-62.

47. There is an American tradition in the sociology of technology. See, for example, S. G. Gilfillan, *The Sociology of Invention* (Cambridge, Mass.: MIT Press, 1935); W. F. Ogburn, *The Social Effects of Aviation* (Boston, Mass.: Houghton Mifflin, 1945); Ogburn and F. Meyers Nimkoff, *Technology and the Changing Family* (Boston, Mass.: Houghton Mifflin, 1955). See also R. Westrum, 'What Happened to the Old Sociology of Technology?', paper presented to the Eighth Annual Meeting of the Society for Social Studies of Science (Blacksburg, Virginia: 3-6 November 1983). A fairly comprehensive view of the present state of the art in German sociology of technology can be obtained from R. Jokisch (ed.), *Techniksoziologie* (Frankfurt: Suhrkamp, 1982). Several studies in the sociology of technology which attempt to break with the traditional approach can be found in W. Krohn, E. T. Layton and P. Weingart (eds), *The Dynamics of Science and Technology, Sociology of the Sciences Yearbook*, Vol. 2 (Dordrecht and Boston, Mass.: Reidel, 1978).

48. R. Johnston, 'The Internal Structure of Technology', in Halmos (ed.), op. cit. note 7, 117-30.

49. G. Dosi, 'Technological Paradigms and Technological Trajectories: A Suggested Interpretation of the Determinants and Directions of Technical Change', *Research Policy*, Vol. 11 (1982), 147-62. Dosi uses the concept of 'technological trajectory', developed by R. R. Nelson and S. G. Winter, 'In Search of a Useful Theory of Innovation', *Research Policy*, Vol. 6 (1977), 36-76.

50. Other approaches to technology based on Kuhn's idea of the community structure of science can be found in Constant, op. cit. note 45, and P. Weingart, 'Strukturen technologischen Wandels. Zu einer soziologische Analyse der Technik', in Jokisch (ed.), op. cit. note 47, 112-41.

51. One is reminded of the first blush of Kuhnian studies in the sociology of science. It was hoped that Kuhn's paradigm concept might be straightforwardly employed by sociologists in their studies of science. Indeed there were a number of studies in which attempts were made to identify phases of science, such as preparadigmatic, normal and revolutionary. It soon became apparent, however, that Kuhn's terms were loosely formulated, could be subject to a variety of interpretations and did not lend themselves to operationalization in any straightforward manner. It has also been argued that this description of science, especially when

paradigms are interpreted as a form of sociometric network or 'invisible college', is not particularly radical. See, especially, T. J. Pinch, 'Kuhn — The Conservative and Radical Interpretations: Are some Mertonians "Kuhnians" and some Kuhnians "Mertonians"?', *4S Newsletter*, Vol. 7, No. 1 (1982), 10-25.

52. See, for example, the inconclusive discussion over whether a Kuhnian analysis applies to psychology in D. S. Palermo, 'Is a Scientific Revolution Taking Place in Psychology?', *Science Studies*, Vol. 3 (1973), 211-44. A notable exception is Barnes's recent contribution to the discussion of Kuhn's work: B. Barnes, T. S. *Kuhn and Social Science* (London: Macmillan, 1982).

53. M. J. Mulkay, 'Knowledge and Utility: Implications for the Sociology of Knowledge', *Social Studies of Science*, Vol. 9 (1979), 63-80.

54. M. Bunge, 'Technology as Applied Science', *Technology and Culture*, Vol. 7 (1966), 329-47.

55. Mulkay, op. cit. note 53, 77.

56. M. Callon, 'The State and Technical Innovation: A Case Study of the Electrical Vehicle in France', *Research Policy*, Vol. 9 (1980), 358-76. The bulk of the empirical material on the development of the electric vehicle has not yet been published. In a series of articles Callon uses examples from his study to illustrate his approach towards technology: see Callon, 'Struggles and Negotiations to Define what is Problematic and what is Not — the Socio-Logic of Translation', in K. D. Knorr, R. Krohn and R. Whitley (eds), *The Social Process of Scientific Investigation, Sociology of the Sciences Yearbook*, Vol. 4 (Dordrecht and Boston, Mass.: Reidel, 1980), 197-219; and Callon, 'Pour une sociologie des controverses technologiques', *Fundamenta Scientiae*, Vol. 2 (1981), 381-99.

57. Noble, op. cit. note 40.

58. For a useful review of Marxist work in this area, see D. Mackenzie, 'Marx and the Machine', *Technology and Culture*, in press.

59. Lazonick, op. cit. note 46.

60. For a provisional report of this study, see Bijker et al., op. cit. note 2. The word 'artefact' denotes material products as well as production processes. The six artefacts which were studied are: aluminium, Bakelite, fluorescent lamp, safety bicycle, Sulzer loom and transistor.

61. Work which might be classed as falling within the EPOR has been carried out primarily at the Science Studies Centre, University of Bath, by Collins, Pinch and Travis, and at the Science Studies Unit, University of Edinburgh, by Harvey and Pickering. See, for example, the studies collected together in Collins (ed.), op. cit. note 11.

62. Collins, op. cit. notes 3, 7.

63. H. M. Collins, 'The Place of the Core-Set in Modern Science: Social Contingency with Methodological Propriety in Science', *History of Science*, Vol. 19 (1981), 6-19.

64. For the purposes of the third stage, the notion of Core-Set may be too limited.

65. See Constant, op. cit. note 45, for a similar evolutionary approach to the description of technological development. Both Constant's and our model seem to arise out of work in evolutionary epistemology: see, for example, S. Toulmin, *Human Understanding*, Vol. 1 (Oxford: Oxford University Press, 1972), and D. T. Campbell, 'Evolutionary Epistemology', in P. A. Schlipp (ed.), *The Philosophy of Karl Popper, The Library of Living Philosophers*, Vol. 14-I (La Salle, Ill.: Open Court, 1974), 413-63. For a review of evolutionary models of technical change, see Jon Elster, *Explaining Technical Change* (Cambridge: Cambridge University Press, 1983).

66. It may be useful to state explicitly that we consider bicycles to be as fully-fledged a technology as, for example, automobiles or aircraft. It may be helpful for readers from outside notorious cycle countries such as The Netherlands, France and Britain, to point out that both the automobile and the aircraft industries are, in a way, descendants from the bicycle industry. Many names occur both in the histories of the bicycle and in the histories of the autocar: Triumph, Rover, Humber, Raleigh, to mention but a few. The Wright brothers both sold and manufactured bicycles before they started to build their flying machines — mostly made out of bicycle parts. See C. F. Caunter, *The History and Development of Light Cars* (London: HMSO, 1957); Caunter, *The History and Development of Cycles (as illustrated by the collection of cycles in the Science Museum); Part I: Historical Survey* (London: HMSO, 1955); C. H. Gibbs-Smith, *The Aeroplane: An Historical Survey of its Origins and Development* (London: HMSO, 1960).

67. J. Woodforde, *The Story of the Bicycle* (London: Routledge and Kegan Paul, 1970).

68. There is no cookbook recipe for how to identify a social group. Quantitative instruments using citation data may be of some help in certain cases. More research is needed to develop operationalizations of the notion of 'relevant social group' for a variety of historical and sociological research sites.

69. Meadows, cited in Woodforde, op. cit. note 67, 49-50.

70. Cited in Woodforde, op. cit. note 67, 122.

71. 'The Stanley Exhibition of Cycles', *The Engineer*, Vol. 69 (7 February 1890), 107-08.

72. This is one of the technological artefacts mentioned in Bijker et al., op. cit. note 2.

73. Woodforde, op. cit. note 67, 47.

74. *Daily Telegraph* (7 September 1877), cited in Woodforde, op. cit. note 67, 42.

75. Two concepts have been used, which can be understood as two distinctive concepts within the broader idea of *stabilization*. *Reification* is used to denote 'social existence' — existence in the consciousness of the members of a certain social group. *Economic stabilization* is used to denote the 'economic existence' of an artefact — its having a market. Both concepts are used in a continuous and relative way; thus requiring phrases such as 'the *degree* of reification of the High Wheeler is *higher* in the group of "young men of means and nerve" than in the group of elderly men'. See Bijker et al., op. cit. note 2.

76. The notion of relevant social group may provide a starting point for formulating theoretical hypotheses about the occurrence of specific closure mechanisms under certain conditions. For a tentative sketch of such a theoretical framework, see W. E. Bijker, 'Collectifs technologiques et styles technologiques: éléments pour un modèle explicatif de la construction sociale des artefacts techniques', paper presented to the Collogue STS 'Travailleur collectif et relations science — production', Lyon, France, 10-11 October 1983. In this paper, the ideas of Ludwik Fleck, op. cit. note 9, are used to relate the structure of social groups to the occurrence of specific closure mechanisms. The concepts 'technological community', 'technological style' and 'inclusion in a technological style' are introduced. See also W. Shrum, 'Scientific Specialties and Technical Systems', *Social Studies of Science*, Vol. 14 (1984), 63-90.

77. Collins, op. cit. note 11.

78. J. B. Dunlop, 'An Improvement in Tyres of Wheels for Bicycles, Tricycles, or other Road Cars', *British Patent No. 10607* (date of application: 23 July 1888).

79. Op. cit. note 71, 107.

80. 'The Stanley Exhibition of Cycles', *The Engineer*, Vol. 67 (22 February 1889), 157-58.

81. Mulkay, op. cit. note 53, 80.

82. W. Grew, *The Cycle Industry, its Origin, History and Latest Developments* (London: Sir I. Pitman & Sons, 1921), 8.

83. The American 'Star' (1881) had a small steering wheel in front of the big wheel.

84. Latour and Woolgar, op. cit. note 10.

85. The existence of different degrees of consensus has not yet been researched amongst Core-Set scientists.

86. See also Latour and Woolgar, op. cit. note 10.

87. Knorr-Cetina, op. cit. note 10.

88. H. M. Collins, 'Son of Seven Sexes: The Social Destruction of a Physical Phenomenon', *Social Studies of Science*, Vol. 11 (1981), 33-62.

89. Pinch, op. cit. note 11.

90. Pickering has confirmed this point to us in personal communication. See also A. Pickering, 'Discovery Claims, Ad Hominem Arguments and Research Programmes: Case Studies in Elementary Particle Physics' (Edinburgh: Science Studies Unit, University of Edinburgh, September 1978, unpublished mimeo).

91. For further details of this controversy, see Pinch, op. cit. note 2. Again we would stress that the example is only illustrative.

92. Advertisements seem to constitute a large and potentially fruitful source for empirical social studies of technology. The considerations which professional advertising designers give to differences between various 'consumer groups' obviously fit our use of different relevant groups. For a fascinating account of the role of advertising in the development of household technology, see Ruth Schwartz Cowan, *More Work For Mother: The Ironies of Household Technology from The Open Hearth to the Microwave* (New York: Basic Books, 1983).

93. *Illustrated London News*, 1880, cited in Woodforde, op. cit. note 67, 60.

94. Woodforde, op. cit. note 67, 89.

95. See L. Croon, Das Fahrrad und seine Entwicklung (Berlin: VDI-Verlag, 1939).

96. See Grew, op. cit. note 82.

97. The concept of 'translation' is fruitfully used in an extended way in Callon, op. cit. note 56: see also M. Callon and J. Law, 'On Interests and their Transformation: Enrolment and Counter-Enrolment', *Social Studies of Science*, Vol. 12 (1982), 615-25, and B. Latour, 'Give Me a Laboratory and I will Raise the World', in Knorr-Cetina and Mulkay (eds), op. cit. note 14, 141-70.

98. E. W. Constant, 'Scientific Theory and Technological Testability: Science, Dynamometers, and Water Turbines in the 19th Century', *Technology and Culture*, Vol. 24 (1983), 183-98.

99. A model of such a 'stage 3' explanation is offered in H. M. Collins, 'An Empirical Relativist Programme in the Sociology of Scientific Knowledge', in Knorr-Cetina and Mulkay (eds), op. cit. note 14, 85-113, esp. 96-97.

100. Historical studies which address the third stage may be a useful guide here. See, for example, D. MacKenzie, 'Statistical Theory and Social Interests: A Case Study', *Social Studies of Science*, Vol. 8 (1978), 35-83, and S. Shapin, 'The Politics of Observation: Cerebral Anatomy and Social Interests in the Edinburgh Phrenology Disputes', in Wallis (ed.), op. cit. note 12, 139-78.

101. Studies which seem to go some way towards meeting the explanatory goals of the third stage are those of Noble, op. cit. note 46, and Lazonick, op. cit. note 46. See also D. MacKenzie, 'Technology, the State and the Strategic Missile: A Preliminary Working Paper' (Edinburgh: Science Studies Unit, University of Edinburgh, 1983, unpublished mimeo).

102. For a more detailed discussion of some methodological and strategical conclusions, drawn from our comparative study of science and technology, see W. E. Bijker and T. J. Pinch, 'La construction sociale de faits et d'artefacts: Impératifs stratégiques et méthodologiques pour une approche unifiée de l'étude des sciences et de la technique', paper presented to 'L'atelier de recherche (III) sur les problèmes stratégiques et méthodologiques des sciences sociales en milieu scientifique et technique' (Paris: 2-3 March 1983).

103. Bruno Latour seems to follow a similar line of argument in his recent plea for what we may call a 'second generation of laboratory studies'; he proposes 'to stick with the methodology developed during laboratory field studies, focusing it not on the laboratory itself but on the construction of the laboratory and its position in the societal milieu': Latour, op. cit. note 97, 143. In order to do this, he has to consider more social groups than the laboratory tribe only. In his study of the Pasteur Laboratory, he actually describes the various roles played by statisticians, veterinarians, farmers, government officials, and the general public.

104. Latour and Woolgar, op. cit. note 10, and Knorr-Cetina, op. cit. note 10.

105. Latour and Woolgar appear to use other data in their study of the construction of TRF; Latour and Woolgar, op. cit. note 10, Chapter 3.

*Trevor Pinch* is a lecturer in Sociology at the University of York. He has carried out research in the sociology of scientific knowledge, especially several case studies of physics. His current interests are in the notion of observation in science and how recent work in the sociology of scientific knowledge can be extended to technology. As well as several articles in the sociology of science Pinch is co-author (with H. M. Collins) of *Frames of Meaning* (London: Routledge and Kegan Paul, 1982). *Wiebe E. Bijker* is a research fellow at the University of Technology, Twente. He studied physics and philosophy of science. His current interests are in a theoretical analysis of technological development. As well as working in the history and sociology of technology, he is involved in 'translating' recent insights from science and technology studies into teaching materials for secondary school science education. See, for example, W. E. Bijker, K. Kortland and A. J. de Wever, *Exact Natuurkunde*, Vols. 1,2,3 (Amsterdam: Meulenhoff Educatief, 1982, 1983, 1984).

*Authors' addresses* (respectively): Department of Sociology, University of York, Heslington, York Y01 5DD, UK; Twente University of Technology, Centre for Studies on Problems of Science and Society, 'De Boerderij', Postbus 217, 7500 AE Enschede, The Netherlands.

# Article 4

Lawrence Lessig

## Code is Law

Almost two decades ago, in the spring of 1989, communism in europe died—collapsed, like a tent, its main post removed. The end was not brought by war or revolution. The end was exhaustion. A new political regime was born in its place across Central and Eastern Europe, the beginnings of a new political society.

For constitutionalists (like me), this was a heady time. I had graduated from law school in 1989, and in 1991 I began teaching at the University of Chicago. At that time, Chicago had a center devoted to the study of the emerging democracies in Central and Eastern Europe. I was a part of that center. Over the next five years I spent more hours on airplanes, and more mornings drinking bad coffee, than I care to remember.

Eastern and Central Europe were filled with Americans telling former Communists how they should govern. The advice was endless. And silly. Some of these visitors literally sold translated constitutions to the emerging constitutional republics; the rest had innumerable half-baked ideas about how the new nations should be governed. These Americans came from a nation where constitutionalism seemed to work, yet they had no clue why.

The Center's mission, however, was not to advise. We knew too little to guide. Our aim was to watch and gather data about the transitions and how they progressed. We wanted to understand the change, not direct it.

What we saw was striking, if understandable. Those first moments after communism's collapse were filled with antigovernmental passion—a surge of anger directed against the state and against state regulation. Leave us alone, the people seemed to say. Let the market and nongovernmental organizations—a new society—take government's place. After generations of communism, this reaction was completely understandable. Government was the oppressor. What compromise could there be with the instrument of your repression?

A certain kind of libertarianism seemed to many to support much in this reaction. If the market were to reign, and the government were kept out of the way, freedom and prosperity would inevitably grow. Things would take care of themselves. There was no need, and could be no place, for extensive regulation by the state.

But things didn't take care of themselves. Markets didn't flourish. Governments were crippled, and crippled governments are no elixir of freedom. Power didn't disappear—it shifted from the state to mafiosi, themselves often created by the state. The need for traditional state functions—police, courts, schools, health care—didn't go away, and private interests didn't emerge to fill that need. Instead, the needs were simply unmet. Security evaporated. A modern if plodding anarchy replaced the bland communism of the previous three generations: neon lights flashed advertisements for Nike; pensioners were swindled out of their life savings by fraudulent stock deals; bankers were murdered in broad daylight on Moscow streets. One system of control had been replaced by another. Neither was what Western libertarians would call "freedom."

About a decade ago, in the mid-1990s, just about the time when this post-communist euphoria was beginning to wane, there emerged in the West another "new society," to many just as exciting as the new societies promised in post-communist Europe. This was the Internet, or as I'll define a bit later, "cyberspace." First in universities and centers of research, and then throughout society in general, cyberspace became a new target for libertarian utopianism. *Here* freedom from the state would reign. If not in Moscow or Tblisi, then in cyberspace would we find the ideal libertarian society.

The catalyst for this change was likewise unplanned. Born in a research project in the Defense Department,[1] cyberspace too arose from the unplanned displacement of a certain architecture of control. The tolled, single-purpose network of telephones was displaced by the untolled and multipurpose network of packet-switched data. And thus the old one-to-many architectures of publishing (television, radio, newspapers, books) were complemented by a world in which anyone could become a publisher. People could communicate and associate in ways that they had never done before. The space seemed to promise a kind of society that real space would never allow—freedom without anarchy, control without government, consensus without power. In the words of a manifesto that defined this ideal: "We reject: kings, presidents and voting. We believe in: rough consensus and running code."[2]

As in post-Communist Europe, these first thoughts about freedom in cyberspace tied freedom to the disappearance of the state. As John Parry Barlow, former lyricist for the Grateful Dead and co-founder of the Electronic Frontier Foundation, declared in his "Declaration of Independence for Cyberspace,"

> Governments of the Industrial World, you weary giants of flesh and steel, I come from Cyberspace, the new home of Mind. On behalf of the future, I ask you of the past to leave us alone. You are not welcome among us. You have no sovereignty where we gather.

35

But here the bond between freedom and the absence of the state was said to be even stronger than in post-Communist Europe. The claim for cyberspace was not just that government would not regulate cyberspace—it was that government *could not* regulate cyberspace. Cyberspace was, by nature, unavoidably free. Governments could threaten, but behavior could not be controlled; laws could be passed, but they would have no real effect. There was no choice about what kind of government to install—none could reign. Cyberspace would be a society of a very different sort. There would be definition and direction, but built from the bottom-up. The society of this space would be a fully self-ordering entity, cleansed of governors and free from political hacks.

I taught in Central Europe during the summers of the early 1990s; I witnessed through my students the transformation in attitudes about communism that I described above. And so I felt a bit of déjà vu when, in the spring of 1995, while teaching the law of cyberspace, I saw in my students these very same postcommunist thoughts about freedom and government. Even at Yale—not known for libertarian passions—the students seemed drunk with what James Boyle would later call the "libertarian gotcha":[3] no government could survive without the Internet's riches, yet no government could control the life that went on there. Real-space governments would become as pathetic as the last Communist regimes: It was the withering of the state that Marx had promised, jolted out of existence by trillions of gigabytes flashing across the ether of cyberspace.

But what was never made clear in the midst of this celebration was *why*. Why was cyberspace incapable of regulation? What made it so? The word itself suggests not freedom but control. Its etymology reaches beyond a novel by William Gibson (*Neuromancer*, published in 1984) to the world of "cybernetics," the study of control at a distance through devices.[4] So it was doubly puzzling to see this celebration of "perfect freedom" under a banner that aspires (to anyone who knows the origin, at least) to perfect control.

As I said, I am a constitutionalist. I teach and write about constitutional law. I believe that these first thoughts about government and cyberspace were just as misguided as the first thoughts about government after communism. Liberty in cyberspace will not come from the absence of the state. Liberty there, as anywhere, will come from a state of a certain kind. We build a world where freedom can flourish not by removing from society any self-conscious control, but by setting it in a place where a particular kind of self-conscious control survives. We build liberty as our founders did, by setting society upon a certain *constitution*.

But by "constitution" I don't mean a legal text. Unlike my countrymen in Eastern Europe in the early 1990s, I am not trying to sell a document that our framers wrote in 1787. Rather, as the British understand when they speak of their "constitution," I mean an architecture—not just a legal text but a way of life—that structures and constrains social and legal power, to the end of protecting fundamental values. (One student asked, "constitution" in the sense of "just one tool among many, one simple flashlight that keeps us from fumbling in the dark, or, alternatively . . . more like a lighthouse that we constantly call upon?" I mean constitution as in lighthouse—a guide that helps anchor fundamental values.)

Constitutions in this sense are built, they are not found. Foundations get laid, they don't magically appear. Just as the founders of our nation learned from the anarchy that followed the revolution (remember: our first constitution, the Articles of Confederation, was a miserable failure of do-nothingness), so too are we beginning to understand about cyberspace that this building, or laying, is not the work of an invisible hand. There is no reason to believe that the foundation for liberty in cyberspace will simply emerge. Indeed, the passion for that anarchy—as in America by the late 1780s, and as in the former Eastern bloc by the late 1990s—has faded. Thus, as our framers learned, and as the Russians saw, we have every reason to believe that cyberspace, left to itself, will not fulfill the promise of freedom. Left to itself, cyberspace will become a perfect tool of control.

Control. Not necessarily control by government, and not necessarily control to some evil, fascist end. But the argument of this book is that the invisible hand of cyberspace is building an architecture that is quite the opposite of its architecture at its birth. This invisible hand, pushed by government and by commerce, is constructing an architecture that will perfect control and make highly efficient regulation possible. The struggle in that world will not be government's. It will be to assure that essential liberties are preserved in this environment of perfect control. As Siva Vaidhyanathan puts it,

While once it seemed obvious and easy to declare the rise of a "network society" in which individuals would realign themselves, empower themselves, and undermine traditional methods of social and cultural control, it seems clear that networked digital communication need not serve such liberating ends.[5]

This book is about the change from a cyberspace of anarchy to a cyberspace of control. When we see the path that cyberspace is on now—an evolution I describe below in Part I—we see that much of the "liberty" present at cyberspace's founding will be removed in its future. Values originally considered fundamental will not survive. On the path we have chosen, we will remake what cyberspace was. Some of that remaking will make many of us happy. But some of that remaking, I argue, we should all regret.

Yet whether you celebrate or regret the changes that I will describe, it is critical to understand how they happen. What produced the "liberty" of cyberspace, and what will change to remake that liberty? That lesson will then suggest a second about the source of regulation in cyberspace.

That understanding is the aim of Part II. Cyberspace demands a new understanding of how regulation works. It compels us to look beyond the traditional lawyer's scope—beyond laws, or even norms. It requires a broader account of "regulation," and most importantly, the recognition of a newly salient regulator.

That regulator is the obscurity in this book's title—Code. In real space, we recognize how laws regulate—through constitutions, statutes, and other legal codes. In cyberspace we must understand how a different "code" regulates— how the software and hardware (i.e., the "code" of cyberspace) that make cyberspace what it is also regulate cyberspace as it is. As William Mitchell puts it, this code is cyberspace's "law."[6] "Lex Informatica," as Joel Reidenberg first put it,[7] or better, "code is law."

Lawyers and legal theorists get bothered, however, when I echo this slogan. There are differences, they insist, between the regulatory effects produced by code and the regulatory effects produced by law, not the least of which is the difference in the "internal perspective" that runs with each kind of regulation. We understand the internal perspective of legal regulation—for example, that the restrictions the law might impose on a company's freedom to pollute are a product of self-conscious regulation, reflecting values of the society imposing that regulation. That perspective is harder to recognize with code. It could be there, but it need not. And no doubt this is just one of many important differences between "code" and "law."

I don't deny these differences. I only assert that we learn something useful from ignoring them for a bit. Justice Holmes famously focused the regulator on the "bad man."[8] He offered a theory of regulation that assumed that "bad man" at its core. His point was not that everyone was a "bad man"; the point instead was about how we could best construct systems of regulation.

My point is the same. I suggest we learn something if we think about the "bot man" theory of regulation—one focused on the regulation of code. We will learn something important, in other words, if we imagine the target of regulation as a maximizing entity, and consider the range of tools the regulator has to control that machine.

Code will be a central tool in this analysis. It will present the greatest threat to both liberal and libertarian ideals, as well as their greatest promise. We can build, or architect, or *code* cyberspace to protect values that we believe are fundamental. Or we can build, or architect, or code cyberspace to allow those values to disappear. There is no middle ground. There is no choice that does not include some kind of building. Code is never found; it is only ever made, and only ever made by us. As Mark Stefik puts it, "Different versions of [cyberspace] support different kinds of dreams. We choose, wisely or not."[9] Or again, code "determines which people can access which digital objects . . . How such programming regulates human interactions . . . depends on the choices made."[10] Or, more precisely, a code of cyberspace, defining the freedoms and controls of cyberspace, will be built. About that there can be no debate. But by whom, and with what values? That is the only choice we have left to make.

My argument is not for some top-down form of control. The claim is not that regulators must occupy Microsoft. A constitution envisions an environment; as Justice Holmes said, it "call[s] into life a being the development of which [cannot be] foreseen."[11] Thus, to speak of a constitution is not to describe a hundred-day plan. It is instead to identify the values that a space should guarantee. It is not to describe a "government"; it is not even to select (as if a single choice must be made) between bottom-up or top-down control. In speaking of a constitution in cyberspace we are simply asking: What values should be protected there? What values should be built into the space to encourage what forms of life?

The "values" at stake here are of two sorts—substantive and structural. In the American constitutional tradition, we worried about the second first. The framers of the Constitution of 1787 (enacted without a Bill of Rights) were focused on structures of government. Their aim was to ensure that a particular government (the federal government) did not become too powerful. And so they built into the Constitution's design checks on the power of the federal government and limits on its reach over the states.

Opponents of that Constitution insisted that more checks were needed, that the Constitution needed to impose substantive limits on government's power as well as structural limits. And thus was the Bill of Rights born. Ratified in 1791, the Bill of Rights promised that the federal government would not remove certain freedoms—of speech, privacy, and due process. And it guaranteed that the commitment to these substantive values would remain despite the passing fancies of normal, or ordinary, government. These values—both substantive and structural—were thus entrenched through our constitutional design. They can be changed, but only through a cumbersome and costly process.

We face the same questions in constituting cyberspace, but we have approached them from the opposite direction.[12] Already we are struggling with substance: Will cyberspace promise privacy or access? Will it enable a free culture or a permission culture? Will it preserve a space for free speech? These are choices of substantive value, and they are the subject of much of this book.

But structure matters as well, though we have not even begun to understand how to limit, or regulate, arbitrary regulatory power. What "checks and balances" are possible in this space? How do we separate powers? How do we ensure that one regulator, or one government, doesn't become too powerful? How do we guarantee it is powerful enough?

Theorists of cyberspace have been talking about these questions since its birth.[13] But as a culture, we are just beginning to get it. As we slowly come to see how different structures within cyberspace affect us—how its architecture, in a sense I will define below, "regulates" us—we slowly come to ask how these structures should be defined. The first generation of these architectures was built by a noncommercial sector—researchers and hackers, focused upon building a network. The second generation has been built by commerce. And the third, not yet off the drawing board, could well be the product of government. Which regulator do we prefer? Which regulators should be controlled? How does society exercise that control over entities that aim to control it?

In Part III, I bring these questions back down to the ground. I consider three areas of controversy—intellectual property, privacy, and free speech— and identify the values within each that cyberspace will change. These values are the product of the interaction between law and technology. How that interaction plays out is often counter-intuitive. My aim in this part is to map that interaction, so as to map a way that we might, using the tools of Part II, preserve the values that are important to us within each context.

Part IV internationalizes these questions. Cyberspace is everywhere, meaning those who populate cyberspace come from everywhere. How will the sovereigns of everywhere live with the claimed "sovereignty" of cyberspace? I map a particular response that seems to me inevitable, and will reinforce the conclusion of Part I.

The final part, Part V, is the darkest. The central lesson of this book is that cyberspace requires choices. Some of these are, and should be, private: Whether an author wants to enforce her copyright; how a citizen wants to protect his privacy. But some of these choices involve values that are collective. I end by asking whether we—meaning Americans—are up to the challenge that these choices present. Are we able to respond rationally—meaning both (1) are we able to respond without undue or irrational passion, and (2) do we have institutions capable of understanding and responding to these choices?

My strong sense is that we are not, at least now, able to respond rationally to these challenges. We are at a stage in our history when we urgently need to make fundamental choices about values, but we should trust no institution of government to make such choices. Courts cannot do it, because as a legal culture we don't want courts choosing among contested matters of values. Congress should not do it because, as a political culture, we are deeply skeptical (and rightly so) about the product of this government. There is much to be proud of in our history and traditions. But the government we now have is a failure. Nothing important should be trusted to its control, even though everything important is.

Change is possible. I don't doubt that revolutions remain in our future. But I fear that it is too easy for the government, or specially powered interests, to dislodge these revolutions, and that too much will be at stake for it to allow real change to succeed. Our government has already criminalized the core ethic of this movement, transforming the meaning of *hacker* into something quite alien to its original sense. Through extremism in copyright regulation, it is criminalizing the core creativity that this network could produce. And this is only the beginning.

Things could be different. They are different elsewhere. But I don't see how they could be different for us just now. This no doubt is simply a confession of the limits of my own imagination. I would be grateful to be proven wrong. I would be grateful to watch as we relearn—as the citizens of the former Communist republics are learning—how to escape these disabling ideas about the possibilities for governance. But nothing in the past decade, and especially nothing in the past five years, has convinced me that my skepticism about governance was misplaced. Indeed, events have only reinforced that pessimism.

# SIX

## Cyberspaces

I'VE SAID WE CAN DISTINGUISH THE INTERNET FROM CYBERSPACE. TO MAKE THE distinctive form of regulation that is the subject of this part salient, we need to say a bit more about this distinction. The Internet is a medium of communication. People do things "on" the Internet. Most of those things are trivial, even if important. People pay bills on the Internet, they make reservations at restaurants. They get their news from the Internet. They send news to family members using e-mail or 1M chat. These uses are important in the sense that they affect the economy and make life easier and harder for those using the Internet. But they're not important in the sense that they change how people live. It's very cool that you can buy books with one click at Amazon. I buy tons (maybe literally) of books I wouldn't otherwise have bought. But my life has not been changed by one-click (even if my bank account has). It's been made easier and more literate, but not anything fundamentally different.

Cyberspace, by contrast, is not just about making life easier. It is about making life different, or perhaps better. It is about making a different (or second) life. It evokes, or calls to life, ways of interacting that were not possible before. I don't mean that the interaction is new—we've always had communities; these communities have always produced something close to what I will describe cyberspace to have produced. But these cyberspace communities create a difference in degree that has matured into a difference in kind. There is something unique about the interactions in these spaces, and something especially unique about how they are regulated.

Life in cyberspace is regulated primarily through the code of cyberspace. Not regulated in the sense of Part I—my point is not that the code makes it easy to know who did what so that penalties can be visited upon those who behaved badly. Regulated in the sense that bars on a prison regulate the movement of a prisoner, or regulated in the sense that stairs regulate the access of the disabled. Code is a regulator in cyberspace because it defines the terms upon which cyberspace is offered. And those who set those terms increasingly recognize the code as a means to achieving the behaviors that benefit them best.

And so too with the Internet. Code on the Internet is also a regulator, and people live life on the Internet subject to that regulation. But my strategy in this chapter is to begin with the more obscure as a way to build recognition about the familiar. Once you see the technique applied to worlds you are unlikely to inhabit, you will recognize the technique applied to the world you inhabit all the time.

Cyberspace is not one place. It is many places. And the character of these many places differ in ways that are fundamental. These differences come in part from differences in the people who populate these places, but demographics alone don't explain the variance. Something more is going on.

Here is a test. Read the following passage, and ask yourself whether the description rings true for you:

I believe virtual communities promise to restore to Americans at the end of the twentieth century what many of us feel was lost in the decades at the beginning of the century—a stable sense of community, of place. Ask those who've been members of such a virtual community, and they'll tell you that what happens there is more than an exchange of electronic impulses in the wires. It's not just virtual bam raising. . . . It's also the comfort from others that a man like Phil Catalfo of the WELL can experience when he's up late at night caring for a child suffering from leukemia, and he logs on to the WELL and pours out his anguish and fears. People really do care for each other and fall in love over the Net, just as they do in geographic communities. And that "virtual" connectedness is a real sign of hope in a nation that's increasingly anxious about the fragmentation of public life and the polarization of interest groups and the alienation of urban existence.1

There are two sorts of reactions to talk like this. To those who have been in "cyberspace" for some time, such talk is extremely familiar. These people have been on different kinds of "nets" from the start. They moved to the Internet from more isolated communities—from a local BBS (bulletin board service), or, as Mike Godwin (the author of the passage) puts it, from a "tony" address like The WELL. For them the Net is a space for conversation, connections, and exchange—a wildly promising location for making life in real space different.

But if you are a recent immigrant to this "space" (the old-timers call you "newbies"), or if all you do on the Internet is check your stocks or look up movie times, you are likely to be impatient with talk like this. When people talk about "community," about special ways to connect, or about the amazing power of this space to alter lives, you are likely to ask, "What is this idea of cyberspace as a place?" For newbies, those who have simply e-mailed or surfed the Web, the "community" of the Net is an odd sort of mysticism. How can anyone think of these pages full of advertisements and spinning icons as a community, or even as a space? To the sober newbie, this just sounds like hype high on java.2

Newbies are the silent majority of today's Net.3 However much one romanticizes the old days when the Net was a place for conversation and exchange, this is not its function for most of its users now. There are exploding communities of bloggers and creativity. But bloggers are still just 3 percent of Internet users; the vast majority of Internet use has no connection to any ideal of community.

Cyberspace has changed in its feel.4 How it looks, what you can do there, how you are connected there—all this has changed. Why it has changed is a complicated question—a complete answer to which I can't provide. Cyberspace has changed in part because the people—who they are, what their interests are—have changed, and in part because the capabilities provided by the space have changed.

But part of the change has to do with the space itself. Communities, exchange, and conversation all flourish in a certain type of space; they are extinguished in a different type of space.5 My hope is to illuminate the differences between these two environments.

The next sections describe different cyber-places. The aim is to build intuitions about how to think through the differences that we observe. These intuitions, in turn, will help us see something about where cyberspace is moving.

# THE VALUES OF A SPACE

Spaces have values.6 They manifest these values through the practices or lives that they enable or disable. As Mark Stefik puts it:

[B]arriers within cyberspace—separate chat rooms, intranet gateways, digital envelopes, and other systems to limit access—resemble the effects of national borders, physical boundaries, and distance. Programming determines which people can access which digital objects and which digital objects can interact with other digital objects. How such programming regulates human interactions—and thus modulates change—depends on the choices made.7

Choices mean that differently constituted spaces enable and disable differently. This is the first idea to make plain. Here is an example.

At the start of the Internet, communication was through text. Media such as USENET newsgroups, Internet Relay Chat, and e-mail all confined exchange to text—to words on a screen, typed by a person (or so one thought).

The reason for this limitation is fairly obvious: The bandwidth of early Net life was very thin. In an environment where most users connected at 1,200 baud, if they were lucky, graphics and streaming video would have taken an unbearably long time to download, if they downloaded at all. What was needed was an efficient mode of communication—and text is one of the most efficient.8

Most think of this fact about the early Net as a limitation. Technically, it was. But this technical description does not exhaust its normative description as an architecture that made possible a certain kind of life. From this perspective, limitations can be features; they can enable as well as disable. And this particular limitation enabled classes of people who were disabled in real-space life.

Think about three such classes—the blind, the deaf, and the "ugly." In real space these people face an extraordinary array of constraints on their ability to communicate. The blind person in real space is constantly confronted with architectures that presume he can see; he bears an extraordinary cost in retrofitting real-space architectures so that this presumption is not totally exclusionary. The deaf person in real space confronts architectures that presume she can hear; she too bears an extraordinary cost in retrofitting these architectures. The "ugly" person in real space (think of a bar or a social club) confronts architectures of social norms that make his appearance a barrier to a certain sort of intimacy. He endures extraordinary suffering in conforming to these architectures.

In real space these three groups are confronted with architectures that disable them relative to "the rest of us." But in cyberspace, in its first iteration, they did not.

The blind could easily implement speech programs that read the (by definition machine-readable) text and could respond by typing. Other people on the Net would have no way of knowing that the person typing the message was blind, unless he claimed to be. The blind were equal to the seeing.

The same with the deaf. There was no need to hear anything in this early Internet. For the first time many of the deaf could have conversations, or exchanges, in which the most salient feature was not that the person was deaf. The deaf were equal to the hearing.

And the same with the "ugly." Because your appearance was not transmitted with every exchange, the unattractive could have an intimate conversation with others that was not automatically defined by what they looked like. They could flirt or play or be sexual without their bodies (in an extremely underappreciated sense) getting in the way. This first version of the Net made these people equal to "the beautiful." In a virtual chat room, stunning eyes, a captivating smile, or impressive biceps don't do it. Wit, engagement, and articulateness do.

The architecture of this original cyberspace gave these groups something that they did not have in real space. More generally, it changed the mix of benefits and burdens that people faced—the literate were enabled and the attractive disabled relative to real space. Architectures produced these enablings and disablings.

I've told this story as if it matters only to those who in real space are "disabled." But of course, "disabled" is a relative term.9 It is more accurate to say that the space changes the meaning of the enabled. A friend—a strikingly beautiful and powerful woman, married, and successful—described for me why she spends hours in political chat spaces, arguing with others about all sorts of political topics:

> You don't understand what it's like to be me. You have lived your whole life in a world where your words are taken for their meaning; where what you say is heard for what it says. I've never had a space, before this space, where my words were taken for what they meant. Always, before, they were words of "this babe," or "wife," or "mother." I could never speak as I. But here, I am as I speak.

Clearly, the space is enabling her, even though one would not have said that in real space she was "disabled."10

Over time, as bandwidth has expanded, this architecture has changed, and so has the mix of benefits and burdens. When graphics entered the Net through the World Wide Web, the blind became "blind" again. As sound files or speech in virtual spaces have been created, the deaf have become "deaf" again. And as chat rooms have started segregating into spaces where video-cams capture real images of the people chatting and spaces where there is just text, the video-unappealing are again unappealing.11 As the architectures change, definitions of who is "disabled" change as well.

My point is not to argue that the Net should not change—though of course, if it can change in ways that minimize the disabling effect of sound and graphics, then it no doubt should."12 However important, my point is not really about the "disabled" at all. I use this example simply to highlight a link—between these structures of code and the world this code enables. Codes constitute cyberspaces; spaces enable and disable individuals and groups. The selections about code are therefore in part a selection about who, what, and, most important, what ways of life will be enabled and disabled.

# CYBER-PLACES

We can build on this point by looking at a number of "communities" that are constituted differently and that constitute different forms of life and by considering what makes these differences possible.

### America Online

America Online (AOL) is an online service provider—"by far the largest ISP in the world"13 with some 12 million subscribers in 1998 and 27 million today.14 But despite having the population of New York and New jersey combined, AOL still describes itself as a "community." A large community perhaps, but a community nonetheless.

This community has a constitution—not in the sense of a written document (though there is that as well), but in the sense of a way of life for those who live there. Its founding vision was that community would make this place sing. So from its start, AOL's emphasis has been on enabling people to interact, through chat, bulletin boards, and e-mail. (Today, AOL hosts the exchange of more messages daily than does the U.S. Post Office.15) Earlier providers, obsessed with providing content or advertising, limited or ignored the possibilities for interaction and exchange, but AOL saw interaction as the stuff that makes cyberspace different. It built itself on building a community and establishing itself as a place where people could say what they wanted.16

This interaction is governed by the rules of the place. Some of these rules are formal, others customary. Among the formal are express terms to which every member subscribes upon joining AOL. These terms regulate a wide range of behaviors in this space, including the behavior of AOL members anywhere on the Internet.17

Increasingly, these rules have become controversial. AOL policies have been called "Big Brother" practices. Arguments that get heated produce exchanges that are rude. But rudeness, or offensiveness, is not permitted in AOL's community. When these exchanges are expunged, claims of "censorship" arise.18

My aim here, however, is not to criticize these rules of "netiquette." AOL also has other rules that regulate AOL members—rules expressed not in contracts but rather through the very architectures of the space. These rules are the most important part of AOL's constitution, but they are probably the part considered last when we think about what regulates behavior in this cyberplace.

Consider some examples:

For most of AOL's life,19 as a member of AOL you could be any one of five people. This was just one amazing feature of the space. When you started an account on AOL, you had the right to establish up to five identities, through five different "screen names" that in effect establish five different accounts. Some users, of course, used the five screen names to give other family members access to AOL. But not everyone used an AOL account like this. Think about the single woman, signing up for her first AOL account. AOL gave her up to five identities that she can define as she wishes—five different personae she can use in cyberspace.

What does that mean? A screen name is just a label for identifying who you are when you are on the system. It need not (indeed, often cannot) be your own name. If your screen name is "StrayCat," then people can reach you by sending e-mail to "straycat@aol.com." If you are online, people can try to talk to you by paging StrayCat on the AOL system; a dialogue would then appear on your screen asking whether you want to talk to the person who paged you. If you enter a chat room, the list of residents there will add you as "StrayCat."

But who is StrayCat? Here is a second dimension of control. StrayCat is who StrayCat says she is. She can choose to define herself as no one at all. If she chooses to place a description of herself in the members' directory, that description can be as complete or incomplete as she wishes. It can be true or false, explicit or vague, inviting or not. A member stumbling across StrayCat, then, in a chat room set up for stamp collectors could get her profile and read that StrayCat lives in Cleveland and is single and female. What happens next is anyone's guess.

Yet this need only be one of StrayCat's five identities. Let's say there is a different persona that StrayCat likes to have when she wanders through chat rooms. She can then select another screen name and define it in the directory as she wishes. Perhaps when StrayCat is having a serious discussion in a newsgroup or political list she prefers to speak as herself. She could then select a screen name close to her own name and define it according to who she really is. At other times StrayCat may like to pretend to be a man—engaging in virtual cross-dressing and all that might bring with it. One of her screen names could then be a man's. And so on. The point is the multiplicity that AOL allows, and the freedom this multiplicity permits.

No one except StrayCat needs to know which screen names are hers. She is not required to publish the full list of her identities, and no one can find out who she is (unless she breaks the rules). (After revealing to the U.S. Navy the name of one of its members so that the Navy could prosecute the person for being a homosexual, AOL adopted a very strict privacy policy that promises never to allow a similar transgression to happen again.)20

So in AOL you were given a fantastic power of pseudonymity that the "code writers" of real space simply do not give. You could, of course, try in real space to live the same range of multiple lives, and to the extent that these lives are not incompatible or inconsistent, you could quite often get away with it. For instance, you could be a Cubs fan during the summer and an opera buff during the winter. But unless you take extraordinary steps to hide your identity, in real space you are always tied back to you. You cannot simply define a different character; you must make it, and more important (and difficult), you must sustain its separation from your original identity.

That is a first feature of the constitution of AOL—a feature constituted by its code. A second is tied to speech—what you can say, and where.

Within the limits of decency, and so long as you are in the proper place, you can say what you want on AOL. But beyond these limits, speech on AOL is constrained in a more interesting way: not by rules, but by the character of the potential audience. There are places in AOL where people can gather; there are places where people can go and read messages posted by others. But there is no space where everyone gathers at one time, or even a space that everyone must sooner or later pass through. There is no public space where you could address all members of AOL. There is no town hall or town meeting where people can complain in public and have their complaints heard by others. There is no space large enough for citizens to create a riot. The owners of AOL, however, can speak to all. Steve Case, the founder of AOL, used to write "chatty" letters to the members as the community's "town mayor."21 Case left AOL in 2005, and apparently no one has stepped into his speaker shoes. AOL does still advertise to all its members and can send everyone an e-mail, but only the owners and those they authorize can do so. The rest of the members of AOL can speak to crowds only where they notice a crowd—and never to a crowd greater than thirty-six (up from twenty-three when the first edition of this book was published).

This is another feature of the constitution of the space that AOL is, and it too is defined by code. That only twenty-three people can be in a chat room at once is a choice of the code engineers. While their reasons could be many, the effect is clear. One can't imagine easily exciting members of AOL into public action, such as picketing the latest pricing policy. There are places to go to complain, but you have to take the trouble to go there yourself. There is no place where members can complain en masse.

Real space is different in this respect. Much of free speech law is devoted to preserving spaces where dissent can occur—spaces that can be noticed, and must be confronted, by non dissenting citizens.22 In real space there are places where people can gather, places where they can leaflet. People have a right to the sidewalks, public streets, and other traditional public forums. They may go there and talk about issues of public import or otherwise say whatever they want. Constitutional law in real space protects the right of the passionate and the weird to get in the face of the rest. But no such design is built into AOL.23 As Dawn Nunziato writes,

> AOL explains in its Community Guidelines that "like any city, we take pride in—and are protective of—our community." Unlike any other city, however, AOL enjoys the unfettered discretion to censor constitutionally-protected speech in its discussion forums and other online spaces, including "vulgar language" (which, it warns, is "no more appropriate online than [it] would be at Thanks-giving dinner"), "crude conversations about sex," and "discussions about . . . illegal drug abuse that imply it is acceptable."24

This is not to romanticize the power of real-space public forums. (Nor is it to pick on AOL: As Nunziato continues, "users seeking stronger protection for their expression might turn to an ISP other than AOL. They will find, however, similar restrictions on speech imposed by many other major ISPs."25) We have become such an apolitical society that if you actually exercised this constitutionally protected right, people would think you were a nut. If you stood on a street corner and attacked the latest tax proposal in Congress, your friends would be likely to worry—and not about the tax proposal. There are exceptions—events can make salient the need for protest—but in the main, though real space has fewer controls through code on who can speak where, it has many more controls through norms on what people can say where. Perhaps in the end real space is much like AOL—the effective space for public speech is limited and often unimportant. That may well be. But my aim here is to identify the feature and to isolate what is responsible for it. And once again, it turns out to be a feature built into the code.

A third feature of AOL's constitution also comes from its code. This is traceability. While members are within the exclusive AOL content area (in other words, when they're not using AOL as a gateway to the Internet), AOL

Thus the architecture of the Net, Abrams suggested, eliminates the need for the constitutional protection. Even better, Abrams went on, the Net protects against prior restraint just as the Constitution did—by ensuring that strong controls on information can no longer be achieved. The Net does what publication of the Pentagon Papers was designed to do—ensure that the truth does not remain hidden.

But there's a second side to this story.
On July 17, 1996, TWA Flight 800 fell from the sky ten miles off the southern coast of Center Moriches, New York. Two hundred and thirty people were killed. Immediately after the accident the United States launched the (then) largest investigation of an airplane crash in the history of the National Transportation Safety Board (NTSB), spending $27 million to discover the cause of the crash, which eventually was determined to have been a mechanical failure. 21

This was not, however, the view of the Internet. From the beginning, stories circulated about "friendly fire"—missiles that were seen to hit the airplane. Dozens of eyewitnesses reported that they saw a streaking light shoot toward the plane just before it went down. There were stories about missile tests conducted by the Navy seventy miles from the crash site.22 The Net claimed that there was a cover-up by the U.S. government to hide its involvement in one of the worst civil air disasters in American history.

The government denied these reports. Yet the more the government denied them, the more contrary "evidence" appeared on the Net.23 And then, as a final straw in the story, there was a report, purportedly by a government insider, claiming that indeed there was a conspiracy—because evidence suggested that friendly fire had shot down TWA 800.24

The former press secretary to President John F. Kennedy believed this report. In a speech in France, Pierre Salinger announced that his government was hiding the facts of the case, and that he had the proof.

I remember this event well. I was talking to a colleague just after I heard Salinger's report. I recounted Salinger's report to this colleague, a leading constitutional scholar from one of the top American law schools. We both were at a loss about what to believe. There were cross-cutting intuitions about credibility. Salinger was no nut, but the story was certainly loony.

Salinger, it turns out, had been caught by the Net. He had been tricked by the flip side of the point Floyd Abrams has made. In a world where everyone can publish, it is very hard to know what to believe. Publishers are also editors, and editors make decisions about what to publish—decisions that ordinarily are driven at least in part by the question, is it true? Statements cannot verify themselves. We cannot always tell, from a sentence reporting a fact about the world, whether that sentence is true.25 So in addition to our own experience and knowledge of the world, we must rely on structures of reputation that build credibility. When something is published, we associate the claim with the publisher. If the New York Times says that aliens have kidnapped the President, it is viewed differently from a story with the identical words published in the National Enquirer.

When a new technology comes along, however, we are likely to lose our bearings. This is nothing new. It is said that the word phony comes from the birth of the telephone—the phony was the con artist who used the phone to trick people who were familiar with face-to-face communication only. We should expect the same uncertainty in cyberspace, and expect that it too, at first, will shake expectations of credibility.

Abrams's argument then depends on a feature of the Net that we cannot take for granted. If there were credibility on the Net, the importance of the Pentagon Papers case would indeed be diminished. But if speech on the Net lacks credibility, the protections of the Constitution again become important.

"Credibility," however, is not a quality that is legislated or coded. It comes from institutions of trust that help the reader separate reliable from unreliable sources. Flight 800 thus raises an important question: How can we reestablish credibility in this space so that it is not lost to the loons?26

In the first edition of this book, that question could only be answered hypothetically. But in the time since, we've begun to see an answer to this question emerge. And the word at the center of that answer is: Blog.

At this writing, there are more than 50 million weblogs on the Internet. There's no single way to describe what these blogs are. They differ dramatically, and probably most of what gets written there is just crap. But it is wrong to judge a dynamic by a snapshot. And the structure of authority that this dynamic is building is something very new.

At their best, blogs are instances of amateur journalism—where "amateur," again, means not second rate or inferior, but one who does what he does for the love of the work and not the money. These journalists write about the world—some from a political perspective, some from the point of view of a particular interest. But they all triangulate across a range of other writers to produce an argument, or a report, that adds something new. The ethic of this space is linking—of pointing, and commenting. And while this linking is not "fair and balanced," it does produce a vigorous exchange of ideas.

These blogs are ranked. Services such as Technorati constantly count the blog space, watching who links to whom, and which blogs produce the greatest credibility. And these rankings contribute to an economy of ideas that builds a discipline around them. Bloggers get authority from the citation others give them; that authority attracts attention. It is a new reputation system, established not by editors or CEOs of media companies, but by an extraordinarily diverse range of contributors.

And in the end, these amateur journalists have an effect. When TWA flight 800 fell from the sky, there were theories about conspiracies that were filtered through no structure of credibility. Today, there are more structures of credibility. So when Dan Rather produced a letter on CBS's 60 Minutes purporting to establish a certain fraud by the President, it took the blogosphere 24 hours to establish this media company's evidence was faked. More incredibly, it took CBS almost two weeks to acknowledge what blogs had established."27 The collaborative work of the blogs uncovered the truth, and in the process embarrassed a very powerful media company. But by contrast to the behavior of that media company, they demonstrated something important about how the Net had matured.

This collaboration comes with no guarantees, except the guarantee of a process. The most extraordinary collaborative process in the context of content is Wikipedia. Wikipedia is a free online encyclopedia, created solely by volunteers. Launched at the beginning of 2001, these (literally thousands of) volunteers have now created over 2 million articles. There are nine major language versions (not including the Klingon version), with about half of the total articles in English.

The aim of the Wikipedia is neutrality. The contributors edit, and reedit, to frame a piece neutrally. Sometimes that effort fails—particularly controversial topics can't help but attract fierce conflict. But in the main, the work is an unbelievable success. With nothing more than the effort of volunteers, the most used, and perhaps the most useful encyclopedia ever written has been created through millions of uncoordinated instances of collaboration.

Wikipedia, however, can't guarantee its results. It can't guarantee that, at any particular moment, there won't be errors in its entries. But of course, no one can make that guarantee. Indeed, in one study that randomly collected entries from Wikipedia and from Encyclopedia Britannica, there were just as many errors in Britannica as in Wikipedia.28

But Wikipedia is open to a certain kind of risk that Britannica is not—maliciousness. In May 2005, the entry to an article about john Seigenthaler Sr. was defaced by a prankster. Because not many people were monitoring the entry, it took four months before the error was noticed and corrected. Seigenthaler wasn't happy about this. He, understandably, complained that it was the architecture of Wikipedia that was to blame.

Wikipedia's architecture could be different. But the lesson here is not its failures. It is instead the extraordinary surprise of Wikipedia's success. There

Imagine one of the programs I could select was a browser with a function we could call "kids-mode-browsing" (KMB). That browser would be programmed to watch on any web page for a particular mark. Let's call that mark the "harmful to minors" mark, or <H2M> for short. That mark, or in the language of the Web, tag, would bracket any content the speaker believes is harmful to minors, and the KMB browser would then not display any content bracketed with this <H2M> tag. So, for example, a web page marked up "Blah blah blah <H2M>block this</H2M> blah blah blah" would appear on a KMB screen as: "Blah blah blah blah blah blah."

So, if the world of the World Wide Web was marked with <H2M> tags, and if browser manufacturers built this <H2M>-filtering function into their browsers, then parents would be able to configure their machines so their kids didn't get access to any content marked <H2M>. The policy objective of enabling parental control would be achieved with a minimal burden on constitutionally entitled speakers.

How can we get (much of the) world of the Web to mark its harmful to minors content with <H2M> tags?

This is the role for government. Unlike the CDA or COPA, the regulation required to make this system work—to the extent it works, and more on that below—is simply that speakers mark their content. Speakers would not be required to block access; speakers would not be required to verify age. All the speaker would be required to do is to tag content deemed harmful to minors with the proper tag.

This tag, moreover, would not be a public marking that a website was a porn site. This proposal is not like the (idiotic, imho) proposals that we create a .sex or .xxx domain for the Internet. People shouldn't have to locate to a red-light district just to have adult material on their site. The <H2M> tag instead would be hidden from the ordinary user—unless that user looks for it, or wants to block that content him or herself.

Once the government enacts this law, then browser manufacturers would have an incentive to build this (very simple) filtering technology into their browsers. Indeed, given the open-source Mozilla browser technology—to which anyone could add anything they wanted—the costs of building this modified browser are extremely low. And once the government enacts this law, and browser manufacturers build a browser that recognizes this tag, then parents have would have as strong a reason to adopt platforms that enable them to control where their kids go on the Internet.

Thus, in this solution, the LAW creates an incentive (through penalties for noncompliance) for sites with "harmful to minors" material to change their ARCHITECTURE (by adding <H2M> tags) which creates a MARKET for browser manufacturers (new markets) to add filtering to their code, so that parents can protect their kids. The only burden created by this solution is on the speaker; this solution does not burden the rightful consumer of porn at all. To that consumer, there is no change in the way the Web is experienced, because without a browser that looks for the <H2M> tag, the tag is invisible to the consumer.

*But isn't that burden on the speaker unconstitutional?* It's hard to see why it would be, if it is constitutional in real space to tell a speaker he must filter kids from his content "harmful to minors." No doubt there's a burden. But the question isn't whether there's a burden. The constitutional question is whether there is a less burdensome way to achieve this important state interest.

*But what about foreign sites? Americans can't regulate what happens in Russia.* Actually, that's less true than you think. As we'll see in the next chapter, there's much that the U.S. government can do and does to effectively control what other countries do.

Still, you might worry that sites in other countries won't obey American law because it's not likely we'll send in the Marines to take out a noncomplying website. That's certainly true. But to the extent that a parent is concerned about this, as I already described, there is a market already to enable geographic filtering of content. The same browser that filters on <H2M> could in principle subscribe to an IP mapping service to enable access to American sites only.

*But won't kids get around this restriction?* Sure, of course some will. But the measure of success for legislation (as opposed to missile tracking software) is not 100 percent. The question the legislature asks is whether the law will make things better off.45 To substantially block access to <H2M> content would be a significant improvement, and that would be enough to make the law make sense.

*But why not simply rely upon filters that parents and libraries install on their computers? Voluntary filters don't require any new laws, and they therefore don't require any state-sponsored censorship to achieve their ends.*

It is this view that I want to work hardest to dislodge, because built within it are all the mistakes that a pre-cyberlaw understanding brings to the question of regulation in cyberspace.

First, consider the word "censorship." What this regulation would do is give parents the opportunity to exercise an important choice. Enabling parents to do this has been deemed a compelling state interest. The kids who can't get access to this content because their parents exercised this choice might call it "censorship," but that isn't a very useful application of the term. If there is a legitimate reason to block this form of access, that's speech regulation. There's no reason to call it names.

Second, consider the preference for "voluntary filters." If voluntary filters were to achieve the very same end (blocking H2M speech and only H2M speech), I'd be all for them. But they don't. As the ACLU quite powerfully described (shortly after winning the case that struck down the CDA partly on the grounds that private filters were a less restrictive means than government regulation):

> The ashes of the CDA were barely smoldering when the White House called a summit meeting to encourage Internet users to self-rate their speech and to urge industry leaders to develop and deploy the tools for blocking "inappropriate speech." The meeting was "voluntary," of course: the White House claimed it wasn't holding anyone's feet to the fire. [But] the ACLU and others . . . were genuinely alarmed by the tenor of the White House summit and the unabashed enthusiasm for technological fixes that will make it easier to block or render invisible controversial speech. . . . [I]t was not any one proposal or announcement that caused our alarm; rather, it was the failure to examine the longer-term implications for the Internet of rating and blocking schemes.46

The ACLU's concern is the obvious one: The filters that the market has created not only filter much more broadly than the legitimate interest the state has here—blocking <H2M> speech—they also do so in a totally non-transparent way. There have been many horror stories of sites being included in filters for all the wrong reasons (including for simply criticizing the filter).47 And when you are wrongfully blocked by a filter, there's not much you can do. The filter is just a particularly effective recommendation list. You can't sue Zagat's just because they steer customers to your competitors.

My point is not that we should ban filters, or that parents shouldn't be allowed to block more than H2M speech. My point is that if we rely upon private action alone, more speech will be blocked than if the government acted wisely and efficiently.

And that frames my final criticism: As I've argued from the start, our focus should be on the liberty to speak, not just on the government's role in restricting speech. Thus, between two "solutions" to a particular speech problem, one that involves the government and suppresses speech narrowly, and one that doesn't involve the government but suppresses speech broadly, constitutional values should tilt us to favor the former. First Amendment values (even if not the First Amendment directly) should lead to favoring a speech regulation system that is thin and accountable, and in which the government's action or inaction leads only to the suppression of speech the government has a legitimate interest in suppressing. Or, put differently, the fact that the government is involved should not *necessarily* disqualify a solution as a proper, rights-protective solution.

The private filters the market has produced so far are both expensive and over-inclusive. They block content that is beyond the state's interest in regulating speech. They are effectively subsidized because there is no less restrictive alternative.

Publicly required filters (which are what the <H2M> tag effectively enables) are narrowly targeted on the legitimate state interest. And if there is a dispute about that tag—if for example, a prosecutor says a website with information about breast cancer must tag the information with an <H2M> tag—then the website at least has the opportunity to fight that. If that filtering were in private software, there would be no opportunity to fight it through legal means. All that free speech activists could then do is write powerful, but largely invisible, articles like the ACLU's famous plea.

It has taken key civil rights organizations too long to recognize this private threat to free-speech values. The tradition of civil rights is focused directly on government action alone. I would be the last to say that there's not great danger from government misbehavior. But there is also danger to free speech from private misbehavior. An obsessive refusal to even consider the one threat against the other does not serve the values promoted by the First Amendment.

*But then what about public filtering technologies, like PICS? Wouldn't PICS be a solution that avoided the "secret list problem" you identified?*

PICS is an acronym for the World Wide Web Consortium's Platform for Internet Content Selection. We have already seen a relative (actually, a child) of PICS in the chapter about privacy: P3P. Like PICS, is a protocol for rating and filtering content on the Net. In the context of privacy, the content was made up of assertions about privacy practices, and the regime was designed to help individuals negotiate those practices.

With online speech the idea is much the same. PICS divides the problem of filtering into two parts—labeling (rating content) and then filtering (blocking content on the basis of the rating). The idea was that software authors would compete to write software that could filter according to the ratings; content providers and rating organizations would compete to rate content. Users would then pick their filtering software and rating system. If you wanted the ratings of the Christian Right, for example, you could select its rating system; if I wanted the ratings of the Atheist Left, I could select that. By picking our raters, we would pick the content we wanted the software to filter.

This regime requires a few assumptions. First, software manufacturers would have to write the code necessary to filter the material. (This has already)

# Article 5

Neil Postman

## Five Things We Need to Know
## About Technological Change

Good morning your Eminences and Excellencies, ladies, and gentlemen.

The theme of this conference, "The New Technologies and the Human Person: Communicating the Faith in the New Millennium," suggests, of course, that you are concerned about what might happen to faith in the new millennium, as well you should be. In addition to our computers, which are close to having a nervous breakdown in anticipation of the year 2000, there is a great deal of frantic talk about the 21st century and how it will pose for us unique problems of which we know very little but for which, nonetheless, we are supposed to carefully prepare. Everyone seems to worry about this—business people, politicians, educators, as well as theologians.

> The human dilemma is as it has always been, and it is a delusion to believe that the technological changes of our era have rendered irrelevant the wisdom of the ages and the sages.

At the risk of sounding patronizing, may I try to put everyone's mind at ease? I doubt that the 21st century will pose for us problems that are more stunning, disorienting or complex than those we faced in this century, or the 19th, 18th, 17th, or for that matter, many of the centuries before that. But for those who are excessively nervous about the new millennium, I can provide, right at the start, some good advice about how to confront it. The advice comes from people whom we can trust, and whose thoughtfulness, it's safe to say, exceeds that of President Clinton, Newt Gingrich, or even Bill Gates. Here is what Henry David Thoreau told us: "All our inventions are but improved means to an unimproved end." Here is what Goethe told us: "One should, each day, try to hear a little song, read a good poem, see a fine picture, and, if possible, speak a few reasonable words." Socrates told us: "The unexamined life is not worth living." Rabbi Hillel told us: "What is hateful to thee, do not do to another." And here is the prophet Micah: "What does the Lord require of thee but to do justly, to love mercy and to walk humbly with thy God." And could say, if we had the time, (although you know it well enough) what Jesus, Isaiah, Mohammad, Spinoza, and Shakespeare told us. It is all the same: There is no escaping from ourselves. The human dilemma is as it has always been, and it is a delusion to believe that the technological changes of our era have rendered irrelevant the wisdom of the ages and the sages.

> . . . all technological change is a trade-off. . . . a Faustian bargain.

Nonetheless, having said this, I know perfectly well that because we do live in a technological age, we have some special problems that Jesus, Hillel, Socrates, and Micah did not and could not speak of. I do not have the wisdom to say what we ought to do about such problems, and so my contribution must confine itself to some things we need to know in order to address the problems. I call my talk *Five Things We Need to Know About Technological Change*. I base these ideas on my thirty years of studying the history of technological change but I do not think these are academic or esoteric ideas. They are the sort of things everyone who is concerned with cultural stability and balance should know and I offer them to you in the hope that you will find them useful in thinking about the effects of technology on religious faith.

## First Idea

The first idea is that all technological change is a trade-off. I like to call it a Faustian bargain. Technology giveth and technology taketh away. This means that for every advantage a new technology offers, there is always a corresponding disadvantage. The disadvantage may exceed in importance the advantage, or the advantage may well be worth the cost. Now, this may seem to be a rather obvious idea, but you would be surprised at how many people believe that new technologies are unmixed blessings. You need only think of the enthusiasms with which most people approach their understanding of computers. Ask anyone who knows something about computers to talk about them, and you will find that they will, unabashedly and relentlessly, extol the wonders of computers. You will also find that in most cases they will completely neglect to mention any of the liabilities of computers. This is a dangerous imbalance, since the greater the wonders of a technology, the greater will be its negative consequences.

Think of the automobile, which for all of its obvious advantages, has poisoned our air, choked our cities, and degraded the beauty of our natural landscape. Or you might reflect on the paradox of medical technology which brings wondrous cures but is, at the same time, a demonstrable cause of certain diseases and disabilities, and has played a significant role in reducing the diagnostic skills of physicians. It is also well to recall that for all of the intellectual and social benefits provided by the printing press, its costs were equally monumental. The printing press gave the Western world prose, but it made poetry into an exotic and elitist form of communication. It gave us inductive science, but it reduced religious sensibility to a form of fanciful superstition. Printing gave us the modern conception of nationwide, but in so doing turned patriotism into a sordid if not lethal emotion. We might even say that the printing of the Bible in vernacular languages introduced the impression that God was an Englishman or a German or a Frenchman— that is to say, printing reduced God to the dimensions of a local potentate.

Perhaps the best way I can express this idea is to say that the question, "What will a new technology do?" is no more important than the question, "What will a new technology undo?" Indeed, the latter question is more important, precisely because it is asked so infrequently. One might say, then, that a sophisticated perspective on technological change includes one's being skeptical of Utopian and Messianic visions drawn by those who have no sense of history or of the precarious balances on which culture depends. In fact, if it were up to me, I would forbid anyone from talking about the new information technologies unless the person can demonstrate that he or she knows some-thing about the social and psychic effects of the alphabet, the mechanical clock, the printing press, and telegraphy. In other words, knows something about the costs of great technologies.

Idea Number One, then, is that culture always pays a price for technology.

## Second Idea

This leads to the second idea, which is that the advantages and disadvantages of new technologies are never distributed evenly among the population. This means that every new technology benefits some and harms others. There are even some who are not affected at all. Consider again the case of the printing press in the 16th century, of which Martin Luther said it was "God's highest and extremest act of grace, whereby the business of the gospel is driven forward." By placing the word of God on every Christian's kitchen table, the mass-produced book undermined the authority of the church hierarchy, and hastened the breakup of the Holy Roman See. The Protestants of that time cheered this development. The Catholics were enraged and distraught. Since I am a Jew, had I lived at that time, I probably wouldn't have given a damn one way or another, since it would make no difference whether a pogrom was inspired by Martin Luther or Pope Leo X. Some gain, some lose, a few remain as they were.

Let us take as another example, television, although here I should add at once that in the case of television there are very few indeed who are not affected in one way or another. In America, where television has taken hold more deeply than anywhere else, there are many people who find it a blessing, not least those who have achieved high-paying, gratifying careers in television as executives, technicians, directors, newscasters and entertainers. On the other hand, and in the long run, television may bring an end to the careers of school teachers since school was an invention of the printing press and must stand or fall on the issue of how much importance the printed word will have in the future. There is no chance, of course, that television will go away but school teachers who are enthusiastic about its presence always call to my mind an image of some turn-of-the-century blacksmith who not only is singing the praises of the automobile but who also believes that his business will be enhanced by it. We know now that his business was not enhanced by it; it was rendered obsolete by it, as perhaps an intelligent blacksmith would have known.

The questions, then, that are never far from the mind of a person who is knowledgeable about technological change are these: Who specifically benefits from the development of a new technology? Which groups, what type of person, what kind of industry will be favored? And, of course, which groups of people will thereby be harmed?

. . . there are always winners and losers in technological change.

These questions should certainly be on our minds when we think about computer technology. There is no doubt that the computer has been and will continue to be advantageous to large-scale organizations like the military or airline companies or banks or tax collecting institutions. And it is equally clear that the computer is now indispensable to high-level researchers in physics and other natural sciences. But to what extent has computer technology been an advantage to the masses of people? To steel workers, vegetable store owners, automobile mechanics, musicians, bakers, bricklayers, dentists, yes, theologians, and most of the rest into whose lives the computer now intrudes? These people have had their private matters made more accessible to powerful institutions. They are more easily tracked and controlled; they are subjected to more examinations, and are increasingly mystified by the decisions made about them. They are more than ever reduced to mere numerical objects. They are being buried by junk mail. They are easy targets for advertising agencies and political institutions.In a word, these people are losers in the great computer revolution. The winners, which include among others computer companies, multinational corporations and the nation state, will, of course, encourage the losers to be enthusiastic about computer technology. That is the way of winners, and so in the beginning they told the losers that with personal computers the average person can balance a checkbook more neatly, keep better track of recipes, and make more logical shopping lists. Then they told them that computers will make it possible to vote at home, shop at home, get all the entertainment they wish at home, and thus make community life unnecessary. And now, of course, the winners speak constantly of the Age of Information, always implying that the more information we have, the better we will be in solving significant problems—not only personal ones but large-scale social problems, as well. But how true is this? If there are children starving in the world—and there are—it is not because of insufficient information. We have known for a long time how to produce enough food to feed every child on the planet. How is it that we let so many of them starve? If there is violence on our streets, it is not because we have insufficient information. If women are abused, if divorce and pornography and mental illness are increasing, none of it has anything to do with insufficient information. I dare say it is because something else is missing, and I don't think I have to tell this audience what it is. Who knows? This age of information may turn out to be a curse if we are blinded by it so that we cannot see truly where our problems lie. That is why it is always necessary for us to ask of those who speak enthusiastically of computer technology, why do you do this? What interests do you represent? To whom are you hoping to give power? From whom will you be withholding power?

I do not mean to attribute unsavory, let alone sinister motives to anyone. I say only that since technology favors some people and harms others, these are questions that must always be asked. And so, that there are always winners and losers in technological change is the second idea.

## Third Idea

Here is the third. Embedded in every technology there is a powerful idea, sometimes two or three powerful ideas. These ideas are often hidden from our view because they are of a somewhat abstract nature. But this should not be taken to mean that they do not have practical consequences.

The third idea is the sum and substance of what Marshall McLuhan meant when he coined the famous sentence, "The medium is the message."

Perhaps you are familiar with the old adage that says: To a man with a hammer, everything looks like a nail. We may extend that truism: To a person with a pencil, everything looks like a sentence. To a person with a TV camera, everything looks like an image. To a person with a computer, everything looks like data. I do not think we need to take these aphorisms literally. But what they call to our attention is that every technology has a prejudice. Like language itself, it predisposes us to favor and value certain perspectives and accomplishments. In a culture without writing, human memory is of the greatest importance, as are the proverbs, sayings and songs which contain the accumulated oral wisdom of centuries. That is why Solomon was thought to be the wisest of men. In Kings I we are told he knew 3,000 proverbs. But in a culture with writing, such feats of memory are considered a waste of time, and proverbs are merely irrelevant fancies. The writing person favors logical organization and systematic analysis, not proverbs. The telegraphic person values speed, not introspection. The television person values immediacy, not history. And computer people, what shall we say of them? Perhaps we can say that the computer person values information, not knowledge, certainly not wisdom. Indeed, in the computer age, the concept of wisdom may vanish altogether.

The consequences of technological change are always vast, often unpredictable and largely irreversible.

The third idea, then, is that every technology has a philosophy which is given expression in how the technology makes people use their minds, in what it makes us do with our bodies, in how it codifies the world, in which of our senses it amplifies, in which of our emotional and intellectual tendencies it disregards. This idea is the sum and substance of what the great Catholic prophet, Marshall McLuhan meant when he coined the famous sentence, "The medium is the message."

## Fourth Idea

Here is the fourth idea: Technological change is not additive; it is ecological. I can explain this best by an analogy. What happens if we place a drop of red dye into a beaker of clear water? Do we have clear water plus a spot of red dye? Obviously not. We have a new coloration to every molecule of water. That is what I mean by ecological change. A new medium does not add something; it changes everything. In the year 1500, after the printing press was invented, you did not have old Europe plus the printing press. You had a different Europe. After television, America was not America plus television. Television gave a new coloration to every political campaign, to every home, to every school, to every church, to every industry, and so on.

That is why we must be cautious about technological innovation. The consequences of technological change are always vast, often unpredictable and largely irreversible. That is also why we must be suspicious of capitalists. Capitalists are by definition not only personal risk takers but, more to the point, cultural risk takers. The most creative and daring of them hope to exploit new technologies to the fullest, and do not much care what traditions are overthrown in the process or whether or not a culture is prepared to function without such traditions. Capitalists are, in a word, radicals. In America, our most significant radicals have always been capitalists—men like Bell, Edison, Ford, Carnegie, Sarnoff, Goldwyn. These men obliterated the 19th century, and created the 20th, which is why it is a mystery to me that capitalists are thought to be conservative. Perhaps it is because they are inclined to wear dark suits and grey ties.

I trust you understand that in saying all this, I am making no argument for socialism. I say only that capitalists need to be carefully watched and disciplined. To be sure, they talk of family, marriage, piety, and honor but if allowed to exploit new technology to its fullest economic potential, they may undo the institutions that make such ideas possible. And here I might just give two examples of this point, taken from the American encounter with technology. The first concerns education. Who, we may ask, has had the greatest impact on American education in this century? If you are thinking of John Dewey or any other education philosopher, I must say you are quite wrong. The greatest impact has been made by quiet men in grey suits in a suburb of New York City called Princeton, New Jersey. There, they developed and promoted the technology known as the stan-dardized test, such as IQ tests, the SATs and the GREs. Their tests redefined what we mean by learning, and have resulted in our reorganizing the curriculum to accommodate the tests.

A second example concerns our politics. It is clear by now that the people who have had the most radical effect on American politics in our time are not political ideologues or student protesters with long hair and copies of Karl Marx under their arms. The radicals who have changed the nature of politics in America are entrepreneurs in dark suits and grey ties who manage the large television industry in America. They did not mean to turn political discourse into a form of entertainment. They did not mean to make it impossible for an overweight person to run for high political office. They did not mean to reduce political campaigning to a 30-second TV commercial. All they were trying to do is to make television into a vast and unsleeping money machine. That they destroyed substantive political discourse in the process does not concern them.

## Fifth Idea

I come now to the fifth and final idea, which is that media tend to become mythic. I use this word in the sense in which it was used by the French literary critic, Roland Barthes. He used the word "myth" to refer to a common tendency to think of our technological creations as if they were God-given, as if they were a part of the natural order of things. I have on occasion asked my students if they know when the alphabet was invented. The question astonishes them. It is as if I asked them when clouds and trees were invented. The alphabet, they believe, was not something that was invented. It just is. It is this way with many products of human culture but with none more consistently than technology. Cars, planes, TV, movies, newspapers—they have achieved mythic status because they are perceived as gifts of nature, not as artifacts produced in a specific political and historical context.

When a technology become mythic, it is always dangerous because it is then accepted as it is, and is therefore not easily susceptible to modification or control. If you should propose to the average American that television broadcasting should not begin until 5 P.M. and should cease at 11 P.M., or propose that there should be no television commercials, he will think the idea ridiculous. But not because he disagrees with your cultural agenda. He will think it ridiculous because he assumes you are proposing that something in nature be changed; as if you are suggesting that the sun should rise at 10 A.M. instead of at 6.

The best way to view technology is as a strange intruder.

Whenever I think about the capacity of technology to become mythic, I call to mind the remark made by Pope John Paul II. He said, "Science can purify religion from error and superstition. Religion can purify science from idolatry and false absolutes."

What I am saying is that our enthusiasm for technology can turn into a form of idolatry and our belief in its beneficence can be a false absolute. The best way to view technology is as a strange intruder, to remember that technology is not part of God's plan but a product of human creativity and hubris, and that its capacity for good or evil rests entirely on human awareness of what it does for us and to us.

## Conclusion

And so, these are my five ideas about technological change. First, that we always pay a price for technology; the greater the technology, the greater the price. Second, that there are always winners and losers, and that the winners always try to persuade the losers that they are really winners. Third, that there is embedded in every great technology an epistemological, political or social prejudice. Sometimes that bias is greatly to our advantage. Sometimes it is not. The printing press annihilated the oral tradition; telegraphy annihilated space; television has humiliated the word; the computer, perhaps, will degrade community life. And so on. Fourth, technological change is not additive; it is ecological, which means, it changes everything and is, therefore too important to be left entirely in the hands of Bill Gates. And fifth, technology tends to become mythic; that is, perceived as part of the natural order of things, and therefore tends to control more of our lives than is good for us.

If we had more time, I could supply some additional important things about technological change but I will stand by these for the moment, and will close with this thought. In the past, we experienced technological change in the manner of sleepwalkers. Our unspoken slogan has been "technology über alles," and we have been willing to shape our lives to fit the requirements of technology, not the requirements of culture. This is a form of stupidity, especially in an age of vast technological change. We need to proceed with our eyes wide open so that we may use technology rather than be used by it.

## Critical Thinking

1. All U.S. schoolchildren learn that the first message Samuel F. B. Morse transmitted over his newly invented telegraph were the words, "What hath God wrought." What they probably do not learn is that Morse was quoting from the poem of Balaam in the Book of Numbers, chapter 23. Read the text of this poem.

2. The overview to this unit presents two ways to understand technical and scientific discoveries. In which camp is Morse? Richard Lewontin, a Harvard geneticist, says ("The Politics of Science," *The New York Review of Books*, May 9, 2002) that "The state of American science and its relation to the American state are the product of war." What does he mean?

# Moore's Law and Technological Determinism:
# Reflections on the History of Technology

Just over a year ago, the arrival in my mailbox of a book I had agreed to review triggered some thoughts about technology I had been meaning to articulate. The book was Ross Bassett's *To the Digital Age: Research Labs, Start-up Companies, and the Rise of MOS Technology* (Baltimore, 2002).[1] In it, Bassett describes the development of metal-oxide semiconductor (MOS) technology, which enabled semiconduc-tor firms to place more and more transistors on a single silicon chip.[2] This became the basis for what is now known as Moore's law, after Gordon E. Moore. In April 1965, Moore, then the director of research and development at the semiconductor division of Fairchild Camera and Instrument Corporation, published a paper in which he observed that the number of transistors that could be placed on an integrated circuit had doubled every year since integrated circuits had been invented and predicted that that trend would continue.[3] Shortly afterward, Moore left Fairchild to cofound Intel—a company, Bassett notes, that staked its future on MOS technology.

It is important to note at the outset that Moore's law was an empirical observation; it is not analogous to, say, Ohm's law, which relates resistance to current. Moore simply looked at the circuits being produced, plotted their density on a piece of semilog graph paper, and found a straight line. Furthermore, he made this observation in 1965, when the integrated circuit was only six years old and had barely found its way out of the laboratory. The name "Silicon Valley" did not even exist; it would be coined at the end of that decade. Nonetheless, Moore's prediction that the number of transistors that could be placed on an integrated circuit would continue to double at short, regular intervals has held true ever since, although the interval soon stretched from twelve to eighteen months.[4]

Moore's law has been intensively studied, mainly by those wondering when, if ever, fundamental physical constraints (such as the diameter of a hydrogen atom) will interrupt the straight line that Moore observed. These studies note the lengthening of the interval mentioned already: chip densities now double about every eighteen to twenty months, although no one is sure why.[5] Analysts have been predicting the failure of Moore's law for years. Interestingly, the moment of its demise seems always to be about ten years from whenever the prediction is made; that is, those writing in 1994 anticipated that it would fail in 2004, while some today put the likely date at about 2015. Obviously one of these predictions will pan out someday, but for now Moore's law is very much in force, as it has been for over forty-five years—a fact from which the lengthening of the dou-bling interval should not distract us. Over the same period, computer-disk memory capacity and fiber-optic cable band-width have also increased at exponential rates. Thus, in 2005 we see memory chips approaching a billion ($10^9$) bits of storage, Apple iPods with forty-gigabyte ($3 \times 10^{11}$ bits) disks, and local networks capable of transmitting a full-length Hollywood feature film in seconds.

But while industry analysts, engineers, and marketing people have studied Moore's law intensively, historians of science and technology have shown less interest. That is surprising, since it cuts to the heart of an issue that they have debated over the years: technological determinism.

Mel Kranzberg and his colleagues organized the Society for the History of Technology in part to foster a view of tech-nology running counter to the notion that technology is an impersonal force with its own internal logic and a trajectory that human beings must follow. The society's founders spoke of a "contextual" approach to technology, in which the linear narrative of events from invention to application was accompanied by an understanding of the context in which those events occurred.[6] They named the society's journal *Technology and Culture* to emphasize the importance of all three words. Of course, the founding of SHOT and the establishment of T&C did not settle the framework for studying technology once and for all, and periodically the concept of determinism is revisited.[7] Nor did the contextual approach remain static. Led by a second genera-tion of scholars including Thomas Parke Hughes, Wiebe Bijker, and Donald MacKenzie, it evolved into the notion (borrowed from elsewhere) of the "social construction" of technology.[8] At the risk of telescoping a complex and rich story, recall that part of the context of the founding of the Society for the History of Technology in 1957 was the Soviets' launch of *Sputnik* and its

**Paul Ceruzzi** is curator of aerospace electronics and computing at the Smithsonian's National Air and Space Museum. A second edition of his book *A History of Modern Computing* appeared in 2004.

effect on the perception of U.S. and British technology.[9] The idea of free peoples choosing their destiny freely was very much on the minds of Americans and Britons, then engaged in a cold war with a nation whose citizens lacked such freedom.

I agree with and support this approach to the history of technology. But it must confront a serious challenge: the steady and unstoppable march of semiconductor density, which has led to the rapid introduction of an enormous number of new products, services, and ways of working and living. Think of all the cultural, political, and social events that have occurred in the West since 1965. Think of our understanding of the history of science and technology today compared to then. Now consider that throughout all of these years, the exponential growth of chip density has hardly deviated from its slope. Can anything other than the limit implied by Planck's constant have an effect on Moore's law?

That Moore's law plays a significant role in determining the current place of technology in society is not in dispute. Is it a determinant of our society? The public and our political leaders believe so. In the popular press, the term "technology" itself is today synonymous with "computers." Historians of technology find that conflation exasperating, as it excludes a vast array of technology-driven processes, such as textiles or food production.

The public acceptance of technological determinism is evident among the many visitors where I work, at the National Air and Space Museum, and a recent essay in this journal indicates that determinism is again very much on the minds of historians of technology as well. In "All that Is Solid Melts into Air: Historians of Technology in the Information Revolution," Rosalind Williams recounts her experiences as dean of students at the Massachusetts Institute of Technology during that institution's transition from a set of internally generated, ad hoc administrative computing systems to one supplied by a commercial vendor, SAP.[10] Williams noted that MIT faculty and administrators felt powerless to shape, much less resist, the administrative model embodied in the new software. Such feelings of powerlessness might be understandable elsewhere, but MIT faculty are supposed to be the masters of new technology—they are the ones who create the science and engineering that underpin SAP's products. How could *they* be powerless?

A close reading of Williams's essay reveals that MIT faculty and staff were not exactly passive consumers of SAP R/3. They may have conformed to the software's rigid structure, but not without a fight. The final implementation of this "reengineering," as it was called, was much more than a simple top-down process. Is that not a refutation of the notion that increases in semiconductor density drive society? If one looked instead at a liberal arts college, less technologically savvy than MIT, would the deterministic nature of computing assert itself more strongly?

Williams used her own institution and her own role as a dean as data points (although she did exclaim "There must be an easier way to do research").[11] I propose that we do the same: look not at other people and institutions but rather at ourselves, historians of technology who live and work in a digital environment and who assert the right to criticize the blind acceptance of the products of the information age. How do we, as individuals, handle the consequences of Moore's law?

I begin with the ground on which we stand—or, more accurately, the chairs in which we sit. We spend our days in offices, staring into computer screens, using software provided by corporations such as Microsoft, Adobe, AOL, Novell, Lotus. We do not design or build the hardware or write the software, nor do we have more than a rudimentary notion of how to repair either when something breaks. "Wizards" install new applications for us; we insert a disk and press "Enter." The computer recognizes when a new device is attached, a process called "plug and play." How far removed this is from the days when many of us used jacks, wrenches, screwdrivers, and other tools to replace broken or worn parts on our cars, reinstalled everything, tested it, and then drove off![12]

We are trying to have it both ways. We pass critical and moral judgment on Harry Truman for his decision to use atomic bombs against Japan, we criticize a museum for showing, out of context, the aircraft that carried the first bomb, yet we ignore our inability to exert more than a smidgen of control over technologies that affect—determine—our daily lives.[13] In her recent book *User Error*, Ellen Rose, a professor of education and multimedia at the University of New Brunswick, writes that when it comes to software people uncritically accept technology without regard to its context or social dimension.[14] This time the villains are not Harry Truman, the Air Force Association, or senior management at the Smithsonian. We are responsible. Historians of technology find determinism distasteful. Yet we validate it every day.

Consider the tools that I and my colleagues used when I began my career as a historian of technology and a teacher:

16 mm movies
Triplicate 3" × 5" library cards (author, title, subject)
5" × 8" note cards, some with edge notches sorted by a knitting needle
35 mm film camera, producing color slides or 8" × 10" black-and-white prints
Blackboard and chalk
Cassette tape recorder
Drafting table, for producing hand-drawn maps and charts
Hewlett-Packard pocket calculator
Microfilm
Mimeograph machine
Overhead transparencies, hand drawn on the fly during a lecture
Photocopier

| Hardware | Software |
|---|---|
| Blackberry or PDA | JPEG image files |
| Compact disks | PDF files (plus Adobe Reader) |
| Cell phone | Electronic mail |
| Digital camera | Instant messaging or chat |
| DSL or cable modem | Groupware (Lotus Notes or Microsoft Outlook) |
| DVD player | Adobe Photoshop |
| GPS receiver | Microsoft Excel |
| MP3 player | Microsoft PowerPoint |
| Laptop computer | Microsoft Word |
| Desktop personal computer | Worldwide Web browser |
| Scanner with digitizing software | Amazon.com |
| Sony MiniDisc recorder | Blackboard.com |
| VoIP telephone | Blogs |
| Wireless ethernet (Wi-Fi) networking device | Google |
| | HTML documents |
| | JSTOR |
| | Listservs, Usenet or similar discussion groups |
| | ProQuest on-line newspaper retrieval |
| | QuickTime Virtual Reality |
| | Turnitin.com |

Preprints or offprints of published papers
Telephone, rotary dial, leased from AT&T
Typed letters, sent through U.S. mail
Typewriter, manual

Now consider the tool set we use today in our daily work of teaching, researching, and writing. This list is based on an informal look around my own office and at nearby universities in Maryland and Virginia where I have taught or lectured. For convenience I divide it into software and hardware. Strictly speaking only hardware obeys Moore's law, but in practice the advances in semiconductor technology allow for more and more complex software products, so both lists are appropriate.

I have probably left some out. Few readers will be enthusiastic users of every device or program or service listed above (though some will be). But I have made my point: Moore's law is at work.

Every three years, as chip capacity quadruples, a new generation of electronic products appears, along with new versions of existing software or new software products. Six years from now probably half the devices in my list of current hardware will be superseded. We see Moore's law at work in the progression of personal computer system software from CP/M to MS-DOS to Windows in its numerous versions, each integrating more and more functions (and triggering antitrust actions, to little avail). We see it, too, in the progression of personal computers, laptops, cell phones, digital cameras, MP3 players, and other devices far more powerful than the computer that accompanied Neil Armstrong, Michael Collins, and Buzz Aldrin to the Moon in 1969.[15]

It is this progression that drives the current relationship between culture and technology. Right now, many of us are abandoning film for digital photography. For those of us who took pleasure in working in a darkroom, this transition is painful. Do we have a choice? I vividly remember getting a pocket calculator and putting away my beloved slide rule.[16] It was a conscious decision that I made with an appreciation of its cultural implications. But who thinks about the wholesale transition to digital technology? Ellen Rose argues that we adopt these things en masse, without questioning them. And if we do not question them, we are at the mercy of those who produce and sell them to us. How can we espouse theories of the social shaping of technology when our daily interaction with technology is driven to such a great extent by the push of engineering?

This phenomenon seems, furthermore, without regard for the themes of gender, race, and class to which historians of technology have devoted so much attention. This journal, for example, has published an excellent study of women's involvement with programming early computers.[17] The popular press carries almost daily reports on, for example, how technologies such as the cell phone are used in less-developed countries lacking extensive wired phone infrastructure, how such technologies are differently adopted in various developed countries, how such devices are manufactured in Asia, or the outsourcing of software production to countries like India.

These are second-order examples of social construction. Silicon Valley firms frequently introduce products that fail in the marketplace, and the consumer plays a role in that process. Race, class, and gender factor into consumers' decisions. But transistor density and memory capacity never stop growing. The MIT faculty may balk at implementing a particular data-base product, but not at the doubling of chip capacity every eighteen months. It is a prerequisite for employment at MIT, Microsoft, or in Silicon Valley that one buy into the perpetu-ation of Moore's law. People who do not believe it must find work elsewhere.

Is this belief, then, an indication of the social construction of computing? I think not. Rather, it is an indication of the reality of technological determinism. Computing power must increase because it can.

## PowerPoint

In an earlier version of this essay I examined the debate over Microsoft PowerPoint as a possible refutation of the thesis of deter-minism. Many scholars have criticized this program. Edward Tufte, the well-known author of books on the visual presentation of information, is especially harsh, arguing that PowerPoint "elevates format over content, betraying an attitude of commercialism that turns everything into a sales pitch."[18] Vint Cerf, coinventor of the Internet protocols, prefers old-fashioned overhead transparencies and typically begins his public talks with the admonition, "Power corrupts; PowerPoint corrupts absolutely." For Cerf it is more of an apology; at most conferences he is the only speaker who does not use the program.[19] Originally I intended to add my own critique, but in the interval between early draft and later revision the debate was flattened by the steamroller of Moore's law. Neither Tufte nor Cerf has made the slightest dent in the adoption of PowerPoint. And if they could not, who can? Two years ago it was still pos-sible to warn scholars not to use PowerPoint. Now that sounds like a crusty old newspaper reporter waxing nostalgic about his old Underwood (and the bottle of bourbon in the top desk drawer).

Comparing PowerPoint to Stalin, as Tufte does, does not advance the debate over technological determinism. Nor will it do to deny determinism because one uses only a fraction of the electronic devices listed above—or even none of them. In a famous and now fairly old essay titled "Why I Am Not Going to Buy a Computer," Wendell Berry raised many of the objections found in more recent critiques, albeit with a succinct eloquence that few can match.[20] One objection not found in many later commentaries that Berry nonetheless advanced was that his wife did the typing for him. That brought him a lot of criticism, of course, but no argument he could have raised would have made a difference. As Ellen Rose points out, even if one writes an essay in longhand, someone else will have to scan or key it into a computer before it can be published.[21] Who is kidding whom? All of these critiques wither before Moore's law. When I was preparing these remarks I found Berry's famous essay not by going to the library and looking for a print copy but by typing the title into Google. The full text came up in seconds. Whether Berry knows or cares that his writings can be found that way, I cannot say. Nor do I know if whoever put the essay onto the Worldwide Web did so with a sense of irony. It does not matter. That is how one retrieves information nowadays.

A common method by which scholars communicate today is via Microsoft Word files attached to e-mail messages. Most publishers and publications (including this journal) ask that manuscripts be submitted as e-mail attachments. Microsoft Word has its flaws; most of us who use it, for example, have encountered instances where the font suddenly changes, randomly, for no appar-ent reason.[22] Word is also a voracious consumer of memory, but thanks to Moore's law that does not matter. Attaching Word files to e-mail is simple and it works, and so the practice is ubiquitous. I compare it to the 4'8½"rail-road gauge, which experts say is slightly narrower than the optimum, in terms of engineering efficiency. That drawback is overshadowed by the virtue of being a standard.[23] But remember that the encoding of text in Word is controlled by Microsoft, and Microsoft has the right to change the code according to its needs—not ours. Indeed, Microsoft has done so in the past, and we may assume that it will do so again.[24] The same holds true of another "standard" now taking hold, Adobe's Portable Document Format (PDF). PDF files also take up a lot of memory, but that is not the problem. The coding of these files is owned by Adobe, not by the person who wrote the words or created the document. Before reading such a file, we have to look at a page of dense legalese that states that we "accept" whatever terms of use Adobe wants us to accept (I have never read it).

One response to these concerns is to adopt "open source" programs that do what Word and Acrobat do but run under some other operating system, such as Linux, and adhere to the GNU general public license. Such programs are available and their numbers are increasing. By definition, their source code is available publicly, without charge, and cannot ever come under the control of a private entity.[25] Users are encouraged to modify the software to fit their needs. The historian who learns how to write open-source code would be the present-day counterpart to one who could repair and modify his own automobile in the dim past.

But can open-source software refute the thesis that historians have no ability to control the pace of digital technology? Thus far, the number of historians of technology who use these programs is miniscule. Perhaps open source will prevail, but the movement is mature and yet has not had much effect on us.

## An Internal Logic at Work

Historians need to be cautious when predicting the future—or, for that matter, assessing the present. Using ourselves as data points, as I (like Rosalind Williams) have done, is also dangerous. Yet the data are there, and it would be foolish to ignore our own actions.

Readers interested in critiques of the pace of digital technology besides the ones cited here can find a range of studies.[26] I have not dwelled more on them because, like everything else, they have had no effect on Moore's law. For the same reason, I do not offer this essay as yet another critique of digitization. My goal is more modest: to ask that we step back from a social constructionist view of technology and consider that, in at least one instance, raw technological determinism is at work. Only then can we begin to make intelligent observations about the details of this process. Ross Bassett's *To the Digital Age* is one such study. There ought to be many more, and they ought to address the question of why the exponential advance of computer power is so impervious to social, economic, or political contexts.

I do not deny that the digital world we inhabit is socially constructed. I am reminded of it every time I observe the celebrity status afforded to Steve Jobs—who, by the way, is not an engineer. Biographies of individuals like Jobs tell how they willed the future into being through the strength of their personalities. One must read these biographies with care, but their arguments are valid. Studying the history of computing in the context of social, political, and economic forces makes sense. It identifies us as like-minded thinkers who do not embrace every new gadget. But if we assert the right to look at technology that way, we must also recognize that in at least one case, Moore's law, an internal logic is at work, and that it is based on old-fashioned hardware engineering that an earlier generation of historians once celebrated.

# Notes

1. My review appeared in the October 2004 issue of this journal, *Technology and Culture* 45 (2004): 892–93.
2. A variant, in which PNP-type transistors alternate with NPN types, is called "complementary MOS," or CMOS, and has the advantage of requiring very little power.
3. Gordon E. Moore, "Cramming More Components onto Integrated Circuits," *Electronics*, 19 April 1965, 114–17.
4. The mathematical relationship described by Moore is $n = 2^{((y-1959) \div d)}$, where n is the number of circuits on a chip, $y$ is the current year, and $d$ is the doubling time, in years. For a doubling time of eighteen months, or $d = 1.5$, this equation predicts chip densities of about one billion in 2005. Chips with that density are not yet available commercially as far as I know, but are being developed in laboratories.
5. For early discussions on this topic among the principals, see Gordon E. Moore, "Progress in Digital Integrated Electronics" (paper presented at the International Electronic Devices Meeting, Washington, D.C., 1–3 December 1975, technical digest 11–13); Robert N. Noyce, "Microelectronics," *Scientific American* 237 (September 1977): 65.
6. See, for example, Stephen H. Cutcliffe and Robert C. Post, eds., *In Context: History and the History of Technology—Essays in Honor of Melvin Kranzberg* (Bethlehem, Pa., 1989).
7. See, for example, Merritt Roe Smith and Leo Marx, eds., *Does Technology Drive History? The Dilemma of Technological Determinism* (Cambridge, Mass., 1994).
8. For example, Donald MacKenzie and Judy Wajcman, eds., *The Social Shaping of Technology*, 2nd ed. (Buckingham, 1999); Wiebe Bijker, Thomas P. Hughes, and Trevor Pinch, eds., *The Social Construction of Technological Systems* (Cambridge, Mass., 1987).
9. Mel Kranzberg, "The Newest History: Science and Technology," *Science*, 11 May 1962, 463–68.
10. Rosalind Williams, "All that Is Solid Melts into Air: Historians of Technology in the Information Revolution," *Technology and Culture* 41 (2000): 641–68. See also her more recent book, *Retooling: A Historian Confronts Technological Change* (Cambridge, Mass., 2002).
11. Williams, "All that Is Solid," 641.
12. I can no longer make such repairs, as the engine and basic components of the car I now drive are inaccessible. Its ignition, fuel, brake, and other systems are all heavily computerized.
13. Robert C. Post, "A Narrative for Our Time: The *Enola Gay* 'and after that, period,'" *Technology and Culture* 45 (2004): 373–95. But see also his "No Mere Technicalities: How Things Work and Why It Matters," *Technology and Culture* 40 (1999): 607–22, which expresses Post's concerns about the way historians of technology react to claims that "life without technology isn't an option."
14. Ellen Rose, *User Error: Resisting Computer Culture* (Toronto, 2003).
15. The Apollo Guidance Computer had a read-write memory capacity of two thousand sixteen-bit words, or four thousand bytes. See the History of Recent Science and Technology project web pages for the Apollo Guidance Computer, http://hrst.mit.edu/ hrs/apollo/public/, accessed July 2005.
16. The calculator was a Hewlett-Packard HP-25C. The letter "C" meant that it used CMOS chips, novel at that time.
17. Jennifer S. Light, "When Computers Were Women," *Technology and Culture* 40 (1999): 455–83.
18. Edward Tufte, "Power Corrupts: PowerPoint Corrupts Absolutely," *Wired*, September 2003, 118–19; also Ian Parker, "Absolute PowerPoint," *New Yorker*, 28 May 2001, 86–87.
19. This is the title of Tufte's article cited above, of course, but I heard Cerf use the phrase on the two occasions when we were on the same program as speakers; we were the only two who did not use PowerPoint.

20. The essay was published in print in various places, but I found it on the Worldwide Web at www.tipiglen.dircon.co.uk/berrynot.html (accessed July 2005).

21. Rose (n. 14 above), 175. She is referring to Neil Postman, who proudly claimed that he wrote all his work by hand.

22. This happened to me as I was preparing this essay.

23. George W. Hilton, *American Narrow Gauge Railroads* (Stanford, Calif., 1990).

24. And this does not address the question whether one can still read the disk on which a document was stored.

25. Paul Ceruzzi, "A War on Two Fronts: The U.S. Justice Department, Open Source, and Microsoft, 1995–2000," *Iterations*, an on-line journal, www.cbi.umn.edu/iterations/ceruzzi.html (accessed July 2005). Among colleagues in SHOT, I note that Bryan Pffafenberger, of the University of Virginia, uses open source software. At home I use several open-source programs, but my employer in general does not allow them at work. GNU, a recursive acronym for "GNU's Not UNIX," is, among other things, an open-source operating system.

26. The best are written by computer-industry insiders. See, for example, Clifford Stoll, *Silicon Snake Oil: Second Thoughts on the Information Superhighway* (New York, 1996); Ben Shneiderman, *Leonardo's Laptop: Human Needs and the New Computing Technologies* (Cambridge, Mass., 2003); Steve Talbott, *The Future Does Not Compute* (Sebastopol, Calif., 1995); Thomas K. Landauer, *The Trouble with Computers: Usefulness, Usability, and Productivity* (Cambridge, Mass., 1995); Donald A. Norman, *The Invisible Computer: Why Good Products Fail, the Personal Computer Is so Complex, and Information Appliances Are the Solution* (Cambridge, Mass., 1998).

## Critical Thinking

1. Early on in *Walden,* Thoreau famously remarks that "Our inventions are wont to be pretty toys, which distract our attention from serious things. They are but an improved means to an unimproved end, an end that it was already but too easy to arrive at. . . . We are in great haste to construct a magnetic telegraph from Maine to Texas; but Maine and Texas, it may be, have nothing important to communicate." Substitute "internet" for "magnetic telegraph." Do you agree or disagree with Thoreau? How do you think Paul Ceruzzi might respond?

2. The two poles of thought that Paul Ceruzzi discusses are usually referred to as social constructivism and technological determinism. Use the internet to explore both. Ceruzzi says that "public acceptance of technological determinism is evident among the many visitors where I work, at the National Air and Space Museum." Why?

3. Who is Moore of Moore's Law?

4. Ceruzzi says that "Moore's law was an empirical observation; it is not analogous to, say, Ohm's law, which relates resistance to current." This implies that Ohm's law is not an empirical observation. Is this true?

5. State clearly what is meant by *technological determinism and social constructivism.*

# Interpersonal Relationships

The more technology becomes integrated into our lives the greater the capacity it has to change our relationships with one another. Such changes can be seen through our communication and interaction with friends and loved ones, as well as in our professional relationships. As our communication expands online, so too do our communities. In light of this, how do we define community? Additionally, in the online world we now have the capacity to create entirely new and different personas. Thus, how does our use of technology impact how we define ourselves? The surge in our personal information being stored and available online allows for other people besides those we have entrusted to have access to us. Marketers, even potential stalkers and bullies have our personal information at their disposal. Are there ramifications to having so much of ourselves online? The advent of the Internet and social media sites have changed how we initiate, form, maintain, and even dissolve relationships with one another. The readings in this section highlight the intricacies of our online personal relationships.

## Learning Objectives

1. Define relationships within the context of this technological age.
2. Describe the various ways we can manage our identities online (i.e. impression management).
3. Compare and contrast in person communities to virtual communities.
4. Assess the benefits and drawbacks of personal information online.

# Article 7

Susan M. Barnes

## Internet Interpersonal Relationships

### Chapter Overview

"Girl meets boy across the Internet and they fall in love." The popular press frequently runs stories about people who make romantic Internet connections, and marry each other. The intimate relationships that develop across the Internet are a stark contrast to early research findings, which argued that CMC would provide low social presence. People get very involved with relationships developed through the exchange of written Internet messages. Due to the lack of physical presence, Internet messages add elements of fantasy to CMC, which can lead to hyperpersonal relationships as discussed in Chapter 1.

Building relationships through the Internet requires people to use different communicative strategies than they would use in face-to-face settings. In contrast to immediate physical first impressions, people can carefully craft messages and manage the impression they communicate to others. Additionally, participants must spend time responding to messages and maintaining correspondence. Chapter 7 explores Internet interpersonal relationships by discussing the following:

- Reasons why people become involved with Internet relationships
- Intimate, social, and professional relationships
- Criteria for examining Internet relationships, which include shared experience, role play, and reciprocity
- Impression management and online relationship building

Building successful relationships using CMC can follow a pattern that is similar to building face-to-face ones. How people meet and the content and the quality of their initial encounter can set the direction of the relationship. Once a relationship is started, the intensity and caliber of the relationship depend on the amount of contact between people (e.g., daily, every few days, weekly, monthly, etc.). In CMC, the pacing of e-mail messages is very important because it reflects what is happening in the relationship. Once a pattern of correspondence is established, psychological reactions can occur when online friends fail to reply to messages at the expected time. Similar to face-to-face friendships, electronic ones are built on regular interaction and reciprocity. According to Chen and Gaines (1998), developing a positive self-image is one motivation for participating in reciprocal CMC relationships. Reciprocity works on the principle of **social exchange** or equity **theory:** An individual attempts to maintain a balance of rewards to costs. Individuals exchanging e-mail messages, participating in discussion lists, and posting personal Web pages must perceive that they receive a benefit from these interactions in order for them to continue.

### Motives for Online Interaction

People who use the Internet have motives. Three main reasons why people use CMC are interpersonal communication, information seeking, and entertainment. Despite the numerous new services that have developed around the Internet, e-mail is the most popular reason for Internet use. According to the Pew Internet and American Life Project (2000), 78 percent of the people surveyed sent e-mail. People also look up information, access government databases, find medical data, view clothing catalogs, shop at cybermalls, buy airline tickets, play games, and order books through the Internet. For entertainment purposes, millions of young American use the Internet to download music.

Using the Internet to maintain or establish human relationships is a primary motivation for Internet use. People exchange e-mail messages, access bulletin boards on Usenet, join discussion groups, exchange instant messages, and chat online. Internet service providers understand the need that people have for connection. For instance, America Online promotes its chat rooms and online forums. People need to meet other people and make friends. The Internet can help to meet this need by enabling people to make both professional and social connections through CMC. Walther and Tidwell (1996) state:

> As many of us are aware, CMC is used quite frequently by managers, academic collaborators, friends, and families, those needing emotional or medically-related social support, and by those who spend hours…playing games using deliberately selected names, genders, and self-descriptions. In doing so, CMC users report—both anecdotally and through social scientific analysis—that there are aspects of their on-line interaction which are interpersonally and stereotypically comparable, or superior to, parallel off-line activities (pp. 300-301).

For some people, the Internet can begin to replace face-to-face encounters and the telephone as a way to stay "in touch" with friends and family. For others, the Internet is an important way to connect with new people and share experiences, advice, and support. Since the early days of the Internet, CMC has been used for support groups, a variety of types of support groups have emerged on the network to help people share information. Early network users first shared information with each other about how to use and program computers. Today, people share information about medical conditions, family problems, and emotional concerns.

## Social Use of the Internet

There are many reasons why people exchange messages over the Internet, including information sharing, engaging in online debate, asking and answering questions, flirting, social contact, playing games, and advocating political positions. For example, the HomeNet study, a field trial at Carnegie Mellon University with the goal of understanding how average people use the Internet, identified the following reasons for Internet use: enjoy myself, get hobby information, learn about local events, read the news, play games, download materials, listen to music, get personal help, meet new people, visit chats and MUDs, influence a group, join a group, get educational information, do schoolwork, get employment information, get product information, buy something, make money, advertise, and sell something. According to Kraut et al. (1997), these reasons fall into four broad categories: entertainment, interpersonal communication, work, and electronic commerce.

One hundred households in the Pittsburgh area participated in the HomeNet study, and extensive study of the participants' Internet usage revealed that people use the Internet primarily for pleasure. Entertainment and personal enjoyment were the major reasons why people logged on to the network. People will regularly exchange e-mail messages with the same people. Often, e-mail correspondence occurs between people who know each other before they begin communicating online. For example, teachers will stay in touch with their students, and recent high school graduates will maintain discussion lists of their friends who have moved away to attend college. People tend to have greater loyalty to e-mail addresses than they do to Web sites because e-mail sustains ongoing exchanges and relationships.

# Online Relationships

Similar to face-to-face contexts, CMC enables two people to develop online relationships. Many of us know people who have met their boyfriend, girlfriend, husband, or wife through the Internet. Couples who are separated by distance often stay in touch through e-mail. Similarly, family members who live in different countries and states can easily communicate with each other through the Internet. Teens and adults report using the Internet to stay connected to friends who have moved away, and parents use e-mail to get in touch with their children's teachers. In business, e-mail has become as important as the telephone for coordinating work activities. E-mail, chat, and instant messenger are all CMC tools that people use to develop and maintain interpersonal relationships.

A study conducted in 1996 by Parks and Floyd (1996) examined personal relationships in Internet newsgroups. They discovered that personal relationships were common and that nearly two-thirds of the participants reported meeting people through the Internet. Women were more likely to make friends, and age did not matter. As relationships developed, their breadth and depth increased. A central characteristic of relational development was the creation of personalized language codes and idioms. Moreover, many Internet relationships incorporate other communication channels, such as telephone calls and the exchange of photographs. A common motive for starting Internet relationships is to meet people from the opposite sex.

## Intimate Relationships

Online dating has received a tremendous amount of press coverage. Web sites have been set up as dating services and chat rooms use names such as The Flirt's Nook, Romance Connection, and Thirtysomething. These electronic spaces are designed for people to meet and chat. Proponents of online romance argue that the Internet is a good way to know someone before meeting in person. However, transforming an Internet relationship into an actual one can be difficult. The romantic images established through the Internet may be built more on fantasy than reality. As a result, people need to take steps to verify that the other person is who and what they say they are. This is generally done by moving from e-mail to other forms of correspondence, such as exchanging letters and photos, viewing each other's personal Web pages, and talking on the telephone.

Internet dating is considered to be a better way to get to know someone. The elimination of physical appearance and gestures helps people learn more about their partner's inner thoughts and interests. Relationships can start off slowly and build over time. People will talk in detail about themselves and their interests. According to Tamosaitis (1995), "words have the power to connect disparate souls from distant lands minus the weighty significances of physicality" (p. 46). Two advantages of Internet dating are the ability of relationships to build over time and the elimination of disruptive nonverbal information.

A disadvantage of online dating is deception. People can make up screen names and write false descriptions about themselves. False descriptions can set up false expectations and illusions. Moreover, the careful crafting of messages can highlight a person's good attributes and disguise negative traits. Some people argue that Internet relationships do not work because they are built on fantasy more than reality. According to Booth and Jung (1996), in online romance, "Romantic lovers project fanciful images onto the objects of their obsessions and never actually see their partners at all. This sort of affection is completely illusory—much like adoring a movie star or model from afar" (p. 194). People can fall in love with the idea of love and project a fantasy image on others.

## Cybersex

The most intimate of all online exchanges is **cybersex**. Cybersex is the exchange of real-time sexually explicit messages through the Internet. Most people who engage in cybersex do it for fun and do not use their real names. However, the innocent sharing of fantasies can lead to more serious relationships. Phlegar (1995) says, "Married people who go online might say that they are neither having real affairs nor short-changing their mates. However, anyone truly addicted to computer sex won't be looking at their behavior rationally and may do serious damage to their marriage without realizing it" (p. 36).

For instance, when a New Jersey man discovered that his wife was exchanging cybersex messages with a man called the Weasel, he sued his wife for divorce. This first case of computer "adultery" made headline news in New York. This "Cybersex Divorce" was called a "groundbreaking suit—an Information Age twist on the most ancient of human foibles (Kennedy, Ben-Ali, & Bertrand, 1996, p. 5). The man claimed that the Weasel had stolen his wife's affections away from him. In contrast to the New Jersey man's reaction to cybersex, Turkle (1995) reported that one wife considered her husband's cybersex experiences to be similar to his reading a sexy novel. For this couple, the husband's cybersex adventures was a way for him to experiment without jeopardizing their marriage. Spouses have different reactions to cybersex encounters.

In addition to cybersexual exchanges, people often disclose sexually explicit information online. Witmer (1997) examined the reasons why people feel safe engaging in sexually explicit online communication. Surveyed individuals did not believe that their Internet activities would affect their careers, and they felt secure about posting risky information on the Internet. Forty-seven percent of the participants believed that the Internet was a private medium. As a result, users perceived a low risk in revealing sexually explicit information. In contrast to the results from this study, additional studies have shown that "private" messages can and do have devastating effects when they are read by other people. Sexually oriented e-mail messages have been sent to employers and people have lost their jobs. For instance, Peter Chung worked in the Seoul office of an investment firm until an e-mail message bragging about his sex life and the degree to which local bankers lavished him with dinners and golf outings was sent to his boss (see Schwartz, 2001). Internet users need to be aware that the messages they exchange with others can be read by third parties, such as systems administrators.

## Case Study: Teens on the Internet

Teenagers are now dating on the Internet. A recent study conducted by the Pew Internet & American Life Project revealed that many American teenagers are now doing so. Face-to-face teen romances can also begin and end online. For many teens, intimate conversations and awkward situations are easier to handle online than in person. Teens can think things over before they reply to a message and they do not have to deal with the immediate reactions of others. Moreover, teens do not have to worry about "freezing up," which could happen in a face-to-face conversation.

Both boys and girls have asked people out using instant messenger and have also ended relationships that way. In addition to maintaining or ending existing relationships, some teens develop Internet-only friendships. Chat rooms are places where teens can meet and arrange dates. Participants frequently ask for an age and sex check. People of similar ages will break off into a separate chat room of only two persons, which is what some teens consider to be an "Internet date." Conversation topics mirror what occurs at a face-to-face teen party. Disembodied Internet relationships limit physical contact between most teens. It is difficult for them to meet a net romance in person because of the challenges of distance, lack of transportation, and lack of financial resources. Many teens consider Internet-only relationships to be fun and fleeting rather than serious. Clark (1998) says that "the focus in the Internet date is on individual gratification, teens experience no sense of obligations to the person with whom they are ephemerally committed. . . . If a person fails to show up at the preappointed time, there are no consequences" (p. 181).

Teens reported that the Internet enables them to express themselves more fully and establish meaningful relationships because CMC allows them to focus on personality and intellect rather than attractiveness and style. Several researchers, including Turkle (1995) and Clark (1998), have observed that teens can use CMC to experiment with roles without worrying about physical sex. For instance, Clark reports that the Internet allows teens "to communicate with one another free from the social and peer pressures toward expressed sexuality" (p. 168).

However, the lack of CMC information can lead to misunderstandings that can hurt or destroy a friendship. When instant messages are used for pranks and deception, they can hurt a relationship. For example, one teen made up a screen name and wrote messages to his friend Jim saying that he knew where Jim lived, Jim's phone number, and other personal information about Jim. However, Jim did not think the prank was funny and the trickery hurt the boys' friendship. Some teens are concerned about online deception and they will only communicate with people they already know. Additionally, teens will ignore messages from strangers or people they do not want to talk to.

In the PEW study, 64 percent of the teens reported that they thought the Internet did not help their family relationships. They expressed a concern about Internet use taking time away from spending time with other family members. Similarly, 79 percent of the parents reported that the Internet has not helped to improve their relationship with their children. Although teens are actively using the Internet to maintain their social relationships with friends, the time they spend online could have an impact on their relationships with other family members.

## Social Relationships

Beyond sharing e-mail messages with friends and family members, chat rooms, discussion groups, and MUDs create electronic environments in which people can meet and socially interact. Chat rooms are places where people can meet each other and participate in online social events; similarly, MUDs and MOOs tend to be socially oriented. Online services have become aware of the need many people have to make connections, and some online services even try to parallel real communities by creating their digital counterparts. Today, CMC is becoming another way for people to meet people, make friends, and interact socially with others.

In addition to making new friends online, e-mail is often used to maintain friendships. In modern society, people frequently move to different cities and the Internet is a way for friends to stay in touch. Virtual communities enable people to meet others with similar interests, and often, friendships can develop from participation in these communities. Members of online communities often arrange face-to-face meetings (see Chapter 11). An advantage of a virtual community is its ability to keep people connected as they change jobs and move to different cities.

## Task-Oriented Relationships

E-mail has become a major method of organizational communication. Task-oriented relationships generally occur in small groups. Problem-solving or task-oriented groups are formed to meet a specific goal or purpose; after the goal is achieved, the group generally disbands. Since the 1970s, CMC has been used to facilitate task-oriented communication between individuals and small groups. The next chapter will describe the types of software and CMC tools that are available to support this type of organizational communication.

As previously stated, early studies on CMC in organizational settings focused on how the narrow bandwidth and lack of nonverbal information would lead to less social presence in the communication exchange. CMC was not considered an appropriate way to get to know someone because it would be more task-oriented and businesslike. However, in the 1980s, researchers (Chesebro, 1985; Hiemstra, 1982) began to notice that a percentage of CMC messages contained socioemotional content. For example, researchers discovered that half of the discussion messages shared on two computer bulletin board services contained jokes, insults, sexual topics, games, stories, and personal information.

Rice and Love (1987) examined the amount and types of CMC content. Specifically they examined socioemotional content, which was defined in Chapter 1, and **task-dimensional content**, which is "interactions that ask for or give information or opinions" (p. 93). They discovered that there is a tendency for active CMC users to add more socioemotional content. "Even a professionally oriented CMC system involving users who do not otherwise know each other can support a reasonable amount of socioemotional content" (p. 101). Nearly 30 percent of the message content examined in the study contained socioemotional information. Although task-oriented relationships are businesslike, with predetermined goals, individuals can use CMC to develop more personalized relationships.

## Online Relationship Development

Unlike face-to-face relationships that develop because of proximity and attraction, Internet relationships often develop from shared interests. For example, there are people participating in thousands of discussion lists. People who engage in group discussions will often privately e-mail other group members. These private exchanges can develop into Internet friendships. On the Internet, interests replace proximity as a primary reason for people meeting and developing friendships.

Human attraction is another reason for establishing relationships. People prefer some people to others. Individuals select and organize information about other people based on the types of behaviors that they think work together. In face-to-face situations, **first impressions** are an important aspect of deciding whether we like or dislike other people. However, first impressions evaluate the personality of an individual with very limited information, primarily physical appearance, and so first impressions are highly susceptible to misperception. For example, studies on first impressions revealed that individuals can jump to quick conclusions about others depending on a variety of factors, including dress, age, and descriptions. Small changes in personal descriptions can alter the ways in which people perceive someone. In a study conducted by Asch (1946), substituting the words *cold, polite,* or *blunt* for the single word *warm* in a list of personality traits altered people's perception of the test subject's personality traits.

Studies conducted on face-to-face versus computer-mediated relationships suggest that people in online relationships are often perceived as more structured or ordered and less spontaneous. According to Wallace (1999), "studies show that what we type is not quite what we would say in person, and others react to this subtle alteration in our behavior. We don't just appear a little cooler, testier, and disagreeable because of the limitations of the medium. Online, we appear to be less inclined to perform those little civilities common to social interactions. Predictably, people react to our cooler, more task-oriented impression and respond in kind" (p. 17). Failure to be civil online can lead to flaming behavior and flame wars. **Flaming** is to speak incessantly and/or negatively about someone or on a relatively uninteresting subject; it is rude behavior by face-to-face standards. One way to prevent flaming is to express more agreement and soften typed disagreements in online conversations. The words people select and their writing style are important communication strategies for presenting themselves online.

## Criteria for Examining Computer-Mediated Interpersonal Relationships

Phillips and Metzger (1976) developed a rhetorical framework for understanding interpersonal relationships. The rhetorical position argues that individuals can take action to alter, enhance, or end relationships. Similar to Karetnick's contextualized framework discussed in the previous chapter, individuals use communicative strategies to maintain friendships. In addition to strategies, the rhetorical view argues that people have goals that influence the way in which strategies are used. Phillips and Metzger contend that individuals seek goals in their interpersonal relationships and that they approach their goal seeking in an orderly manner, which can be described and critiqued in ways similar to as public discourse. The rhetorical framework has six standards for identifying interpersonal behavior: sharing common experience, security and satisfaction, understanding the other, role play, reciprocity, and benefit.

A rhetorical approach is being used to discuss online interactions because it is through the effective use of language that online relationships are built. Language in either a spoken or written form enables individuals to take action and learn to enhance or to end relationships with others. Thus, the six criteria of the rhetorical framework can be applied to relationships that develop through different CMC genres. Examining Internet interpersonal relationships can be easier than analyzing face-to-face ones because actual electronic interactions are often recorded and can be analyzed in detail. In contrast, researchers examining face-to-face relationships must record exchanges and make transcripts or rely on secondhand accounts.

Unlike to face-to-face relationships, relationships that form through CMC are built on written rather than spoken words. There are two reasons why written language is an important aspect of online relationship building. First, people who talk over extended periods of time develop a **private language** with their e-mail friends. Private language develops when language is used idiosyncratically by CMC correspondents who share assigned meanings for words and acronyms. Second, e-mail is different from face-to-face interactions because all conversations can be recorded and saved for future reference. Saved messages can indicate milestones in the relationship, for example, a birthday message from an e-mail friend can be printed and saved. Unlike face-to-face conversations, electronic ones can be re-read and can reappear in future messages with comments and reactions. Replying to email, the frequency of contact, and the development of private language all contribute to the building of successful online relationships.

### Relationships Build over Time

The elimination of social information in CMC makes participants communicate in a single verbal/linguistic mode. Consequently, it takes more "real time" for participants to exchange the same number of messages in CMC than it does face-to-face. This approach to CMC is called the **social information processing (SIP) theory**. SIP is built on the following ideas. First, communicators' motives for affiliation with others encourage them to develop relationships and will overcome the limitations of a medium. Second, communicators will adapt their communication strategies to the medium in an effort to acquire social information and achieve social goals. Finally, relationship building takes time and CMC relationship development is slower than establishing face-to-face relationships.

Walther's (1994) research revealed that socioemotional expression was greater when interaction between participants occurred over a longer period of time. He states, "Interpersonal impressions did develop over extended time interaction in CMC, and they developed more slowly than in FtF [Face-to-Face] interaction" (477). Additionally, research has revealed that differences between face-to-face and computer-mediated relationships occur in the initial stage of interaction but tend to dissipate over time. However, a factor that influences the development of relational correspondence in CMC is whether participants expect the relationship to be ongoing and possibly lead to future contact. People who believe their relationships are ongoing will work harder to use CMC to maintain the relationship.

When people come together on-and offline, they often form a type of minisociety, complete with legislative, executive, and judicial components. People engaging in relationships must decide on what to do and believe, they must be able to carry out their decisions, and they must have a way of settling disputes. They must also agree on a common definition of what is being exchanged.

Interpersonal relationships can be complementary, symmetrical, or parallel. **Complementary relationships** are based on differences between the partners; for example, one person is dominant and the other is submissive, or one person has knowledge about a subject that the other needs. In contrast, **symmetrical relationships** are based on similarities; for instance, both partners tend to be dominant or both tend to be submissive. In CMC, symmetrical relationships are built around mutual interests. **Parallel relationships** are based on a combination of complementary and symmetrical interactions. For example, one person is dominant and the other is submissive when making decisions about finances, but the roles switch when entertainment decisions are being made. Relationships in which people babble independently without fulfilling some type of complementary, symmetrical, or parallel shared needs are really nothing more than acquaintanceships.

## Shared Experience

Relationships must build substantive meanings for the participants sharing the experience. Montgomery (1996) states, "The meanings associated with partners' communicative acts, both verbal and nonverbal, define relationship events like arguments, lovemaking, flirtation, play, discussions, apologies, and so forth" (p. 125). It is through the sharing of experiences and events that people develop a sense of the nature of their relationship. Relationships involve two or more people sharing a common experience for meeting some basic human goal.

Short-term goals are generally defined by the situation in which people encounter each other, and goals are negotiated between the individuals. For example, a student contacts his or her professor to get help understanding a homework assignment, or members of a work group use e-mail to coordinate their meetings and activities. Long-term goals require more time and include building one's self-esteem or developing a friendship. The first step in building a shared experience is understanding the situation or context in which the communication occurs. This is particularly important in CMC because individuals can encounter other people from geographically and culturally diverse backgrounds.

When CMC is a supplement to face-to-face encounters, the participants generally understand the context. For instance, when teachers and students communicate through e-mail, they understand each other's roles and the rules of behavior. However, when people first come together in an Internet discussion list, they may not understand the nature of the communication context because the lack of shared face-to-face experiences can make online conversations difficult to interpret. Quoting portions of an e-mail message can help to establish a shared context for the exchange (Figure 7.1).

Dissimilar external factors, such as linguistic differences. cultural differences, age factors, and gendered discourse can inhibit the building of shared meaning between communicators. However, once participants take the time to understand the different points of view being articulated, group members can share a common experience. Moreover, sharing birthday greetings, births, deaths, and other significant events online can help to create a bond between individuals.

## Security and Satisfaction

Another factor in establishing relationships both on-and offline is security and satisfaction. Security develops from the feeling that one fits into society, and satisfaction is ascribed to the awareness that others have verified one's identity. Phillips and Metzger (1976) state, "Security is sought largely through public means, and satisfaction is the product of private and intimate arrangements" (p. 107). Relationship bonding requires a feeling of security because both partners must feel secure in what is going on. For example, for one person to be in charge requires the other to give permission. If one partner gives permission to the other to take charge, who is really in charge? In any relationship, each partner assigns value and the person who assigns the highest value to the relationship will do more to keep it working. In CMC relationships, the person who assigns the highest value to the relationship will write longer messages and spend more time online maintaining the relationship.

In addition to interpersonal correspondence, the medium helps to create feelings of satisfaction. According to Williams and Rice (1983), the interactive characteristic of new media can satisfy interpersonal needs because these media are flexible enough to personalize information. As a result, computer networks can help foster a sense of social presence. **Social presence** is reflected in how participants in a communication exchange would evaluate the medium that is being used on the following criteria: unsociable-sociable, insensitive-sensitive, cold-warm, and impersonal-personal (Figure 7.2). For example, people generally expect a business letter to have less social presence than a face-to-face meeting.

Two factors that relate to social presence are interactivity and the public versus private aspect of the interaction. As previously stated, CMC is interactive and the nature of the interactivity depends on whether the online interaction occurs in synchronous or asynchronous time. Unlike face-to-face encounters, Internet conversations do not obviously occur in a public or private setting. Witmer's study on risky communication, described earlier in this chapter, revealed that people often consider their e-mail messages to be private. But system administrators at corporations and universities can monitor messages, and e-mail can be forwarded to others without our knowledge. People sitting alone at home typing their inner thoughts into the computer tend to perceive the experience as a private one. However, others can read many computer-mediated exchanges.

Message          1
To:              Sue
From:            Pat
Re:              Meeting

Let's get together in June to talk about the book project.

pat

Message          2
To:              Pat
From:            Sue
Re:              RE: Meeting

>Let's get together in June to talk about the book project.

That's a good idea. But, the early part of June would be better for me because I'm going on vacation in the middle of June.

Sue

Message          3
To:              Sue
From:            Pat
Re:              RE: Meeting

>>Let's get together in June to talk about the book project.

[Notice the double >>because this line was first sent two messages ago.]

>That's a good idea. But, the early part of June would be >better for me because I'm going on vacation in the middle of >June.

How about June 4th at 10 : 30 A.M. at my office.

pat

Message 4
To:              Pat
From:            Sue
Re:              RE: Meeting

>How about June 4th at 10 : 30 A.M. at my office.

Sounds great! I'll be there.

Pat

Notice how the quoting clarifies the message and creates continutity between messages. People often read 20–50 messages per day and messages can be forgotten or lost. Requoting eliminates ambiguity and make easier to understand messages.
From: Wendy

**Fig 7.1 Quoting in Message Exchanges**

Dear Folks:

"I'd like to know 'What significant artifact you have in your living environment that represents you or something about yourself?" In my case I would say the yellow paint color of my living room! I call the room my sunshine room. It's a happy place made more so by the bright, cheerful color. I also have painted murals on the exterior of my home (soon to be refreshed) that represent blue skies and summer flowers I would like to enjoy year round. Every time I come into my driveway, I feel transported to an upbeat day no matter what the weather.

Wendy

**Fig. 7.2 Message with High Social Presence**

Source: Wendy Snetsinger. Used by permission.

Despite confusion over the public-private nature of CMC, it can support feelings of both security and satisfaction. For example, Hauben and Hauben (1997) argue that by electronically interacting with others, individuals can begin to feel more secure. They provide the following example:

When I started using ForumNet (a chat program similar to irc, but smaller—[Now called icb]) back in January 1990, I was fairly shy and insecure. . . . I had a few close friends but was slow at making new ones. Within a few weeks, on ForumNet, I found myself able to be open, articulate, and well-liked in this virtual environment. Soon, this discovery began to affect my behavior in "real" face-to-face interaction. I met some of my computer friends in person and they made me feel so good about myself, like I really could be myself and converse and be liked and wanted (William Carroll, cited in Hauben & Hauben, 1997, p. 17).

CMC enables socially reticent individuals to develop interpersonal skills because it removes the social pressure of immediate face-to-face reactions from others. Moreover, some people seem to feel more secure about expressing their personal feelings to others online. Individuals who are shy and do not like to speak in front of small groups can use email as a way to express themselves. For instance, shy students will often use e-mail as a way to communicate with their professors. A study by Mazur, Burns, and Emmers-Sommer (2000) examined the effects of communication apprehension and relational interdependence in online relationships. They discovered that people who are communicatively apprehensive perceived higher levels of relational interdependence with online partners. These findings support the idea that socially shy individuals could use CMC to build and develop interpersonal relationships.

Additionally, CMC can help individuals who are experiencing professional or personal problems. Sproull and Faraj (1996) state, "Despite the fact that participants in electronic groups may be surrounded by people at work or school, at least some of them feel alone in facing a problem or a situation" (p. 128). The feeling of facing a problem alone can lead a person to believe that he or she is at fault. Online support groups help to normalize experiences and allow people who share similar problems to meet.

Online groups that share common interests are also likely to share common problems, and members of these groups can provide support for each other. Many different support groups can be accessed through the Internet. Moore (1995) says, "America Online, for instance, has Monday meetings for infertility, chronic fatigue, and 'Marital Blisters.' On Tuesday, there is an AA meeting, a support group for depression, one for eating disorders, a meeting of Adult Children of Alcoholics, and a forum for Panic Support" (pp. 67–68). Electronic support groups exist for every topic from breast feeding to people with cerebral palsy. Today, computer networks have developed into a medium that facilitates the person to person sharing of emotional and informational support.

For some individuals, CMC can be a preferred method of communication. For example, Murray (1991), in her ethnographic study of IBM employees, revealed that employees choose e-mail as a medium of communication to express logical, well-argued statements. E-mail is generally followed by a telephone call or face-to-face conversation. Beginning an interaction through e-mail removes personal and emotional matters from the initial conversation and makes discussions more rationally oriented.

Because e-mail eliminates immediate face-to-face reactions from others, some people find it a superior way to present issues and problems that need solutions. Separating the people from the problems enables individuals to discuss their problems in a less emotional context. Moreover, e-mail provides an opportunity for socially reticent individuals to express themselves in ways that can lead to an improved sense of security and satisfaction.

## Understanding the Other

Understanding the other, a basic concept from the writings of George Herbert Mead (1932, 1934), was discussed in the previous chapter. According to Phillips and Metzger (1976), "Each individual in a relationship is able to monitor his (or her] behavior as well as take the position of the other in order to perform an analysis of the situation in which he [or she] finds himself [or herself]. This helps him [or her] find the most effective approach to facilitate goal accomplishment" (p. 182). Unlike face-to-face encounters, CMC can make understanding the other difficult because people can more easily misrepresent themselves. Consider the following e-mail story:

> I started corresponding with a woman I encountered on a discussion network. She had a job at a major university facility and I documented her existence. She lived in the same town as my friend's aged mother, and so I asked her to look in. She did, reported pleasant encounters with the old woman. Then she reports that her daughter is "hooked on drugs," her ex husband is harassing. She reports tales from her past that pass beyond all that is reasonable and reports she is now doing three therapy sessions a week with her psychiatrist. Shall I take this seriously. She is looking in on my friend's mother. I am, frankly, worried, and I know, I hope, I will be more cautious next time (cited in Barnes, 2001, p. 117).

As in face-to-face encounters, our *first Internet impression* of others may prove to be wrong. Initial impressions both on- and offline are often quick, inaccurate judgements. Therefore, most discussion groups recommend **lurking** and becoming familiar with individuals and the group's dynamics before joining the conversation. Eager new members frequently embarrass themselves. For example, a student who joined an academic discussion list sent a nasty message to the group's leading academic, calling this professor a "cranky old man." This student had not done his homework and did not understand the professor's role in the group as a provocative writer or his professional reputation. As a result, the professor first appeared to the student as "cranky" rather than insightful. After reading more messages posted to the group, the student realized his error and apologized to everyone.

Dual perspective is an aspect of relationship building that can influence how we understand other people. **Dual perspective** is a state of mind that takes into account the realization that the other person may see the world through entirely different eyes. Moreover, it is often important to discover exactly how that other person sees the world in order to adjust your own behavior. Through the understanding that an individual has the capacity to influence others, the individual has a responsibility when he or she does so. Dual perspective enables people to monitor their language and address themselves directly to the needs of the rhetorically sensitive person.

With casual acquaintances, we only have a limited view of the ways in which they perceive the world. This also tends to be true about Internet relationships. When we meet someone through CMC, the conversation is restricted to text and people can control their reactions and opinions. Interactions are not always spontaneous. Individuals can use **negative spontaneity** to carefully craft their messages to create the "right" impression. Therefore, it is important in CMC to observe the behaviors and roles of others. Spending time carefully reading messages will help you better understand the perspectives of Internet friends and members of online groups.

## Role Play

Role play both on-and offline is important in the formation of relationships. According to Phillips and Metzger (1976), "Behaviors possible are projected as roles, roles are systematically played and are purposeful. They need to be ratified through the response of the other. Successful ratification enhances self-esteem" (p. 182). People can play a variety of roles in CMC. They can be themselves in discussion lists, create a pseudonym in a chat room, or invent a character to play in an online game.

An online participant's perception of the computer-mediated genre can influence the participant's behavioral roles. Saunders, Robey, and Vaverek (1994) researched status roles in computer conferences and discovered that occupational roles apply to CMC. For instance, in online medical contexts, doctors are viewed as high-status professionals and they "tend to send more sentences to low-status individuals than vice versa" (p. 465). Similarly, in computer-assisted instruction, teachers assume high online centrality. Social roles established in face-to-face contexts are frequently transferred into online encounters. Saunders, Robey, and Vaverek (1994) concluded that "advocates of equalitarian social interaction clearly cannot depend on technology alone to overcome the status differentials inherent in occupations and other social roles" (p. 469).

Unlike roles established in professionally oriented CMC, social roles are more difficult to establish. As in face-to-face situations, social roles emerge as people interact with each other. For example, many discussion groups have a **list guru**, a person who sparks the fires of debate and assumes a leadership position. The leadership role of the list guru will influence the formation of Internet friendships developed through online groups. For instance, a complementary relationship can develop between a list guru and a person who needs information or advice. A well-published academic list guru developed a number of complementary relationships with young scholars who wanted to get published. They exchanged e-mail and instant messages about different book ideas, and the list guru provided advice about dealing with publishers.

A leadership role established in one discussion group does not necessarily transfer to another one. Therefore, some people oppose **cross-posting** messages, or moving e-mail from one online discussion group to a different one. Whittle (1997) contends, "Some participants object to wider distribution of their posts on the grounds that cross-posting of their works might expose them to ridicule or loss of status, or because the original context might easily be lost" (p. 134). Expertise and status on one list do not necessarily transfer to another.

The roles we assume in both professional and social online contexts can influence the nature of relationships that we develop. Therefore, it is important to clearly communicate these roles to others.

## Relationships are Built on Reciprocity

Both on-and offline, interpersonal relationships are developed through reciprocal exchanges. Phillips and Metzger (1976) say, "Each person, consciously or unconsciously, conducts a review of his ongoing relationships and, following the pleasure principle, acts to maintain those that satisfy and diminish or extinguish those that do not. Since both parties to a relationship have equivalent opportunity, maintenance of a relationship is a reciprocal process. Something must be exchanged" (p. 182). For successful relationships to occur, people must feel that a beneficial exchange is taking place. For example, people can exchange professional information and provide emotional support for each other. The following are examples of beneficial online relationships from the HomeNet study:

> One professional in the sample gets information from and sends information to a group discussing income tax regulation. . . . A woman has joined an on-line support group dealing with her chronic illness. And many of the teenagers in the sample exchange daily electronic mail with other kids in their high school, supplementing the endless conversations they have on the telephone and in person (Kraut, 1995, page 2).

Responding to e-mail messages is the first step in building reciprocal online relationships. Whittle (1997) states, "Although net culture is fairly flexible about e-mail turnaround time, the nature of the communication should factor in your decision of when and how to respond, if at all" (p. 53). However, a distinction is generally made between professional and casual use of e-mail. Professional correspondents usually expect a quick reply to their e-mail unless you are out of town. Casual e-mail messages can be read and answered at your convenience.

Responses to online messages can broaden or narrow the exchange depending on whether the response focuses on portions of the original message, offers new ideas, or asks questions to move the conversation in a different direction. Whittle (1997) provides some examples:

- JaneD comments that abortion is wrong and gives three reasons to support her belief. RichM responds by rebutting each of the three reasons and offers four reasons why a woman's right to choose should take precedence over moral judgements about abortion in making law. (Broadening)
- JaneD responds by pointing out that all four of RichM's reasons are based on the assumption that morality cannot be legislated, and she rebuts that assumption by pointing out that ALL legislation is based on morality—i.e., society's concept of right and wrong. (Narrowing)
- Another participant jumps in and comments that the separation of church and state demands that all morality be kept out of all legislation. (Diverting). (1997, p. 71).

When people divert or make outrageous statements to others, many people respond with silence. Ignoring statements is an easy way to deal with inappropriate messages or behavior. Moreover, silence can be used as an avoidance strategy. "A negative use of silence is to drop out of a discussion without comment rather than face up to the weakness of one's position" (Whittle, 1997, p. 71). Rather than reply to criticism, some people will just not respond. Often, no response is perceived as a negative reaction and the person can lose credibility. Additionally, not responding to e-mail can end an online relationship.

In online communication, it is possible to cultivate skill with reciprocity. A small amount of reflected listening can enable an individual to bring the other person's message to the screen so it can be answered line-for-line (Figure 7-3). Quoting sections of previous messages encourages online discussion for two reasons. First, it helps readers contextually understand who and what the writer is replying to. Second, it supports the idea of reciprocity by providing direct feedback to the message sender. Reflected listening is a style of interaction that was used by psychologist Carl Rogers, and it was applied to a computer program called *ELIZA*, one of the first bots ever programmed. Reflected listening is an effective technique for developing reciprocity between online correspondents, and the *ELIZA* program shows that it works well in text-only exchanges (Figure 7.4). Online writers need to learn how to write messages that foster responses. Otherwise, their messages will be ignored and the individual will be unable to develop computer-mediated relationships.

**MESSAGE ONE FROM PHILLIP TO THE GROUP**
Date: Wed, 31 Aug 1994 22 : 17 EDT
From: Phillip M. G.
Subject: Re: real life vs. cyberspace
> Robert B. asks . . .
> And how does everyone feel now that you met F2F? Did "it"
> live up to expectations? Does whether "it" did or did not
> meet your expectations effect your relationships?
>
> None of my business, really, but Phillip did ask for input.
>
PMG: Well, gee whiz, you don't have to do things just because I
PMG: ask. But it would be interesting to find out. Since I
PMG: was at the epicenter, I confess, I was overwhelmed. Too
PMG: many important people coming all at once and not enough
PMG: time to spend with any of them. Of course, it was not
PMG: enough --and too much --at the same time.

PMG: But, a hazard of the internet is that we often do not
PMG: encounter whole people. You do not know who I am off
PMG: list. I can conceal features of my personality I do not
PMG: want you to know about. What if I wore Depends?

**MESSAGE 2 ROBERT'S ANSWER TO PHILLIP**
Date: Wed, 31 Aug 1994 19 : 51 EST
From: Robert B.
Subject: Re: real life vs. cyberspace
Phillip:
I thought everyone knew you wore Depends. Whoops. Ah. . . ahem. Umm. . . ah. . . suspends! I mean. . . suspend. . . ers. Yeah. I thought everyone knew you wore susPENDers. Yeah. Like Larry King. Harum.
(skitter skitter skitter fade out)

**MESSAGE 3 PHILLIP'S ANSWER TO ROBERT**
Date: Thur, 1 Sept 1994 20 : 18 EDT
From: Phillip
Subject: Re: real life vs. cyberspace
You are quite right, you know? I do wear suspenders. How
could you have ever known.
PMG

**MESSAGE 4 ROBERT'S ANSWER TO PHILLIP**
Date: Fri, 02 Sep 1994 00 :15 :18 -0600
From: Robert B.
Subject: Re: real life vs. cyberspace
I occasionally wonder what you look like. If I let myself ponder the fact that I am talking with people I have never met and know precious little about in a very informal manner, I get a bit woozy.

**Fig 7.3 A Series of Reciprocal E-mail Exchanges.** The following is a series of exchanges between two members of a discussion group. Most of the members had met face-to-face and they were discussing their face-to-face, versus online relationships. The first message, written by Phillip, was responding to a message written by Robert. Notice how Phillip first quotes Robert and then adds his comments.

Source: Adapted from Barnes, 2001.

Men are all alike
IN WHAT WAY
They're always bugging us about something or other.
CAN YOU THINK OF A SPECIFIC EXAMPLE
Well, my boyfriend made me come here.
YOUR BOYFRIEND MADE YOU COME HERE . . . .
You are like my father in some ways.
WHAT RESEMBLANCE DO YOU SEE
You are not very aggressive but I think you don't want me to notice that.
WHAT MAKE [SIC] YOU THINK I AM NOT VERY AGGRESSIVE
You don't argue with me.
WHY DO YOU THINK I DON'T ARGUE WITH YOU
You are afraid of me.
DOES IT PLEASE YOU TO BELIEVE I AM AFRAID OF YOU
My father is afraid of everybody.
WHAT ELSE COMES TO MIND WHEN YOU THINK OF YOUR FATHER
Bullies.
DOES THAT HAVE ANYTHING TO DO WITH THE FACT THAT YOUR BOYFRIEND MADE YOU COME HERE

Source: Weizenbaum, 1976, pp. 3–4.

**Fig 7.4 Example of an ELIZA Exchange.** An early computer program developed to use reflected listening was called ELIZA. ELIZA was programmed to emulate the conversational style of a Rogerian psychologist, and the software encouraged people to talk to the program because it gave the illusion of listening and responding. The following is an excerpt from an ELIZA exchange. First to speak is a young woman. Her statement is followed by the computer's response in capital letters.

## CMC Impression Management Model

At times, people prefer mediated communication over face-to-face communication because they can more effectively control the positive impression made on others. A study conducted by Hancock and Dunham (2001) revealed "that impressions formed in the CMC environment were less detailed but more intense than those formed face-to-face" (p. 325). This finding supports the theory that hyperpersonal relationships develop through CMC.

To further examine impression management in CMC, O'Sullivan (2000) developed an **impression management model** for understanding interpersonal mediated communication. The impression management model "views mediated communication channels as a tool for managing self-relevant information in pursuit of self-presentational goals" (p. 403). The model combines both mass media and interpersonal theories, and its focus is on people and the media they use rather than technology characteristics. Uses and gratifications media research, described in Chapter 4, is applied to interpersonal relationships by considering the media tools that people use to pursue communication and relational goals.

The model also incorporates elements of **symbolic interactionism,** a perspective that asserts human interaction is mediated by the use of symbols. According to Wood (1992),"symbolic interaction refers to a process in which humans interact with symbols to construct meanings. Through symbolic interactions we acquire information and ideas, understand our own experiences and those of others, share feelings, and come to know other people" (p, 63).

Impression management focuses on the relational partners' concept of self and how people present themselves to others. Self-presentation theory is based on Goffman's research, discussed in the previous chapter. People can select different media tools to communicate messages and present themselves. According to 0'Sullivan (2000), "Individuals are seen as working to regulate what information about oneself is known (and what [is] not known) by others in order to mange the impression that others have of them" (pp. 405–406). People develop communication strategies to manage the ways in which they present themselves to interactional partners. When using CMC tools, such as e-mail, chat, or instant messenger, the missing visual and aural information is seen as an opportunity to regulate information exchanged between two partners. Individuals select communication tools based on the benefit and cost of how each tool can be used to meet communication goals. As stated earlier, teenagers often use CMC in the dating process to control and experiment with their self-identity. The ambiguity of CMC provides more freedom to teens for experimentation and also allow them to regulate the nature, amount, and timing of information shared (Figure 7.5).

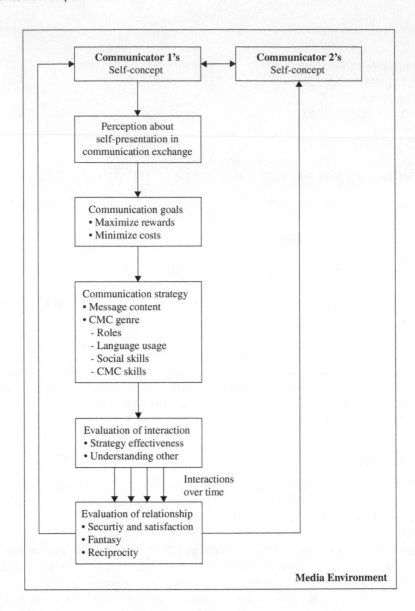

**Fig 7.5 Impression Management in CMC**

Based on O'Sullivan (2000) and adapted to conform to Phillips & Metzger (1976) and terminology used in this text.

Communicative competence and social skills also influence the communication exchange. As described in Chapter 5, the symbolic form of language used in CMC adds new types of communication competence skills that are different from those of face-to-face interaction. In addition to traditional writing skills, online communicators need to know how to use graphic accents and acronyms. Moreover, the medium itself can influence the understanding of messages. The lack of visual and aural information can lead to misunderstanding, and therefore, communicators need to add emotional cues to text-only exchanges. In addition to linguistic and computer skills, CMC requires social skills that include the ability to manage interactions.

When O'Sullivan applied this model to a study of individuals involved in romantic relationships, he discovered that people would select different methods of communication depending on the perceived threat or support for self-presentation. A preference for CMC increased when self-presentation was threatened. People realize that CMC can help minimize the effect of embarrassing or unattractive information. Similarly, in business contexts, CMC can be used to present rational arguments and eliminate emotionally charged social cues. The information management model can help us better understand the ways in which people select CMC as a medium for interpersonal communication and relationship development.

# Summary

People have reasons for using the Internet, including keeping in touch with friends and family, information seeking, and entertainment. The most popular reason for using the Internet is sending e-mail messages. E-mail can be used to develop intimate, social, and professional relationships. The six standards (sharing experiences, security and satisfaction, understanding the other, role play, reciprocity, and benefit) described in Phillips and Metzger's rhetorical framework for interpersonal behavior can be found in Internet relationships. These standards can be used to help evaluate the quality of relationships that are built through CMC.

A key aspect of Internet relationship building is reciprocity—individuals need to exchange messages for the relationship to continue. Message styles can both encourage and discourage a response. As a result, online friends need to work on establishing communication strategies that will build relationships. Impression management models enable us to better understand why people choose different media to communicate interpersonal messages. The model examines how people present themselves to others, goals of the exchange, the strategies used in the communication exchange, evaluation of the exchange, and evaluation of the relationship.

# TERMS

**Complementary relationships** are based on differences between the partners; for example, one person is dominant and the other is submissive.

**Cross-posting** messages is forwarding an e-mail message sent to one discussion group to a different group.

**Cybersex** is the exchange of real-time sexually explicit messages through the Internet.

**Dual perspective** is a state of mind that takes into account the realization that the other person may see the world through entirely different eyes.

# Article 8
Crispin Thurlow, Laura Lengel, and Alice Tomic

## Online Communities: Real or Imagined?

### OVERVIEW
### KEY TERMS

| | |
|---|---|
| community | imagined communities |
| Gemeinschaft and Gesellschaft | social networks |
| Sociability and locality | hybridity |

### MAIN OBJECTIVES

- Critique the notion that online communities are either good or bad.
- Distinguish between descriptive and normative definitions of community.
- Consider theories of 'community' and social network theory.
- Highlight the hybrid forms of on-and offline community networking.

### ONLINE COMMUNITY: ALL GOOD OR ALL BAD?

In Basic Theory: Unit 3, we looked at the major discourses of hype and hysteria that have surrounded all new technologies of communication, and, most recently, new media like the internet and web. One excellent example of the way in which these competing discourses play out with regards to CMC can be found in people's ideas about online communities and the impact of new communication technologies on offline communities. These are ideas which can be heard from CMC scholars and lay people alike – have a look at these two quotes:

> Computer networks isolate us from one another, rather than bring us together . . . .
> Computers teach us to withdraw, to retreat into the warm comfort of their false reality . . . . only the illusion of community can be created in cyberspace. (Stoll, 1995: 58, 137)
> **www** For weblinks and resources visit the CMC website at <www.sagepub.co.uk/resources/cmc>

> The internet has opened a whole new frontier that has brought every person in the world together in one place. The internet is a world within itself; it is a virtual community of hundreds of millions of citizens from every corner of the planet . . . No longer do personal differences separate the seven billion citizens of the world's 244 nations; we are now one people united together. (www.intergov.org)

As with these quotes, commentators – be they academics, journalists or the people next door – try to persuade us into taking one of two extreme points of view about the connection between new technology and community. These positions are sketched in Box CI3:1.

---

**BOX CI3:1 GOOD TECHNOLOGY, BAD TECHNOLOGY**

- **Negative position:** Communication technologies like the internet are to blame for the loss of *real*, offline communities and so-called online communities are not *proper* communities anyway.
- **Positive position:** New communication technologies, and especially the internet, make possible exciting, *new* communities and help reinvigorate or enhance existing offline communities.

---

We've chosen to italicize what we see as some problematic words in these two positions. As we discussed in Central Issues: Unit 2, it's worth while being a little wary when people make assumptions about something being 'real', 'proper' or 'new', and especially when they opt for emotive language like 'false reality' and 'one people united', as in the quotes from Stoll and InterGov. © Just as we saw with the notions of 'group' and of 'flaming' in Basic Theory: Units 5-6, it's also always useful to start by establishing some kind of definitional clarity about terms which people otherwise take for granted. So, before we start looking at *online* communities, one of the first things we need to ask ourselves is 'What exactly is it people mean when they talk about **community?'**

© Remember also that the dichotomy between 'real' and 'virtual' often implies that any-thing 'virtual' isn't real or proper.

# WHAT IS [OR WAS] A COMMUNITY?

One important way of starting to address this question is to follow the ideas of sociologists Colin Bell and Howard Newby (1971), who distinguished between what they called *empirical descriptions* and *normative prescriptions*. In other words, it's important to separate the ways people try to describe what a particular community is actually like (e.g. where it is and who belongs to it) from the ways people promote or prescribe their own particular idea of what they think community should be like. The fact of the matter is that community doesn't mean the same thing to everyone, and discussions about the nature of online communities, and their relative strengths and weaknesses, invariably get caught up between what they are and what they should be – or, alternatively, what they are not and what they shouldn't be.

Think about it for a moment. Think about all the ways we hear the word 'community' being used around us on a daily basis: 'the African-American community', 'the international community', 'the village community', 'the gay community', 'the local community', 'the European Community', 'the Irish community', 'the farming community'. It's really hard to imagine how this word can possibly mean the same thing in the context of 'international community' as it does, say, in 'farming community'. The fact is that 'community' is a bit of a buzz-word. We hear people talking about community in all sorts of different ways and for various purposes. Most of the time it's a convenient label for a whole range of feelings and ideas about people in tight-knit, clearly identified, politically coherent collectives. In fact 'community' is often used as a rhetorical device for communicating a sense of comforting or reassuring togetherness. This is what CMC scholar Lynne Cherny (1999: 255) says is the *symbolic* use of 'community': 'In both academic literature and more popular media reports, the word "community" is often invoked in a symbolic way, with a utopian subtext.'

Such is the complexity and significance of the term for people that there's been a fairly long tradition of scholarship known as Community Studies, and much of this work comes from sociologists. In trying to define community, most sociologists look to identify the main characteristics of community. In this regard, one idea proposed many years ago by the German sociologist Ferdinand Tönnies was the distinction between what he called ***Gemeinschaft*** (pronounced 'guh-mine-shaft'), which are small, rural, intimate communities, and ***Gesellschaft*** (pronounced 'guh-zel-shaft'), which, by contrast, are large, urban, impersonal societies. For our purposes, it's the first of these which describes what are often seen as traditional or 'real' forms of community: a village where everybody more or less knows everybody else, and where people encounter each other almost daily.

Nowadays so few people live in small rural communities like these that the notion of community has obviously had to change. The question is whether locality or territoriality is a defining feature of community. Can we describe a collection of people as a community only if they're in close physical or geographical proximity to one another? For most people the answer is clearly no. You don't have to be living next door to someone – or even in the same country – to feel close to them, to share an interest with them or a sense of belonging. It's for this reason that a more useful distinction to be drawn is that between **sociability** and **locality**. This refers to the way that communities may be defined either in terms of the shared social interactions of its members or in terms of a shared geographical location. Some communities, like the old-fashioned country village, will obviously be characterized by both, but it's not necessarily true of all communities.

Technical labels like these become useful conceptual tools for scholars, who need to be able to be more specific about what they mean when talking about something as apparently vague as 'community'. To proceed critically, therefore, it's important to be clear about what type or form of community is being spoken about (e.g. village community, urban community, international community, virtual community). Wherever possible, it's also best to avoid evaluative terms like 'real', 'authentic', 'proper' and 'genuine' when describing a community. After all, one person's idea of a 'real community' is quite possibly someone else's idea of a shallow, loosely affiliated gathering.

## DOES CMC DESTROY [TRADITIONAL] COMMUNITY?

### BOX CI3:2 AND STILL THE WORLD'S GETTING WORSE . . .

*I can watch thirty-four channels of TV, I can get on the fax and communicate with people anywhere, I can be everywhere at once, I can fly across the country, I've got call waiting, so I can take two calls at once. I live everywhere and nowhere. But I don't know who lives next door to me. Who's in the next flat? Who's in 14B? ... Community to me means simply the actual little system in which you are situated, sometimes in your office, sometimes at home with your furniture and your food and your cat, sometimes talking in the hall with the people in 14B ... I think it's absolutely necessary for our spiritual life today to have community where we actually live. (Hillman and Ventura, 1992: 40–3)*

The prescriptive take on community in Box CI3:2 is clearly one which is premised on community being based on local-ity. What's more, psychoanalyst John Hillman and Journalist Michael Ventura are evidently concerned about what they see as the negativity of technologies of communication on their sense of community. All this technology, they say, and still the world's getting worse. This is a common anxiety about online communication. Within the field of CMC, writers such as Jon Stratton (1997) and Joseph Lockard (1997) pass strong judgement on what they see as the 'moral distraction' and 'myth' of virtual communities. Both Stratton and Lockard feel that online communities inevitably lead to people evading offline or 'real life' difficulties, problems and social issues. It's something like this: while you sit chatting with your cyber-buddies, the people next door may be being robbed and a house a block away is burning down!

Well known CMC scholar Nancy Baym (1998, 2000) has spent many years studying and writing about online communities, and she examines a range of criticisms which people level at online communities: the lack of commitment between members, the lack of moral cohesion, the lack of global access, and so on. However, she also points to the lack of empirical evidence to confirm the effects of online participation on offline community. For Baym, the accusation that online communication is somehow responsible for the 'loss' of offline community is problematic for several reasons, but one in particular:

> It is fundamentally reductionist to conceptualize all 'virtual communities' as a single phenomenon and hence to assess them with a single judgement ... [there are] countless thousands of online groups that vary tremendously. Some groups are surely bad for offline life, but there's certainly no reason to believe that most are. (1997: 63)

In Central Issues: Unit 7 we look again at how the internet sometimes stands accused of impacting negatively on offline life and so we'll leave this issue for the time being.

## DOES CMC ENABLE [PROPER] COMMUNITY?

> *The question of whether or not one can find community online is asked largely by those who do not experience it. Committed participants in email, bulletin boards, chat lines [and] MUDs . . . have no problem in accepting that communities exist online, and that they belong to them. (Haythornthwaite et al., 1998: 212)*

What then of the argument that, far from breaking down traditional communities, communication technologies and CMC are in fact restoring and creating them? Well, there have been many conflicting points of view. Most famously, Howard Rheingold (1993) claimed the following: 'CMC liberates interpersonal relations from the confines of physical locality and thus creates opportunities for new, but genuine ... communities.' © Many commentators, like Stoll at the start of this unit, are sceptical about claims made for online communities. Is it really possible, they ask, to have 'proper' communities in cyberspace? Writers like Joseph Lockard (1997: 225) feel that online community is a poor substitute for the 'real' thing; he concludes: 'To accept only communication in place of a community's manifold functions is to sell our common faith in community vastly short.'

Is, then, the online community nothing more than a virtual substitute for the 'real' community of yesteryear? In Basic Theory: Units 4–6 we've already seen a great deal of research evidence which refutes earlier accusations that CMC is necessarily asocial, cold, task-focused, and so on. We've also seen how large numbers of people have in fact begun to establish complex arrangements of long-standing, meaningful social relationships online. It's precisely with this in mind that Rheingold feels the case for online communities is clear:

© Howard Rheingold is most famous for his early writings about 'virtual communities'. He maintains his own website dedicated to this issue and more recent phenomena like Smart Mobs [**www** CI3:1].

> Online communities are social aggregations that emerge from the net when enough people carry on those public discussions long enough, with sufficient human feeling, to form webs of personal relationships. (1993: 5)

So, according to Rheingold, communities are almost inevitable and are constituted on the basis of social interaction, the length of people's involvement and the strength of their feelings. Basically, people are in community with each other wherever they do things together for long enough and when they *feel* like they're a community.

At this point, it's worth turning again to Baym (1997) to see what she has to say as a scholar who, like Rheingold, has actually spent so long studying and participating in online communities herself. She argues that, however important, common interest alone is unlikely to be sufficient to build and sustain a strong sense of community. Baym draws on the key ideas of Benedict Anderson, who proposes that the thing we ought to be looking at is the style in which communities are imagined. In his now famous treatise, Anderson (1983: 15) states that 'all communities larger than primordial villages of face-to-face contact are imagined' – hence **imagined communities**. This doesn't mean that communities are not 'real' in the sense that they're not meaningful to people and can't act as powerful influences in people's lives -they are indeed both meaningful and powerful. What Anderson does mean, however, is that 'community' is not about numbers or places, it's about activities and feelings. Baym identifies four ways in which she sees community emerging through social processes: forms of expression (e.g. our talking about our communities), identity (e.g. our sense of shared group identity), relationship (e.g. our connections and interactions with others in the community) and norms (e.g. the rules and conventions we agree to live by together).

What's the conclusion of all this? Well, all we can suggest is that, while society *may* be losing one type of community, this is not to say that it's losing community altogether. In other words, online communities may not be 'traditional' communities but it seems to us that they're communities nonetheless – communities not of common location, sure, but of common interest and feeling. Like offline communities, they're also communities of practice and memory – people feel a part of online communities, they talk about their online friendship networks as communities, and they share a history of interacting together (Cherny, 1999).

# RELATIONAL WEBS: SOCIAL NETWORKS ON THE NET

As we hope you can see, it's really important to disentangle from the ideology of community exactly what it is that people feel is lacking or being threatened when they bemoan the loss of 'real life' or 'traditional' community. Similarly, what is it that other people are experiencing when they describe their CMC as 'communal'? Perhaps the best way of doing this is simply to be more specific and use a more operationalized notion of community; that is, do define community in more concrete ways. So, for example, in talking about community we might be thinking of some, or all, of the following variables:

- Being in face-to-face contact and/or having regular contact.
- Having shared goals and/or producing and using shared commodities.
- Having the opportunity for dialogue and social interaction.
- Having a common cultural heritage or history.
- Enjoying unique communal features and/or developing 'organic' social formations (e.g. people often like to be able to say, 'This is the way we do things round here.').

Along these lines, one alternative approach to thinking about online communities in more practical terms is to think of them as social networks. In this sense, CMC scholars like Barry Wellman and Caroline Haythornthwaite (e.g. 2002) have sought to describe community structures rather than rely on more subjective or discursive accounts. For them, 'community' is a term best used to characterize the strength of relationships between people in an extensive network.©

> © Networks are regarded as being larger than groups which have clearly defined boundaries; networks tend to be more extensive and dispersed.

> Social network analysis examines patterns of resource exchange among actors to determine how and what resources flow from one actor to another. Regular patterns of relations – i.e. specific types of resource exchange – reveal themselves as social networks, with actors as nodes and relations between actors as connectors between nodes. Social network analysis strives to derive social structure empirically, based on *observed* exchanges among actors. (Haythornthwaite *et al.*, 1998: 214, emphasis ours)

According to social network scholars, CMC is more than capable of supporting strong, multiple ties between people. Just as roads are the material infrastructure which supports the flow of commercial exchanges offline, the internet is the material infrastructure which supports social exchanges online. What's more, the internet can also increase the range of social networks by enabling people to connect with even more people than before.

---

**BOX CI3:3 THE TIES THAT BIND ...**

According to the Social Network perspective, the strength of ties between people is measured in terms of their closeness, intimacy and interconnectedness. This may vary depending on two sets of factors:

- What kind of tie it is, e.g. work or leisure.
- What kind of people are tied, e.g. adults or teens.
- What social positions they have, e.g. teacher or student.
- Where they are located, e.g. dose or far apart.
- What mode of communication is being used, e,g. online or offline.
- The frequency of contact between people.
- The amount and diversity of information exchanged.
- The number of different communication modes used.

Research by Haythornthwaite and Wellman has shown how stronger ties are those where participants communicate more frequently, about a range of different topics and using several different modes of communication (e.g. FtF, online and telephone).

---

Just like offline, online participants may be bound together by strong, intermediate, or weak ties. Furthermore, social networks may be either specialized or multiplex; that is, with participants bonded through a single shared interest and a primary focus of discussion, or free to wander off-topic and discuss all sorts of other issues and concerns. Studies of computer-assisted social networks have shown that the stronger the ties and the more multiplex the activities, the more like a community a network will be.

## HYBRIOITY: GRAFTING THE NEW ON TO THE OLD

In their discussion of community networking, Haythornthwaite and her colleagues (1998: 213) also make the following very astute observation:

> Just as modern neighborhood ties do not fulfill all of a person's community needs, membership in a single online community rarely meets all of a person's needs for information, support, companionship, and a sense of belonging. Virtual communities are only part of a person's multiple communities of interest, kinship, friendship, work, and locality. (1998: 213)

In social network terms, what they are saying is that online communities don't just have people wandering off-topic, but also offline. In fact, most well established online communities show participants often meeting FtF as well. Whether they are 'virtual' or 'real', no communities exist in splendid isolation. As Baym (1998: 63) concludes:

© What Baym says here is clearly related to Howard's notion, of 'embedded media' (see p. 75).

Online groups are woven into the fabric of offline life rather than set in opposition to it. The evidence includes the pervasiveness of offline contexts in online interaction and the movement of online relationships offline.©

Baym also notes that online communities are in fact heavily influenced by pre-existing structures which enable, and encourage, people to feel (or imagine) themselves part of a community. Some of the factors which therefore need to be taken into consideration when evaluating online communities are:

- *External contexts*, e.g. are community members already work colleagues or individuals participating from home and who've never met?
- *Temporal structure*, e.g. is the CMC synchronous as asynchronous?
- *System infrastructure*, e.g. are members completely anonymous?
- *Group purposes*, e.g. what are the aims of the group? how closely are they having to, or wanting to, work together towards some goal or other?
- *Participant characteristics*, e.g. are members all men or all women or a mixture of both?

Not only does this mean that online communities are shaped by the extent of their embeddedness in the 'real world', it also means that online communities are often simply offline communities which have come online. In other words, these are supposedly 'traditional' communities which are exploring new ways for their members to be in community with each other. The distinction between online and offline communities is not so neat after all and you are more likely to find hybrid examples than anything else.

## PUTTING COMMUNITY IN PERSPECTIVE

**BOX CI3:4 OPENING WELCOME FROM LAMBDAMOO**

*Welcome to LambdaMOO!*
**********************

Running Version 1.8.1r0 of LambdaMOO

PLEASE NOTE:

LambdaMOO is a new kind of society, where thousands of people voluntarily come together from all over the world. What these people say or do may not always be to your liking; as when visiting any international city, it is wise to be careful who you associate with and what you say. The operators of LambdaMOO have provided the materials for the buildings of this community, but are not responsible for what is said or done in them. In particular, you must assume responsibility if you permit minors or others to access LambdaMOO through your facilities. The statements and viewpoints expressed here are not necessarily those of the wizards, Pavel Curtis, Stanford University, or PlaceWare Inc, and those parties disclaim any responsibility for them.

Thomas Bender (in Jones, 1995) is highly critical of what he sees as value-laden attempts to recapture traditional communities regardless of the quality of human relationships that may or may not have characterized them. What he means by this is that people who bemoan the loss of 'real' community and who ridicule the notion of online communities are often appealing to a romantic ideal of what traditional communities were really like.

In fact, long before Bender, Jackson (in Bell and Newby, 1971: 48) noted how the notion of *Gemeinschaft* is inevitably based on fallacious assumptions about the nature of traditional societies – their homogeneity, for example – and end up 'harking back to some pre-existing, rural utopia'. In other words, just because people live within a few blocks of each other doesn't mean they all get along. In fact, even small communities can suffer from conflict and divisions. Jon Stratton (1997: 267) is a little bit more hard-hitting. Commenting on claims made about how wonderful virtual communities are, he notes that, in the Global North, 'community' always carries a nostalgic connotation of pre-modern (or traditional or rural) communities.

[Community] refers to a mythic understanding of the essential 'sharedness' of a way of life before the fragmentation of interpersonal interaction and the loss of taken-for-granted moral order brought about by the founding modern changes – secularization, urbanization, capitalism, industrialization, and, of course, the nation-state . . . We can begin to see that, far from being innocent, the American mythologization of the internet as a community represents a nostalgic dream for a mythical early modern community which reasserts the dominance of the white middle-class male and his cultural assumptions.

In this sense, it all very much depends on what people understand by the term 'community' (i.e. meanings and feelings) and what they hope to achieve when talking about community (i.e. motives and ideologies). It also makes a difference who's talking about community. Is it the marketing director of AOL pitching to new customers with the promise of online friendship, love and support? Or is it your local politician trying to persuade you to pay more tax for amenities and care facilities in your neighbourhood? What, for example, are InterGov (see p. 108) and LambdaMOO (see Box CI3:4) hoping to achieve in their descriptions, do you think?

A critical awareness of the social transformations that have occurred and continue to occur with or without technology will be our best ally as we incorporate CMC into contemporary social life. (Jones, 1995: 33)

As we've said before, and as Steven Jones reminds us here, debates about the social impact of the internet invariably dovetail with what scholars elsewhere are saying about the post-industrial, information societies in which many of us live nowadays. It's usually the broader economic, social and cultural changes which make people feel uneasy and unsettled. It's perhaps not surprising, therefore, that people are often found to be searching for the kind of stability and security which they think being a part of a community will bring. Where for some people this means fighting for exclusive, traditional forms of offline community, for others it means turning to the internet to sustain and perhaps extend their existing social networks.

# REVIEW

In this unit, we started by looking at the two most extreme positions sometimes taken in relation to online communities. We then considered different approaches to the notion of 'community', distinguishing between descriptive and normative perspectives, and the definitions of sociality and locality. Next we returned to discuss the ideas that CMC is responsible for the loss of traditional, offline communities, and that online communities are not 'real' communities. We then looked at the social network approach to community, which led us to consider hybrid forms of offline-online community. We concluded by putting the notion of community into perspective with reference to broader social transformations.

# STIMULUS READINGS AND RESOURCES

Centre for the Study of Online Communities [**www** CI3:3].

Research Center for Virtual Environments and Behavior [**www** CI3:4].

Baym, N.K. (2000). Chapter 4 – 'I think of them as friends': Interpersonal relationships in the online community. In *Tune in, log on: Soaps, fandom, and online community*. Thousand Oaks, CA: Sage.

Brown, J. (2001). Three case studies. In C. Werry and M. Mowbray (eds), *Online Communities: Commerce, community action and the virtual university* (pp. 33–46). Upper Saddle River, NJ: Prentice Hall.

Driskell, R.B. and Lyon, L. (2002). Are virtual communities true communities? Examining the environments and elements of community. *City and Community*, 1 (4): 373–90.

Haythornthwaite, C. (2002). Strong, weak and latent ties and the impact of new media. *The Information Society*, 18 (5), 1–17.

## IDEAS FOR FURTHER DISCUSSION AND INVESTIGATION

*Note*: The ideas covered in this unit are closely linked with Fieldwork: Unit 5, where we focus on community building in metaworlds and visual chat.

(1) In thinking about both the idea of hybrid forms of community and issues of identity online, have a look at Trinidad Online (**www** CI3:5). Have a look also at the extracts (**www** CI3:6) from an ethnographic study of this site conducted by British scholars Daniel Miller and Don Slater. How do they discuss the integration between the online and offline versions of the Trinidadian community? How does the website look to communicate, support and promote their national identity?

(2) Webrings [see **www** CI3:7] are basically a way of people grouping together by linking all their websites. One of the major listings of web rings is at Webring.com [**www** CI3:8], which, in February 2003, boasted, 'We bring the internet together!' with 3.05 million unique visitors, 24 million hits, 60,500 rings, 975,800 active sites, 500,000+ registered users and 3,800+ contributing members. Have a look at some web rings. Would you describe them as networks or communities?

# Article 9

Vanessa M. Buote *, Eileen Wood, and Michael Pratt

## Exploring Similarities and Differences Between Online and Offline Friendships: The Role of Attachment Style

### article info

Article history:
Available online 7 January 2009

### Keywords:

Attachment style
Online and offline relationships
Friendships Computers and friendships
Friendship quality

### abstract

The present study merges the fields of attachment and friendships and compares these in online and off-line environments. Although currently we know a great deal about the importance of friendships and attachments for healthy development, there is no research to guide our understanding of how attach-ment style and friendship characteristics are evidenced in online contexts. Participants completed surveys to assess attachment style, friendships (online and offline), as well as interactions with friends and friendship quality. The extent to which individuals sought out online friends did not differ as a func-tion of attachment style. Friendship quality differed as function of attachment style, while differences among attachment styles for other friendship characteristics resulted only when context (online versus offline) was simultaneously considered.

## Introduction

Online social interaction has become a focal point for discussion in today's society. For example, articles concerning Facebook, My-space or other online interaction mediums, with titles such as "My-Space can bring shy kids out of their shells" (msnbc, 2008), "Yahoo to offer single user profile" (the Globe and Mail, 2008) and "Oxford University fines students with the aid of Facebook" (The Times on-line, 2008), are commonplace in both online and hardcopy news outlets. Given the surging interest and use of the Internet as a med-ium for engaging in social interactions, it is surprising how little re-search is available to explain how social relationships function in online and offline contexts and for whom social interactions are or are not enhanced through online interactions. This is especially true of friendships, even though friends provide one of the most important social relationships throughout development (Hartup & Stevens, 1997; Richey & Richey, 1980). Friends can act as role models, supporters, advisors, reference groups, listeners, allies, critics, and companions (Buote et al., 2007; Richey & Richey, 1980; Tokuno, 1986). Friendship relationships provide a context for acceptance, sense of belonging and assistance (Buote et al., 2007; Tokuno, 1986; Weiss, 1974). Given the vast number of opportunities to form friendships in online contexts, it is important to examine whether online friendships differ from traditional off-line face-to-face friendships. In addition, the study further exam-ines whether online or offline friendships differentially benefit individuals with different social histories. Specifically, the study compares friendships on and offline for individuals with differing attachment styles.

* Corresponding author. Tel.:+ 1 519 884 1970.
E-mail address: buot2090@wlu.ca (V.M. Buote).

Attachment theory has been widely studied in past literature (e.g., Bartholomew, 1990; Griffin & Bartholomew, 1994; Schindler, Thomasius, Sack, Gemeinhardt, & Kuster, 2007; Tanaka et al., 2008). Developed by Bowlby (1969), attachment theory assumes that all individuals are born with behavioural control systems that aid with survival (Bowlby, 1969). Initially, these systems guide infants and children to engage in survival-based behaviours such as those that allow the child to maintain close proximity to the primary caregiver, and to seek food and warmth from their caregiver. These early interactions of the child and caregiver allow the child to develop an internal working model of the world. In turn, these internal working models guide the child's thoughts, behaviours, and affect, and permit the infant to have a set of expectations of how others will behave and react; essentially, how a relationship functions (Weimer, Kerns, & Oldenburg, 2004). Bowlby (1969) believed that the primary caregiver acted as a "secure base" from which the child could explore their surroundings and return to if they experienced fear, illness or fatigue or if the distance between the self and the caregiver was too large. This conceptualization of a "secure base" that one turns to in time of vulnerability is valuable in making the distinction between an attachment figure, and simply a relationship, whether it be a friend, playmate or peer. While a child seeks their attachment figure in time of need, a child seeks a playmate when he is happy, content and confident that his/her caregiver is in close proximity (Bowlby, 1969). Thus, the difference between an attachment figure and a non-attachment figure is reflected in the desire for the attachment figure when undergoing a difficult time, and the need for proximity.

0747-5632/$ -see front matter © 2008 Elsevier Ltd. All rights reserved. doi:10.1016/j.chb.2008.12.022

During adolescence and adult life, shifts in attachment figures typically occur. While the adolescent remains attached to the primary caregiver, he/she typically also becomes strongly attached to persons outside the family (Bowlby, 1969). It is believed that the attachment relationship that adolescents and adults have is at least partly a reflection of their attachment (or internal working models) as infants, and that the initial parental attachment style is predictive of attachment in other non-parental relationships throughout the lifespan, such as romantic relationships and friendships (Bowlby, 1969; Bowlby, 1973; Zimmerman, 2004). As such, the manner in which adolescents interact with this new attach-ment figure should mirror childhood behaviours (Bowlby, 1969). Just as young children will possess relationships that are not specifically attachment relationships, adolescents will have attachment relationships and non-attachment relationships. Attachment relationships would be somewhat parallel to early childhood attachment relationships, in that in time of need, or when undergoing a crisis or difficult time, the adolescent would seek out their attachment figure, perhaps a best or close friend. Non-attachment figures, perhaps more superficial friendships, might be sought out when one wants to have fun, is happy, and has no immediate concerns or fears.

Attachment style can be organized into four categories (Bartholomew & Horowitz, 1991) based on two dimensions (See Fig. 1). The first dimension provides a model of the self, in which the self is viewed either positively or negatively.

A positive view of self is reflected in a sense of worthiness of love and support whereas a negative view sees oneself as not meriting love and support from others. The second dimension of self presents a model of others, wherein others are perceived either positively or negatively. A positive view of others is manifested in the belief that others are trustworthy, available and accepting, while a negative view of others leads to the belief that others are unreliable and rejecting. Together, this model results in four attach-ment styles-one Secure style and three Insecure styles (i.e., Preoccupied, Dismissing and Fearful). An individual characterized as having a Secure attachment style has a positive view of themselves and of others, and therefore, feels worthy of others' love and support, views others as responsive and accepting and is comfortable with intimacy and closeness. An individual having a Preoc-cupied attachment style has a negative view of themselves but a positive view of others, which leads to a sense of personal unworthiness with respect to love and support, but a sense that others are responsive and accepting. As a result, this individual strongly depends on others' acceptance to feel positively about him/herself. To achieve self-acceptance, this individual would try to gain the accept-ance of others and this would most probably be evidenced through seeking excessive closeness. A Fearful attachment style is distin-guished by both a negative view of the self and a negative view of others. This style is similar to the preoccupied attachment style in feelings of unworthiness of love and support, however the fearful attachment style also leads to the belief that others are rejecting and untrustworthy. As a result, a fearful individual avoids relationships with the goal of protecting the self, as s/he typically feels s/he will eventually be disappointed by the relationship.

The Dismissing attachment style is characterized by a positive view of the self and a negative view of others, leading this individual to dismiss the importance of relationships and try to remain independent (Bartholomew & Horowitz, 1991; Griffin & Bartholomew, 1994).

Some past research has been conducted on the association between attachment style and traditional face-to-face friendships. Overall, individuals with a secure attachment style seem to fare best. They report greater companionship (Saferstein, Neimeyer, & Hagans, 2005), cooperativeness (Schulman, Elicker, & Sroufe, 1994), intimacy (Bartholomew & Horowitz, 1991), emotional closeness (Zimmerman, 2004) and friendship quality (Liebermam, Doyle, & Markiewicz, 1999), and lower conflict (Liebermam et al., 1999) than insecurely attached individuals. In addition, secure individuals are typically socially competent (Schulman et al., 1994) and have good conflict resolution skills (Liebermam et al., 1999). Among individuals with insecure attachments, those with a preoccupied attachment style report similar levels of companionship to secure individuals (Mikulincer & Nachshon, 1991; Saferstein et al., 2005) have highly intimate friendships, display emotional expressivity and rely on others, which likely reflects their strong desire to validate themselves through excessively close relationships (Griffin & Bartholomew, 1994). This is also evident in much higher levels of self-disclosure than those with secure styles (Mikulincer & Nachshon, 1991; Saferstein et al., 2005). Interestingly however, preoccupied participants report less satisfaction with their relationships (Brennan & Shaver, 1995; Feeney, 1994). Dismissing and fearful styles, on the other hand, experience very different relationships with their friends. Specifically, they experience lower levels of companionship (Saferstein et al., 2005). In addition they report challenges with self-disclosure and intimacy (Bartholomew & Horowitz, 1991; Mikulincer & Nachshon, 1991) while experiencing higher levels of friendship conflict (Saferstein et al., 2005). Further, individuals with dismissing styles demonstrate lower levels of emotional expressivity, care-giving and reliance on others than those with secure attachments (Bartholomew & Horowitz, 1991). These findings with "face-to face"/"offline" friendship underscore the important contribution of attachment style to friendship relationships. The current study explores whether these findings transfer to an "online" context.

Online social exchanges occur through many diverse outlets, including, blogs, chat rooms emails, networking, gaming, personal profile sites (e.g., Facebook). Indeed, research indicates that one of the predominant uses of the Internet is for interpersonal communication (Gross, 2004; Lenhart, Madden, & Hitlin, 2005). In addition, those who use the Internet for chatting and social exchange purposes are among those who use the Internet most heavily (Dryburgh, 2001; NetValue, 2002, as cited in Brignall & Valey, 2005). Among adolescents and young adults, many report developing both close and casual friendships online (14% and 25%, respectively; Wolak, Mitchell, & Finkelhor, 2002).

Preliminary investigations of these "new" types of friendships yield contradictory outcomes. On the one hand, consistent with displacement theory, online friendships are depicted as "weaker" relationships (e.g., Kraut et al., 1998; Nie, 2001) as evidenced through less interdependence, understanding, commitment and self-disclosure, as well as less convergence of social networks Model of Self (Dependence).

| Model of Other (Avoidance) | | Model of Self (Dependence) | |
| --- | --- | --- | --- |
| | | Positive (low) | Negative (high) |
| | Positive (low) | Secure | Preoccupied |
| | Negative (high) | Dismissing | Fearful |

**Fig. 1. Bartholomew and Horowitz' adult attachment model.**

and less discussion, with exchanges being limited to a smaller variety of topics (Chan & Cheng, 2004; Parks & Roberts, 1998; Scott, Mottarealla, & Lavooy, 2006). In strong contrast to these findings, other researchers endorse online friendships as an alternate venue for experiencing positive, beneficial relationships that are meaningful, close and long lasting (Bargh, McKenna, & Fitzsimons, 2002; McKenna, Green, & Gleason, 2002).

Given the vast body of research that documents the impact of underlying constructs such as attachment for relationships in general, and the growing body of work that indicates the important role of attachment style in traditional "face-to-face"/"offline" friendships, it is critical to examine whether attachment style impacts in these new online friendship contexts. The many opportunities to communicate in an asynchronous and anonymous nature while using the Internet may provide an opportunity for some individuals to differentially affect friendships as a function of attachment style. For example, less socially skilled individuals may be able to utilize asynchrony as an opportunity for reflection, planning, and as a result may be able to present themselves more effectively. Alternatively, the absence of immediate feedback (both verbally and behaviourally) may be detrimental to relationship building. Attachment style provides a framework for predicting who may or may not benefit from the unique characteristics of onine exchanges. For example, Insecure individuals, who typically have less friendship experience, might benefit from the many opportunities to practice initiating friendships without the tremendous costs associated with face-to-face relationships. In addition, they can practice initiating interactions through many diverse venues' (e.g., blogs, personal profiles, and games). However, it is also possible that the virtual environment could further limit successful friendship formation for individuals with insecure attachment styles. Specifically, using the Internet to interact prohibits some very important social information such as gestures, facial expressions, proximity which may be critical for both participants to interpret the importance of what is being said and the reaction to what has been said (e.g., Kiesler, Siegel, & McGuire, 1984). Although Internet communications afford some socio-emotional communication both through the text and emoticons (Baron, 2008), these sources of information are not as robust and prevalent as is available in face-to-face interaction. The absence of these key elements of interaction might be particularly problematic for individuals who may need more support in their relationships. Examination among the specific attachment styles will permit greater understanding of how online and offline contexts differ and for whom online versus offline contexts impact the most.

In summary, this study explored three questions. The first question examined the prevalence of online and offline friendships in the lives of late adolescents. The second question investigated how often adolescents use online venues to initiate friendships. The third question explored the role of attachment style in understanding adolescents' evaluations of their online and offline friendships. Consistent with past research key positive and negative characteristics of friendship were examined; quality, intimacy, self-disclosure, satisfaction and conflict resolution (e.g., Aikins, Bierman, & Parker, 2005; Hays, 1984; Richey & Richey, 1980; Tokuno, 1986; Weiss, 1974).

## 1.1 Design

The present quasi-experimental design uses attachment style as the independent variable. The dependent variables include friendship quantity, online friendship seeking, online and offline friendship quality, intimacy, self-disclosure, satisfaction and conflict resolution.

## 2. Method

### 2.1. Participants

A total of 141 participants (46 males, 88 females, 7 failed to respond) were recruited from a participant pool at a mid-sized Canadian university. The mean age of participants was 19.14 years (SD = 1.94). Participants self-reported ethnic descent was follows; 55.32% European, 12.77% Asian, 3.42% Indo, 21. 99% "other" and 6.16% of participants did not indicate ethnicity. Participants received course credit for participating. All participants were treated in accordance with APA ethical guidelines.

Participants were grouped according to attachment style based on their response to the Relationship Questionnaire (Bartholome w & Horowitz, 1991).[1] In total, 47 participants (33.33%) were categorized as having a secure attachment style, 29 participants (20.56%) had a dismissing attachment style, 25 (17.73%) participants had a preoccupied style, and 40 (28.37%) participants were categorized as exhibiting a fearful attachment style. The number of males and females and ages in each of the 4 attachment style groups was as follows; Secure (16 males, 26 females, 5 unidentified; Mage = 19.33 (SD = 2.52)), Dismissing (12 males, 16 females, 1 unidentified; Mage = 18.86 (SD = 1.77)), Preoccupied (10 males, 14 females, 1 unidentified; Mage = 18.84 (SD = 1.62)) and Fearful (8 males, 32 females; $M_{age}$ = 19.33 (SD = 1.87)). A ONEWAY ANOVA resulted in no significant differences in age as a function of attachment style, F = (3, 131) = .65, p = .60.

---

[1] Participants were categorized based on the prototypical attachment pattern they considered most similar to themselves. In 21 cases, participants identified themselves equally for more than one style. These participants were randomly assigned to one of the two styles, using the procedures outlined by Bartholomew (2008).

Given the focus on technology in this study, three ONEWAY ANOVAs were used to test for possible differences among the four attachment styles for (1) computer comfort, (2) time spent online completing school work and (3) time spent online for entertainment purposes as a function of attachment style. Results were non-significant, largest F, $F(3,134) = .74$, $p = .53$, indicating similar levels of comfort and time spent online for all attachment styles.

## 2.2 Measures

Participants completed 8 measures over two sessions. In the first session, participants completed only the attachment measure. All other measures (demographic and friendship-related measures) were completed in a second session. The attachment, demographic, and friendship measures were completed in hard copy form and all other measures were completed online.

### 2.2.1 Attachment style

Attachment style was assessed by Bartholomew and Horowitz's (1991) Relationship Questionnaire measure, which is designed to gauge general attachment style by using participants' perception of how they behave and feel in relationships. This measure consists of four paragraphs, each describing one of the four attachment styles. Participants read each paragraph and rated, on a 7-pt scale (1 = very similar to me, 7 = not at all similar to me), the extent to which the content in each paragraph reflected themselves. An example of this scale is "It is easy for me to become emotionally close to others. I am comfortable depending on them and having them depend on me. I don't worry about being alone or having others not accept me." (secure attachment).

## 2.3 Demographics and friendship information

Participants completed a survey. Initial questions asked participants to identify their age, gender, and ethnicity. This was followed by 3 measures regarding friendships in general and online friendships in particular, and 1 measure assessing computer comfort.

### 2.3.1 Friendship quantity and type

Participants indicated the total number of friendships they had and, out of those friendships, how many were online friendships and how many were offline friends.

### 2.3.2 Friendship seeking

Online friendship seeking was assessed through two questions: In the past, how often have you tried to meet new people online (through such things as MSN, chat rooms, online games, groups, Facebook, etc.)? and Currently, how often have you tried to meet new people online (through such things as MSN, chat rooms, online games, groups, Facebook, etc.)? Participants used a 7-pt Likert-type scale for both questions with anchors being 1 (never) to 7 (always).

### 2.3.3 Friend nomination

Participants were asked to nominate their closest (a) online and (b) offline friend. In order to ensure consistency in the definitions of online and offline friendships, participants were given the following definitions at the outset of the questionnaire.

When we talk about an online friendship we mean one where you first met your friend online (through such things as msn, chat rooms, online games groups, Facebook, etc.) and you use the internet to interact with your friend. When we talk about an offline friend we mean one in which you met and now interact with your friend almost all of the time on a face-to-face level.

Participants indicated the gender and age for each of these friends. Participants were asked to identify, "How emotionally close do you feel to this person?"

For the closeness questions, a Likert-type scale ranging from Not close at all (1) and Extremely Close (7) was used.

### 2.3.4 Computer comfort

Participants completed a 3-item computer comfort scale (Wood, Mueller, Willoughby, Specht, & Deyoung, 2005) using a Likert-type scale ranging from 1–5, with higher scores indicating less comfort. An item from this scale is "In general, how at ease do you feel about using computers". Cronbach's alpha was .95.

Each of the following questionnaires were completed twice; once in reference to their online friend and once in reference to their offline friend. The ordering of the questionnaire was counterbalanced across participants.

### 2.3.5 Friendship quality

Friendship quality was assessed by the McGill Friendship Questionnaire-Friend's Functions (Mendelson & Aboud, 1999). This questionnaire is comprised of 30 items and measures the degree to which six friendship functions (stimulating companionship, help, intimacy, reliable alliance, self-validation and emotional security) are fulfilled by a particular friend. Participants indicated their level of agreement with each statement on an 8-pt. Likerttype scale, ranging from never (1) to always (8). An item from this scale is "helps me do things". Cronbach alphas were .97 and .99 for the offline and online versions, respectively.

### 2.3.6 Intimacy
Intimacy was measured using the Intimacy Scale (IS; Walker & Thompson, 1983). This scale measures an individual's perceived intimacy in a particular relationship and is comprised of 17 items. A 7-pt Likert-type scale was used (1 = never, 7 = always) for responding. A scale item is "He/She cares about the way I feel". Cronbach alphas were .95 and .98 for the offline and online versions, respectively.

### 2.3.7 Self-disclosure
The level of self-disclosure in which participants engage with their nominated friends was measured by the Self-Disclosure Index (Miller, Berg, & Archer, 1983). This questionnaire is comprised of 10 intimate topics and participants are asked to rate the extent to which they have disclosed information pertaining to these topics to their friend on a 5-pt Likert-type scale (1 = not at all; 5 = disclosed fully and completely). An example from this scale is "My worst fears". Cronbach alphas were .91 and .92 for the offline and online versions, respectively.

### 2.3.8 Friendship satisfaction
Friendship satisfaction was measured by the satisfaction subscale of the McGill Friendship Questionnaire-Respondent's Affection (MFQ-RA; Mendelson & Aboud, 1999). Participants completed this 7-item subscale in reference to one person. Participants identified their level of agreement with each of the 7 items using a 9-pt scale ranging from —4 (very much disagree) to +4 (very much agree) (which were then recoded as 1–9). An item from this scale is "pleased with my friendship with". Cronbach alphas were .97 and .98 for the offline and online version.

### 2.3.9 Conflict resolution
Conflict resolution style was assessed by the Conflict Resolution Style Inventory (CRSI, Kurdek, 1994). This 16-item questionnaires asks participants to rate the extent to which they engage in a specific conflict resolution behaviour within a particular relationship on a scale from 1 (never) to 5 (always). The scale reflects four conflict resolution styles, which include (1) positive problem solving (characterized by compromise and negotiation; "Focusing on the problem at hand") (2) conflict engagement (losing control and verbally attacking the other person; "Launching personal attacks") (3) withdrawal (tuning out the other person and refusing to discuss the issue; "Remaining silent for long periods of time") and (4) compliance (giving in and not defending oneself; "Not be willing to stick up for myself"). Reliability using Cronbach alphas was .79 for the offline and .83 for the online version.

### 2.4. Procedure
There were two phases to this study. The first phase involved collecting attachment style data. These data were collected in the participants' classrooms. The Bartholomew and Horowitz (1991) Relationship Questionnaire was projected via Powerpoint. Participants indicated their responses using electronic scanning forms.

Participants completed the second phase in a computer laboratory. The three sections of the computer survey were counterbalanced.

## 3. Results
Two sets of analyses were conducted. The first set of analyses focused on the presence of friends and online friendship seeking behaviour as a function of attachment style. The second set of analyses examined the relationship of attachment style and friendship characteristics.[2]

### 3.1 Examination of number of friends and likelihood of seeking online friends
A 2 (online versus offline friend) **x** 4 (attachment style) repeated measures ANOVA was computed to determine whether the number of friends differed as a function of the source of friendship and attachment style.[3] Participants reported more offline (M = 11.29, SD = 11.70) than online (M = 2.9, SD = 11.70) friendships, $F(1, 133) = 25.82$, $p = <.001$. The number of overall friendships differed as a function of attachment style, $F(3, 133) = 2.70$, $p = .05$. Post hoc comparisons indicated that the Secure participants reported more friends (M = 9.83, SD = 1.76) than the Preoccupied (M = 4.94, SD = 2.33) and Fearful participants (M = 4.56, SD = 1.86) The interaction was not significant, $F(3, 133) = 1.88$, $p = .14$.

Two analyses were conducted to examine the likelihood of seeking out online friendships. One analysis looked at current behaviour and the other at past behaviour. The two ONEWAY ANOVAs (current, past) were non-significant, largest $F(3, 128) = 1.90$, $p = .13$.

---

[2] Covariates were reported for all analyses that yielded significant outcomes. In each case, the covariates were significant.
[3] Test for the number of friends were significant ($F(3, 133) = 5.67$, $p < .001$ and $F(3, 133) = 4.93$, $p < .003$ for online and offline respectively. The variation in the number of friends identified may reflect differences in individuals' understanding of what constitutes friendship.

In summary, participants with secure attachment styles have more friends than those with fearful or preoccupied attachments and most friends that were reported were offline friendships. However, the extent to which participants sought friendships online (presently and in the past) did not differ by attachment style.

## 3.2 Friendship characteristics as a function of attachment style

Five friendship characteristics were examined (friendship quality, intimacy, self disclosure, satisfaction, and conflict resolution). In each of these analyses, a 2 (friendship type) x 4 (attachment style) repeated measures ANOVA was computed with friendship serving as the within subjects variable and attachment style as the between subjects variable. In addition, closeness of both the online and offline friendship were included as covariates, as this variable could potentially impact on other friendship related variables. Closeness of the online friendship and offline friendships were included as separate variables, in order to assess their unique contributions, as they were not significantly correlated, $r(74) = -.058$, $p = .62$.[4]

### 3.2.1 Friendship quality

The 2 (friendship type) x 4 (attachment style) repeated measures ANOVA yielded no significant main effect of friendship type, $F(1, 65) = 1.81$, $p = .18$. However, the main effect for attachment style was significant, $F(3, 65) = 2.69$, $p = .05$. Specifically, post hoc comparisons indicated that participants with a fearful attachment style (M = 5.90, SD = 1.38) reported higher friendship quality rat- ings than those with a preoccupied attachment (M = 5.09, SD = 2.04) (for remaining means see Table 1).

### 3.2.2 Intimacy

The 2 (friendship type) x 4 (attachment style) repeated measures ANOVA assessing friendship intimacy yielded no significant main effects or interactions, largest $F(3, 66) = 1.32$, $p = .28$ (for attachment style).

### 3.2.3 Self-disclosure

The 2 (friendship type) **x 4** (attachment style) repeated measures ANOVA examining self-disclosure yielded no significant main effect for either friendship type or attachment style, largest F, $F(1, 66) = .56$, $p = .46$. However, a significant interaction emerged, $F(3, 66) = 2.67$, $p = .05$ (See Fig. 2). To examine the interaction, four paired t-tests were computed (one test per attachment style) to determine if differences existed between online and offline friendship self-disclosure. Results indicated that for Secure, Dismissing and Preoccupied groups, there was significantly more self disclosure with offline friends than online friends, smallest t, $t(15) = 2.25$, $p = .02$ (See Table 1 for means). For the Fearful group, however, there was no significant difference in the level of self-disclosure within the online and offline friendships. In addition, post hoc comparisons were computed to examine attachment style as a function of selfdisclosure separately for online friendships and offline friendships. Results of the post hoc comparisons for offline friends yielded no significant comparisons. In contrast, significant post hoc comparisons for online friendships indicated that Fearful participants reported self-disclosure more so than the Secure participants.

### 3.2.4 Satisfaction

The 2 (friendship type) **x 4** (attachment style) repeated measures ANOVA assessing friendship satisfaction yielded no significant main effects for either friendship type or attachment style, largest $F(1, 66) = 1.16$, $p = .29$. However, the interaction was significant, $F(3, 66) = 2.93$, $p = .04$ (See Fig. 3). To examine whether online and offline friendship satisfaction differed within each attachment style, four paired t-tests were computed. Results indicated that Secure, Dismissing and Fearful participants reported significantly greater satisfaction with their offline than online friendships, smallest t, $t(15) = 2.50$, $p = .02$. Preoccupied participants' satisfaction with their offline and online friendships did not differ significantly, $t(10) = 1.38$, $p = .20$ (see Table 1 for means).

### 3.2.5 Conflict resolution

To investigate the use of each of the four types of conflict resolution strategies within the friendship, 4 separate 2 (friendship type) **x 4** (attachment style) repeated measures ANOVAs were computed. All analyses resulted in non-significant main effects and interactions, largest F, $F(1, 66) = 2.12$, $p = .10$.

## 4 Discussion

Youth today clearly use both online and offline outlets as a source for friendships. Interestingly, overall, more friendships continue to be forged and maintained in offline contexts. This overall finding may be a function of developmental level such that these youths would have spent more of their time in close contact with others and would, at this point in development, have had fewer

---

[5] Levene's Tests of Equality variance were conducted for each measure with no significant findings for the measures regarding friendship characteristics (i.e., quality intimacy, self-disclosure, satisfaction and conflict resolution).

opportunities to forge online friends. However, it appears to be the case that attachment style might yield fundamental differences in what online and offline friendships can offer.

Although extant literature regarding social interaction and attachment style would suggest that attachment style would play a critical role in an individual's assessment of their friendships (e.g., Mikulincer & Nachshon, 1991; Saferstein et al., 2005), the present study suggested that attachment style alone provides a fairly limited impact on friendship assessment. What is clear, however, is that when attachment style does play a critical role in friendship assessment, it is when the context of the friendship is examined. Specifically, in a number of cases, attachment style impacts friendship differently when individuals relate to online or offline contexts.

With respect to friendship quality, the only two groups to differ significantly were the participants with a fearful and the preoccupied attachment style—both groups who typically hold a negative view of themselves in terms of worthiness for close relationships. Perhaps the more interesting finding is the lower quality of friendship reported by participants with a preoccupied style. Recalling that all groups nominated a friend, this group was the only one to be identified as experiencing lower quality relative to any other group. Given that Fearful participants typically have low levels of companionship, self-disclosure and intimacy (e.g., Bartholomew & Horowitz, 1991; Mikulincer & Nachshon, 1991; Saferstein et al., 2005), which likely results in less experience with relationships, and friendships in particular, it is possible that by asking participants to choose a friend as a referent, the participants with a fearful style are overestimating the quality of that friendship.

**Table 1**
**Means and standard deviations by attachment style.**

| | | | Secure | Proccupied | Dismissing | Fearful | Overall sample |
|---|---|---|---|---|---|---|---|
| Friendship quantity | Offline | M | 13.40 | 8.92 | 16.93 | 6.90 | 11.35 |
| | | SD | 18.02 | 10.26 | 21.54 | 9.33 | 15.97 |
| | Online | M | 5.82 | 2.11 | 1.40 | 2.12 | 3.18 |
| | | SD | 19.05 | 3.43 | 2.40 | 4.99 | 11.42 |
| Friendship quality | Offline | M | 6.91 | 6.13 | 6.74 | 6.60 | 6.72 |
| | | SD | 1.49 | 2.15 | 1.82 | 1.45 | 1.04 |
| | Online | M | 4.56 | 4.05 | 4.90 | 5.19 | 4.82 |
| | | SD | 2.37 | 3.43 | 2.90 | 2.32 | 2.02 |
| | Marginal means | | 5.74 | 5.09 | 5.82 | 5.90 | 5.64 |
| | | | 1.41 | 2.04 | 1.73 | 1.38 | .82 |
| Intimacy | Offline | M | 6.15 | 5.61 | 6.06 | 5.85 | 6.02 |
| | | SD | 1.14 | 1.65 | 1.35 | 1.12 | .94 |
| | Online | M | 4.31 | 4.07 | 4.43 | 4.60 | 4.37 |
| | | SD | 1.80 | 2.61 | 2.14 | 1.76 | 1.60 |
| Self-disclosure | Offline | M | 3.13 | 2.97 | 3.04 | 2.90 | 3.06 |
| | | SD | 1.02 | 1.46 | 1.20 | .99 | .71 |
| | Online | M | 1.90 | 2.09 | 2.22 | 2.40 | 2.13 |
| | | SD | 1.33 | 1.92 | 1.57 | 1.30 | 1.00 |
| Friendship satisfaction | Offline | M | 8.44 | 7.63 | 8.00 | 7.79 | 8.09 |
| | | SD | 1.38 | 1.99 | 1.63 | 1.41 | .95 |
| | Online | M | 6.14 | 6.15 | 6.51 | 6.64 | 6.36 |
| | | SD | 2.31 | 3.32 | 2.72 | 2.25 | 1.95 |
| Conflict resolution engagement | Offline | M | 1.98 | 2.44 | 1.92 | 2.11 | 2.13 |

|  |  |  | Secure | Proccupied | Dismissing | Fearful | Overall sample |
|---|---|---|---|---|---|---|---|
|  |  | SD | 1.42 | 2.04 | 1.67 | 1.38 | .83 |
|  | Online | M | 2.01 | 2.40 | 1.60 | 1.86 | 1.93 |
|  |  | SD | 1.42 | 2.04 | 1.68 | 1.38 | .76 |
| Positive problem solving | Offline | M | 3.75 | 3.40 | 3.64 | 3.64 | 3.55 |
|  |  | SD | 1.24 | 1.78 | 1.52 | 1.20 | .77 |
|  | Online | M | 2.95 | 2.98 | 3.06 | 3.31 | 3.07 |
|  |  | SD | 1.72 | 2.48 | 2.03 | 1.68 | 1.02 |
| Withdrawal | Offline | M | 1.83 | 2.38 | 2.00 | 2.09 | 1.97 |
|  |  | SD | 1.23 | 1.83 | 1.50 | 1.24 | .74 |
|  | Online | M | 2.01 | 2.43 | 2.32 | 2.21 | 2.20 |
|  |  | SD | 1.54 | 2.22 | 1.82 | 1.50 | .83 |
| Compliance | Offline | M | 2.02 | 2.40 | 2.12 | 2.24 | 2.09 |
|  |  | SD | 1.46 | 2.10 | 1.72 | 1.42 | .78 |
|  | Online | M | 1.88 | 2.18 | 1.56 | 1.97 | 1.88 |
|  |  | SD | 1.31 | 1.89 | 1.54 | 1.28 | .73 |

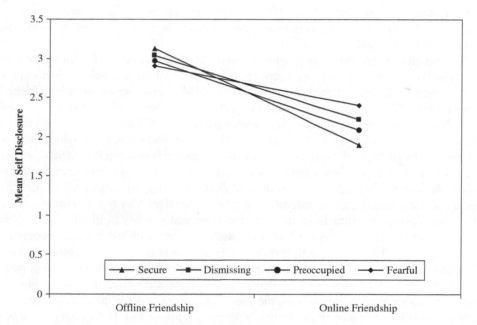

**Fig. 2. Self-disclosure as a function of friendship type and attachment style.**

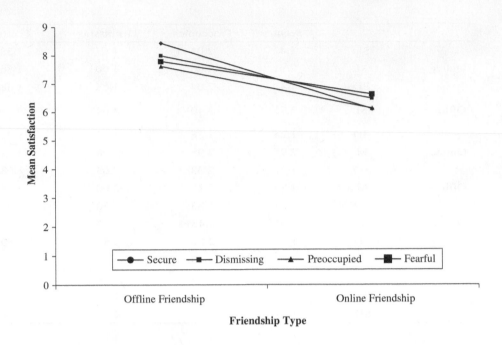

**Fig. 3. Friendship satisfaction as a function of friendship type and attachment style.**

Thus, with fewer examples to compare the nominated friendship to, and having overcome the challenges in trusting others with the nominated friend, the friendship may seem higher in quality then it would be rated by others. Notably, visual inspection of the means suggests that the high friendship quality reported by

participants with a fearful attachment style may be a reflection of higher perceived quality for online than offline contexts.

Secure, Dismissing and Preoccupied participants discriminated between offline and online friendships and engaged in more self-disclosure with their offline friends. Fearful participants self-disclosed to a similar extent with both friendships, which resulted in more self-disclosure with online friends than was engaged in by those with other attachment styles. These findings suggest that while individuals with a secure, dismissing and preoccupied attachment style exhibit more caution, and limit the information they reveal to online friends, individuals with a fearful attachment are less vigilant and are apt to disclose more personal information. While this might be perceived to be problematic, it is also possible that an online friendship is beneficial and advantageous for individuals with a fearful attachment. Again, given the negative view of others held by those with a fearful attachment style, asynchronous opportunities available through the Internet may allow these individuals the opportunity to reflect on their partner's comments, and to plan and reconsider their statements and the statements of others. Therefore, this type of communication might allow them to feel more secure in their interactions, resulting in greater self-disclosure, and possibly facilitating friendship development. Given that past findings seem to be contradictory in terms of which style discloses more, with some studies finding that secure individuals disclose more information (e.g., Grabill & Kerns, 2000; Pistole, 1993) and others indicating that insecure participants self-disclose more (Mikulincer & Nachshon 1991; Saferstein et al., 2005), these results are consistent with a portion of past findings.

Notably, while all other attachment styles discriminated between offline and online friendships in their reports of satisfaction, and reported greater satisfaction with offline friends, the Preoccupied style did not make this distinction. Individuals with a Preoccupied style typically report lower levels of satisfaction with most types of face-to-face relationships (Brennan & Shaver, 1995; Feeney, 1994), as they feel they are not benefitting from the relationships and/or not receiving back what they put into the relationships in return. Lower satisfaction ratings may also be reflective of an inaccurate perception of the relationship, although in our findings, participants with a preoccupied attachment did report lower friendship quality, which would be consistent with lower satisfaction ratings. Therefore, given that those with a Preoccupied style typically feel lower levels of satisfaction with most face-to-face relationships, an online friendship would not be expected to be reported as highly satisfactory, which is consistent with minimal past research indicating that participants with a preoccupied style were less satisfied with their online friendships (Jiali, 2007).

Past research indicates that securely attached individuals typically reported greater friendship intimacy (Bartholomew & Horowitz, 1991; Mikulincer & Nachshon, 1991) than those with an insecure attachment. Similarly, individuals with a secure attachment style have been found to have good conflict resolution skills relative to those with an insecure attachment (Liebermam et al., 1999) setting up the expectation that differences might occur. In both cases our outcomes did not support our expectations. Perhaps this is a function of the categorization of individuals. In the previous work, categories of attachment were defined as secure versus insecure. Our more fine grained classification system might remove small trends. Alternatively, evaluation of friendships might be skewed or inflated within particular attachment styles (i.e., Fearful and Preoccupied (Mikulincer, Orbach, & Lavnieli, 1998). Given that little research has directly compared the four attachment styles, with some contrasting the larger grouping of secure versus insecure attachments, it is important that we investigate the more subtle differences within each of the attachment styles.

On the whole, our findings suggest that there are differences between online and offline friendships and that these differences are experienced differently as a function of attachment style. Friendships were equally high in quality, intimacy and self-disclosure (evidenced by the non-significant main effects of friendship type), providing convergent evidence that online friendships present a positive and beneficial alternative to offline friendships. Past literature would suggest that offline friendships result in higher levels of self-disclosure, understanding, commitment (Chan & Cheng, 2004; Scott et al., 2006), cooperation (Schulman et al., 1994) and intimacy (Bartholomew & Horowitz, 1991), but this is not uniform for all individuals, only for some.

In this study, attachment style predicted friendship characteristics when the friendship context was taken into account. In particular, individuals with fearful and preoccupied attachment styles experienced friendships differently, and more negatively, than their peers for contexts where they meet face-to-face with their friends. These findings are concerning but consistent with previous literature suggesting that these groups may require additional practice, and aid in friendship development. One thing our findings suggest is that online sources may provide a starting point to navigate friendships. Initiating an online friendship might seem less risky and easier to initiate, as there less to less cost associated with this type of friendship. Furthermore, the potential for asynchronous and anonymous Internet interactions allows the opportunity for self-presentation strategies and reflection and thought before engaging in online conversation. Similarly, newer developments in Internet communication (i.e., using emoticons, informal communications, typed emotional statements, plays on language; Baron, 2008; Danet & Herring, 2003; Nishimaru, 2003) may provide alternative ways for less socially skilled individuals to express themselves. The findings of our exploratory study set out the challenges for future research. Specifically, if we are to understand how online contexts can be a potential source for facilitating difficult social relationships especially for individuals who traditionally experience challenges in relationship building, we need to determine which online features in particular are most supportive, how long it takes for any benefits to be realized and whether any benefits would transfer to offline contexts.

## Acknowledgements

We would like to thank Tamsynn Moodley, Samantha Germanakos and Jennifer Newman for their invaluable assistance conducting this research. Please direct all enquiries about the manuscript to Vanessa Buote, Department of Psychology, Wilfrid Laurier University, Waterloo, Ontario, N2L 3C5 and email, buot2090@wlu.ca.

## References

Aikins, W. A., Bierman, K. L., & Parker, J. G. (2005). Navigating the transition to junior high school: The influence of pre-transition friendship and self-system characteristics. Social Development, 14, 42–60.

Bargh, J. A., McKenna, K. Y. A., & Fitzsimons, G. M. (2002). Can you see the real me? Activation and Expression of the 'true self' on the internet. Journal of Social Issues, 58, 33–48.

Baron, N. S. (2008). Always on: Language in an online and mobile world. NY: Oxford University Press.

Bartholomew, K. (1990). Avoidance of intimacy: An attachment perspective. Journal of Social and Personal Relationships, 7, 147–178.

Bartholomew, K. (2008). Self report measures of adult attachment. Retrieved October 1st, 2008. Available from http://www.sfu.ca/psyc/faculty/ bartholomew/selfreports.htm.

Bartholomew, K., & Horowitz, L. M. (1991). Attachment styles among young adults: A test of a four-category model. Journal of Personality and Social Psychology, 61, 226–244.

Bowlby, J. (1969). Attachment and loss: Vol. 1. Attachment. New York: Basic Books. Bowlby, J. (1973). Attachment and loss: Vol. 2. Separation. New York: Basic Books.

Brennan, K. W., & Shaver, P. R. (1995). Dimensions of adult attachment, affect regulation and romantic relationships functioning. Personality and Social Psychology Bulletin, 21, 267–283.

Brignall, T. W., III & Valey, T. V. (2005). The impact of internet communications on social interaction. Sociological Spectrum, 25, 335–348.

Buote, V. M., Pancer, S. M., Pratt, M. W., Adams, G., Birnie-Lefcovitch, S., Polivy, J., et al. (2007). The importance of friends: Friendship and adjustment among 1st- year university students. Journal of Adolescent Research, 22, 665–689.

Chan, D. K. S., & Cheng, D. H. L. (2004). A comparison of offline and online friendship qualities at different stages of relationship development. Journal of Social and Personal Relationships, 21, 305–320.

Danet, B., & Herring, S. C. (2003). Introduction: The multilingual internet. Journal of Computer Mediated Communication, 9(1). Available online at http:// jcmc.indiana.edu/vol9/issue1/editors.html. Date retrieved: December 4, 2008.

Dryburgh, M. (2001). Changing our ways: Why Canadians use the Internet. Statistics Canada. Retrieved April 30th, 2008. Available from http://www.statcan.ca/ english/IPS/Data?56F0006XIE.htm.

Feeney, J. A. (1994). Attachment style, communication patterns and satisfaction across the life cycle of marriage. Personal Relationships, 1, 333–348.

Grabill, C. M., & Kerns, K. A. (2000). Attachment style and intimacy in friendship.
Personal Relationships, 7, 363–378.

Griffin, D., & Bartholomew, K. (1994). Models of the self and other: Fundamental dimensions underlying measures of adult attachment. Journal of Personality and Social Psychology, 67, 430–445.

Gross, E. F. (2004). Adolescent Internet use: What we expect, what teens report.
Journal of Applied Developmental Psychology, 25, 633–649.

Hartup, W. W., & Stevens, N. (1997). Friendships and adaptation in the life course.
Psychological Bulletin, 121, 355–370.

Hays, R. B. (1984). The development and maintenance of friendship. Journal of Social and Personal Relationships, 1, 75–98.

Jiali, Y. (2007). Attachment style differences in online relationship involvement: An examination of interaction characteristics and relationship satisfaction.
CyberPsychology & Behavior, 10, 605–607.

Kiesler, S., Siegel, J., & McGuire, T. M. (1984). Social psychological aspects of computer-mediated communication. American Pscyhologist, 39, 1123–1143.

Kraut, R., Patterson, M., Lundmark, V., Kiesler, S., Mukpadhyay, T., & Scherlis, W.
(1998). Internet paradox: A social technology that reduces social involvement and psychological well being? American Psychologist, 53, 1017–1031.

Kurdek, L. A. (1994). Conflict resolution styles in gay, lesbian, heterosexual nonparent, and heterosexual parent couples. Journal of Marriage and the Family, 56, 705–722.

Lenhart, A., Madden, M., & Hitlin, P. (2005). Teens and technology: Youth are leading the transition to a fully wired and mobile nation. Washington, DC: Pew Internet & American Life Project.

Liebermam, M., Doyle, A., & Markiewicz, D. (1999). Developmental patterns in security of attachment to mother and father in late childhood and early adolescence: Associations with peer relations. Child Development, 70, 202–213.

McKenna, K. Y. A., Green, A. S., & Gleason, M. E. J. (2002). Relationship formation on the internet: What's the big attraction? Journal of Social Issues, 58, 9–31.

Mendelson, M. J., & Aboud, F. E. (1999). Measuring friendship quality in late adolescents and young adults: McGill Friendship Questionnaires. Canadian Journal of Behavioural Science, 31, 130–132.

Mikulincer, M., & Nachshon, O. (1991). Attachment styles and patterns of self- disclosure. Journal of Personality and Social Psychology, 61, 321–331.

Mikulincer, M., Orbach, I., & Lavnieli, D. (1998). Adult attachment style and affect regulation: Strategic variations in subjective self–other similarity. Journal of Personality and Social Psychology, 75, 436–488.

Miller, L. C., Berg, J. H., & Archer, R. L. (1983). Openers: Individuals who elicit intimate self-disclosure. Journal of Personality and Social Psychology, 44, 1234–1244.

MySpace can bring shy kids out of their shells(2008). Retrieved on April 30th, 2008. Available from http://www.msnbc.msn.com/ id/24161656/.

Nie, N. H. (2001). Sociability, interpersonal relations and the internet: Reconciling conflicting findings. American Behavioral Scientist, 45(3), 420–435.

Nishimaru, Y. (2003). Linguistic innovations and interactional features of casual online communication in Japanese. Journal of Computer Mediated Communication, 9(1). Available online at http://jcmc.indiana.edu/vol9/issue1/ nishimura.html. Date retrieved: December 4, 2008.

Oxford University fines students with the aid of Facebook (2008). Retrieved on April 24th, 2008. Available from http://www .timesonline.co.uk/tol/life_and_style/ education/article3768282.ece.

Parks, M. R., & Roberts, L. D. (1998). 'Making MOOsic': The development of personal relationships on line and a comparison to their off-line counterparts. Journal of Social and Personal Relationships, 15, 517–537.

Pistole, M. C. (1993). Attachment relationships: Self-disclosure and trust. Journal of Mental Health Counseling, 15, 94–106.

Richey, M. H., & Richey, H. W. (1980). The significance of best-friend relationships in adolescence. Psychology in the Schools, 17, 536–540.

Saferstein, J. A., Neimeyer, G. J., & Hagans, C. L. (2005). Attachment as a predictor of friendship qualities in college youth. Social Behaviour and Personality, 33, 767–776.

Schindler, A., Thomasius, R., Sack, P.-M., Gemeinhardt, B., & Kuster, U. (2007). Insecure family bases and adolescent drug abuse: A new approach to family patterns of attachment. Attachment & Human Development, 9, 111–126.

Schulman, S., Elicker, J., & Sroufe, L. A. (1994). Stages of friendship growth in preadolescence as related to attachment history. Journal of Social and Personal Relationships, 11, 341–361.

Scott, V. M., Mottarealla, K. E., & Lavooy, M. J. (2006). Does virtual intimacy exist? A brief exploration into reported levels of intimacy in online relationships. CyberPsychology & Behaviour, 9, 759–761.

Tanaka, N., Hasui, C., Uji, M., Hiramura, H., Chen, Z., Shikai, N., et al. (2008). Correlates of the categories of adolescent attachments styles: Perceived rearing, family function, early life events and personality. Psychiatry and Clinical Neurosciences, 62, 65–74.

Tokuno, K. A. (1986). The early adult transition and friendships: Mechanisms of support. Adolescence, 21, 593–606.

Walker, A. J., & Thompson, L. (1983). Intimacy and intergenerational aid and contact among mothers and daughters. Journal of Marriage and the Family, 45, 841–849. Weimer, B. L., Kerns, K. A., & Oldenburg, C. M. (2004). Adolescents' interactions with a best friend: Associations with attachment style. Journal of Experimental Child Psychology, 88, 102–120.

Weiss, R. (1974). The provisions of social relationships. In Z. Rubin (Ed.), Doing unto others (pp. 17–27). Englewood Cliffs, NJ: Prentice Hall.

Wolak, J., Mitchell, K. J., & Finkelhor, D. (2002). Close online relationships in a national sample of adolescents. Adolescence, 37(147), 441–455.

Wood, E., Mueller, J., Willoughby, T., Specht, J., & Deyoung, T. (2005). Teachers' Perceptions: Barriers and supports to using technology in the classroom. Education, Communication and Information, 5, 183–206.

Yahoo to offer single user profile (2008). Retrieved on April 24th, 2008. Available from http://www.theglobeandmail.com/servlet/story/RTGAM.20080424. wgtyahoounity0424/BNStory/PersonalTech/.

Zimmerman, P. (2004). Attachment representations and characteristics of friendship relations during adolescence. Journal of Experimental Child Psychology, 88, 83–101.

Russell B. Clayton

# The Third Wheel: The Impact of Twitter
# Use on Relationship Infidelity and Divorce

Prepared by: R. Eric Landrum, *Boise State University*

## Learning Outcomes

*After reading this article, you will be able to:*
• Appreciate the research design utilized to study the impact of Twitter use on relationship status.
• Practice the interpretation of statistical results in order to draw conclusions about psychological ideas.

## Introduction

The Introduction of Social Networking Sites (SNSs) such as MySpace, Facebook, and Twitter have provided a relatively new platform for interpersonal communication and, as a result, have substantially enhanced and altered the dynamics of interpersonal relationships.[1-7] Twitter, once deemed merely an "information network,"[8] is now considered one of the most popular SNSs, with more than 554 million active users, competing with Facebook, Google + , and LinkedIn.[9] Although Facebook and MySpace have received a great deal of empirical attention,[3,6] research investigating the effects of Twitter use on interpersonal relationships has been somewhat limited, despite Twitter's increasing popularity. Thus, the current study's aim is to examine the effects of Twitter use on romantic relationships.

### Evolution of Twitter as a SNS

Since its creation in 2006, the microblogging site Twitter has accumulated more than 554 million active registered users with 58 million tweets per day.[10] Twitter provides users a communication platform to initiate and develop connections in real time with thousands of people with shared interests.[11] It is also a way to get to know strangers who share the details of their daily lives.[12] As Chen[13] notes, Twitter evolved from an online information network where users responded to a simple question: "What are you doing right now?" to a social network that provides a "new economy of info-sharing and connectivity" between people.[10] Johnson and Yang[14] found that those who have Twitter accounts use the site primarily to give and receive advice, gather and share information, and meet new people.

The primary source for providing and obtaining information on Twitter is by reading or communicating 140-character personal updates, now known as "tweets," to those who opt to "follow" the tweeter. Additional features allow users to retweet, abbreviated as RT, others' tweets and privately direct message, or DM, other users. Twitter users can also have public conversations with others by using "@replies" and can engage in larger conversations by hashtagging ("#") words or phrases. Tweets, RTs, @replies, and hashtags are sent to a public newsfeed viewable by others, unless the user designates his or her tweets as private. Twitter updates can be sent to the newsfeed using mobile phone text messaging from Twitter's mobile phone website, phone applications, and from a user's Twitter home web page.[8,14] Although users can access Twitter across many electronic devices,[8,14] Twitter user interactivity is still somewhat limited compared to other SNSs.

While other SNSs, such as Facebook, allow users to share information about their daily lives on their Facebook newsfeeds, or directly communicate with other users via online chat, Twitter does not provide users the same functionality. Twitter does, however, allow users to post photos, videos, and check-ins that display on the Twitter newsfeed through third-party sites, such as Instagram (photos/videos) and Foursquare (check-ins). Although the method of sharing information varies between Facebook and Twitter, the type of information that can be shared publicly is similar. Therefore, the researcher speculates that the effects of Twitter usage on relationships may parallel those of Facebook. For this reason, the researcher will briefly highlight recent literature pertaining to the effects of SNS use on romantic relationships.

### SNSs' effects on romantic relationships

The evolution of SNSs, as well as their increasing popularity, has provided communication and psychology researchers with an avenue to investigate, more than ever, computer-mediated communication. As a result, scholars have compiled a body of research that has systematically investigated the dynamic, complex interactions between SNS use, health, and romantic relationship outcomes.[1,3–7,15–24] While SNSs may be beneficial in helping users keep in touch with others,[16] research has shown that excessive SNS use can be detrimental to romantic relationships.[3] As Tong[17] notes, relationships, both personal and imper-sonal, are social in nature, and therefore involve one's social networks. Since Twitter and Facebook use "maps on to one's social networks almost isomorphi-cally, SNSs' potential role in the process of relationship maintenance and termination seems quite likely."[17(p1)]

In fact, several studies have found that Facebook-induced jealousy, partner survelliance, posting ambiguous information, compulsive Internet use, and online portrayal of intimate relationships can be damaging to romantic relationships.[18–21] Additionally, Lyndon[22] found that Facebook monitoring leads to negative relationship outcomes, such as online and offline relationship intrusion, which may induce jealousy among romantic partners.[23] Marshall[24] found that remaining friends on SNSs, specifically Facebook, after a breakup delays the healing process. One possible explanation for this delay could be due to romantic partners taking advantage of the information Facebook provides of their ex-partner.[17] This type of information visibility, which occurs not only on Facebook but also on Twitter, may lead to similar relationship outcomes for the latter SNS.

Since Twitter now allows users to interact in a similar way as Facebook (i.e., write posts and upload images, videos, and location check-ins), the researcher theorizes that the effects of Twitter use on interpersonal relationships are comparable to those associated with Facebook. Thus, one additional aim of this study is to examine if Twitter uses parallels that of Facebook with regard to negative relationship outcomes.[3]

## The current study

The current study is grounded in the methodological framework of Clayton et al.'s[3] survey study examining the influence of Facebook use on romantic relationships. Clayton et al.'s[4] study of 205 Facebook users found that Facebook-related conflict mediated the relationship between Facebook use and negative relationship outcomes (i.e., cheating, breakup, and divorce). This indirect effect was more pronounced for those in relatively newer relationships of 3 years or less.[3] To understand the influence of Twitter usage on romantic relationships, this study used the same mediating variable, now termed "Twitter-related conflict," as well as the negative relationship outcome items.[3] The researcher conceptualized Twitter-related conflict as whether Twitter use increases relationship complications in intimate romantic relationships. Negative relationship outcomes were conceptualized as whether Twitter use influences the likelihood for emotional cheating, physical cheating, relationship breakup, and divorce. As a result, the researcher predicted that active Twitter use and negative relationship outcomes would be positively related and that Twitter-related conflict would mediate the relationship between active Twitter use and negative relationship outcomes.

Clayton et al.'s[3] study found a moderating effect on the mediational relationship for those who are, or have been, in relationships of 3 years or less. Therefore, the current study hypothesizes that the length of the romantic relationship will moderate the indirect effect on the relationship between active Twitter use and negative relationship outcomes. Based on this examination of the literature, the author hypothesizes the following:

H1: The relationship between active Twitter use and negative relationship outcomes will be positively related.

H2: Twitter-related conflict will mediate the relationship between active Twitter use and negative relationship outcomes.

H3: The indirect effect of active Twitter use on negative relationship outcomes through Twitter-related conflict will be greater for those who are, or have been, in shorter duration relationships.

# Method

## Participants

An online survey was created on qualtrics.com and distributed to Twitter users via the researcher's Twitter account, as well as *The Huffington Post*'s Twitter account. The survey was tweeted a total of 20 times to followers. The total number of users the survey link was tweeted to, not including possible retweets, exceeded 3.4 million Twitter users. The final number of participants was 581 Twitter users. All participants were 18 years of age or older. The participants' ages ranged from 18 to 67 years ($M = 29$, $SD = 8.9$). Most participants (62%) were Caucasian, 15% Asian, 12% Hispanic, 6% African American, and 5% Native American. The majority of participants (63%) were male. This study was approved by the university's Institutional Review Board.

## Materials

Following Clayton's[3] methodology, a 20-question survey was designed using qualtrics.com. The survey included demographic questions, as well as questions about participants' perceived levels of Twitter use. Additionally, participants were asked if they had encountered relationship conflict with their current or former partner as a result of Twitter use. Participants were also asked if Twitter use had led to breakup or divorce, emotional cheating, and physical cheating with a current or former partner.

### Relationships

The researcher asked the participants to indicate if their partner or former partner had a Twitter account. Those who indicated that their former partner or spouse did not have a Twitter account were not included in further analyses because some items pertained to participants' perceived levels of their current or former partner's Twitter use ($n = 67$). In order for the researcher to understand to whom the participants' answers were directed, the survey also instructed participants to answer the question, "Are you currently in a romantic relationship?" If the participants answered, "Yes," they were then asked to type how many months or years they had been in the relationship with their current partner. If participants answered "No," the researcher could analyze their data in connection with the participants' former partners. After screening participants' responses for initial criteria, the total number of participants included for analyses was 514. Of the 514 participants, 386 (75%) participants responded that they were in a romantic relationship, while 128 (25%) reported being single.

### Active Twitter use

Following Rubin's[25] active audience construct and Chen's[13] Twitter use items, active Twitter use was measured by asking participants to rate the following five statements: "How often do you log in into Twitter?" "How often do you Tweet?" "How often do you @replies?" "How often do you direct message followers?" and "How often do you scroll the Twitter newsfeed?" Data were gathered using a Likert-type scale where A = "never," B = "monthly," C = "weekly," D = "daily," E = "hourly," and F = "more than hourly." The Cronbach's alpha for the scale was 0.90. To create a multiplicative index of Twitter use, participants indicated how many hours per day, and how many days per week, they used Twitter. On average, participants used Twitter for 52 minutes per day ($SD = 66.3$), five days per week ($SD = 2.3$).

### Twitter-related conflict

The current study adapted the items in Clayton et al.'s[3] Facebook-related conflict scale (Cronbach's $\alpha = 0.85$) to measure Twitter-related conflict. Such items included, "How often do you have an argument with your significant other as a result of excessive Twitter use?" and "How often do you have an argument with your significant other as a result of viewing friends' Twitter profiles?" The questions were answered using a Likert scale ranging from A = "never" to F = "always." The Cronbach's alpha for the scale was 0.94.

**Negative relationship outcomes.** The current study used Clayton et al.'s[3] negative relationship outcome questions (Kuder Richardson [KR-20]=0.70) to measure the criterion variable. Such items included, "Have you emotionally cheated on your significant other with someone you have connected or reconnected with on Twitter?" "Have you physically cheated on your significant other with someone you have connected or reconnected with on Twitter?" and "Has Twitter led to a breakup/ divorce?" The researcher condensed the answers into dichotomous yes/no answer choices. Once averaged, the KR-20 measure of reliability was 0.72 (see Table 1).

### Table 1
**Means, standard deviations, correlations, and alpha reliabilities[a] for variables**

|  | M | SD | 1 | 2 | 3 |
|---|---|---|---|---|---|
| 1. Active Twitter use | 3.36 | 1.0 | (0.90) | | |
| 2. Twitter-related conflict | 2.77 | 1.4 | 0.52*** | (0.94) | |
| 3. Negative relationship outcomes | 1.17 | 0.30 | 0.33*** | 0.53*** | (0.72) |

[a] On diagonal in parentheses.

*$p < 0.05$; **$p < 0.01$; ***$p < 0.001$.

## Results

To test the aforementioned hypotheses, moderation–mediation regression analyses using bootstrapping resampling methods were conducted according to the specifications set out by Andrew Hayes's PROCESS for SPSS using model four for simple mediation and model seven to test for moderation–mediation.[26] As Figure 1 shows, active Twitter use was entered as the independent variable (X), Twitter-related conflict as the mediator variable (M), length of romantic relationship as the moderator variable (W), and negative relationship outcomes was entered as the criterion variable (Y) in the model.

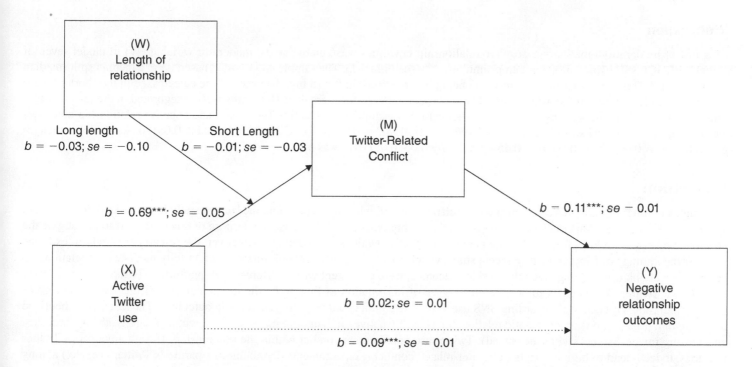

**Figure 1** Andrew Hayes's mediation–moderation model 7 conceptual diagram. Path coefficients for simple moderation–mediation model analysis. Note. Model four is the same as model seven excluding the moderator variable (W). Dotted line denotes the effect of active Twitter use on negative relationship outcomes when Twitter-related conflict is not included as a mediator. * $p < 0.05$; ** $p < 0.01$; *** $p < 0.001$.

## *Mediation*

As a test of simple mediation, Twitter-related conflict was entered as the mediator variable (M) in model four of Hayes's PROCESS[26] (see Figure 1). Data analysis using 1,000 bootstrap simulations[26] revealed that the total effect between active Twitter use negative relationship outcomes was positively associated (*effect* = 0.09, *SE* = 0.01, $p < 0.001$ [95% CI 0.07, 0.12]), supporting H1 (see Table 2). Moreover, active Twitter use exerted an indirect effect on negative relationship outcomes through Twitter-related conflict (*effect* = 0.07, *SE* = 0.01, p < 0.001 [95% bias-corrected bootstrap CI 0.06, 0.09]), while the direct relationship between active Twitter use and negative relationship outcomes was not significant (*effect* = 0.02, *SE* = 0.01, $p = 0.082$ [95% CI − 0.01, 0.05]), supporting H2 (see Table 2). This indirect effect is statistically different from zero, as revealed by a 95% bias-corrected bootstrap confidence interval,[26] and indicates that Twitter-related conflict mediates the relationship between active Twitter use and negative relationship outcomes.

**Table 2**
**Total, direct, and indirect effects**

|  | Negative relationship outcomes as criterion | | | | |
| --- | --- | --- | --- | --- | --- |
|  | Effect | SE | t | LLCI | ULCI |
| Total effect of active Twitter use | 0.09 | 0.01 | 7.90*** | 0.07 | 0.12 |
| Direct effect of active Twitter use | 0.02 | 0.01 | 1.75 | −0.01 | 0.05 |
|  | Effect | Boot SE |  | BootLLCI | BootULCI |
| Indirect effect of active Twitter use | 0.07*** | 0.01 | — | 0.06 | 0.09 |

*Note.* Number of bootstrap samples for bias-corrected bootstrap confidence intervals: 1,000. Level of confidence for all confidence intervals: 95.

*p < 0.05; **p < 0.01; ***p < 0.001.

## Moderation

As a test of moderation–mediation, negative relationship outcomes was entered as the moderator variable (W) in model seven of Hayes's PROCESS[26] using 1,000 bootstrap simulations[26] (see Figure 1). The sample was divided based upon a median split (median = 18 months). Those participants who reported being in a relationship for 18 months or less were categorized in the shorter length group ($n = 194$), whereas those who reported being in relationships for more than 18 months were categorized in the longer length group ($n = 181$). The moderating effect on the indirect relationship between active Twitter use and negative relationship outcomes was not significant for the shorter length group (*effect* = 0.01, *SE* = 0.02, *p* = 0.337 [95% CI − 0.02, 0.05]) or for the longer length group (*effect* = 0.02, *SE* = 0.03, *p* = 0.454 [95% CI −0.03, 0.08]). H3 was not supported.

# Discussion

Although a number of variables can contribute to relationship infidelity and separation, the current study hypothesized that SNS use, specifically Twitter use, can contribute to negative relationship outcomes. Therefore, the purpose of this study was to investigate the relationship between active Twitter use and negative romantic relationship outcomes. Moreover, the researcher sought to examine whether the findings of Clayton et al.'s[3] recent study, which concluded that Facebook-related conflict fully mediated the relationship between Facebook use and negative relationship outcomes, were consistent with a different SNS platform—Twitter.

Since Twitter allows users to share similar types of information as Facebook, the researcher argued that Twitter outcomes may parallel those of Facebook regarding SNS use, romantic conflict, and negative relationship outcomes. The researcher theorized that if an individual who is in a romantic relationship is highly active on Twitter (e.g., tweeting, direct messaging others, check-ins, and posting images to the Twitter newsfeed), Twitter use could create conflict within the relationship. If high amounts of Twitter use does, indeed, lead to high amounts of Twitter-related conflict (i.e., arguments pertaining to a partner's Twitter use, etc.) among romantic partners, it is plausible to speculate that such conflict could lead to unfavorable relationship outcomes such as cheating, breakup, or divorce. The results from this study largely support these propositions. In contrast to recent findings,[3] the length of the relationship did not moderate the mediational effect, suggesting that relationship maturity may not influence negative relationship outcomes in terms of Twitter use.

The results of this study partially replicate Clayton et al.'s[3] findings regarding Facebook use and negative relationship outcomes. Based on the findings from both[3] studies, Twitter and Facebook use can have damaging effects on romantic relationships. That is, when SNS use becomes problematic in one's romantic relationship, risk of negative relationship outcomes may follow. In contrast, recent reports have shown that SNS conflict can be reduced when partners share joint accounts.[27] Furthermore, recent SNS applications have been developed to facilitate interpersonal communication between partners by providing a private, secure, and organized environment for two people to share, such as the 2life app[28] for iPhone users. Whether this type of app reduces SNS-related conflict between romantic partners is yet to be determined.

## Limitations and implications for further research

The current study has several limitations. The sample included participants who were told before starting the survey that they would be answering questions regarding Twitter use and romantic relationship outcomes, and this may have skewed the data. Additionally, some items were left to participants' interpretation, such as the word "excessive" when answering questions about Twitter-related conflict. Moreover, social desirability is an unavoidable issue when it comes to self-reported data, particularly when the issues under investigation are sensitive, as in the current study. Since the online survey link was distributed by the researcher's Twitter account and *The Huffington Post*'s Twitter account, the current study's sample is limited to only those who use Twitter and who follow the researcher or *The Huffington Post*'s profile on Twitter. This limitation significantly limits the generalizations of the findings. Future research should investigate if engaging in high levels of other SNS usage, such as Instagram and LinkedIn, also predicts negative relationship outcomes. Additional future research should explore other mediators in the current study's model, such as relationship quality and satisfaction.

# Conclusion

The results from this study show that active Twitter use leads to greater amounts of Twitter-related conflict among romantic partners, which in turn leads to infidelity, breakup, and divorce. Results from the current study and Clayton et al.'s[3] study demonstrate that Twitter and Facebook use can have damaging effects on romantic relationships.

# Author Disclosure Statement

No competing financial interests exist.

# References

1. Boyd D, Ellison BN. Social network sites: definition, history, and scholarship. *Journal of Computer-Mediated Communication* 2007; 13.
2. Choi JH. (2008) Living in cyworld: contextualising cy-ties in South Korea. In Bruns A, Jacobs J, eds. *Uses of blogs.* New York: Peter Lang, pp. 173–186.
3. Clayton R, Nagurney A, Smith J. Cheating, breakup, and divorce: is Facebook use to blame? *Cyberpsychology, Behavior, & Social Networking* 2013; 16:717–720.
4. Ellison BN, Steinfield C, Lampe, C. The benefits of Facebook "friends": exploring the relationship between college students' use of online social networks and social capital. Journal of *Computer-Mediated Communication* 2007; 12: article 1.
5. Lampe C, Ellison BN, Steinfield C. Social capital, self-esteem, and use of online social network sites. *Journal of Applied Developmental Psychology* 2008; 29:434–445.
6. Raacke J, Bonds-Raacke J. MySpace and Facebook: applying the uses and gratifications theory to exploring friend-networking sites. *Individual Differences Research Group* 2008; 8:27–33.
7. Fox J, Warber K. Romantic relationship development in the age of Facebook: an exploratory study of emerging adults' perceptions, motives, and behaviors. *Journal of Cyberpsychology, Behavior, & Social Networking* 2013; 16:3–7.
8. About Twitter. https://twitter.com/about (accessed Jun. 20, 2013).
9. 2010 Best social networking site reviews and comparisons. http://social-networking-websites-review.toptenreviews.com (accessed Dec. 28, 2013).
10. Statistics Brain. Twitter statistics. www.statisticbrain.com/twitter-statistics/ (accessed Jun. 20, 2013).
11. Sarno D. On Twitter, mindcasting is the new lifecasting. Los Angeles Times, Mar. 11, 2009. http://latimesblogs.latimes.com/technology/2009/03/on-twitter-mind.html (accessed Jan. 12, 2014).
12. Thompson C. Brave new world of digital intimacy. The New York Times, Sep. 5, 2008. www.nytimes.com/2008/09/07/magazine/07awareness-t.html?_r 5 1&pagewanted 5 all (accessed Dec. 29, 2013).
13. Chen G. Tweet this: a uses and gratifications perspective on how active Twitter use gratifies a need to connect with others. *Journal of Computers in Human Behavior* 2011; 27:755–762.
14. Johnson P, Yang S-U. Uses and gratifications of Twitter: an examination of user motives and satisfaction of Twitter use. Paper presented at the Annual Convention of Association for Education in Journalism and Mass Communication in Boston, MA.
15. Clayton R, Osborne R, Miller B, et al. Loneliness, anxiousness, and substance use as predictors of Facebook use. *Computers in Human Behavior* 2013; 29:687–693.
16. Joinson AN. (2008) "Looking at," "looking up" or "keeping up with" people? Motives and uses of Facebook. In: *Proceedings of the 26th Annual SIGCHI Conference on Human Factors in Computing Systems (Florence, Italy, April 5–10, 2008), CHI'08.* New York: ACM Press, pp. 1027–1036.
17. Tong ST. Facebook use during relationship termination: uncertainty reduction and surveillance. *Cyberpsychology, Behavior, & Social Networking* 2013; 16:788–793 .
18. Utz S, Beukeboom CJ. The role of social network sites in romantic relationships: effects on jealousy and relationship happiness. *Journal of Computer-Mediated Communication* 2011; 16:511–527.
19. Tokunaga RS. Social networking site or social surveillance site? Understanding the use of interpersonal electronic surveillance in romantic relationships. *Computers in Human Behavior* 2011; 27:705–713.
20. Kerkhof P, Finkenauer C, Muusses, LD. Relational consequences of compulsive internet use: a longitudinal study among newlyweds. *Human Communication Research* 2011; 37:147–173.
21. Papp LM, Danielewicz J, Cayemberg C. "Are we Facebook official?" Implications of dating partners' Facebook use and profiles for intimate relationship satisfaction. Cyberpsychology, Behavior, & Social Networking 2012; 15:85–90.
22. Lyndon A, Bonds-Raacke J, Cratty AD. College students' Facebook stalking of ex-partners. *Cyberpsychology, Behavior, & Social Networking* 2011; 14:711–716.
23. Muise A, Christofides E, Desmarais S. More information than you ever wanted: does Facebook bring out the green-eyed monster of jealousy? *Cyberpsychology & Behavior* 2009; 12:441–444.
24. Marshall T. Facebook surveillance of former romantic partners: associations with postbreakup recovery and personal growth. *Cyberpsychology, Behavior, & Social Networking* 2012; 15:521–526.
25. Rubin AM. (2009) Uses and gratifications: an evolving perspective on media effects. In Nabi RL, Oliver MB, eds. *The SAGE handbook of media processes and effect.* Washington, DC: Sage, pp. 147–159.
26. Hayes AF. (2013) *Introduction to mediation, moderation, and conditional process analysis: a regression-based approach.* New York: Guilford Press.

27.  Buck S. (2013) When Facebook official isn't enough. Mashable.com . http://mashable.com/2013/08/04/social-mediacouples/ (accessed Jan. 10, 2014).

28.  2 For Life Media Inc. (2013) 2Life App description. www.2life.io (accessed Sep. 28, 2013).

## Critical Thinking

1.  The development of social networking is developing rapidly and changing daily. Why is it important that this article was published in 2014 rather than in 2009? Explain.

2.  Some fairly complex results appear in this journal article. What are the takeaway messages that you have after reading the complete article? What reservations might you have about the results and what they mean?

## Internet References

**Is constant texting good or bad for your relationship?**

   http://www.psychologytoday.com/blog/meet-catch-and-keep/201403/ is-constant-texting-good-or-bad-your-relationship.

**The effect of technology on relationships**

   http://www.psychologytoday.com/blog/happiness-in-world/201006/the-effect-technology-relationships

# The Adultery Arms Race

Prepared by: Patricia Hrusa Williams, University of Maine at Farmington

## Learning Outcomes

*After reading this article, you will be able to:*
- Explain how technology is influencing cheating and infidelity in relationships.
- Identity different technological options and apps available to monitor partner's mobile phones and devices.
- Analyze the effects of being able to spy on a partner's activities through technology.

Jay's wife, Ann, was supposed to be out of town on business. It was a Tuesday evening in August 2013, and Jay, a 36-year-old IT manager, was at home in Indiana with their 5-year-old daughter and 9-year-old son when he made a jarring discovery. Their daughter had misplaced her iPad, so Jay used the app Find My iPhone to search for it. The app found the missing tablet right away, but it also located all the other devices on the family's plan. What was Ann's phone doing at a hotel five miles from their home?

His suspicions raised, Jay, who knew Ann's passwords, read through her e-mails and Facebook messages. (Like others in this story, Jay asked that his and Ann's names be changed.) He didn't find anything incriminating, but neither could he imagine a good reason for Ann to be at that hotel. So Jay started using Find My iPhone for an altogether different purpose: to monitor his wife's whereabouts.

Two nights later, when Ann said she was working late, Jay tracked her phone to the same spot. This time, he drove to the hotel, called her down to the parking lot, and demanded to know what was going on. Ann told him she was there posing for boudoir photos, with which she planned to surprise him for his upcoming birthday. She said the photographer was up in the room waiting for her.

Jay wanted to believe Ann. They'd been married for 12 years, and she had never given him cause to distrust her. So instead of demanding to meet the photographer or storming up to the room, Jay got in his car and drove home.

Still, something gnawed at him. According to Ann's e-mails, the boudoir photo shoot had indeed taken place—but on the previous day, Wednesday. So her being at the hotel on Tuesday and again on Thursday didn't make sense. Unless . . .

In an earlier era, a suspicious husband like Jay might have rifled through Ann's pockets or hired a private investigator. But having stumbled upon Find My iPhone's utility as a surveillance tool, Jay wondered what other apps might help him keep tabs on his wife. He didn't have to look far. Spouses now have easy access to an array of sophisticated spy software that would give Edward Snowden night sweats: programs that record every keystroke; that compile detailed logs of our calls, texts, and video chats; that track a phone's location in real time; that recover deleted messages from all manner of devices (without having to touch said devices); that turn phones into wiretapping equipment; and on and on.

Jay spent a few days researching surveillance tools before buying a program called Dr. Fone, which enabled him to remotely recover text messages from Ann's phone. Late one night, he downloaded her texts onto his work laptop. He spent the next day reading through them at the office. Turns out, his wife had become involved with a co-worker. There were thousands of text messages between them, many X-rated—an excruciatingly detailed record of Ann's betrayal laid out on Jay's computer screen. "I could literally watch her affair progress," Jay told me, "and that in itself was painful."

One might assume that the proliferation of such spyware would have a chilling effect on extramarital activities. Aspiring cheaters, however, need not despair: software developers are also rolling out ever stealthier technology to help people conceal their affairs. Married folk who enjoy a little side action can choose from such specialized tools as Vaulty Stocks, which hides photos and videos inside a virtual vault within one's phone that's disguised to look like a stock-market app, and Nosy Trap, which displays a fake iPhone home screen and takes a picture of anyone who tries to snoop on the phone. CATE (the Call and Text Eraser) hides texts and calls from certain contacts and boasts tricky features such as the ability to "quick clean" incriminating evidence by shaking your smartphone. CoverMe does much of the above, plus offers "military-grade encrypted phone calls." And in the event of an emergency, there's the nuclear option: apps that let users remotely wipe a phone completely clean, removing all traces of infidelity.

But every new app that promises to make playing around safer and easier just increases the appetite for a cleverer way to expose such deception. Some products even court both sides: a partner at cate walked me through how a wife could install the app on her husband's phone to create a secret record of calls and texts to be perused at her leisure. Which may be great from a market-demand standpoint, but is probably not so healthy for the broader culture, as an accelerating spiral of paranoia drives an arms race of infidelity-themed weapons aimed straight at the consumer's heart.

Every tech trend has its early adopters. Justin, a 30-year old computer programmer from Ohio, is at the vanguard of this one.

Justin first discovered cate on the September 21, 2012, episode of *Shark Tank*, ABC's venture-capital reality show. The Call and Text Eraser, pitched specifically as a "cheating app," won $70,000 in seed money on the program. Justin knew he had to have it.

His girlfriend at the time—we'll call her Scarlett—was "the jealous type," forever poking through his smartphone and computer. Not that he could blame her, given that she'd already busted him once for having sex with another woman. "It took a lot of talking and a lot of promising that it wouldn't happen again," he told me over e-mail. (I found Justin through a user review of CATE.) "So her wanting to check up on me was understandable," he allowed. "But at the same time, it was my business and if I wanted to share I would have."

Even a not-so-jealous girlfriend might have taken exception to many of the messages on Justin's phone: "casual texting" (that is, flirting) with other women, "hard core" (explicitly sexual) texting, texts arranging "hookups." In the past, he'd been busted repeatedly for such communiqués. (Scarlett is not the only girlfriend with whom Justin has found monogamy to be a challenge.) With CATE, all Justin had to do was create a list of contacts he didn't want Scarlett to know about, and any incriminating texts and phone calls with those contacts got channeled directly into a pass-code-protected vault.

CATE is just one of many tools Justin uses to, as he puts it, "stay one step ahead." His go-to method for exchanging explicit photos is Snapchat, the popular app that causes pics and videos to self-destruct seconds after they are received. (Of course, as savvy users know, expired "snaps" aren't really deleted, but merely hidden in the bowels of the recipient's phone, so Justin periodically goes in and permanently scrubs them.) And for visuals so appealing that he cannot bear to see them vanish into the ether, he has Gallery Lock, which secretes pics and videos inside a private "gallery" within his phone.

Justin wound up cheating on Scarlett "several more times" before they finally broke up—a pattern he's repeated with other girlfriends. Oh, sure, he enjoys the social and domestic comforts of a relationship ("It's always nice to have someone to call your girl"). He understands the suffering that infidelity can cause ("I have been cheated on so I know how much it hurts"). He even feels guilty about playing around. But for him, the adrenaline kick is irresistible. "Not to mention," he adds, "no woman is the same [and] there is always going to be someone out there who can do something sexually that you have never tried." Then, of course, there's "the thrill of never knowing if you are going to get caught."

All of which makes it more than a little troubling that, while laboring to keep one semiserious girlfriend after another in the dark with privacy-enhancing apps, Justin has been equally aggressive about using spy apps to keep a virtual eye on said girlfriends.

Justin has tried it all: keystroke loggers, phone trackers, software enabling him to "see text messages, pictures, and all the juicy stuff . . . even the folder to where your deleted stuff would go." He figures he's tried nearly every spy and cheater app on the market, and estimates that since 2007, he has "kept tabs," serially, on at least half a dozen girlfriends. "The monitoring is really just for my peace of mind," he says. Plus, if he catches a girlfriend straying, "it kind of balances it out and makes it fair." That way, he explains, if she ever busts him, "I have proof she was cheating so therefore she would have no reason to be mad."

Not that Justin is immune to the occasional flash of jealousy. More than once, he has gone out to confront a girlfriend whose phone revealed her to be somewhere other than where she'd claimed to be. One relationship ended with particularly dramatic flair: "The phone went to the location off of a country road in the middle of nowhere and there she was having sex in the backseat of the car with another man." A fistfight ensued (with the guy, not the girlfriend), followed later by "breakup sex" (vice versa). One year on, Justin says, "I still don't believe that she has figured out how I found out."

Justin knows that many folks may find his playing both sides of the cheating-apps divide "twisted." But, he reasons, "I am doing it for my safety to make sure I don't get hurt. So doesn't that make it right??"

Right or wrong, cheating apps tap into a potentially lucrative market: While the national infidelity rate is hard to pin down (because, well, people lie), reputable research puts the proportion of unfaithful spouses at about 15 percent of women and 20 percent of men—with the gender gap closing fast. And while the roots of infidelity remain more or less constant (the desire for novelty, attention, affirmation, a lover with tighter glutes . . .), technology is radically altering how we enter into, conduct, and even define it. (The affairs in this piece all involved old-school, off-line sex, but there is a growing body of research on the devastation wrought by the proliferation of online-only betrayal.) Researchers regard the Internet as fertile ground for female infidelity in particular. "Men tend to cheat for physical reasons and women for emotional reasons," says Katherine Hertlein, who studies the impact of technology on relationships as the director of the Marriage and Therapy Program at the University of Nevada at Las Vegas. "The Internet facilitates a lot of emotional disclosure and connections with someone else."

At the same time, privacy has become a rare commodity. Forget the National Security Agency and Russian mobsters: in a recent survey conducted in the United Kingdom, 62 percent of men in relationships admitted to poking around in a current or ex-partner's mobile phone. (Interestingly, among women, the proportion was only 34 percent. So much for the stereotype of straying guys versus prying gals.) On the flip side, according to the Pew Research Center's Internet and American Life Project, 14 percent of adults have taken steps to hide their online activity from a family member or romantic partner. Therapists say they're seeing more spouses casually tracking each other as well as more clashes over online spying, and lawyers are starting to recommend digital-privacy clauses for prenup and postnup agreements. Such clauses aim to prevent spouses from using personal texts, e-mails, or photos against each other should they wind up in divorce court.

Tech developers by and large didn't set out looking to get involved. As is so often the case with infidelity, it just sort of happened. Take Find My iPhone. Apple did not create the app with suspicious lovers in mind, but users pretty quickly realized its potential. Dr. Fone is marketed primarily as a way to recover lost data. Likewise, messaging apps such as Snapchat have many more uses than concealing naughty talk or naked photos, but the apps are a hit with cheaters.

The multipurpose nature and off-label use of many tools make it difficult to gauge the size of this vast and varied market. The company mSpy offers one of the top-rated programs for monitoring smartphones and computers; 2 million subscribers pay between $20 and $70 a month for the ability to do everything from review browsing history to listen in on phone calls to track a device's whereabouts. Some 40 percent of customers are parents looking to monitor their kids, according to Andrew Lobanoff, the head of sales at mSpy, who says the company does basic consumer research to see who its customers are and what features they want added. Another 10 to 15 percent are small businesses monitoring employees' use of company devices (another growing trend). The remaining 45 to 50 percent? They could be up to anything.

Apps marketed specifically as tools for cheaters and jealous spouses for the most part aren't seeing the download numbers of a heavy hitter like, say, Grindr, the hookup app for gay men (10 million downloads and more than 5 million monthly users). But plenty have piqued consumer interest: The private- textingand- calling app CoverMe has more than 2 million users. TigerText, which (among other features) causes messages to self-destruct after a set amount of time, has been downloaded 3.5 million times since its introduction in February 2010. (It hit the market a couple of months after the Tiger Woods sexting scandal, though the company maintains that the app is not named for Woods.)

Once the marketplace identifies a revenue stream, of course, the water has been chummed and everyone rushes in for a taste. By now, new offerings are constantly popping up from purveyors large and small. Ashley Madison, the online-dating giant for married people (company slogan: "Life is short. Have an affair."), has a mobile app that provides some 30 million members "on the go" access to its services. Last year, the company introduced an add-on app called BlackBook, which allows users to purchase disposable phone numbers with which to conduct their illicit business. Calls and texts are placed through the app much as they are through Skype, explains the company's chief operating officer, Rizwan Jiwan. "One of the leading ways people get caught in affairs is by their cellphone bill," he observes. But with the disposable numbers, all calls are routed through a user's Ashley Madison account, which appears on his or her credit-card statements under a series of business aliases. "The phone number isn't tied to you in any way."

Both sides of the arms race have ego invested in not getting outgunned. Stressing Ashley Madison's obsession with customer privacy, Jiwan boasts that the shift from computers to mobile devices makes it harder for members to get busted. "It's much more difficult to get spyware on phones," he told me. But mSpy's Lobanoff pushed back: "All applications can be monitored. Let me make it clear for you. If you provide us what application you would like to track, within two weeks we can develop a feature to do that." It all boils down to demand. For instance, he notes, after receiving some 300 calls from customers looking to monitor Snapchat, the company rolled out just such a feature.

Lobanoff admits that iPhones are tougher to monitor than phones from other brands, because Apple is strict about what runs on its operating system (although many Apple users "jailbreak" their devices, removing such limits). Which raises the question: Is an iPhone a good investment for cheaters worried about being monitored—or would it too tightly restrict their access to cheating apps? Such are the complexities of modern infidelity.

Of course, no app can remove all risk of getting caught. Technology can, in fact, generate a false sense of security that leads people to push limits or get sloppy. Justin has had several close calls, using cate to conceal indiscreet texts and voicemails but forgetting to hide explicit photos. When a girlfriend found a naked picture of him that he'd failed to delete after sexting another woman, Justin had to think fast. "The way I talk my way out of it is that I say I was going to send it to her." Then, of course, there is the peril of creeping obsolescence: after several months, regular upgrades to the operating system on Justin's phone outpaced cate's, and more and more private messages began to slip through the cracks. (A scan of user reviews suggests this is a common problem.)

Virtual surveillance has its risks as well. Stumbling across an incriminating e-mail your partner left open is one thing; premeditated spying can land you in court—or worse. Sometime in 2008 or 2009, a Minnesota man named Danny Lee Hormann, suspecting his wife of infidelity, installed a GPS tracker on her car and allegedly downloaded spyware onto her phone and the family computer.

His now-ex-wife, Michele Mathias (who denied having an affair), began wondering how her husband always knew what she was up to. In March 2010, Mathias had a mechanic search her car. The tracker was found. Mathias called the police, and Hormann spent a month in jail on stalking charges. (It's worth noting that a second conviction, specifically for illegally tracking her car, was overturned on appeal when the judge ruled that joint ownership gave Hormann the right to install the GPS tracker.)

Staying on the right side of the law is trickier than one might imagine. There are a few absolute no-nos. At the top of the list: never install software on a device that you do not own without first obtaining the user's consent. Software sellers are careful to shift the legal burden onto consumers. On its site, mSpy warns that misuse of the software "may result in severe monetary and criminal penalties." Similarly, SpyBubble, which offers cellphone-tracking software, reminds its customers of their duty to "notify users of the device that they are being monitored." Even so, questions of ownership and privacy get messy between married partners, and the landscape remains in flux as courts struggle to apply old laws to new technology.

In 2010, a Texas man named Larry Bagley was acquitted of charges that he violated federal wiretapping laws by installing audio-recording devices around his house and keystroke-monitoring software on his then-wife's computer. In his ruling, the district judge pointed to a split opinion among U.S. circuit courts as to whether the federal law applies to "interspousal wiretaps." (The Fourth, Sixth, Eighth, Tenth, and Eleventh Circuit Courts said it does, he noted; the Second and Fifth said it doesn't.) Similarly, in California, Virginia, Texas, Minnesota, and as of this summer New York, it is a misdemeanor to install a GPS tracker on someone's vehicle without their consent. But when a vehicle is jointly owned, things get fuzzy.

"I always tell people two things: (1) do it legally, and (2) do it right," says John Paul Lucich, a computer-forensics expert and the author of *Cyber Lies*, a do-it-yourself guide for spouses looking to become virtual sleuths. Lucich has worked his share of ugly divorces, and he stresses that even the most damning digital evidence of infidelity will prove worthless in court—and potentially land you in trouble—if improperly gathered. His blanket advice: Get a really good lawyer. Stat.

Such apps clearly have the potential to blow up relationships, but the question now may be whether they can be used to salvage them as well. Many of the betrayed partners I spoke with believe they can.

A couple of years ago, Ginger discovered that her husband, Tim, was having an affair with a woman he'd met through a non-profit on whose board he sat. (As Ginger tells it, this was a classic case of a middle-aged man having his head turned by a much younger woman.) The affair lasted less than a year, but it took another eight months before Tim's lover stopped sending him gifts and showing up in awkward places (even church!).

Ginger and Tim decided to tough it out—they've been married for 35 years and have two adult children—but that took some doing. For the first year and a half, certain things Tim did or said would trigger Ginger's anxiety. He would announce that he was going to the store; Ginger would fire up her tracking software to ensure he did just that. Business travel called for even more elaborate reassurances. "When he was away, I would be like, 'I want you to FaceTime the whole room—the bathroom, the closet; open the hallway door.'"

Ginger's anxiety has dimmed, but not vanished. She still occasionally uses Find My iPhone to make sure Tim is, in fact, staying late at the office. "And we use FaceTime all the time. He knows that if I try to FaceTime him, he'd better answer right then or have a very, very good reason why he didn't."

Jay and Ann, of the boudoir photo shoot, also decided to try to repair their marriage. When he first confronted her with a record of her texts, Ann denied that the sex talk was ever more than fantasy. But when Jay scheduled a polygraph, she confessed to a full-blown, physical affair.

As hard as it has been for Jay, one year later he reports that tech tools are helping. Ann's affair grew out of her sense of neglect, Jay told me: "She wasn't getting the attention she wanted from me, so she found someone else to give it to her." To strengthen their bond, Jay and Ann have started using Couple, a relationship app geared toward promoting intimacy by setting up a private line of communication for texts, pics, video clips, and, of course, updates on each person's whereabouts. Every now and again, Jay sneaks a peek at Find My iPhone. He also has set his iPad to receive copies of Ann's texts. "I don't know if she realizes I'm doing that," he told me. But in general, she understands his desire for extra oversight. "She's like, 'Whatever you want.'"

In fact, post-affair surveillance seems to be an increasingly popular counseling prescription. Even as marriage and family therapists take a dim view of unprovoked snooping, once the scent of infidelity is in the air, many become enthusiastically pro-snooping—initially to help uncover the truth about a partner's behavior but then to help couples reconcile by reestablishing accountability and trust. The psychotherapist and syndicated columnist Barton Goldsmith says he often advocates virtual monitoring in the aftermath of an affair. Even if a spouse never exercises the option of checking up, having it makes him or her feel more secure. "It's like a digital leash."

And that can be a powerful deterrent, says Frank, whose wife of 37 years learned of his fondness for hookers last February, after he forgot to close an e-mail exchange with an escort. "He had set up a Gmail account I had no idea he had," Carol, his wife, told me. Frank tried to convince her that the e-mails were just spam, even after she pointed out that the exchange included his cell number and photos of him.

Frank agreed to marriage counseling and enrolled in a 12-step program for sexual addiction. Carol now tracks his phone and regularly checks messages on both his phone and his computer. Still, she told me sadly, "I don't think that I'm ever going to get the whole story. I believe he thinks that if I know everything, the marriage will come to an end."

For his part, Frank—who comes across as a gruff, traditional sort of guy, uneasy sharing his feelings even with his wife—calls Carol's discovery of his betrayal "excruciating," but he mostly seems angry at the oversexed culture that he feels landed him in this mess. He grumbles about how "the ease and the accessibility and the anonymity of the Internet" made it "entirely too easy" for him to feed his addiction.

Frank has clearly absorbed some of the language and lessons of therapy. "As well as it is a learned behavior to act out, it is a learned behavior not to," he told me. He doesn't much like his wife's having total access to his phone, but he claims that his sole concern is for the privacy of others in his 12-step group, who text one another for support. Frank himself clearly feels the tug of his digital leash. "Now that she checks my phone and computer, I have a deterrent."

Even as he calls virtual surveillance "a powerful tool," though, Frank also declares it a limited one. No matter how clever the technology becomes, there will always be workarounds. For someone looking to stray, "absolutely nothing is going to stop it," says Frank, emphatically. "Nothing."

## Critical Thinking

1. Have you ever spied on the cell phone or Internet activities of a romantic partner or loved one? How did you do it and why? What did you learn and how did it make you feel?
2. How has technology and virtual surveillance changed the nature of intimate relationships and cheating? What are ethical, legal, and emotional issues surrounding spying on partners which need to be considered?
3. How can technological surveillance and our digital trail be used to help restore trust between partners who have experienced infidelity?

## Internet References

**American Association for Marriage and Family Therapy: Infidelity**
www.aamft.org/imis15/content/Consumer_Updates/Infidelity.aspx
**Beyond Affairs Network**
http://beyondaffairs.com/
**Dear Peggy: Extramarital Affairs Resource Center**
http://www.dearpeggy.com/

**Michelle Cottle** is a senior writer for National Journal.

# Article 12

Stephen Marche

## Is Facebook Making Us Lonely?

Prepared by: Kurt Finsterbusch, *University of Maryland, College Park*

Social media—from Facebook to Twitter—have made us more densely networked than ever. Yet for all this connectivity, new research suggests that we have never been lonelier (or more narcissistic)—and that this loneliness is making us mentally and physically ill. A report on what the epidemic of loneliness is doing to our souls and our society.

## Learning Outcomes

*After reading this article, you will be able to:*
• Know the trends in loneliness over the past several decades.
• Understand the role of Facebook in present-day loneliness.
• Understand the effects of loneliness on the mental and physical health of individuals and on society.

Yvette Vickers, a former *Playboy* playmate and B-movie star, best known for her role in *Attack of the 50 Foot Woman*, would have been 83 last August, but nobody knows exactly how old she was when she died. According to the Los Angeles coroner's report, she lay dead for the better part of a year before a neighbor and fellow actress, a woman named Susan Savage, noticed cobwebs and yellowing letters in her mailbox, reached through a broken window to unlock the door, and pushed her way through the piles of junk mail and mounds of clothing that barricaded the house. Upstairs, she found Vickers's body, mummified, near a heater that was still running. Her computer was on too, its glow permeating the empty space.

The *Los Angeles Times* posted a story headlined "Mummified Body of Former Playboy Playmate Yvette Vickers Found in Her Benedict Canyon Home," which quickly went viral. Within two weeks, by Technorati's count, Vickers's lonesome death was already the subject of 16,057 Facebook posts and 881 tweets. She had long been a horror-movie icon, a symbol of Hollywood's capacity to exploit our most basic fears in the silliest ways; now she was an icon of a new and different kind of horror: our growing fear of loneliness. Certainly, she received much more attention in death than she did in the final years of her life. With no children, no religious group, and no immediate social circle of any kind, she had begun, as an elderly woman, to look elsewhere for companionship. Savage later told *Los Angeles* magazine that she had searched Vickers's phone bills for clues about the life that led to such an end. In the months before her grotesque death, Vickers had made calls not to friends or family but to distant fans who had found her through fan conventions and Internet sites.

Vickers's web of connections had grown broader but shallower, as has happened for many of us. We are living in an isolation that would have been unimaginable to our ancestors, and yet we have never been more accessible. Over the past three decades, technology has delivered to us a world in which we need not be out of contact for a fraction of a moment. In 2010, at a cost of $300 million, 800 miles of fiber-optic cable was laid between the Chicago Mercantile Exchange and the New York Stock Exchange to shave three milliseconds off trading times. Yet within this world of instant and absolute communication, unbounded by limits of time or space, we suffer from unprecedented alienation. We have never been more detached from one another, or lonelier. In a world consumed by ever more novel modes of socializing, we have less and less actual society. We live in an accelerating contradiction: the more connected we become, the lonelier we are. We were promised a global village; instead we inhabit the drab cul-de-sacs and endless freeways of a vast suburb of information.

At the forefront of all this unexpectedly lonely interactivity is Facebook, with 845 million users and $3.7 billion in revenue last year. The company hopes to raise $5 billion in an initial public offering later this spring, which will make it by far the largest Internet IPO in history. Some recent estimates put the company's potential value at $100 billion, which would make it larger than the global coffee industry—one addiction preparing to surpass the other. Facebook's scale and reach are hard to comprehend: last summer, Facebook became, by some counts, the first website to receive one trillion page views in a month. In the last three months of 2011, users generated an average of 2.7 billion "likes" and comments every day. On whatever scale you care to judge Facebook—as a company, as a culture, and as a country—it is vast beyond imagination.

Despite its immense popularity, or more likely because of it, Facebook has, from the beginning, been under something of a cloud of suspicion. The depiction of Mark Zuckerberg, in *The Social Network*, as a bastard with symptoms of Asperger's syndrome, was nonsense. But it felt true. It felt true to Facebook, if not to Zuckerberg. The film's most indelible scene, the one that may well have earned it an Oscar, was the final, silent shot of an anomic Zuckerberg sending out a friend request to his ex-girlfriend, then waiting and clicking and waiting and clicking—a moment of superconnected loneliness preserved in amber. We have all been in that scene: transfixed by the glare of a screen, hungering for response.

When you sign up for Google + and set up your Friends circle, the program specifies that you should include only "your real friends, the ones you feel comfortable sharing private details with." That one little phrase, *Your real friends*—so quaint, so charmingly mothering—perfectly encapsulates the anxieties that social media have produced: the fears that Facebook is interfering with our real friendships, distancing us from each other, making us lonelier; and that social networking might be spreading the very isolation it seemed designed to conquer.

Facebook arrived in the middle of a dramatic increase in the quantity and intensity of human loneliness, a rise that initially made the site's promise of greater connection seem deeply attractive. Americans are more solitary than ever before. In 1950, less than 10 percent of American households contained only one person. By 2010, nearly 27 percent of households had just one person. Solitary living does not guarantee a life of unhappiness, of course. In his recent book about the trend toward living alone, Eric Klinenberg, a sociologist at NYU, writes: "Reams of published research show that it's the quality, not the quantity of social interaction, that best predicts loneliness." True. But before we begin the fantasies of happily eccentric singledom, of divorcées dropping by their knitting circles after work for glasses of Drew Barrymore pinot grigio, or recent college graduates with perfectly articulated, Steampunk-themed, 300-square-foot apartments organizing croquet matches with their book clubs, we should recognize that it is not just isolation that is rising sharply. It's loneliness, too. And loneliness makes us miserable.

We know intuitively that loneliness and being alone are not the same thing. Solitude can be lovely. Crowded parties can be agony. We also know, thanks to a growing body of research on the topic, that loneliness is not a matter of external conditions; it is a psychological state. A 2005 analysis of data from a longitudinal study of Dutch twins showed that the tendency toward loneliness has roughly the same genetic component as other psychological problems such as neuroticism or anxiety.

Still, loneliness is slippery, a difficult state to define or diagnose. The best tool yet developed for measuring the condition is the UCLA Loneliness Scale, a series of 20 questions that all begin with this formulation: "How often do you feel . . . ?" As in: "How often do you feel that you are 'in tune' with the people around you?" And. "How often do you feel that you lack companionship?" Measuring the condition in these terms, various studies have shown loneliness rising drastically over a very short period of recent history. A 2010 AARP survey found that 35 percent of adults older than 45 were chronically lonely, as opposed to 20 percent of a similar group only a decade earlier. According to a major study by a leading scholar of the subject, roughly 20 percent of Americans—about 60 million people—are unhappy with their lives because of loneliness. Across the Western world, physicians and nurses have begun to speak openly of an epidemic of loneliness.

The new studies on loneliness are beginning to yield some surprising preliminary findings about its mechanisms. Almost every factor that one might assume affects loneliness does so only some of the time, and only under certain circumstances. People who are married are less lonely than single people, one journal article suggests, but only if their spouses are confidants. If one's spouse is not a confidant, marriage may not decrease loneliness. A belief in God might help, or it might not, as a 1990 German study comparing levels of religious feeling and levels of loneliness discovered. Active believers who saw God as abstract and helpful rather than as a wrathful, immediate presence were less lonely. "The mere belief in God," the researchers concluded, "was relatively independent of loneliness."

But it is clear that social interaction matters. Loneliness and being alone are not the same thing, but both are on the rise. We meet fewer people. We gather less. And when we gather, our bonds are less meaningful and less easy. The decrease in confidants—that is, in quality social connections—has been dramatic over the past 25 years. In one survey, the mean size of networks of personal confidants decreased from 2.94 people in 1985 to 2.08 in 2004. Similarly, in 1985, only 10 percent of Americans said they had no one with whom to discuss important matters, and 15 percent said they had only one such good friend. By 2004, 25 percent had nobody to talk to and 20 percent had only one confidant.

In the face of this social disintegration, we have essentially hired an army of replacement confidants, an entire class of professional carers. As Ronald Dworkin pointed out in a 2010 paper for the Hoover Institution, in the late 40s, the United States was home to 2,500 clinical psychologists, 30,000 social workers, and fewer than 500 marriage and family therapists. As of 2010, the country had 77,000 clinical psychologists, 192,000 clinical social workers, 400,000 nonclinical social workers, 50,000 marriage and family therapists, 105,000 mental-health counselors, 220,000 substance-abuse counselors, 17,000 nurse psychotherapists, and 30,000 life coaches. The majority of patients in therapy do not warrant a psychiatric diagnosis. This raft of psychic servants is helping us through what used to be called regular problems. We have outsourced the work of everyday caring.

We need professional careers more and more, because the threat of societal breakdown, once principally a matter of nostalgic lament, has morphed into an issue of public health. Being lonely is extremely bad for your health. If you're lonely, you're more likely to be put in a geriatric home at an earlier age than a similar person who isn't lonely. You're less likely to exercise. You're more likely to be obese. You're less likely to survive a serious operation and more likely to have hormonal imbalances. You are at greater risk of inflammation. Your memory may be worse. You are more likely to be depressed, to sleep badly, and to suffer dementia and general cognitive decline. Loneliness may not have killed Yvette Vickers, but it has been linked to a greater probability of having the kind of heart condition that did kill her.

And yet, despite its deleterious effect on health, loneliness is one of the first things ordinary Americans spend their money achieving. With money, you flee the cramped city to a house in the suburbs or, if you can afford it, a McMansion in the exurbs, inevitably spending more time in your car. Loneliness is at the American core, a by-product of a long-standing national appetite for independence: The Pilgrims who left Europe willingly abandoned the bonds and strictures of a society that could not accept their right to be different. They did not seek out loneliness, but they accepted it as the price of their autonomy. The cowboys who set off to explore a seemingly endless frontier likewise traded away personal ties in favor of pride and selfrespect. The ultimate American icon is the astronaut: Who is more heroic, or more alone? The price of self-determination and self-reliance has often been loneliness. But Americans have always been willing to pay that price.

Today, the one common feature in American secular culture is its celebration of the self that breaks away from the constrictions of the family and the state, and, in its greatest expressions, from all limits entirely. The great American poem is Whitman's "Song of Myself." The great American essay is Emerson's "Self-Reliance." The great American novel is Melville's *Moby-Dick*, the tale of a man on a quest so lonely that it is incomprehensible to those around him. American culture, high and low, is about self-expression and personal authenticity. Franklin Delano Roosevelt called individualism "the great watchword of American life."

Self-invention is only half of the American story, however. The drive for isolation has always been in tension with the impulse to cluster in communities that cling and suffocate. The Pilgrims, while fomenting spiritual rebellion, also enforced ferocious cohesion. The Salem witch trials, in hindsight, read like attempts to impose solidarity—as do the McCarthy hearings. The history of the United States is like the famous parable of the porcupines in the cold, from Schopenhauer's *Studies in Pessimism*—the ones who huddle together for warmth and shuffle away in pain, always separating and congregating.

We are now in the middle of a long period of shuffling away. In his 2000 book *Bowling Alone*, Robert D. Putnam attributed the dramatic postwar decline of social capital—the strength and value of interpersonal networks—to numerous interconnected trends in American life: suburban sprawl, television's dominance over culture, the self-absorption of the Baby Boomers, and the disintegration of the traditional family. The trends he observed continued through the prosperity of the aughts, and have only become more pronounced with time: the rate of union membership declined in 2011, again; screen time rose; the Masons and the Elks continued their slide into irrelevance. We are lonely because we want to be lonely. We have made ourselves lonely.

The question of the future is this: Is Facebook part of the separating or part of the congregating; is it a huddling-together for warmth or a shuffling-away in pain?

Well before facebook, digital technology was enabling our tendency for isolation, to an unprecedented degree. Back in the 1990s, scholars started calling the contradiction between an increased opportunity to connect and a lack of human contact the "Internet paradox." A prominent 1998 article on the phenomenon by a team of researchers at Carnegie Mellon showed that increased Internet usage was already coinciding with increased loneliness. Critics of the study pointed out that the two groups that participated in the study—high-school journalism students who were heading to university and socially active members of community-development boards—were statistically likely to become lonelier over time. Which brings us to a more fundamental question: Does the Internet make people lonely, or are lonely people more attracted to the Internet?

The question has intensified in the Facebook era. A recent study out of Australia (where close to half the population is active on Facebook), titled "Who Uses Facebook?," found a complex and sometimes confounding relationship between loneliness and social networking. Facebook users had slightly lower levels of "social loneliness"—the sense of not feeling bonded with friends—but "significantly higher levels of family loneliness"—the sense of not feeling bonded with family. It may be that Facebook encourages more contact with people outside of our household, at the expense of our family relationships—or it may be that people who have unhappy family relationships in the first place seek companionship through other means, including Facebook. The researchers also found that lonely people are inclined to spend more time on Facebook: "One of the most noteworthy findings," they wrote, "was the tendency for neurotic and lonely individuals to spend greater amounts of time on Facebook per day than nonlonely individuals." And they found that neurotics are more likely to prefer to use the wall, while extroverts tend to use chat features in addition to the wall.

Moira Burke, until recently a graduate student at the Human-Computer Institute at Carnegie Mellon, used to run a longitudinal study of 1,200 Facebook users. That study, which is ongoing, is one of the first to step outside the realm of selfselected college students and examine the effects of Facebook on a broader population, over time. She concludes that the effect of Facebook depends on what you bring to it. Just as your mother said: you get out only what you put in. If you use Facebook to communicate directly with other individuals—by using the "like" button, commenting on friends' posts, and so on—it can increase your social capital. Personalized messages, or what Burke calls "composed communication," are more satisfying than "one-click communication"—the lazy click of a like. "People who received composed communication became less lonely, while people who received one-click communication experienced no change in loneliness," Burke tells me. So, you should inform your friend in writing how charming her son looks with Harry Potter cake smeared all over his face, and how interesting her sepia-toned photograph of that tree-framed bit of skyline is, and how cool it is that she's at whatever concert she happens to be at. That's what we all want to hear. Even better than sending a private Facebook message is the semipublic conversation, the kind of back-and-forth in which you half ignore the other people who may be listening in. "People whose friends write to them semi-publicly on Facebook experience decreases in loneliness," Burke says.

On the other hand, nonpersonalized use of Facebook—scanning your friends' status updates and updating the world on your own activities via your wall, or what Burke calls "passive consumption" and "broadcasting"—correlates to feelings of disconnectedness. It's a lonely business, wandering the labyrinths of our friends' and pseudo-friends' projected identities, trying to figure out what part of ourselves we ought to project, who will listen, and what they will hear. According to Burke, passive consumption of Facebook also correlates to a marginal increase in depression. "If two women each talk to their friends the same amount of time, but one of them spends more time reading about friends on Facebook as well, the one reading tends to grow slightly more depressed," Burke says. Her conclusion suggests that my sometimes unhappy reactions to Facebook may be more universal than I had realized. When I scroll through page after page of my friends' descriptions of how accidentally eloquent their kids are, and how their husbands are endearingly bumbling, and how they're all about to eat a homecooked meal prepared with fresh local organic produce bought at the farmers' market and then go for a jog and maybe check in at the office because they're so busy getting ready to hop on a plane for a week of luxury dogsledding in Lapland, I do grow slightly more miserable. A lot of other people doing the same thing feel a little bit worse, too.

Still, Burke's research does not support the assertion that Facebook creates loneliness. The people who experience loneliness on Facebook are lonely away from Facebook, too, she points out; on Facebook, as everywhere else, correlation is not causation. The popular kids are popular, and the lonely skulkers skulk alone. Perhaps, it says something about me that I think Facebook is primarily a platform for lonely skulking. I mention to Burke the widely reported study, conducted by a Stanford graduate student, that showed how believing that others have strong social networks can lead to feelings of depression. What does Facebook communicate, if not the impression of social bounty? Everybody else looks so happy on Facebook, with so many friends, that our own social networks feel emptier than ever in comparison. Doesn't that *make* people feel lonely? "If people are reading about lives that are much better than theirs, two things can happen," Burke tells me. "They can feel worse about themselves, or they can feel motivated."

Burke will start working at Facebook as a data scientist this year.

John Cacioppo, the director of the Center for Cognitive and Social Neuroscience at the University of Chicago, is the world's leading expert on loneliness. In his landmark book, *Loneliness*, released in 2008, he revealed just how profoundly the epidemic of loneliness is affecting the basic functions of human physiology. He found higher levels of epinephrine, the stress hormone, in the morning urine of lonely people. Loneliness burrows deep: "When we drew blood from our older adults and analyzed their white cells," he writes, "we found that loneliness somehow penetrated the deepest recesses of the cell to alter the way genes were being expressed." Loneliness affects not only the brain, then, but the basic process of DNA transcription. When you are lonely, your whole body is lonely.

To Cacioppo, Internet communication allows only ersatz intimacy. "Forming connections with pets or online friends or even God is a noble attempt by an obligatorily gregarious creature to satisfy a compelling need," he writes. "But surrogates can never make up completely for the absence of the real thing." The "real thing" being actual people, in the flesh. When I speak to Cacioppo, he is refreshingly clear on what he sees as Facebook's effect on society. Yes, he allows, some research has suggested that the greater the number of Facebook friends a person has, the less lonely she is. But he argues that the impression this creates can be misleading. "For the most part," he says, "people are bringing their old friends, and feelings of loneliness or connectedness, to Facebook." The idea that a website could deliver a more friendly, interconnected world is bogus. The depth of one's social network outside Facebook is what determines the depth of one's social network within Facebook, not the other way around. Using social media doesn't create new social networks; it just transfers established networks from one platform to another. For the most part, Facebook doesn't destroy friendships—but it doesn't create them, either.

In one experiment, Cacioppo looked for a connection between the loneliness of subjects and the relative frequency of their interactions via Facebook, chat rooms, online games, dating sites, and face-to-face contact. The results were unequivocal. "The greater the proportion of face-to-face interactions, the less lonely you are," he says. "The greater the proportion of online interactions, the lonelier you are." Surely, I suggest to Cacioppo, this means that Facebook and the like inevitably make people lonelier. He disagrees. Facebook is merely a tool, he says, and like any tool, its effectiveness will depend on its user. "If you use Facebook to increase face-to-face contact," he says, "it increases social capital." So if social media let you organize a game of football among your friends, that's healthy. If you turn to social media instead of playing football, however, that's unhealthy.

"Facebook can be terrific, if we use it properly," Cacioppo continues. "It's like a car. You can drive it to pick up your friends. Or you can drive alone." But hasn't the car increased loneliness? If cars created the suburbs, surely they also created isolation. "That's because of how we use cars," Cacioppo replies. "How we use these technologies can lead to more integration, rather than more isolation."

The problem, then, is that we invite loneliness, even though it makes us miserable. The history of our use of technology is a history of isolation desired and achieved. When the Great Atlantic and Pacific Tea Company opened its A&P stores, giving Americans self-service access to groceries, customers stopped having relationships with their grocers. When the telephone arrived, people stopped knocking on their neighbors' doors. Social media bring this process to a much wider set of relationships. Researchers at the HP Social Computing Lab who studied the nature of people's connections on Twitter came to a depressing, if not surprising, conclusion: "Most of the links declared within Twitter were meaningless from an interaction point of view." I have to wonder: What other point of view is meaningful?

Loneliness is certainly not something that Facebook or Twitter or any of the lesser forms of social media is doing to us. We are doing it to ourselves. Casting technology as some vague, impersonal spirit of history forcing our actions is a weak excuse. We make decisions about how we use our machines, not the other way around. Every time I shop at my local grocery store, I am faced with a choice. I can buy my groceries from a human being or from a machine. I always, without exception, choose the machine. It's faster and more efficient, I tell myself, but the truth is that I prefer not having to wait with the other customers who are lined up alongside the conveyor belt: the hipster mom who disapproves of my high-carbon-footprint pineapple; the lady who tenses to the point of tears while she waits to see if the gods of the credit-card machine will accept or decline; the old man whose clumsy feebleness requires a patience that I don't possess. Much better to bypass the whole circus and just ring up the groceries myself.

Our omnipresent new technologies lure us toward increasingly superficial connections at exactly the same moment that they make avoiding the mess of human interaction easy. The beauty of Facebook, the source of its power, is that it enables us to be social while sparing us the embarrassing reality of society—the accidental revelations we make at parties, the awkward pauses, the farting and the spilled drinks, and the general gaucherie of face-to-face contact. Instead, we have the lovely smoothness of a seemingly social machine. Everything's so simple: status updates, pictures, your wall.

But the price of this smooth sociability is a constant compulsion to assert one's own happiness, one's own fulfillment. Not only must we contend with the social bounty of others; we must foster the appearance of our own social bounty. Being happy all the time, pretending to be happy, actually attempting to be happy—it's exhausting. Last year a team of researchers led by Iris Mauss at the University of Denver published a study looking into "the paradoxical effects of valuing happiness." Most goals in life show a direct correlation between valuation and achievement. Studies have found, for example, that students who value good grades tend to have higher grades than those who don't value them. Happiness is an exception. The study came to a disturbing conclusion:

Valuing happiness is not necessarily linked to greater happiness. In fact, under certain conditions, the opposite is true. Under conditions of low (but not high) life stress, the more people valued happiness, the lower were their hedonic balance, psychological well-being, and life satisfaction, and the higher their depression symptoms.

The more you try to be happy, the less happy you are. Sophocles made roughly the same point.

Facebook, of course, puts the pursuit of happiness front and center in our digital life. Its capacity to redefine our very concepts of identity and personal fulfillment is much more worrisome than the data mining and privacy practices that have aroused anxieties about the company. Two of the most compelling critics of Facebook—neither of them a Luddite— concentrate on exactly this point. Jaron Lanier, the author of *You Are Not a Gadget*, was one of the inventors of virtualreality technology. His view of where social media are taking us reads like dystopian science fiction: "I fear that we are beginning to design ourselves to suit digital models of us, and I worry about a leaching of empathy and humanity in that process." Lanier argues that Facebook imprisons us in the business of self-presenting, and this, to his mind, is the site's crucial and fatally unacceptable downside.

Sherry Turkle, a professor of computer culture at MIT who in 1995 published the digital-positive analysis *Life on the Screen*, is much more skeptical about the effects of online society in her 2011 book, *Alone Together*: "These days, insecure in our relationships and anxious about intimacy, we look to technology for ways to be in relationships and protect ourselves from them at the same time." The problem with digital intimacy is that it is ultimately incomplete: "The ties we form through the Internet are not, in the end, the ties that bind. But they are the ties that preoccupy," she writes. "We don't want to intrude on each other, so instead we constantly intrude on each other, but not in 'real time.'"

Lanier and Turkle are right, at least in their diagnoses. Selfpresentation on Facebook is continuous, intensely mediated, and possessed of a phony nonchalance that eliminates even the potential for spontaneity. (Look how casually I threw up these three photos from the party at which I took 300 photos!) Curating the exhibition of the self has become a 24/7 occupation. Perhaps not surprisingly, then, the Australian study "Who Uses Facebook?" found a significant correlation between Facebook use and narcissism: "Facebook users have higher levels of total narcissism, exhibitionism, and leadership than Facebook nonusers," the study's authors wrote. "In fact, it could be argued that Facebook specifically gratifies the narcissistic individual's need to engage in self-promoting and superficial behavior."

Rising narcissism isn't so much a trend as the trend behind all other trends. In preparation for the 2013 edition of its diagnostic manual, the psychiatric profession is currently struggling to update its definition of narcissistic personality disorder. Still, generally speaking, practitioners agree that narcissism manifests in patterns of fantastic grandiosity, craving for attention, and lack of empathy. In a 2008 survey, 35,000 American respondents were asked if they had ever had certain symptoms of narcissistic personality disorder. Among people older than 65, 3 percent reported symptoms. Among people in their 20s, the proportion was nearly 10 percent. Across all age groups, one in 16 Americans has experienced some symptoms of NPD. And loneliness and narcissism are intimately connected: a longitudinal study of Swedish women demonstrated a strong link between levels of narcissism in youth and levels of loneliness in old age. The connection is fundamental. Narcissism is the flip side of loneliness, and either condition is a fighting retreat from the messy reality of other people.

A considerable part of Facebook's appeal stems from its miraculous fusion of distance with intimacy, or the illusion of distance with the illusion of intimacy. Our online communities become engines of self-image, and self-image becomes the engine of community. The real danger with Facebook is not that it allows us to isolate ourselves, but that by mixing our appetite for isolation with our vanity, it threatens to alter the very nature of solitude. The new isolation is not of the kind that Americans once idealized, the lonesomeness of the proudly nonconformist, independent-minded, solitary stoic, or that of the astronaut who blasts into new worlds. Facebook's isolation is a grind. What's truly staggering about Facebook usage is not its volume—750 million photographs uploaded over a single weekend—but the constancy of the performance it demands. More than half its users—and one of every 13 people on Earth is a Facebook user—log on every day. Among 18 to 34-yearolds, nearly half check Facebook minutes after waking up, and 28 percent do so before getting out of bed. The relentlessness is what is so new, so potentially transformative. Facebook never takes a break. We never take a break. Human beings have always created elaborate acts of self-presentation. But not all the time, not every morning, before we even pour a cup of coffee. Yvette Vickers's computer was on when she died.

Nostalgia for the good old days of disconnection would not just be pointless, it would be hypocritical and ungrateful. But the very magic of the new machines, the efficiency and elegance with which they serve us, obscures what isn't being served: everything that matters. What Facebook has revealed about human nature—and this is not a minor revelation—is that a connection is not the same thing as a bond, and that instant and total connection is no salvation, no ticket to a happier, better world or a more liberated version of humanity. Solitude used to be good for self-reflection and self- reinvention. But now we are left thinking about who we are all the time, without ever really thinking about who we are. Facebook denies us a pleasure whose profundity we had underestimated: the chance to forget about ourselves for a while, the chance to disconnect.

## Critical Thinking

1. What are the advantages of social media for mental health?
2. What are the tradeoffs for time using social media?
3. What in your opinion are the best ways to use social media?

## Create Central

www.mhhe.com/createcentral

## Internet References

**Global X Social Media Index ETF**
http://www.globalxfunds.com/SOCL
**Social Science Information Gateway**
http://sosig.esrc.bris.ac.uk
**Sociology Web Resources**
http://www.mhhe.com/socscience/sociology/resources/index.htm
**Sociology—Study Sociology Online**
http://edu.learnsoc.org
**Sociosite**
http://www.topsite.com/goto/sociosite.net
**Socioweb**
http://www.topsite.com/goto/socioweb.com
**The American Studies Web**
http://lamp.georgetown.edu/asw

# Article 13

## Are Women More at Risk for Crimes Using Digital Technology?

**Selected, Edited, and with Issue Framing Material by:**
Elizabeth Schroeder, EdD, MSW, *Elizabeth Schroeder Consulting*

**YES: Danielle Keats Citron**, from "Law's Expressive Value in Combating Cyber Gender Harassment," *Michigan Law Review* (vol. 108, no. 3, 2009)

**NO: Rebecca Eckler**, from "Finding Out What Men Are Up To: Some Women Pride Themselves on Their Cyber-Sleuth Skills," *Macleans* (September 28, 2009)

## Learning Outcomes

*As you read the issue, focus on the following points:*
• Does online anonymity increase abuse and harassment? Why?
• Is the preservation of anonymity for the sake of the masses worth the cost of abuse to the few?

### ISSUE SUMMARY

**YES:** Professor of law at University of Maryland Law School, Danielle Keats Citron argues that women face higher rates of gender-based cyber harassment and it creates a gender divide online where women are disenfranchised from full participation.

**NO:** Rebecca Eckler asserts that women are equal opportunity offenders in the realm of digital crime and that women have used online tactics to harass men in increasingly greater numbers.

## Where Do You Stand?

The online universe of the Internet along with other computer-assisted digital technologies has, for many, opened a virtual "wild west" of criminal opportunities. The relative anonymity of digital interactions in digital and virtual environments creates a fertile environment for abuse and harassment.

While law enforcement agencies report increased incidences of digital stalking and other forms of cyber harassment, research suggests that cyber crime does not divide neatly along gender lines.

In the YES and NO selections, two different perspectives on the gendered patterns of cyber-based behavior are presented. Citron examines the scope of cyber harassment arguing that the prevalence of gender-based online abuse inhibits women's potential participation in digital environments. Eckler presents a counter-narrative in which women have embraced technology as a way to engage in male-focused harassment and stalking behavior.

In "Law's Expressive Value in Combating Cyber Gender Harassment," Citron examines how the bulk of cyber gender harassment is focused on women. This online targeting of women, Citron posits, inhibits women from free and full participation in the Internet world. According to Citron, while cyber gender harassment "encompasses various behaviors," three core features characterize cyber gender harassment and make it a gendered form of abuse that is primarily experienced by women: "(1) its victims are female, (2) the harassment is aimed at particular women, and (3) the abuse invokes the targeted individual's gender in sexually threatening and degrading ways" (p. 378).

In "Finding Out What Men Are Up To: Some Women Pride Themselves on Their Cyber-Sleuth Skills," Eckler examines how women appropriate technology to flip the power narrative in order to cyber-stalk men. The anonymity of new technology and the relative ease of access the technology provides afford opportunities for anyone with the inclination to engage in invasive online activities. Women's online activities allow them to furtively spy on current and former relationships using purloined passwords. Other technological advances allow both men and women to engage in mischief that ranges from prank calls to fake text messages.

# YES

Danielle Keats Citron

## Law's Expressive Value in Combating Cyber Gender Harassment

## Introduction

The harassment of women online is a pernicious and widespread problem.[1] It can be severe, involving threats of sexual violence, doctored photographs of women being suffocated, postings of women's home addresses alongside the suggestion that they should be raped, and technological attacks that shut down feminist blogs and websites.[2] Cyber harassment is a uniquely gendered phenomenon—the majority of targeted individuals are women,[3] and the abuse of female victims invokes gender in threatening and demeaning terms.[4]

Such harassment has a profound effect on targeted women. It discourages them from writing and earning a living online.[5] It interferes with their professional lives. It raises their vulnerability to offline sexual violence. It brands them as incompetent workers and inferior sexual objects. The harassment causes considerable emotional distress.[6] Some women have committed suicide.[7]

To avoid future abuse, women assume gender-neutral pseudonyms or go offline, even if it costs them work opportunities.[8] Others curtail their online activities.[9] For the "digital native"[10] generation, forsaking aspects of the internet means missing innumerable social connections. Although online harassment inflicts the most direct costs on targeted individuals, it harms society as well by entrenching male hierarchy online.

But no matter how serious the harm that cyber gender harassment inflicts, the public tends to trivialize it. Commentators dismiss it as harmless locker-room talk, characterizing perpetrators as juvenile pranksters and targeted individuals as overly sensitive complainers.[11] Others consider cyber gender harassment as an inconvenience that victims can ignore or defeat with counterspeech.[12] Some argue that women who benefit from the internet have assumed the risks of its Wild West norms.[13] Although the arguments differ, their message is the same—women need to tolerate these cyber "pranks" or opt out of life online. This message has the unfortunate consequence of discouraging women from reporting cyber gender harassment and preventing law enforcement from pursuing cyber-harassment complaints.[14]

The trivialization of harms suffered by women is nothing new.[15] Society ignored or downplayed domestic violence's brutality for over 200 years.[16] No term even existed to describe sexual harassment in the workplace until the 1970s, despite the pervasiveness of the practice.[17] In light of this history, the current refusal to take seriously the cyber harassment of women is as unsurprising as it is disappointing.

Due to the internet's relative youth, this is an auspicious time to combat the trivialization of cyber gender harassment before it becomes too entrenched. If it continues unabated, cyber harassment could very well be the central front of struggles against sexual harassment in the coming decades given our increasing dependence on the net. More people make friends, apply for jobs, and discuss policy online than ever before, shifting their social and professional interactions to the net and with it the risk of sexual harassment.[18] As the market leans toward more realistic sensory experiences in virtual worlds and as these sites become more popular, cyber gender harassment may more closely approximate conventional notions of sexual violence. For instance, Second Life users' avatars have reportedly been forced to perform sexually explicit acts after being given malicious code.[19] These developments, and others like them, would further threaten gender equality in our digital age.

Wrestling with the marginalization of cyber sexual harassment is a crucial step in combating its gender-specific harms. Law has a crucial role to play in this effort. Law serves different functions here. It can deter online harassment's harms by raising the costs of noncompliance beyond its expected benefits. Law can also remedy such harm with monetary damages, injunctions, and criminal convictions. My article *Cyber Civil Rights* explored antidiscrimination, criminal, and tort law's role in preventing, punishing, and redressing cyber harassment.[20] In this piece, I explore law's other crucial role: educating the public about women's unique suffering in the wake of cyber harassment and potentially changing societal responses to it. Because law is expressive, it constructs our understanding of harms that are not trivial. The application of a cyber civil rights legal agenda would reveal online harassment for what it truly is—harmful gender discrimination. It would recognize the distinct suffering of women, suffering that men ordinarily do not experience or appreciate as harmful.

Once cyber harassment is understood as gender discrimination and not as a triviality to be ignored, women are more likely to complain about it rather than suffer in silence. Law enforcement could pursue cyber harassment complaints rather than just counseling women to get off their computers and seek help only if their harassers confront them offline. As a result, some perpetrators might curtail their bigoted assaults. Viewing cyber harassment as gender discrimination could become part of our cultural understandings and practices. As with workplace sexual harassment and domestic violence, changing the norms of acceptable conduct may be the most potent force in regulating behavior in cyberspace. An antidiscrimination message is crucial to harness law's moral and coercive power.[21]

. . . [This article] explores the gendered nature of online harassment.[22] It first defines the phenomenon of cyber gender harassment. It then explores the distinct harms that such online abuse inflicts on targeted women and society.

## Cyber Harassment Through a Feminist Lens

Online harassment is a problem that has a profound impact on women's lives but is little understood. Just as society ignored sexual harassment until scholars and courts recognized it as sex discrimination, a definition of cyber gender harassment is crucial to understanding and tackling its distinct harms to women. No working definition has been constructed, perhaps because cyber gender harassment has been relegated to the shadows of our thinking. This [article] fills that void and provides an account of the gendered nature of online harassment, highlighting its distinct effect on targeted women and society.

### Understanding Cyber Gender Harassment

Although cyber gender harassment encompasses various behaviors, it has a set of core features: (1) its victims are female, (2) the harassment is aimed at particular women, and (3) the abuse invokes the targeted individual's gender in sexually threatening and degrading ways.[23]

While cyber attackers target men, more often their victims are female.[24] The nonprofit organization *Working to Halt Online Abuse* has compiled statistics about individuals harassed online. In 2007, 61% of the individuals reporting online abuse identified themselves as women while 21% identified themselves as men.[25] In 2006, 70% of online harassment complainants identified themselves as women.[26] Overall, from 2000 to 2008, 72.5% of the 2,519 individuals reporting cyber harassment were female and 22% were male.[27] Forty-four percent of the victims were between the ages of 18 and 40,[28] and 49% reportedly had no relationship with their attackers.[29] Similarly, the Stalking Resource Center, a branch of the National Center for Victims of Crimes, reports that approximately 60% of online harassment cases involve male attackers and female targets.[30]

Academic research supports this statistical evidence. The University of Maryland's Electrical Engineering and Computer Department recently studied the threat of attacks associated with the chat medium Internet Relay Chat.[31] Researchers found that users with female names received on average 100 "malicious private messages," which the study defined as "sexually explicit or threatening language," whereas users with male names received only 3.7.[32] According to the study, the "experiment show[ed] that the user gender has a significant impact on one component of the attack thread (i.e., the number of malicious private messages received for which the female bots received more than 25 times more private messages than the male bots . . . )" and "no significant impact on the other components on the attack threat[,]" such as attempts to send files to users and links sent to users.[33] The study explained that attacks came from human chat users who selected their targets, not automated scripts programmed to send attacks to everyone on the channel, and that "male human users specifically targeted female users. . . ."[34]

### Distinct Impact on Targeted Women

Cyber gender harassment invokes women's sexuality and gender in ways that interfere with their agency, livelihood, identity, dignity, and well-being. The subsequent injuries are unique to women because men do not typically experience sexual threats and demeaning comments suggesting their inferiority due to their gender.[35]

First, cyber gender harassment undermines women's agency over their own lives. Online threats of sexual violence "literally, albeit not physically, penetrate[ ]" women's bodies.[36] They expose women's sexuality, conveying the message that attackers control targeted women's physical safety.[37] The rape threats are particularly frightening to women as one in every six women has experienced an attempted or completed rape as a child or adult.[38] Such threats discourage women from pursuing their interests in cyberspace. For instance, women shut down their blogs and websites.[39] They retreat from chat rooms. A 2005 Pew Internet and American Life Project study attributed an 11 percent decline in women's use of chat rooms to menacing comments.[40] Women limit their websites' connectivity to a wider, and potentially threatening, audience by password protecting their sites.[41] They close comments on blog posts, foreclosing positive conversations along with abusive ones.[42] The harassment scares women away from online discourse "by making an example of those females who [do] participate" with "very real threats of rape."[43]

Cyber harassment also affects women's agency in their offline lives. For instance, a woman stopped going to the gym because her anonymous harassers encouraged her law school classmates to take cell phone pictures of her and post them online.[44] After posters warned a female blogger that she needed to watch her back because they knew where she lived, the woman "g[o]t an alarm" and "started [carrying a] bat to and from the car when [she] went to work at night."[45] Kathy Sierra's cyber harassment experience left her fearful to attend speaking engagements and even to leave her yard: "I will never feel the same. I will never *be* the same."[46] Another woman explained: cyber threats had a "major impact on me both online and offline—I removed my name from my Website and my Internet registration. I rented a mailbox to handle all snail mail related to the Website, and I changed my business and home phone numbers . . ."[47] As Ms. Sierra noted, "[h]ow many rape/fantasy threats does it take to make women want to lay low? Not many. . . ."[48]

Online harassment replicates in cyberspace the autonomy erosion that female employees have long experienced in real space. Workplace sexual harassment exposes and exploits a female employees' sexuality. Verbal sexual abuse and displays of pornography make female employees "feel physically vulnerable" to attack.[49] Female employees leave their jobs or seek transfers to escape hostile work environments in much the same way that women shut down income-generating sites or limit access to their blogs to avoid cyber abuse.

Second, cyber gender harassment undermines women's ability to achieve their professional goals. It may impair women's work directly, such as technological attacks designed to shutter feminist websites or postings designed to discourage employees from hiring women.[50] It may take a more indirect form of professional sabotage by discrediting women's competence in their careers.[51] Assertions that "[t]his is why women are TOO STUPID to think critically and intelligently about film; AND business for that matter" and "why don't you make yourself useful and go have a baby"[52] appear designed to generate feelings of inferiority and to discourage women from engaging in professional activities online. Rape threats and sexually menacing comments have a similar effect. This sort of intimidation is unique to women—men are not routinely told that they belong in the kitchen or bedroom instead of earning a living online.

The abuse harms targeted individuals' careers because employers routinely rely on search engines to collect intelligence on job applicants and may discover negative postings about them. Employers may decline to interview or hire targeted women not because they believe the malicious postings but because it is simply easier to hire individuals who don't come with such baggage. Moreover, candidates with impressive online reputations are more attractive to employers than those who lack them. Indeed, an online presence is crucial to obtaining work in certain fields. Noted technology blogger Robert Scoble explains that women who don't blog are "never going to be included in the [technology] industry."[53] This parallels workplace sexual harassment's interference with women's economic opportunities.[54] Demeaning verbal abuse can be so severe that women leave their jobs,[55] just as online intimidation has pushed women out of the blogosphere.[56] It impairs women's work opportunities by making clear to them that they will be viewed and judged by traditional and subordinate female roles,[57] in much the way that cyber gender harassment does.

Third, women sustain harm to their identities *as women*. Women may feel impelled to compromise their female identity by "passing" as men to prevent discrimination.[58] . . .

Fourth, cyber harassment harms women's dignity and sense of equal worth.[59] Online assaults objectify women, reducing them to their body parts.[60] For instance, posters on the message board AutoAdmit described one targeted female student as a "dumbass bitch . . . [who] I wish to rape . . . in the ass"[61] and stated that another has "huge fake titties."[62] Harassers further humiliate women by reducing them to *diseased* body parts. For example, a poster says of one woman, "just don't FUCK her, she has herpes."[63] They make clear that women have worth only as sex objects.

Such objectification injures women by signaling that they are nothing but things to be used by men, not persons with feelings.[64] Online rape threats say to women "[y]ou claim to be a full human being, but you are much less than that. You are a mere thing . . . . [whose] autonomy can be snatched away, your feelings ignored or violated."[65] Women feel rejected and less worthy.[66] A victim explained: "someone who writes 'You're just a cunt!' is not trying to convince me of anything but my own worthlessness."[67] Martha Nussbaum considers the online objectification of women an attempt to "restor[e] the patriarchal world before the advent of sex equality, the world in which women were just tools of male purposes . . . . [and] had no right to be more than tits and cunt."[68]

Sexual harassment in the workplace similarly treats women as moral subordinates and undermines their self-respect.[69] Employers and co-workers who refer to female workers as "nice pieces of ass" or "stupid pair of boobs" cause women to see themselves as less equal and able than men.[70] As Kathryn Abrams develops in her work, sexual inquiries, jokes, and innuendos in the workplace have the effect of reminding women that they are viewed as objects of sexual derision, not colleagues worthy of respect and equal treatment.[71]

Last, cyber harassment inflicts unique harms to women's physical and emotional well-being. Posts providing women's home addresses alongside the suggestion that they have rape fantasies or should be raped have led to offline stalking and rape. Women also fear that online threats of sexual violence will be realized. Women's anxiety may be particularly acute as the posters' anonymity eliminates cues—such as the identity or location of the person who made the threat or a joking tone of voice—that might diminish concerns about the threat. Women's emotional distress often produces physical symptoms, such as anorexia nervosa, depression, and suicide. Women experience similar symptoms in the face of workplace sexual harassment.

This destructive phenomenon not only has profound consequences for individual women, but for society as well, as the next Section demonstrates. . . .

# Notes

1. Although its scope is difficult to estimate, one study suggests that approximately 40 percent of female internet users have experienced cyber harassment. Azy Barak. *Sexual Harassment on the Internet*, 23 Soc. Sci. Computer Rev. 77, 81 (2005); *see also* Francesca Philips & Gabrielle Morrissey, *Cyberstalking and Cyberpredators: A Threat to Safe Sexuality on the Internet*, 10 Convergence: Int'l J. Res. into New Media Techs. 66, 72 (2004) (estimating that one-third of female internet users have been harassed online). Any existing statistical evidence surrounding cyber gender harassment is likely to underestimate the phenomenon as women tend to underreport it due to feelings of shame and embarrassment. *See* Att'y Gen. to Vice President, Cyberstalking: A New Challenge for Law Enforcement and Industry (1999), http:// www.usdoj.gov/criminal/cybercrime/cyberstalking.htm [hereinafter Rep. on Cyberstalking]. This is unsurprising given women's underreporting of workplace sexual harassment. Louise Fitzgerald et al., *Why Didn't She Just Report Him?*, 51 J. Soc. Issues 117, 119–21 (1995).
2. Danielle Keats Citron, *Cyber Civil Rights*, 89 B.U.L. Rev. 61, 69–75 (2009).
3. L.P. Sheridan & T. Grant, *Is Cyberstalking Different?*, 13 Psychol., Crime & L. 627, 637 (2007) (citing various studies suggesting that the majority of cyber stalking victims were female and their online stalkers were less likely to be ex-partners of the victims).
4. *See* Barak, *supra* note 1, at 78–79.
5. Posting of Louisa Garib to On the Identity Trail, *Blogging White Female, Online Equality and the Law*, http://www.anonequity.org/weblog/archives/2007/08/ blogging_while_female_online_i.php (Aug. 21, 2007, 23:59 EST).
6. *See* Ellen Nakashima, *Sexual Threats Stifle Some Female Bloggers*, Wash. Post. Apr. 30, 2007, at A1.
7. *See* B.J. Lee. *When Words Kill: Suicide spurs bid to regulate the net in South Korea*, Newsweek.com, Oct. 15, 2008. http://www.newsweek.com/id/164013.
8. Nakashima, *supra* note 6; *see also, e.g.,* Posting of womensspace to Women's Space, *Blogging White Female. Hacking as Sexual Terrorism*, http://www.womensspace.org/phpBB2/2007/08/06/bloggingwhile-female-men-win-hacking-as-sexual-terrorism/ (Aug. 6. 2007) (explaining that she shut down her women's issues website due to cyber harassment that included threats of violence, technological attacks, and publication of her home address).
9. *See* Posting of Louisa Garib to On the Identity Trail, *supra* note 5.
10. A digital native is "a person for whom digital technologies already existed when they were born." and who has "grown up with digital technology such as computers, the Internet, mobile phones and MP3s." Wikipedia, Digital Native, http://en.wikipedia.org/wiki/Digital_native (last visited Aug. 29. 2009).
11. Posting of Rev. Billy Bob Gisher to Less People Less Idiots. *Silence of the hams*, http://lessidiots.blogspot.com/2007/04/silence-of-hams.html (Apr. 3, 2007, 16:19 EST) (on file with author).
12. Posting of Markos Moulitsas to Daily Kos, *Death threats and blogging*, http://www.dailykos.com/story/2007/4/12/22533/9224 (Apr. 11, 2007, 23:45 PDT).
13. Posting of Susannah Breslin to The XX Factor, *Is Blogging While Female Really So "Perilous"?*, Slate, http://www.slate.com/blogs/blogs/xxfactor/archive/2009/03/13/is-blogging-while-female-reallyso-perilous.aspx (Mar. 13, 2009. 17:03 EST) (arguing that the web is an equal-opportunity attack forum and thus urging women to "get over yourselves"); Comment of Fistandantalus to Posting of Rev. Billy Bob Gisher to Less People Less Idiots, *Silence of the hams,* http://lessidiots .blogspot.com/2007/04/silence-of-hams.html (on file with author).
14. *See, e.g.,* Paul Bocij, Cyberstalking: Harassment in the Internet Age and How to Protect Your Family 17 (2004).
15. Robin West. Caring for Justice 96 (1997).
16. *Id.*
17. Catharine A. MacKinnon, Sexual Harassment of Working Women: A Case of Sex Discrimination xi (1979).
18. *See, e.g.,* Posting of Danielle Citron to Concurring Opinions, *Zuckerberg's Law on Data Sharing, Not Puffery*, http://www.concurringopinions.com/archives/2009/07/zuckerbergs-law-on-datasharing-not-puffery.html (July 16, 2009, 12:32 EST) (explaining that as of July 2009, Facebook had 250 million members, up from 150 million in January 2009).
19. Michael Tennesen, *Avatar Acts: When the Matrix Has You, What Laws Apply to Settle Conflicts?*, Sci. Am., July 2009, at 27; *see also* Regina Lynn, *Virtual Rape Is Traumatic, but Is It A Crime?*, Wired.com Comment.—Sex Drive, May 4, 2007, http://www.wired.com/culture/lifestyle/commentary/sexdrive/2007/05/sexdrive_0504; Posting on Tech FAQ, *Second Life virtual rape,* http://www.tech-faq.com/blog/secondlife-virtual-rape.html (last visited Aug. 29. 2009) (explaining that a Belgian user of Second Life was forced to perform sexually explicit acts after being given a "voodoo doll," a piece of code that takes the form of a regular object such as a cup or pen but in fact takes control of your avatar).
20. Citron, *supra* note 2.
21. *Cf.* Kimberlé Williams Crenshaw, *Race, Reform, and Retrenchment: Transformation and Legitimation in Antidiscrimination Law,* 101 Harv. L. Rev. 1331, 1335 (1988) (describing the importance of an antidiscrimination message to combat racial subordination).

22. Brian Leiter aptly calls social networking sites that house and encourage such gender harassment "cyber–cesspools." Brian Leiter, Cleaning Cyber–Cesspools: Google and Free Speech 1 (Nov. 21, 2008) (unpublished manuscript, on file with author).

23. Online harassment is also targeted at gay men—the harassment similarly invokes targeted individuals' gender in a sexually threatening manner. For instance, anonymous posters on the high school gossip site Peoples Dirt noted that named male students were gay and threatened them with violence. A posting under a male student's name asserted "we know your [sic] g@y . . . just come out of the closet . . . and you should choke on a dick and die." Posting of Danielle Citron to Concurring Opinions, *Peoples Dirt, Now Terrorizing High Schoolers Everywhere,* http://www.concurringopinions.com/archives/2009/05/peoplesdirt-now-terrorizing-high-schoolers-everywhere.html (May 18, 2009, 15:05 EST) (alteration in original). Anonymous posters on the Encyclopedia Dramatica site direct sexually threatening taunts to named gay men. Posters accused a man of having an incestuous relationship with his brother and a bestial relationship with his dog. Encyclopedia Dramatica, Chris Cocker, http://www.encyclopediadramatica.com/Chris_Crocker (last visited Aug. 29, 2009).

24. Sheridan & Grant, *supra* note 3, at 67. A 2003 study of 169 individuals who reportedly experienced cyber harassment found that 62.5 percent of the respondents were female. Paul Bocij, *Victims of Cyberstalking: An Exploratory Study of Harassment Perpetrated via the Internet,* FIRST MONDAY, Oct. 6, 2003, http://firstmonday.org/htbin/cgiwrap/bin/ojs/index.php/fm/articlc/view/1086/1006. The harassment consisted of threatening or abusive email messages, threats or abusive comments via IM messages, threats or abusive comments in chat rooms, the posting of false rumors in chat rooms, impersonation of individuals in e-mail messages to friends, and encouragement of others to harass or threaten the respondent. *Id.*

25. WORKING TO HALT ONLINE ABUSE, 2007 CYBERSTALKING STATISTICS 1, http://www.haltabuse.org/resources/stats/2007Statistics.pdf. Eighteen percent of those reporting cyber harassment did not report their gender. *Id.*

26. WORKING TO HALT ONLINE ABUSE, 2006 CYBERSTALKING STATISTICS 1. http://www.haltabuse.org/resources/stats/2006Statistics.pdf.

27. WORKING TO HALT ONLINE ABUSE, CYBERSTALKING COMPARISON STATISTICS 2000–2008 1. http://www.haltabuse.org/resources/stats/Cumulative2000–2008.pdf. Five and one-half percent of the reporting individuals refused to provide their gender to the organization. *Id.*

28. *Id.*

29. *Id.* at 2.

30. Christine Petrozzo & Sarah Stapp, *To catch a predator: How some cyber–agencies help victims fight back against online aggression.* DAILY ORANGE (Syracuse. N.Y.), Jan. 24. 2008. http://media.www.dailyorange.com/media/storage/paper522/news/2008/01/24/News/To.Catch.A.Predator-3165676.shtml#cp_article_tools.

31. *See* Robert Meyer & Michael Cukier, *Assessing the Attack Threat due to IRC Channels, in* PROCEEDINGS OF THE INTERNATIONAL CONFERENCE ON DEPENDABLE SYSTEMS AND NETWORKS 467 (2006), *available at* http://www.enre.umd.edu/content/rmeyer-assessing.pdf. Chat rooms using IRC protocol permit live conversations via the internet, containing as many as several thousand people, whereas other chat programs such as MSN messenger and Yahoo focus on two-person conversations. *Id.* Users can join existing discussions or create new ones. BOCIJ. *supra* note 14, at 126. "Estimates of the number of publicly accessible channels available [on IRC] range from 100,000 to more than 580,000." *Id.* (citation omitted).

32. Meyer & Cukier, *supra* note 31, at 469. The researchers used simulated users with female names Cathy, Elyse, Irene, Melissa, and Stephanie, and simulated users with male names Andy, Brad, Dan, Gregg, and Kevin. *Id.* at 469–70.

33. *Id.* at 470.

34. *Id.* at 471.

35 This statement is particularly true for heterosexual men who are less likely to face sexual intimidation by women or homosexual men, but less true for gay men who confront sexual taunts when others perceive them as effeminate. *See* Jerry Finn, *A Survey of Online Harassment at a University Campus,* 19 J. INTERPERSONAL VIOLENCE 468 (2004).

36. WEST, *supra* note 15, at 102–03 (discussing real space rape) (emphasis omitted).

37. *See* Martha Nussbaum, *Objectification and Ressentiment* 18–20 (Nov. 21–22, 2008) (unpublished manuscript, on file with author).

38. LENORA M. LAPIDUS ET AL., THE RIGHTS OF WOMEN: THE AUTHORITATIVE ACLU GUIDE TO WOMEN'S RIGHTS 180 (4th ed. 2009) (describing incidence of rape in United States). To the extent that we see men experience threats of sexual violence online, the victims are gay men. *See* Posting of Danielle Citron to Concurring Opinions, *supra* note 23.

39. Sheridan & Grant, *supra* note 3, at 637.

40. *See Female Bloggers Face Harassment,* WOMEN IN HIGHER EDUC., June 2007, at 5.

41. Nakashima, *supra* note 6 (explaining that women attacked online by anonymous posters suspend their blogging, turn to private forums, or use gender-neutral pseudonyms).

42. *See* Comment of Alyssa Royse to Posting of Alyssa Royse to BlogHer, *supra* note 71.

43. Comment of C.L. to Posting of Danielle Citron to Concurring Opinions.*Cyber Harassment: Yes, It is a Woman's Thing,* http://www.concurringopinions .com/archives/2009/03/cyber_harassmen.html (March 12, 2009, 22:37 EST).

44. *See* Ellen Nakashima, *Harsh Words Die Hard on the Web; Law Students Feel Lasting Effects of Anonymous Attacks,* WASH. POST, Mar. 7, 2007, at A1.

45. Tracy L.M. Kennedy, *An Exploratory Study of Feminist Experiences In Cyberspace,* 3 CYBERPSYCHOL., & BEHAV. 707, 716 (2000).

46. Dahlia Lithwick, *Fear of Blogging: Why women shouldn't apologize for being afraid of threats on the Web.* SLATE, May 4, 2007. http://www.slate.com/ id/2165654 (internal quotation marks omitted).

47. Kennedy, *supra* note 99, at 716.

48. Valenti, *supra* note 35 (internal quotation marks omitted).

49. Kathryn Abrams, *Gender Discrimination and the Transformation of Workplace Norms,* 42 VAND. L. REV. 1183, 1206 (1989) [hereinafter Abrams, *Transformation*].

50. *See supra* notes 80–81 and accompanying text (describing activities of Anonymous).

51. *See, e.g.,* Posting of Alyssa Royse to BlogHer, *supra* note 38.

52. *Id.*

53. Nakashima. *supra* note 6 (internal quotation marks omitted).

54. *See* Vicki Schultz. *Reconceptualizing Sexual Harassment,* 107 YALE L.J. 1683. 1763–65 (1998) (conceptualizing hostile-work-environment harassment as a means for men to preserve dominance in favored types of work by undermining women's effectiveness on the job through demeaning comments, deliberate sabotage, and refusals to provide women support they need on the job).

55. Kathryn Abrams, *The New Jurisprudence of Sexual Harassment,* 83 CORNELL L. REV. 1169, 1207 (1998) [hereinafter Abrams, *New Jurisprudence*].

56. Posting of John Hawkins to Right Wing News, *Blogging While Female Part 2: Five Women Bloggers Talk About Gender Issues And The Blogosphere,* http://www.rightwingnews.com/mt331/2008/03/blogging_while_female_part_2_5_1.php (Mar. 18, 2008 11:30 EST) (interviewing blogger Ann Althouse).

57. Abrams, *New Jurisprudence, supra* note 109, at 1208.

58. *See* KENJI YOSHINO, COVERING: THE HIDDEN ASSAULT ON OUR CIVIL RIGHTS 22, 144 (2006) [hereinafter YOSHINO, COVERING]. Discrimination has long forced women to pass as men to gain access to professions or relationships that would otherwise have remained unavailable to them. *See* also. *e.g.,* MARJORIE GARBER, VESTED INTERESTS: CROSS–DRESSING & CULTURAL ANXIETY 67–70 (1992). Kenji Yoshino identifies films such as *Yentl* and *Boys Don't Cry* as examples of female passing. Kenji Yoshino, *Covering,* 111 YALE L.J. 769, 926 & n.880 (2002) [hereinafter Yoshino, *Covering*].

59. As Leslie Meitzer elegantly develops in her article *Spheres of Dignity: Conceptions and Functions in Constitutional Law* (on file with author), the term dignity implicates a variety of values, including dignity as equality. I aim to use the term dignity here to refer to the value harmed by conduct that demeans, devalues, and denigrates women due to their gender.

60. Nussbaum, *supra* note 91, at 5–6; *see also* WEST, *supra* note 15. at 146 (explaining that sexual harassment objectifies women, inflicting a dignitary injury).

61. First Amended Complaint at ¶ 25. Doe v. Ciolli, No. 307CV00909 CFD (D. Conn. Nov. 8. 2007) (internal quotation marks omitted).

62. *Id.* at ¶ 18 (internal quotation marks omitted).

63. *Id.* at ¶ 21 (internal quotation marks omitted).

64. Nussbaum. *supra* note 91, at 3–4.

65. *Id.* at 8 (internal quotation marks omitted).

66. Kennedy, *supra* note 99, at 717.

67. *Id.* at 715 (internal quotation marks omitted).

68. Nussbaum, *supra* note 91, at 19.

69. Abrams, Transformation, *supra* note 103, at 1208. *See generally* DEBORAH HELLMAN, WHEN IS DISCRIMINATION WRONG? (2008) (exploring when and why discrimination is morally wrong).

70. Kathryn Abrams, *Title VII and the Complex Female Subject,* 92 MICH. L. REV. 2479, 2529–30 (1994).

71. *E.g.,* Abrams, *New Jurisprudence, supra* note 109, at 1207–08.

DANIELLE KEATS CITRON is the Lois K. Macht Research Professor of Law at the University of Maryland Francis King Carey School of Law.

# NO

**Rebecca Eckler**

# Finding Out What Men Are Up To:
# Some Women Pride Themselves
# on Their Cyber-Sleuth Skills

On a recent episode of the reality show *Keeping Up with the Kardashians,* Kourtney Kardashian tells her sister Kim she has her boyfriend's old phone. "Have you gone through it?" Kim asks Kourtney excitedly. What's the point, Kourtney wants to know. "What do you mean what is the point?" Kim asks. "You want to know what your boyfriend is up to." Then, speaking directly to the camera, Kim proudly says, "I can break into any phone, can get any code, can get into any voice mail." She's not the only phone-email snooper out there. One of the main characters on the show *Entourage* just dropped a woman who listened to one of his phone messages when he was in the shower.

Ali Wise, a stunning 32-year-old New Yorker, was arrested in July on felony charges of computer trespass and eavesdropping after allegedly hacking into the voice mail of Nina Freudenberger, an interior designer and socialite. Hacking "isn't the sort of crime that normally comes to mind when you think of a pretty young publicist who attends glam parties on a nightly basis," says Remy Stern, founder of Cityfile, a gossip website that has followed the story. "It was a little more juicy because she wasn't accused of hacking into her boyfriend's voice mail; the victim was another woman . . . who may have been involved with an ex-boyfriend of hers."

Wise used software called SpoofCard to hack into the voice mail. The SpoofCard can be bought online and, according to information on the product's website, "offers the ability to change what someone sees on their caller ID display when they receive a phone call." You simply dial SpoofCard's toll-free number or local access number in your country and then enter your PIN (like a calling card). What comes up on a person's phone is a number that's not yours.

The SpoofCard is meant to be used, mostly it seems, for crank calls and for other times people want to hide their number. But, obviously, it's being misused. The Internet is rife with information about how to break into someone's voice mail using a SpoofCard. "I'll tell you how," writes one snooper. "Call up SpoofCard and when they ask you to enter the number you want to show [up] on the caller ID, you enter your boyfriend's number.

When they ask you to enter the number you want to call, you enter your boyfriend's number again, and, bingo, you'll get into his messages. This works because it tricks the cellphone to think the cell is calling into the voice message system." The deviousness doesn't end there. "Now remember," another writes, "when you get into the voice message, you must quickly change the password so you can always access the voice mail messages."

According to a friend of Wise's, when the police asked her if she had used a SpoofCard, her answer was, "Of course I used a SpoofCard." It was as if they had asked a meat lover if they ate steak.

Wise stepped down from her job at Dolce & Gabbana, and has become fodder for New York gossip rags. But to some women she's become, if not a hero, at least relatable. Movie producers have begged to option her story.

On a recent night out, five women laughed at stories of breaking into men's voice mails. "I would wait until he went into the shower," said one, "and I would manically try and figure out his password." Another admitted that for years she has broken into her boyfriend's, and ex-boyfriend's, email and voice mail accounts. "It's really not that hard. Men are stupid. If you know their Interac password, that's generally their code for all their other PDAs," she said. One woman is so skilled at figuring out passwords, she can hear someone type in the phone digits, and from the tones of the numbers, figure out the code. "I want to see if they're up to no good," she laughs.

Obviously, serial snooping isn't just for the rich and famous. The founder of Toronto-based Blue Star Investigations Inc. International, Allen Brik, has been a private detective for 15 years. He says this kind of invasion of privacy has exploded in the past five years. "It's not always easy, but it's certainly doable." It's strictly illegal, he says, and shouldn't be done, "but people want to know they can trust someone. They're not thinking with their heads about right or wrong."

Brik agrees that men "don't often change their password. They usually use their date of birth or their middle names. Women are more creative." (He hasn't changed any of his passwords in 12 years.) It's not only females who snoop, he says, but the majority are women. "I think it comes down to men cheating more."

A judge could turn Wise's case, due in court in October, into an "example" à la Paris Hilton's jail stint. "I do hope that no prison time is involved," says Stern. "A much better punishment would be to require her to have those godawful orange jumpsuits worn by American prisoners redesigned by Dolce & Gabbana. That might make it all worth it."

**REBECCA ECKLER** is a Canadian journalist and an author whose work has appeared in *Elle, Maclean's,* and *Mademoiselle.* She is also a columnist for *Post City Magazines* in Toronto.

# Technology and Education

Chalk and a chalkboard were once seen as essential for a well-equipped classroom. But those have now been replaced by smartboards and computers set-up for multi-media presentations in both primary and secondary education. Not only do new technological devices change the ways students learn and relate to educational content, they also change how teachers deliver such content and materials. Teachers now use video games, videos, interactive visual enhancements, and other high impact technology to accommodate student learning. Technology in the educational landscape has impacted the personal relationships students have with one another, their teachers, and their parents. The educational landscape has broadened to include online programs and distance learning in attempts to provide educational opportunities to those who might not be able to participate in traditional educational programs. However, could it be true that even with more people having access to expanding educational technology that the benefits are still eluding those who need it most? Further, have new technological developments standardized education by focusing too much on serving quantities of students, while ignoring quality? Technology has changed the entire system of education and we can be certain that more changes are to come in the future. The readings presented in this section cover different technological developments and explore the impact of such changes on the educational landscape.

## Learning Objectives

1. Provide examples of technological developments that have become commonplace in today's schools.
2. Critically examine the educational changes that have taken place and what changes in educational technology will take place in the future.
3. Identify the impact technology has on individual students, teachers, and the classroom environment.
4. Contemplate how to decrease the knowledge gap while keeping technological development intact.

119

# Article 14

Janet Holland and John Holland

## Implications of Shifting Technology in Education

Prepared by: Rebecca B. Evers, *Winthrop University*

### Learning Outcomes

*After reading this article, you will be able to:*
• Assess the changing trends in technology.
• Reflect on your gaps in technological knowledge and skills.
• Implement research-based technology practices.

### Instructional Gaps

While talking to an engineer volunteering to work with middle and high school students on a robotics competition, he expressed his surprise at how the students did not have a basic understanding of simple everyday concepts like clockwise and counter-clockwise. A school nurse complained how sick students came into her office and when handed a phone to call their parents, they did not know how. At a recent workshop presentation for middle and high school students they were told to e-mail the information to the group leader then to their own account. It was surprising how many did not know how to do it. How can this be happening in this day and age? Were the students not taught the knowledge and skills through authentic experiences, did they not have access to the technology, are they using different terms or formats for communications? These events cause one to wonder what the root causes might be and to think about whether they need to be addressed. If so, how, especially when considering ourselves to be in this technologically advanced era?

### Shifting Technologies

From simple observations, reading magazines, newspapers, and Internet articles, to watching the TV news we are seeing many new technologies arrive and old ones go away, so it is important to reflect on what we are gaining and losing in the shuffle. Think about the recent losses of or declines in the markets for stopwatches, calculators, compasses, print cameras, network TV, portable radios, tapes, CDs, DVDs, GPS units, big box games, rolodex organizers, maps, books, magazines, newspapers, travel agents, and greeting cards; just to name a few. Locally the large bookstores and news stands have disappeared, video stores closed, office supply store stocks dwindle, no local printing presses anymore, even the local newspaper is making deep cuts in hardcopy, while working to develop an online presence.

Radios and TVs are being challenged at every turn to keep people interested in their nearly real time media. We have a younger generation often more interested in what the Internet has to offer than the traditional entertainment options. The newer media offers a more personalized, interactive method of learning, socializing, and entertainment on a reduced or no cost basis.

The major greeting card companies are slowly reducing employees. This is happening as digital card use continues to grow with the added features of audio, video, and animation provided at a reduced or no cost basis. The selling of card stock paper for self-printed cards, again demonstrates the digital shift towards increasing user control. We are seeing traditional magazines and books going to digital formats. According to various popular press articles, more books are being sold as e-texts than as hard copy or paperback combined. Learners now have small, compact, increased access using mobile devices. The subsequent increase in self-publication software and apps provides a way for anyone to publish then share globally within a richer media platform while bypassing editor restrictions.

It seems like the current level of expectation to produce more at a faster pace has resulted in writing being shorthanded in most of our everyday communications. Elementary classroom teachers have been discussing whether students still need to know how to physically write with everything going digital today. Though typing electronically is quick, voice command typing is even faster. In addition, digital writing offers the support of immediate spelling and grammar checking. It is not fool proof and still requires a good foundation in writing basics. With the decline of writing checks for bill payments and an increase in electronic banking transactions, it is also reducing the need for handwriting. So, when reflecting on how handwriting has been so centrally necessary to building and preserving our culture, it takes a shift in mindset to see it should still be preserved even if performed electronically. I believe we can all agree, no matter what medium is used, students still need to have the knowledge and command of effective two-way communication skills including recording their thoughts, knowledge, opinions, discoveries, and inventions in a clear and concise way.

No sooner do we have to decide whether to save writing skills, and then smartphones arrive with their heavy and direct affect on new technology shifts. Most students are now packing an impressive set of apps used for learning, sharing, and even entertainment, all in their pocket with access at an all time high. One smartphone app called TuneIn (2012) currently advertises access to over 70,000 radio stations and two million podcasts with listeners from 230 countries. Talk about seductive and personalized, just shake your phone and it will locate similar stations, how sweet is that? It is only logical to see where this could be headed with continued growth. How long until our cars are standard equipped with this expanded access? Imagine the possibilities of students having this type of access to timely International news and the ability to hear reports in different languages, as we become a more global society.

Many of the older technology declines are directly attributable to technology shifts with quick direct open access through the Internet, for personal e-mail, chat, social media, new and improved software, tools, mobile devices, and apps. As a result, digital alternatives are quickly taking the place of our more traditional tools with the lure of small, mobile, quick, easy to use devices, improved quality, with increased user control and choice. It is not a bad thing, but there are implications, whether it is simply a new medium, or whether we might be missing some of the underlying bits of important knowledge needed to carry us forward in a digital era.

## Technology Growth Areas

Where are consumers spending their money in the tech sector? According to CNN Money (2012), the "7 Fastest-Growing tech companies" include Cirrus Logic, making circuit components for tablets, Biadu China's search engine with a custom personalized homepage based on the users' search patterns, Apple's voice recognition phone, IGI Phototonics fiber lasers, 3D Systems creating three dimensional parts found in smartphones and other devices produced, Priceline online international travel booking, and Acme Packet security gateways reflecting the incredible growth and profits within the industry. The same consumer desires mentioned earlier are also reflected here with fast-personalized searches, shifts toward voice-activated communications, use of mobile devices, and increasing globalization.

Growth of technologies in the workplace are expanding to improve innovations and to expand the bottom line. The Deloitte Technology Trends annual report called "Elevate IT for digital business" (2012) examines actionable practices used to achieve improvements within five major technology forces over the past several years: analytics, mobility, social, cloud, and cyber security. Areas targeted for growth include; social business, gamification, mobility, user empowerment, cloud services, big data, geospatial visualization, digital identities, measured innovation, and outside-in architecture. Author's Cearley and Claunch (2012) (*The Top 10 Technology Trends for 2012*) point to Gartner's annual list reflecting the tremendous growth in mobile computing in the workplace. The top 10 strategies include, "media tablets and beyond, mobile-centric applications and interfaces, contextual and social user experiences, Internet of things, app stores and marketplaces, next-generation analytics, big data, in-memory computing, extreme low-energy servers, and cloud computing" (Cearley & Claunch, 2012, p. 1). It looks like one can find different items when looking at the various listings but it is easy to see major overlapping trends in mobile and social technologies. The current workplace knowledge-based economies are requiring more high-level creative thinking skills with workers adept in problem solving within expanded global markets.

Oftentimes, areas of growth in the workplace extend into the educational arena at some point in time. The "NMC Horizon Report > 2012 K-12 Edition", research from the Consortium of School Networking (CoSN), and the International Society for Technology in Education (ISTE) provides a list of the top emerging technologies, trends, and challenges impacting teaching, learning, and creative inquiry over the next five years. Within one year it is anticipated adoption will increase for, cloud computing, collaborative environments, mobiles, apps, and tablet computing. In two to three years adoption of digital identity, game-based learning, learning analytics, and personal learning environments is anticipated. From four to five years, augmented reality, natural user interfaces, semantic applications, and tools for assessing twenty-first century learning skills. Key trends are reflecting the shift towards more access, mobility, online, hybrid, and authentic active challenge-based collaborative learning models to develop leadership and creativity (NMC Horizon Report, 2013, p. 1).

According to authors Trucano, Hawkins, and Iglesias in EduTech (2012) blog article called "Ten trends in technology use in education in developing countries that you may not have heard about" provides a list of instructional technology trends in developing countries including, "tablets, social learning networks, translations, the great firewall of . . . everywhere, earlier and earlier, special needs, e-waste, open data, big brother data, getting school leadership on board, going global locally" (Trucano, Hawkins, & Iglesias, 2012, p. 1). The list reflects the trend towards increasing mobility and social learning within globalized learning environments.

With the release of mobile broadband wireless multiport Internet access, gaining Internet access on the go is ever more accessible, not only at home and from hotels, but literally traveling in the passenger seat riding the highways of America. It is arguably a step forward when exercising the potential for Internet access while becoming an effective use of what would normally be down time, now used productively. This is not to advocate working 24/7 but to create flexibility for hectic schedules. In the next section, we will examine some of the current best research-based instructional practices to see how they can be aligned with the use of new technologies.

## Literature-Based Current Best Educational Practices

New technologies offer a great way to invigorate instruction, whether in traditional classrooms, online, or in blended learning environments. We are finding many new digital tools allow learners to actively research, collaborate, innovate, and share their ideas. Collaborative tools can be used to increase knowledge acquisition quickly and efficiently while making global connections for broader perspectives. Providing meaningful integration of new technologies through the careful selection of quality tools aligning to best instructional practices can alter how learners and instructors engage with concepts and each other to achieve powerful learning. The following sections provide some background knowledge on the current best instructional practices found in the research literature used as the bases for aligning instructional needs directed towards technology enhanced teaching and learning.

## Mobility

One of the biggest trends in education is the ability to be mobile. *Time* magazine. April 1 (2013) states the percentage of U.S. phones that are smartphones has reached 57%. According to Apple's released reports, more than 40 billion apps were downloaded for the iPhone, iPad and the iPod Touch, in 2012. It is hard to deny the success realized with approximately 83 million iPads sold by the third fiscal quarter of 2012 (Nations, 2013). To put their impact into perspective, iPads have now surpassed Mac OS sales with the new mobile iOS (Caulfield, 2011). These sales reflect the strong consumer demand for this new media. There are many iPad contenders such as Amazon, Archos, Disgo, Acer, Asus, HTC, Google, Android, Motorola, Toshiba, BlackBerry, Sony, Samsung, Microsoft, Dell, Vizio, HP, and the e-book readers including the Kindle, Kobo, and Nook. Users are drawn to the sleek design, small portable size, long battery life, in store support, inexpensive, intuitive natural interface, with a vast number of quality content apps to run on the mobile devices, as well. Learning can then be extended beyond the classroom to working from home, on the go, and in the field. "We really have reached the point where we do have magic, and thus we have the opportunity to ask what we should do with it" (Quinn, 2012, p. 3). In the corporate environment educational applications range from training, performance support, increased access, and collaboration to learning. In the educational setting, learners are gaining new content, communicating, capturing information, analyzing data, presenting, sharing, and even using location based activities. "To have mobile learning work well, power has to shift from instructors and managers to the learners themselves" (Woodill, 2011, p. 165). It is a self-directed or do-it-yourself (DIY) approach to learning.

## Problem-Based Learning

Problem-Based Learning is an instructional method in which learners, usually working in teams, are given complex authentic problems or challenges and are asked to solve them. This approach is often used to increase learner interactions by working together collaboratively. Teams determine the needs, and work through the steps to solve the problem. Barrows (1986) describes problem-based learning as a way to motivate students' solutions through self-directed explorations while gaining additional practice. Problem-solving models of instruction are based on contributions from Dewey (1916, 1938). Dewey defined a problem as anything giving doubt or uncertainty. His active learning experiences included providing an appropriate learning topic, which was important and relevant.

## Inquiry Learning

The researchers Bigge and Shermis (2004), Holcomb (2004), Joyce and Calhoun (1998), Van Zee 2001), and others define inquiry learning as capitalizing on students' interests in discovering something new or finding alternatives to unsolved questions or problems. Learners often work together to conduct research, experiment, synthesize, classify, infer, communicate, analyze, draw conclusions, evaluate, revise, and justify findings. In inquiry learning, students are responsible for problem solving, discovery, and critical thinking in order to construct new knowledge through active experiences. "Inquiry teaching requires a high degree of interaction among the learner, the teacher, the materials, the content, and the environment. Perhaps the most crucial aspect of the inquiry method is that it allows both students and teachers to become persistent askers, seekers, interrogators, questioners, and ponderers" (Orlich, Harder, Callahan, Trevisan, & Brown, 2007, p. 296).

## Motivating Learning

Keller's (1983) ARC (attention, relevance, confidence, satisfaction) model of motivation provides insight into providing motivating instructional learning environments. In general, gaining attention involves capturing learner interest, stimulating inquiry, and maintaining it. Relevance includes identifying learner needs, aligning them to appropriate choices and responsibilities, and building on prior experiences. Confidence includes building positive expectations, support, competence, and success. Satisfaction includes providing meaningful opportunities to apply new knowledge and skills, reinforcement, and positive accomplishments. In Gagne (1985) "Conditions of learning" he indicated it is necessary to gain students' attention before they will be able to learn. Ongoing studies in the field of educational motivation continued to expand with additional research by Wlodkowsky (1999), Brophy (1983, 1998), and others. They determined that additional traits of motivated learners include the desire to learn, work, meet a need, personal value, reach a goal, complete tasks, engaging, curiosity, successful effort or ability, achievement, and personal responsibility. In a constructivist framework, motivation includes both individual and group generated knowledge and concepts.

## Communications and Collaborations for Learning

In the learning environment building professional relationships through collaborating, coaching, and mentoring are all social interactions directed towards learning to share ideas, give and receive feedback, and offer support (Carr, Herman, Harris, 2005). The concepts of social learning can be traced to Bruner (1961) and Vygotsky (1978) and others. Quality instructional design directed towards technology-enhanced learning requires a great deal of student interaction. Promoting learner-to-learner interactions can increase engagement through negotiations, reflections, and shared understandings. The interactions allow students to expand viewpoints and build social connections to each other. Dialogue directed towards learning can provide students a way to expand ideas, extend concepts, and apply theory in authentic ways to solve challenges. "The focus of this work is ongoing engagement in a process of purposeful inquiry designed to improve student learning" (Carr, Herman, Harris, 2005, p. 1–2). "Collaboration forms the foundation of a learning community online-it brings students together to support the learning of each member of the group while promoting creativity and critical thinking" (Palloff, Pratt, 2005, p. xi). Some of the constructivists contributing to social learning included Piaget (1969), Jonassen (1995), and Brookfield (1995). Social presence creates the "feeling of community and connection among learners, has contributed positively to learning outcomes and learner satisfaction with online courses" (Palloff, Pratt, 2005, p. 7). Researchers finding a strong connection between social presence and improved learning, interaction, and satisfaction include Picciano (2002), Gunawardena and Zittle (1997), Kazmer (2000), and Murphy, Drabier, and Epps (1998). With the wide range of collaborative tools available for communications and collaboration, it forms the perfect foundation for social interactions and collaboration directed towards learning.

## Multimedia Rich Learning

Multimedia refers to the use of text, graphics, sound, video, animation, simulation, or a combination of media. By appropriately aligning rich media to the content message, it can provide additional clarity and increase student focus rather than detract from it. Using a variety of media can increase interest and motivation while allowing unique opportunities to reach diverse learners. Mayer conducted many studies from comparing lessons presenting content with words, to lessons presenting content with words and relevant visuals (R. C. Clark & Mayer, 2003; Mayer 2001). The results have consistently demonstrated the positive impact of appropriate instructional visual selections. "Rich media can improve learning if they are used in ways that promote effective cognitive processes in learners" (Reiser & Dempsey, 2007, p. 315). Whether an educator prescribes to the learning principles of Skinner in the 30's by changing behavior, the 70's cognitive psychology focus on memory and motivation, the 80's constructivist focus on real world application, or a mixture of approaches, multimedia, used effectively, can help students to learn. Some media considerations include: gaining and keeping attention, memorability using an appropriate speed, level of difficulty, comprehension, placement, easy access, media matching the purpose, image content value, discovery, and level of interaction to improve effectiveness. "Ultimately good learning environments begin with the principles of learning and instruction, but require evaluation, revisions, and fine tuning to balance these competing values and ensure that the benefits are accrued for all intended learners" (Alessi & Trollip, 2001, p. 41). Multimodal learning can include a wide range of multimedia and interactive tools used to engage learners, thereby providing multiple modes of interfacing within the system.

## Diverse Learners

Students learn in different ways and have unique abilities and preferences on how they best acquire new information. The exceptionalities in intellectual ability, communications, sensory, behavioral, physical, and combinations sometimes require special learning accommodations. One benefit digital tools can provide is the unique interface differing from traditional computing with gesture controlled navigation, the offering of computer-assisted programs, ability to increasing the size and contrast for text, images, audio, audio readers, audio text recording, audio commands, video media, interactive and collaborative tools to target specific learning needs. In addition, there is an increase in multi-language support. This can include assistance for both special needs, low and high, as well as the ever-increasing diversity of learners from all over the world joining our classes and workplaces.

## Globalization

With the tremendous increase in travel, immigration, and communication technologies the world is becoming more diverse, connected, and interdependent. Globalization has accelerated the exchange of ideas and perspectives thereby increasing the overall knowledge base. Current digital tools provide increased opportunities for extending content and perspectives to transform knowledge into innovative. Using integrated curriculums, team teaching, and media rich instructional technologies, and forming partnerships, and fostering innovation, we can create knowledge and skills to prepare learners to work in future markets. Success in global markets, as we are now experiencing, demands successful interactions with a diverse, wide range of individuals and cultures. It begins with intercultural knowledge, skills, and respect for our combined contributions and strengths. As educators, we need to become international stewards sharing insights and preparing learners for the future. The dramatic increase in mobility and digital communications now "connects people and facilitates transnational understanding" in ways not previously possible (Bryan & Vavrus, 2005, p. 184). As a result, the international information infrastructure allows learners to interact and share multimedia resources easily with anyone across the globe. Current technology tools easily allow for original creations and global sharing.

It seems like it would be beneficial to offer classes on global language basics including key functional survival skill words through the use of immersive practice with multiple-languages. Subsequently, providing the potential to foster international relationships, travel, and commerce needed for an increasingly global society.

## Active Hands-On Learning

Hands-on refers to the learning activity involving practice on actual equipment, or in this case digital tools. The learning activity is designed with the goal of promoting the transfer of knowledge through application. In an active learning environment students are active, working in teams, and socialization is directed toward learning productively. "Students must be actively involved in the learning process if their classroom experience is to lead to deeper understandings and the building of new knowledge. Students (and adults, as I have discovered) need to hear it, touch it, see it, talk it over, grapple with it, confront it, question it, laugh about it, experience it, and reflect on it in a structured format if learning is to have any meaning and permanence" (Nash, 2009, p. xi). The dialogue provides time for learners to digest new information, exchange ideas, and engage with others in authentic, active hands-on ways for expanded perspectives, and memorable learning experiences.

## Creative Learning

Open-ended digital tools allowing for original solutions to problems or challenges provide the perfect environment for creative thinking. Students can demonstrate understanding through a wide variety of digital resources to present and share their unique solutions. It is critical to develop learners who can think beyond the box and lead us to new innovations. Simply reading and testing over material will not develop the creative, original thinking needed to move our society forward. Instructors often use Bloom's Taxonomy (1956) to ensure inclusion of high-level knowledge and skills as can be found in original creative work.

## Learning New Content with Practice

The main consideration when selecting content resources is the relevance to the desired topic, and how clear the main ideas are communicated to learners. Providing learners with a graphic organizer is a nice way to show what will be studied by providing a brief overview of the content. By isolating facts, concepts, and generalizations, it makes it easier to understand new content. The higher level of knowledge integration teaches learners how items are related, similar, different, and how to compare so they can understand more complex relationships. Interactions with the content and others can provide additional practice to better retain new information. Some instructional activities are designed to provide learners with opportunities for review of previously learned information through repetition. Some digital tools provide the needed practice activities by using repetition to ensure retention into long-term memory. It is important to identify the objectives and align them with the learning activity.

## Feedback, Support, and Assessment

By providing learners with timely information about their actions they will know how they compare to the desired level of criteria. "We should ensure that they receive feedback about their success and failure, are appropriately resourced with support to ultimately succeed, and ideally can share tasks and learning with one another" (Quinn, 2012, p. 24). Learner feedback can take many different forms such as traditional instructor exams with rating scales or comments for students. Another alternative is to use student self-evaluations using checklists or rubrics for individual or group work to learn to monitor their own success. Sometimes instructors will also use checklists or rubrics for evaluation and providing student feedback. Instructors can use a pretest to assess learners' current level of knowledge, diagnostic test to assess areas of strengths and weakness, formative assessments to measure ongoing progress, and summative letter grade assessments to make judgments on the quality and completion of projects. The data gathered by the instructor can be used to monitor learning and make adjustments as needed as the course progresses or for changes to be made before teaching the lesson, unit, or module again. It is important to identify the desired learning of "behaviors, activities, and knowledge you will be evaluating" (Orlich, Harder, Callahan, Trevisan, & Brown, 2007, p. 332). Instruction can include the teaching of knowledge, performance skills, and attitudes such as found in collaborative group work. Another consideration is whether the learning goal aligns to standards and provides feedback in this regard to students, parents, instructors, and administrators, as needed.

## Objectives for Learning

Mager's (1975) model for objectives, indicates quality objectives including the following three elements: 1) statement of the conditions or context of performance, 2) statement of the task, and 3) measurable way to evaluate the performance. Meaningful objectives are the backbone for instructors to create learning activities designed for knowledge to be retained, transferred, and applied to similar situations. It is accomplished by providing a specific statement of what learners will be able to do when they complete the lesson. A measureable performance objective statement describes the behavior students will demonstrate at the end of the lesson, the conditions under which they will be demonstrated, and the criteria for acceptable performance. Identifying the objectives becomes the guiding force for the selection of appropriate digital tools to get to the desired learner outcomes.

## Flipped Classroom

Flipped classrooms are a more recent trend used to transform the way instructors are providing information by inverting traditional classroom lectures into online video and screencast presentations, so learners can view them prior to attending class. At home, learners can watch step-by-step explanations of concepts with visual examples to better understand complex concepts. The digital presentations allow each student to learn at their own pace with the ability to pause and replay as much as needed, on their own personal schedule when they are the most receptive to learning, to acquire the needed foundation knowledge. Class time is then flipped, so students complete homework and practice activities applying the new concepts in class. When attending class, students are engaged in studentto-student interactions, collaborations, and critical thinking with the instructor serving as a facilitator to support learners, as needed. The classroom is transformed into an active, authentic, learning environment where students can deal with complex issues related to the content topic. The Flipped classroom can be an alternative to traditional lecture-based models or can be used as a blended learning environment to engage student learning. Screencast technology is often used to leverage learning outside of class, so a teacher can spend more time facilitating project-based learning during class. This is most commonly being done using teacher-created videos that students view outside of class time. Then, the learners spend class time on problem solving, thereby increasing interactions between students and instructors. With the tremendous growth and availability of mobile devices, learners have ever improving abilities to view the videos on their own time. As noted, this just keeps increasing the chances the class time can be spent on problem-based collaborative learning.

## Emerging Technologies

On a *CBS This Morning* show segment called "Gadgets and Gizmos Galore" with Brian Cooley, he reported on the 2013 Las Vegas, NV, International Consumer Electronics Show. He talked about how we are starting to move into a post-mobile era. It does not mean getting rid of mobile devices but rather seeing a merger of devices such as computers, phones, TV, and tablets so we will not be thinking about what device we are using. One example of this trend is the movement towards hybrids such as the Phablet, where the phone and tablet are combined. Cooley also talked about exciting developments through body gesturing such as Vuzix's®™ eye motion control, Leap Motion's®™ sensor on the device screen controlled by hand movements, and InteraXon's®™ Muse headband reading brainwaves for device control. Within ten years we may no longer be using the mouse and touchscreen technology. It seems like the new devices will have the potential to increase usability access for diverse learners while being a more tactile and engaging way to interact with technology resources.

## Conclusions and Future Implications

When searching the literature for recommendations practitioners could consider, when dealing with shifting technologies and the pursuit of quality learning environments within the K-12 setting, a Freakonomics podcast provides some insight. Stephen Dunbar's (2011) podcast tells about how the New York City Department of Education pilot program called "School of One" personalized educational plans so each individual student has a chance to excel. Dunbar interviewed the program founders Joel Rose, Chris Rush, and chancellor Joel Klein. They implemented a technology algorithm, similar in concept to what is used to personalize Pandora radio, to analyze how each individual student learns the best. Based on the analysis results, learning was customized the next day to maximize learning efficiency. The learning modality was also aligned to how each individual student learned best; whether alone, in small or large groups, synchronously or asynchronously to practice learning concepts. One shared success story pertained to a student who initially took ten to twelve exposures to learn, but after targeting how this individual student learned best, the number of exposures was reduced to two to three. Rather than guessing what students have learned, it is statistically analyzed at the individual level to ensure it is happening through personalization. Along the same line, the U.S. Department of Education report (2012) states

> The realization of productivity improvements in education will most likely require a transformation of conventional processes to leverage new capabilities supported by information and communications technologies. In sum, rigorous evidence is needed to support effective practices to foster the adoption of efficient, effective paths to learning.

We have three sets of insightful recommendations for higher education. They include "growth, even with the accompanying pains, is generally welcome because it provides energy, new ideas, and attention to innovations. Often, however, a snazzy new technology becomes the sole focus, not the ideas or innovative uses that lead to improved learning" (Wilson, 2005, p. 1). It is important to consider instructional needs alongside new and emerging technologies aligned to desired outcomes. If we do not, we may find ourselves marching towards obsolescence as we fail to adapt to changing educational goals, objectives, and new technologies. "Most universities are using the same methods to teach all of the same stuff. This is very dangerous as the world is changing so quickly that entire fields and bodies of knowledge risk being outdated/outmoded very quickly" (Moravec, 2013, p. 1). Moravec goes on to state we "need to stop behaving as consumers of education, but become creators, producers, and prosumers. At the same time, learning needs to become more immersive and personally-meaningful (subjective experiences) to each learner" (Moravec, 2013, p. 2). In a video interview with Douglas Rushkoff, he makes a good comment about how students need to ask themselves the following questions. "Am I learning? Am I becoming a smarter more innovative human being? That's what's going to serve you in the real job market of tomorrow. By the time the corporation has told the city college what skills it wants from its future workers you are going to graduate and those skills will have changed anyway" (Rushkoff, 2013, p. 3). The factory and banking models are no longer relevant and students are now demanding interactive, relevant learning experiences, as they well should.

Recommendations for business training include actionable improvements to add measurable value to the company. With the influx of digital natives into the workplace, social technology use is increasing. "Leading enterprises today are applying social technologies like collaboration, communication and content management to social networks—the connected web of people and assets that impact on a given business goal or outcome—amplified by social media from blogs to social networking sites to content communities. Yet it's more than tools and technology. Businesses are being fundamentally changed as leaders rethink their core processes and capabilities with a social mindset to find new ways to create more value, faster" (Ramsingh, 2012, p. 1). According to author Ron Zamir, keeping "learners engaged and motivated in training through rich media, bite-sized content and gamification are essential for creating training that is both palatable to the learner and creates real workplace change" (Zamir, 2013, p. 1). Zamir's goal is to design innovative solutions to create better training using new technologies "not just simply rehashing old, unchanged content" (Zamir, 2013, p. 1). Other current trends found from the Training Zone (2013) website include the integration of rich media, mobile learning, online learning, conferencing, and the shift to globalization. It is critical to first know the learners and organizational goals to better meet their needs. The best training is personalized, accessible, and engaging in both the training and support materials offered. The technology itself is not the magic bullet, it is what you do with it to reach the business goals. The training is a means to an end, with the end resulting in a positive impact.

Integrating quality research-based instructional practices as new technologies are released is one way to fight against knowledge gaps at all levels. When one analyzes the learning needs, goals, and objectives, then selects and aligns the best tools to accomplish the tasks, one increases opportunities for exceptional learning.

Looking at where we need to be going with technology infused education, *eSchool News* has an article called eSN Special Report: Keeping students on a path to graduation. The author states "educators are determined to find that relevance by giving students more of the skills they'll need to succeed in a globally competitive economy—the so-called "twenty-first-century skills" such as problem solving, critical thinking, communication, and collaboration" (Nastu, 2012, p. 1). By integrating technology through meaningful applications, learners are more likely to stay the course needed for college and future careers. Students tend to learn best through the application of concepts to functions via meaningful work tasks, integrating those concepts through authentic relevant connections.

With so many tremendous technological shifts happening, we need to be mindful of the missing bits of information which still need to be taught. Ask people from all walks of life what is missing, what are we no longer teaching that needs to be included no matter what medium is used? Keeping in mind, the knowledge and skills valued by our society are also in a state of flux.

The concepts of collaboration and social interactions directed towards learning can continue to play a great role in the digital transitions. Could we be at a point where we think those brains, properly educated and trained to collect data, to think about problems through deeper root cause evaluation processes might be ready to start coming up with solutions to issues, concerns, and problems? Could we be ready to embrace a little change? Might we be ready to start exploring ways to maximize the potential of each individual? This article points to the need to conduct various needs analyses, identify relevant learning goals and align them to current best research-based instructional practices, no matter what technologies are selected, while staying flexible and adaptable to the changes that are sure to come.

A story by Sugata Mitra from NPR's Ted Radio called Unstoppable Learning is a wonderful example of the resilience of learners. He found by putting computers in villages in rural India, that the residents who had never seen computers before, with absolutely no resources to teach them taught themselves how to use them. My favorite quote was "you gave us a machine that only works in English, so we taught ourselves English to use it" (Mitra, 2013). By providing challenges then standing back to watch we will be amazed at what the human spirit of inquiry is capable of learning.

In looking at the New Horizons Report (2013) for K-12, Higher Education, and online resources for new and emerging technologies in industry, there are some very exciting new developments happening from augmented reality, wearable technologies, 3D printing, and much more. It will be fun to see how these technologies can be used effectively to have a positive impact on learning.

Closing suggestions for future researchers include: continue to examine effective ways to personalize instruction, examine goals and learners, tailor instruction or training specifically to the learner. Then, we may find the keys to additional innovations in teaching, training, and learning.

# References

Alessi, S., Trollip, S. (2001). *Multimedia for learning: Methods and development,* 3rd Edition. Allyn & Bacon, A Pearson Education Company, Needham Heights: MA.

Bryan, A., & Vavrus, F. (2005). The promise and peril of education: The teaching of in/tolerance in an era of globalization. *Globalization, Societies and Education,* 3(2), 183–202. Doi:10.1080/14767720500167033

Carr, J., Herman, N., & Harris, D. (2005). *Creating dynamic schools through mentoring, coaching, and collaboration.* Association for Supervision and Curriculum Development, Alexandria: VA.

Caulfield, B. (2011). Apple now selling more iPads than Macs; iOS eclipses Dell and HP's PC Businesses. Retrieved March 17, 2013 from http://www.forbes.com/sites/briancaulfield/2011/07/19/apple-didnt-just-sell-more-ipads-than-macs-ios-has-now-eclipsed-dell-and-hps-pc-business-too/

Cearley, D., Claunch, C. (2012). The top 10 technology trends for 2012. Retrieved Jan. 12, 2013 from: http://www.junctionsolutions.com/gartner-insights-the-top-10-technology-trends-for-2012/

CNN Money, 7 Fastest-Growing tech companies, Retrieved Nov. 2, 2012 from http://money.cnn.com/gallery/technology/2012/09/06/fastest-growing-tech-companies.fortune/index.html

Cooley, B. (2013). CBS This Morning, Gadgets and gizmos galore. Retrieved Jan. 8 from: http://www.cbsnews.com/video/watch/?id=50138517n

Deloitte, (2012). Tech trends 2012: Elevate IT for digital business. Retrieved Jan. 12, 2013 from: http://www.deloitte.com/view/en_US/us/Services/consulting/technology-consulting/technology-2012/index.htm?id=us_google_techtrends_02212&gclid=CIuI7Nqb47QCFYp_QgoduSsAcw

Dunbar, S. (2011). How is a bad radio station like our public-school system? A Freakonomics Radio Podcast Encore. Retrieved May 21, 2013 from: http://www.freakonomics.com/2011/12/21/how-is-a-bad-radio-station-like-our-public-school-system-a-freakonomics-radio-podcast-encore/

Hawkins, R. (2010). 10 global trends in ICT and education. Retrieved Jan. 12, 2013 EduTech: A World Bank Blog on ICT use in Education from: http://blogs.worldbank.org/edutech/10-global-trends-in-ict-and-education

Mitra, S. (2013). Unstoppable learning. NPR, Ted Radio Hour. Retrived May 23, 2013 from: http://www.npr.org/2013/04/25/179010396/unstoppable-learning

Moravec, J. (2013). The university of the future: Marching toward obsolescence? Education Futures. Retrieved May 21, 2013 from: http://www.educationfutures.com/2013/04/08/uni-future/

Nash, R. (2009). The active classroom: Practical strategies for involving students in the learning process. Corwin Press, Thousand Oaks: CA.

Nastu, J. (2012). eSN Special Report: Keeping student on a path to graduation, *eSchool News,* Retrieved Nov. 2, 2012 from: http://www.eschoolnews.com/2011/02/22/esn-special-report-keeping-students-on-a-path-to-graduation/?ast=95&astc=8784

Nations, D. (2013). How many iPads have been sold? Retrieved March 17, 2013 from: http://ipad.about.com/od/iPad-FAQ/a/How-Many-iPads-Have-Been-Sold.htm

New Media Consortium (2013). NMC Horizon Report. K-12 Education Edition and Higher Education Edition. Retrieved May 21, 2013 from: http://www.nmc.org/publications

Orlich, D., Harder, R., Callahan, R., Trevisan, M., & Brown, A. (2007). Teaching strategies: A guide to effective Instruction, 8th Edition. Houghton Mitllin Company, Boston: MA.

Palloff, R., Pratt, K. (2005). *Collaborating online: Learning together in the community.* Jossey-Bass, A John Wiley & Sons Inc. Imprint, San Francisco: CA.

Quinn, C. (2012). *The mobile academy mlearning for higher education.* Jossey-Bass a John Wiley & Sons, Inc. Imprint, San Francisco: CA.

Ramsingh, K. (2012). Reimagining business with a social mindset. Deloitte Tech Trends. Retrieved May 21, 2013 from: http://deloitteblog.co.za.www102.cpt1.host-h.net/2012/03/28/reimagining-business-with-a-social-mindset-%E2%80%93-deloitte-tech-trends-2012/

Reiser, R. & Dempsey, J. (2007). *Trends and issues in instructional design and technology,* Second Edition. Pearson, Merrill Prentice Hall, Upper Saddle River: NJ.

Rushkoff, D. (2013). Education in present shock: An interview with Douglas Rushkoff. Education Futures. Retrieved May 21, 2013 from: http://www.educationfutures.com/2013/05/03/education-in-present-shock-an-interview-with-douglas-rushkoff/

Training Zone (2013). Learning Technologies 2013. Retrieved May 25, 2013 from: http://www.trainingzone.co.uk/features/Technology

Trucano, M., Hawkins, R., & Iglesias C. (2012). Ten trends in technology use in education in developing countries that you may not have heard about, EduTech: A World Bank Blog on ICT use in Education Retrieved Jan. 12, 2013 from: http://blogs.worldbank.org/edutech/some-more-trends

Tuneln Radio, Retrieved Nov. 2, 2012 from http://tunein.com/press/

U.S. Department of Education (2012). Understanding the implications of online learning for educational productivity. Office of Educational Technology. Retrieved May 21, 2013 from: http://www.ed.gov/edblogs/technology/research/

Wilson, B. G. (2005). Choosing our future. Retrieved May 21, 2013 from: http://carbon.ucdenver.edu/~bwilson/ChoosingOurFuture.html

Woodill, G. (2011). *The mobile learning edge: Tools and technologies for developing your teams.* The McGraw-Hill Companies, New York: NY.

Zamir, R. (2013). Corporate training trends in 2013. Retrieved May 25, 2013 from: http://www.allencomm.com/2013/02/corporate-training-trends-in-2013/

## Critical Thinking

1. The sections on shifting technologies and technology growth discuss an array of changes and new devices/software coming to market. Which of these new technologies will have the most impact on your personal life? Explain why and how it will impact your personal life.

2. Some sections of the article provide an overview of the current best educational practices. Which of these practices will have the most impact on your teaching practices? Do not consider finances, but think about your content area or grade level and technology expertise. Explain why and how it will impact your teaching. Now consider if and how your answers to these two questions are similar.

3. In their conclusion the authors ask, ". . . what is missing, what are we no longer teaching that needs to be included no matter what medium is used?" Ask two to three teachers with different years of teaching experience this question and include your own answer. Reflect on the implications of your findings.

## Internet References

**Center for Implementing Technology in Education**
http://www.cited.org/

**International Society for Technology in Education**
http://www.iste.org/

**US Department of Education- Use of Technology in Teaching and Learning**
http://www.ed.gov/oii-news/use-technology-teaching-and-learning

# Article 15

Curtis J. Bonk

## "For Openers: How Technology is Changing School"

Whether you're sailing around the world, homebound with the flu, or just in the market for more flexible learning, thanks to the Internet, schooling never stops.

Sometimes it takes a major catastrophe to transform how we deliver schooling. In 2005, in the aftermath of Hurricanes Katrina and Rita, websites went up in Louisiana, Texas, and Mississippi to help educators, students, families, and school districts deal with the crisis. The Mississippi Department of Education (2005) announced free online courses at the high school level, and institutions from 38 states provided more than 1,300 free online courses to college students whose campuses had been affected by the hurricanes (Sloan-C, 2006).

Health emergencies in recent years have also caused educators to ponder the benefits of the Web. In 2003, during the SARS epidemic in China, government officials decided to loosen restrictions on online and blended learning (Huang & Zhou, 2006). More recently, as concerns about the H1N1 virus mounted, many U.S. schools piloted new educational delivery options, such as free online lessons from Curriki (www.curriki.org) and Smithsonian Education (www.smithsonianeducation. org). Microsoft has even offered its Microsoft Office Live free of charge to educators dealing with H1N1. The software enables teachers to share content, lesson plans, and other curriculum components, while students access the virtual classroom workspace, chat with one another on discussion topics, and attend virtual presentations.

## Blended Learning Is Here

The focus today is on continuity of learning, whether learning is disrupted because of a hurricane or the flu—or because of other factors entirely. Schools may have difficulty serving students who live in rural areas; reduced budgets may limit the range of learning that a school can offer; people young and old involved in serious scholarly, artistic, or athletic pursuits may find it difficult to adhere to the traditional school structure.

In light of these developments, some school districts are resorting to blended learning options. They are using tools like Tegrity (www.tegrity.com); Elluminate (www.elluminate.com); and Adobe Connect Pro (www.Adobe.com/products/acrobat connectpro) to provide online lectures. Many are developing procedures for posting course content and homework online. Some are trying phone conferencing with Skype (www.skype.com) or Google Talk (www.google.com/talk). Others are evaluating digital textbooks and study guides. Still others are sharing online videos from places like Link TV (www.linktv.org); FORA, tv (http:// fora.tv); or TeacherTube (www.teachertube.com), with teachers often asking students to post their reflections in blogs or online discussion forums. Many schools have begun to foster teamwork by using Google Docs (http://docs.google. com) and wikis. Although some schools use e-mail to communicate messages district-wide, others are experimenting with text messaging or Twitter (http://twitter.com).

The wealth of information available online is also changing teaching practices. Teachers can access free online reference material, podcasts, wikis, and blogs, as well as thousands of free learning portals, such as the Periodic Table of Videos (www. periodicvideos.com) for chemistry courses and the Encyclopedia of Life (www.eol.org) for biology. Science teachers can use portals devoted to Einstein (www.alberteinstein.info); Darwin (www.darwin-online.org.uk); or Goodall (www.janegoodall. org). English teachers can find similar content repositories on Poe (www.eapoe.org); Shakespeare (http://shakespeare.mit.edu); and Austen (www.janeausten.org), to name just a few.

## High School—Online

Tools like these enable great flexibility in learning. When I take a break from work and jog across my campus, smack in the middle of it I come to Owen Hall, home of the Indiana University High School (http://iuhighschool.iu.edu). Indiana University High School (IUHS) students can take their courses online or through correspondence or some combination of the two. Students range from those who live in rural settings to those who are homebound, homeschooled, pregnant, or gifted. Some are Americans living in other countries; some are natives of other countries whose parents want them to have a U.S. education. Some are dropouts or students academically at risk. Still others are teenagers about to enter college who need advanced placement courses or adults who want to finish their high school degrees (Robbins, 2009). Across the board, many of the 4,000 students enrolled in IUHS simply did not fit in the traditional U.S. high school setting.

Take 16-year-old Evren Ozan (www.ozanmusic.com), the Native American flute prodigy whose music I've enjoyed for several years. I'm listening to him as I write this sentence. Many of Evren's vast accomplishments—he's been recording music since he was 7 years old—would not have been possible without the online and distance education experiences he benefited from during his teen years when most of his peers were attending traditional high schools. Also attending IUHS is 15-year-old Ania Filochowska, a Polishborn violinist who has studied with several great masters of the violin in New York City since 2005. Similarly, Kathryn Morgan enrolled in IUHS so she could continue her quest to become a professional ballerina. With the flexibility of online courses and degrees, Kathryn danced full-time and pursued an apprenticeship with the New York City Ballet.

Then there is the amazing story of Bridey Fennell. Bridey completed four IUHS courses while enjoying a five-month sailboat journey with her parents and two sisters from Arcaju, Brazil, to Charleston, South Carolina. Ship dock captains and retired teachers proctored her exams in port, and she practiced her French lessons on different islands of the Caribbean. Her sister Caitlin posted updates about their daily activities to her blog, and elementary students in the Chicago area monitored the family's journey and corresponded with Caitlin.

## We All Learn

All this raises the question of why so many people only see the benefits of online learning for musicians, dancers, athletes, and other performers or for those affected by some calamity. I personally benefited from nontraditional education a quarter of a century ago when I was taking correspondence and televised courses from the University of Wisconsin. Back then, I was a bored accountant, and distance learning was my only way out. It got me into graduate school and changed my life. I now speak, write books, and teach about the benefits of distance learning.

The 21st century offers us far more options to learn and grow intellectually. Today more than a million people in the United States alone are learning online.

To make sense of the vast array of Web-based learning opportunities possible today, I have developed a framework based on 10 *openers*—10 technological opportunities that have the potential to transform education by altering where, when, and how learning takes place. The openers form the acronym WE-ALL-LEARN. [1] They include

- Web searching in the world of e-books.
- E-learning and blended learning.
- Availability of open-source and free software.
- Leveraged resources and open courseware.
- Learning object repositories and portals.
- Learner participation in open information communities.
- Electronic collaboration.
- Alternate reality learning.
- Real-time mobility and portability.
- Networks of personalized learning.

Online and blended learning opportunities are just one opener (opener #2). Lets look at two more.

## Web Searching in the World of e-Books

A decade ago, books were limited to being physical objects. Today, all that has changed. Government, nonprofit, and corporate initiatives are placing greater emphasis on digital book content.

The digital textbook project in Korea (www.dtbook.kr/eng), for instance, is being piloted in 112 schools with hopes of making textbooks free for all Korean schools by 2013. Digital textbooks include such features as dictionaries, e-mail applications, forum discussions, simulations, hyperlinks, multimedia, data searching, study aids, and learning evaluation tools.

Right behind Korea is California, which is steeped in a huge deficit. Governor Arnold Schwarzenegger is seeking ways out. One direction is a greater emphasis on digital education (Office of the Governor, 2009). By using digital books, California not only addresses its budgetary problems, but also assumes a leadership role in online learning. Officials in the state plan to download digital textbooks and other educational content into mobile devices that they will place in the hands of all students.

Some digital book initiatives are taking place at the district level. Vail School District in Arizona has adopted an approach called Beyond Textbooks (http://beyondtextbooks.org), which encourages the use of Web resources and shared teacher lesson plans geared to meet state standards (Lewin, 2009). Rich online videos, games, and portals of Web materials as well as podcasts of teacher lectures extend learning at Vail in directions not previously possible.

Innovative companies and foundations are also finding ways to offer free textbooks. Flat World Knowledge (www .flatworldknowledge.com) offers free online textbooks and also sells print-on-demand softcover textbooks, audio textbooks, and low-cost ancillary or supplemental materials, such as MP3 study guides, online interactive quizzes, and digital flashcards connected to each book. Using an open-content, Web-based collaborative model, the CK-12 Foundation (http://ckl2.org) is pioneering the idea of free FlexBooks that are customizable to state standards.

Digital books on mobile devices will move a significant chunk of learning out of traditional classroom settings. Hundreds of thousands of free e-books are now available online. You can search for them at places like Google; Many-Books.net (http:// manybooks.net); LibriVox (www.librivox.org); the World Public Library (http://worldlibrary.net); the Internet Archive (www. archive.org); Bookyards. com (www.bookyards.com); and other e-book sites. Ironically, the majority of the top 25 best sellers on the Kindle are actually free (Kafka, 2009). We have entered the era of free books.

## Real-Time Mobility and Portability

Mobile learning is the current mantra of educators. More than 60,000 people around the planet get mobile access to the Internet each hour (Iannucci, 2009), with 15 million people subscribing each month in India alone (Telecom Regulatory Authority of India, 2009). Also, if just one percent of the 85,000 applications for the iPhone (Marcus, 2009) are educational, thousands of possible learning adventures are at one's fingertips. It's possible to access grammar lessons, language applications, Shakespearean plays or quotes, physics experiments, musical performances, and math review problems with a mobile phone.

Online classes and course modules as well as teacher professional development are now delivered on mobile devices. As mobile learning advocate John Traxler (2007) points out, mobile professional development options are especially important in developing countries in Africa.

Mobile learning is not restricted to phones, of course. Laptops, iPods, MP3 players, flash memory sticks, digital cameras, and lecture recording pens all foster mobile learning pursuits as well as greater learning engagement. Educators need to thoughtfully consider where, when, and how to use such devices.

For instance, rather than ban mobile technologies, school officials might encourage students to record lectures with their pens or digital devices and listen to them while studying for quizzes and final exams. Or teachers might make available snippets of content that students can download to their mobile devices—such as French grammar lessons or quick guides to concepts in the study of chemistry, the human nervous system, or cell biology (Bonk, 2009).

When we think about mobile learning, we often just think of a mobile learner. But the deliverer of the learning might also be mobile. With the Web, our learning content might come from a climb up Mount Everest, expeditions to the Arctic or Antarctic, research at the bottom of an ocean, NASA flights far above us, or sailing adventures across the planet.

Michael Perham (www.sailmike.com) and Zac Sunderland (www.zacsunderland.com), for instance, each blogged and shared online videos of their record-setting solo sailing journeys around the globe. Amazingly, they each completed their adventures last summer at the tender age of 17. I could track their daily experiences and post comments in their blogs. They were my highly mobile teachers. I also learn from Jean Pennycook, a former high school science teacher who now brings scientific research on penguins in the Antarctic to classrooms around the world (see www.windows.ucar.edu/tour/link=/people/postcards/penguin_post.html).

## Trends in the Open World

Given these myriad learning opportunities on the Web, you might wonder what is coming next. Here are some predictions.

- *Free as a book.* Digital books will not only be free, but readers will also be able to mix and match several of their components. E-books and classrooms will increasingly embed shared online video, animations, and simulations to enhance learning.
- *The emergence of super e-mentors and e-coaches.* Super e-mentors and e-coaches, working from computer workstations or from mobile devices, will provide free learning guidance. As with the gift culture that we have seen in the open source movement over the past two decades, some individuals will simply want to share their expertise and skills, whereas others may want practice teaching. Many will be highly educated individuals who have always wanted opportunities to teach, coach, or mentor but who work in jobs that do not enable them to do so. Those with the highest credibility and in the most demand will have human development or counseling skills (perhaps a master's degree in counseling); understand how to use the Web for learning; and have expertise in a particular domain, such as social work, nursing, accounting, and so forth.
- *Selecting global learning partners.* Peers don't need to live down the street; they could be anywhere on the planet. Tools like Ning (www.ning.com) and Google Docs and resources like ePals (www.epals.com) and iEARN (International Education and Research Network; www.iearn.org) make global interactions ubiquitous. Global peer partners will form mini-school communities and unique school-based social networking groups. Projects might include learning how to cope with

natural disasters, engaging in cultural exchanges, designing artwork related to human rights, exploring the effects of global warming, and learning about threats to animal habitats.

- *Teachers everywhere.* Soon students will be able to pick their teachers at a moment's notice. Want a teacher from Singapore, the Philippines, the United Kingdom, or Israel? They will be available in online teacher or mentor portals as well as preselected and approved by local school districts or state departments. Some will be displayed on a screen as students walk into school; students might consult this individual during a study hall period or review session.
- *Teacher as concierge.* The notion of a teacher will shift from a deliverer of content to that of a concierge who finds and suggests education resources as learners need them.
- *Informal = formal.* Informal learning will dramatically change the idea of "going to school," with a greater percentage of instructors being informal ones who offer content, experiences, and ideas to learners of all ages. Such individuals will include explorers on expeditions, researchers in a science lab, and practitioners in the workplace.
- *International academic degrees.* Consortia of countries will band together to provide international education using online courses and activities with the goal of offering a high school or community college degree.
- *Dropouts virtually drop back in.* The U.S. government will offer free online courses for high school dropouts and those needing alternative learning models (Jaschik, 2009). Such courses, as well as multiple options for learning, may lure students back to pick up a secondary or postsecondary degree. Interactive technology enhancements will appeal to teenagers and young adults savvy with emerging tools for learning.
- *The rise of the super blends.* As schools are faced with continued budgetary constraints and with the plethora of free courses, learning portals, and delivery technologies available, blended learning will become increasingly prevalent in K-12 education. Determining the most effective blend will be a key part of effective school leadership.
- *The shared learning era.* In the coming decade, the job of a K-12 teacher will include the willingness to share content with teachers in one's school district as well as with those far beyond. Teachers will also be called on to evaluate shared content.
- *Personalized learning environments.* Open educational resources (OER) and technologies like shared online videos podcasts, simulations, and virtual worlds will be available to enhance or clarify any lesson at any time (Bonk & Zhang, 2008). For example, Wendy Ermold, a researcher and field technician for the University of Washington Polar Science Center, conducts research in Greenland and in other northern locations on this planet. While out on the icebreakers or remote islands, she listens to lectures and reviews other OER content from MIT, Stanford, Seattle Pacific University, and Missouri State University to update her knowledge of physics and other content areas. The expansion of such free and open course content options will personalize learning according to particular learner needs or preferences.
- *Alexandrian Aristotles.* Learners will emerge who have the modern-day equivalent of the entire ancient library of Alexandria on a flash memory stick in their pocket or laptop. They will spend a significant amount of time learning from online tools and resources, will be ideal problem finders and solvers, and will set high personal achievement standards.

## Open for Business

The world is open for learning. In addition to blended learning, e-books, and mobile learning, we are witnessing an increase in learner generation of academic content, collaboration in that content generation, and customization of the learning environment at significantly reduced costs and sometimes for free.

The 10 openers I suggest, push educators to rethink models of schooling and instruction. They are converging to offer the potential for a revolution in education—which is already underway.

## Endnote

1. For a full discussion of the We-All-Learn framework, see my book, *The World Is Open; How Web Technology Is Revolutionizing Education* (Jossey-Bass, 2009).

## References

Bonk. C.J. (2009). *The world is open: How Web technology is revolutionizing education.* San Francisco: Jossey-Bass.

Bonk, C. J., & Zhang, K. (2008). *Empowering online learning: 100+activities for reading, reflecting, displaying, and doing.* San Francisco: Jossey-Bass.

Huang, R., & Zhou, Y. (2006). Designing blended learning focused on knowledge category and learning activities: Case sudies from Beijing. In C. J. Bonk & C. R. Graham (Eds.), *Handbook of blended learning: Global perspectives, local designs* (pp. 296–310), San Francisco: Pfeiffer.

Iannucci, B. (2009, January 7). *Connecting everybody to everything.* Nokia Research Center, Stanford University POMI (Programmable Open Mobile Internet), NSF research advisory meeting.

Jaschik, S. (2009, June 29). U.S. push for free online courses. *Inside Higher Ed.* Available: www.insidehighered.com/news/2009/06/29/ccplan.

Kafka, P. (2009, December). The secret behind the Kindle's best-selling e-books: They're not for sale. *CNET News.* Available: http://news.cnet.com/8301-1023_310422538-93.html.

Lewin, T. (2009, August 9). In a digital future, textbooks are history, *The New York Times.* Available: w ww.nytimes.com/2009/08/09/education/09textbook.html.

Marcus, M. B. (2009, October 5). Pull yourself from that iPhone and read this story. USA *Today.* Available: www.usatoday.com/printedition/life/20091005/appaddiction05_st.art.htm.

Mississippi Department of Education. (2005, September). *Katrina recovery information.* Available: www.mde.k12.ms.us/Katrina.

Office of the Governor. (2009, May 6). Gov Schwarzenegger launches first-in-nation initiative to develop free digital textbooks for high school students (Press Release). Sacramento, CA: Author. Available: http://gov.ca.gov/press-release/12225.

Robbins, R. (2009, June 9). Distance students are "a varied and interesting lot." *Herald Times Online.* Available: www.heraldtimesonline.com/stories/2009/06/08/schoolnews.qp2930970.sto.

Sloan-C (2006, August 8). The Sloan Consortium honored for post-hurricane delivery of online courses. The Sloan semester. Available: www.sloan-c.org/sloansemester.

Telecom Regulatory Authority of India. (2009, June). Information note to the press (Press Release No 54/2009). Available: www.trai.gov.in/WriteReadData/trai/upload/PressReleases/687/pr1june09no54.pdf.

Traxler, J. (2007, June). Defining, discussing, and evaluating mobile learning: The moving finger writes and having writ . . . *International Review of Research in Open and Distance Learning,* 8(1). Available: www.irrodl.org/index.php/irrodl/article/view/346/875.

## Critical Thinking

1. Make a list of the ways that you use technology to learn or teach.
2. Work with a small group of peers to share your technology-use lists. Make a team list of all the ways you can teach or learn with technology.
3. Go online and open the Horizon Report: www.nmc.org/pdf/2010-Horizon-Report.pdf. Select one of the Six Top Technologies to research further. Explain how you might use the new information in your school.

**Curtis J. Bonk** is Professor of Instructional Systems Technology at Indiana University. He is the author of *The World Is Open: How Web Technology Is Revolutionizing Education* (Jossey-Bass, 2009) and coauthor, with Ke Zhang, of *Empowering Online Learning: 100+ Ideas,* for *Reading, Reflecting, Displaying, and Doing* (Jossey-Bass, 2008). He blogs at TravelinEdMan (http://travelinedmanblogspot.com); curt@worldisopen.com.

# Article 16

Beth Pyle and Keri Esslinger

## Utilizing Technology in Physical Education:
## Addressing the Obstacles of Integration

Prepared by: Rebecca B. Evers, *Winthrop University*

The use of technology to enhance the educational experience has become a standard within all content areas. Physical education is not exempt from this standard, although implementation of technology use has been difficult because of the unique nature of the physical education classroom environment. The authors discuss the obstacles that teachers and administrators face while integrating technology into the physical education environment, as well as approaches that can be taken to overcome those obstacles.

## Learning Outcomes

*After reading this article, you will be able to:*
• Justify reasons to overcome the roadblocks to integrating technology into physical education.
• Develop a lesson plan with two appropriate implementations of technology.

Technology and physical education (PE) are often considered at opposite ends of the educational spectrum—one sedentary and the other requiring movement. Tony Hall, in his keynote lecture given at the *International Association of Physical Education in Higher Education 2011 Conference,* addressed this very dilemma, suggesting that interactive technology needs be a solution to, rather than a reason for, "the serious contemporary educational and societal problems of inactivity, hypokinetic, and sedentary living" (Hall, 2012, p. 106). However, establishing or crossing the bridge with technology on one side and PE on the other can be difficult because of two major roadblocks—those from the perceptions of administrators and those self-imposed by physical educators. These roadblocks are not insurmountable, but they do require a plan, resting on the important idea that technology should enhance teaching, not replace it (Juniu, 2011).

## Administrative Roadblocks

Administrators and faculty technology committees often overlook the technology needs of PE. This oversight is not necessarily intentional but more often occurs because they are unaware of the technology possibilities within PE or because of financial restraints. Administrators may not consider the gymnasium a classroom. For instance, an interactive whiteboard is often out of the question in a gymnasium because of Internet capabilities, wiring, and safety concerns and because the gym is a multipurpose facility—often used for lunch, assemblies, interscholastic competitions, band and choral concerts, and so forth. Although having a separate classroom for PE would be ideal, it is rarely the reality, and many do not see retrofitting an older gymnasium with technology as being cost effective.

## Self-Imposed Roadblocks

Even as administrators often overlook how technology and PE can be partnered, physical educators may also overlook obvious links that could create this needed relationship. Most physical educators recognize the positives of technology in education but may not know how to implement them into the curriculum without taking away from activity time. Utilizing technology without adequate prep time for teachers to master its use may result in technology taking away from student learning and activity time (Sinclair, 2002). The key to maximizing the positive effects of technology in PE is to enlarge the physical educator's knowledge base. By starting small and enlisting the help of colleagues—with more than one person making an effort—the PE teacher can share and lessen frustration during the learning curve. For instance, creating a web page for PE on the school's website is a viable first step. Successfully implementing one piece of technology within PE will affirm its importance. It is also imperative that physical educators make administrators and technology committee members aware of the technology needs within PE.

## Teacher Preparation

In teacher education, technology is frequently an area in which all student teachers must demonstrate competence. Teacher preparation universities need to address how they are preparing future teachers in PE (Liang, Walls, Hicks, Clayton, & Yang, 2006) and emphasize the need for teacher candidates to meet technology standards (Southern Regional Education Board, n.d.). For instance, in Kentucky, technology is one of ten standards on which teacher candidates are evaluated. The candidate must display his or her ability to implement technology to (a) support instruction; (b) access and manipulate data; (c) enhance professional growth and productivity; (d) communicate and collaborate with colleagues, parents, and the community; and (e) conduct research (Kentucky Teacher Standards, 2008). The National Council for Accreditation of Teacher Education (NCATE) also emphasizes the importance of technology for teachers and for student learning.

## Technology in PE

Technology can be implemented in a number of areas within the teaching of PE: unit and lesson plan preparation; classroom management; communication with parents and students; instruction and feedback; and assessment. However, too often physical educators implement technology only to meet the standards without discovering the how, why, and when to best use the technologies available ("Does Technology," 2012). Technology should be used to enhance student learning, to save time, and to motivate the student and the teacher. Technology should not be used just to meet state or district requirements. The challenge is how to find best uses of technology for PE.

### Class preparation

The most common and accessible way for PE teachers to use technology is in their preparation for the school year. Numerous websites to which teachers can refer are available in this area: www.pecentral.com; www.aahperd.org/naspe; www.braingym.com; www.pe4life.org; www.letsmove.gov; and www.spark.org. At these sites, physical educators can find inspiration for units, outlines, lesson plans, and national and state standards as well as new ideas to augment their knowledge and experiences. In addition, physical educators from around the United States and the world can collaborate, share ideas, and problem solve, thereby further expanding their knowledge bases. Sharing via the Internet is also a valuable tool for new teachers as they prepare for their classes.

### Classroom management

Keeping students meaningfully active is the primary goal of physical educators, but this is sometimes a difficult task. Music is a great addition to physical activities, useful for getting the students moving faster, keeping them motivated and moving, or calming them down. Software such as *GarageBand* (www.apple.com/ilife/garageband)—a tool that can create, write, or edit music as well as record songs—is advantageous to use in PE (Miller, n.d.). It allows a PE teacher to create musical loops with sound effects that the teacher then plays to signal students to move from station to station. For example, one piece of music can designate time for working at a station; a sound effect can signal equipment return at that station; another piece of music can then cue transition from one station to another; and a sound effect can signal students to begin the next station. This musical loop can be repeated until the students have moved through all the stations. Because the music is set up on a continuous loop, the PE teacher no longer needs to turn the music off and on manually or remotely to signal student rotation but can move freely about the gym, providing instruction and immediate feedback as well as monitoring off-task behavior.

### Communication

A PE web page is a great technology tool with which to keep students, parents, colleagues, administrators, school board members, and the community informed. Daily PE routines, special events, review worksheets, exams, PE policies, and so forth can all be communicated to stakeholders via the Internet. Also, having an area on the web page for parents and other viewers to submit questions and concerns provides an additional opportunity for communication. PE advocacy is yet another reason for such a web page. Links to community recreation opportunities and tips on health and wellness can promote lifetime physical activity for the entire family.

However, a PE web page is only valuable if its contents are up-to-date; reading information that is 2 years old will not give others, including administrators, the impression that technology is important. PE teachers must have a systematic strategy in place to keep information current. For example, the organizational concept of only *handle it once* can be utilized to ensure timely information. PE teachers can write their units and assignments right into their web page while they plan, rather than having to plan, transfer, and update.

## Instruction and feedback

Physical educators are often their own worst enemies when it comes to technology because they sense that technology operates against the very soul of their mission: to help students be physically active! *Technology and PE* appears to be an oxymoron, but the terms can complement each other. Video game consoles such as Wii (Nintendo, 2013), pedometers, heart rate monitors, iPads, active apps, interactive whiteboards, digital video recorders, and so forth can all be used to help students understand the relationships among the key components of physical education: motor skills, fitness, and physical activity. For example, a PE teacher may use a camcorder to record, share, and critique a student's performance. In their research, Banville and Polifki (2009) found a student's ability to learn and perform motor skills increased with the use of digital video recorders. Furthermore, digital videos are teacher friendly because they can be recorded and played back without any interruption to instructional time (Banville & Polifko, 2009).

Another application of technology to enhance instruction and feedback is to make available videos of appropriate skill performance and game play. Such videos can be used during the teaching, review, and assessment portions of a PE unit. Every day brings a new app for nutritional tracking, video feedback, PE rules, workout routines, and so forth. The number of apps and the rate at which they are hitting the market is astounding. Many schools are now providing iPads for each student or portable learning labs, so the possibilities of using apps for direct instruction and feedback are limitless.

## Assessment

Although much of the physical skill assessment done in PE is time consuming by nature, technology can be a time saver if used properly (Graham, Holt-Hale, & Parker, 2013). For instance, to save precious in-class time for physical activity, teachers can assess cognitive knowledge with exams given online outside of class time; feedback on these exams can be immediate. Another advantage is that record keeping for student attendance and grades can be linked directly to the teacher's grade-reporting system for easy access and distribution from various mobile devices such as tablets, iPads, or smart phones. Students can also utilize these devices to selfassess motor performance by analyzing their skills immediately through videos. In addition, using software such as MovieMaker (Microsoft, 2013), students can showcase the application of their PE knowledge and skill through the creation of instructional and performance movies. Technology makes this type of authentic assessment more meaningful for the student and the teacher (Kovar, Combs, Campbell, Napper-Owen, & Worrell, 2012).

## Conclusion

Despite the roadblocks, a partnership of technology and PE is workable and beneficial for all involved. Frustrated by early failures with technology, many physical educators may give up or under-utilize technology just to say they are using it. The ability to understand technology may appear to some a natural-born trait; however, just like the acquisition of any skill-related endeavor in PE, time on task makes the difference. Once they invest the time and effort to learn technology, teachers who use it for unit and lesson plan preparation, classroom management, communication with parents and students, instruction and feedback, and assessment can save enormous amounts of time and energy. Truly, developing and improving the partnership between technology and PE is vital for student learning and needs to be a priority for all stakeholders—physical educators, administrators, classroom teachers, parents, and students.

## References

Apple, Inc. (2013). GarageBand [Computer software]. Cupertino, CA: Author. Available from http://www.apple.com/ilife/garageband/

Banville, D., & Polifko, M. F. (2009). Using digital video recorders in physical education. *Journal of Physical Education, Recreation & Dance, 80*(1), 17–21. doi:10.1080/07303084.2009.10598262

Does technology in physical education enhance or increase the time available to engage in physical activity? (2012), *Journal of Physical Education, Recreations & Dance, 83*(7), 53–56.

Graham, G., Holt-Hale, S. H., & Parker, M. (2013). *Children moving: A reflective approach to teaching physical education.* New York, NY: McGraw-Hill.

Hall, T. (2012). Emplotment, embodiment, engagement: Narrative technology in support of physical education, sport and physical activity. *Quest, 64*(2), 105–115. doi:10.1080/00336297.2012.669324

Juniu, S. (2011). Pedagogical uses of technology in physical education. *Journal of Physical Education, Recreation & Dance, 82*(9), 41–49. doi:10.1080/07303084.2011.10598692

Kentucky Education Professional Standards Board. (2008). *Kentucky teacher standards.* Retrieved from http://www.kyepsb.net/teacherprep/standards.asp

Kovar, S. K., Combs, C. A., Campbell, K., Napper-Owen, G., & Worrell, V.J. (2012). *Elementary classroom teachers as movement educators.* New York, NY: McGraw-Hill.

Liang, G., Walls, R. T., Hicks, V. L., Clayton, L. B., & Yang, L. (2006). Will tomorrow's physical educators be prepared to teach in the digital age? *Contemporary Issues in Technology and Teacher Education,* 6(1), 143–156.

Microsoft, Inc. (2013). MovieMaker [computer software]. Redmond, WA. Retrieved from http://windows.microsoft.com/en-us/windows-live/movie-maker#tl=overview

Miller, A. (n.d.). Podcasting tool: GarageBand [web page]. Retrieved from https://sites.google.com/site/adammillerphysedandhealth/podcast

Nintendo of America, Inc. (2013). Wii [Video game system]. Redmond, WA: Author. Retrieved from http://www.nintendo .com/wii

Sinclair, C. (2002). A technology project in physical education. *Journal of Physical Education, Recreation & Dance,* 73(6), 23–27. doi:10.1080/07303084.2002.10607823

Southern Regional Education Board. (n.d.). *Technology standards for teachers.* Retrieved from http:/www.sreb.org/page/1380/

## Critical Thinking

1. Review the roadblocks mentioned in the article. Then develop an argument for using technology to overcome two of the administrative and two of the self-imposed roadblocks.
2. Use the websites in the article and mentioned here to find at least three technologies (software or devices) to support your teaching. Write a letter to your principal or school board explaining how these tools would enhance students' skills and help them develop a healthy lifestyle.
3. To help your principal/school board understand the practical use of technology in physical education and support your request for technology, develop one or two lesson plans using the technology you have requested.

## Internet References

**iPhys-Ed.com**
   http://www.iphys-ed.com/technology-in-pe
**PE Central**
   http://www.pecentral.org/
**The PE Geek**
   https://thepegeek.com/

# Technology and Young Children: How 4–7 Year Olds Perceive Their Own Use of Computers

In the past century, the introduction of new media such as films, radio and television, has spawned debate and research concerning the (educational) benefits for children versus the fears related to (over)exposure. In this millennium, the opportunities and concerns regarding widely accessible Information and Communications Technologies (ICTs) are no different. Society's perceptions of technology and expectations for its use are important. Those notions impact the use of computers at home, as well as shape the course of implementation in educational settings. While many assert that computers do not have a place at the hands of young children, others contend that those who do not embrace new media may be in danger of losing touch with the popular culture of young children and their families.

While the debate in favor of and against young children's computer use rages on, there is little dispute that today, children are using computers even before they know how to read and write. However, research is lacking on how young children use computers and what the (intentional and unintentional) effects are. This is especially true in the Netherlands. Current literature is dominated by investigations conducted in the United States. Studies involving young children and computers have increased in recent years, with greater emphasis on exploring innovative applications for this age range and only a few examining usage patterns. Of those studies that look at how children are using computers, most rely on parent and caregiver reports; and very few involve asking children directly about how they perceive their own use of computers. In analyzing the 60 structured interviews and 1852 questionnaire responses from parents and caregivers in the England, [it was] found:

- *Frequency:* 53% of the children in the 0–6 age range use computers on a typical day, usually for less than 1 hour.
- *Type:* Children's favorite type of application was playing games, either on websites (especially those associated with BBC television programs) or on CD/DVD.
- *Gender:* When listing website favorites, boys' and girls' preferences were the same for the first three rankings (CBeebies, CBBC, and Nickolodeon Junior, respectively), but differed in the fourth and fifth rankings. Boys preferred Bob the Builder and Thomas the Tank Engine, while girls liked Barbie and the Tweenies.
- *Parental attitude:* Parents were overwhelmingly positive about their children using computers, noting their acquisition of computing skills as well as software-specific knowledge and skills as beneficial. Concerns about the children using computers were not expressed.

Perhaps even more problematic is the prevalence of "few facts and many opinions" about the use of computers by young children. The need for increased research into young children's computer use has been expressed by researchers and practitioners. Though early, this call is garnering response, as exemplified by programs and projects undertaken on both sides of the Atlantic such as:

- Technology and Young Children Special Interest Forum within the [American] National Association for the Education of Young Children (NAEYC); and
- Children's Awareness of Technology (CHAT) and
- Developmentally Appropriate Technology in Early Childhood (DATEC), sponsored by the European Union. . . .

As early as the 1990s, young children's attitudes towards computers [have been studied]. Data were collected from 1990 to 1994 and examined the impact of computer use on children in grade 1–3 (6–9 year olds) from Japan, the USA and Mexico. The results showed that computer exposure in school had a positive impact on children's attitudes towards computers and that children's perceptions of computers were not related to their home country. Studies such as this have not been conducted in the Netherlands. Therefore, the research reported in this paper focuses on computer attitudes, computer use and computer skills of pre-K–grade 2 children (4–7 year olds), an age range slightly younger than the children who were involved in the study reported above. Better insight in computer use and attitudes of young children informs the debate of the desirability of young children's exposure to computers at home as well as in educational settings.

As with an educational resource, equitable use is worthy of consideration. . . . Gender differences in attitudes towards computers for children in grade 1–3 [were not found], girls' participation in technology-related activities has been a serious concern in the last decade. Perhaps even more disquieting is the 'digital divide,' now generally defined as "situations in which there is a marked gap in access to or use of ICT devices". The digital divide usually exists when a group's access to ICT differs along one or more dimensions of social, economic, cultural, or national identity. In this study, we explore whether indications can be found for a digital divide in this age range with respect to gender, socio-economic status and (ethnic) minority versus (ethnic) majority groups in the Dutch society. Studies with older children have shown that lower-income students have less access to computers in the home, and use computers at school more often for repetitive practice; whereas higher-income students have far greater access to computers in the home and use computers at school more often for more sophisticated, intellectually complex applications. . . . Very few of the already scarce studies looking at computer use in this age range, examine the access to ICT with regard to gender and ethnic minorities. What we do know . . . [from one] study:

- Considerable inequality of access to ICT in the home: In this study, 28 children were from English families, 17 from Bangladeshi families, and 3 from another ethnic origin (African and Kosovan). 26 of the 48 households contained a computer, but only 3 of these were in Bangladeshi homes.
- Young girls are as likely as young boys to be using a home computer.
- Middle-class parents tend to be more involved in their children's computer use than lower class parents.
- No evidence that home advantages in terms of technology access directly influenced computer use at school.

The finding that girls and boys are equally likely to be using a home computer is consistent with the findings of a previous study. However, the finding that home advantages do not influence computer use at school is especially interesting, as it is contradicted by the beliefs of early years educators who responded to an earlier . . . survey.

The study reported in this article took place in the Netherlands, and speaks to the need for better insight into how children are using computers, how they experience computers, and differences associated with gender and ethnicity. With the ultimate aim of understanding how Dutch 4–7 year olds perceive their own use of computers, the following four research questions were formulated:

1.  Is access to computers outside school associated with gender, age, socio-economic status or ethnic group?
2.  What activities do young children do on the computer, in and out of school?
3.  To what extent are they able to conduct these activities independently or with help?
4.  What attitudes do young children have?
5.  Are differences in the use, skills or attitudes associated with gender, age, socio-economic status and ethnic group?

# Methods

## Participants

Children in pre-kindergarten (pre-K) through second grade (Dutch groups 1–4) from two schools participated. In total, 167 children (82 boys and 85 girls) were involved in the study. The age range varied between 4 and 8 years. The Dutch school system starts at the age of 4 when children start in pre-K, and is compulsory from kindergarten (K) starting at age 5. In the Netherlands, 98% of all 4-year olds attend pre-K. In this study we explored in and out of school use of computers. For this reason we prefer not to use age level, but to use grade level as an indicator of age. In the Dutch school system most four year olds attend pre-K, most 5 year old attend K, the 6 year olds are in grade 1 and the most 7 year olds are in grade 2. Learning to read and to write, as well as basic arithmetic starts in grade 1, but preparatory activities are carried out in pre-K and K.

Regardless of nationality, children were classified as native Dutch or Dutch immigrants. In accordance with national guidelines, native Dutch children were defined as those whose parents were both born in the Netherlands; children of one or more parents born in another country were categorized as Dutch immigrants. Both schools were located in the same city of 150,000. One school, hereafter referred to as "Southside," is located on the outskirts of town, in an area of lower socio-economic status and many second and third generation immigrant families from Morocco or Turkey with Arab-Berber or Turkish ethnic backgrounds, respectively. Teachers in this school openly share their ongoing concerns about pupil welfare and regularly conduct home visits. 81 children from this school participated in the study. 36 were classified as Dutch natives, and can be considered as belonging to the ethnic majority; while 45 were classified as immigrants and belonging to the ethnic minorities present in this part of town. In this study, we consider the immigrants of Southside to represent ethnic minorities and compare them with the Dutch natives from Southside as a representation of an ethnic majority group.

The other school, hereafter referred to as, "Central," is located in the city center, with primarily middle class children attending. Pupil welfare issues are less common in this school, and home visits by teachers are rarely made. This school is the only school in the region that offers instruction in English for long-term visiting children whose parents work in international companies or at the local university. Children attend the English language class a few hours each day, but spend the majority of their time in their home class with the Dutch children. In addition, the school prides itself on their Early English program, teaching English as a second language to Dutch-speaking children from pre-K onwards, which is exceptional in the Dutch education system. From this school, 86 children participated, with 58 classified as Dutch natives (ethnic majority) and 33 as immigrants. It should be noted, however, that this group of immigrants is much more mixed than those from Southside, and cannot be classified as an ethnic minority group.

. . . [W]e view the Southside population to represent low socio-economic status and the Central population to represent middle socio-economic status.

Both schools had similar technology facilities: one or two computers in each classroom and computer clusters in one or more hallways. Southside has a technology coordinator who manages the infrastructure and also worked with the children on a weekly basis. This school prides itself on their approach to technology integration, which begins with the pre-K groups. In contrast, Central assigns the role of technology coordinator to a regular class room teacher, whose main task is to manage the infrastructure including, when necessary coordination with the service provider. Both schools used the same third-party provider for technology services.

## Data Collection

In a preliminary study conducted in 2003, experience was ac quired in collecting data with children of this age level. The data for this study were collected through one-on-one interviews with the children. The interviews contained closed questions and were designed to take less than 15 min each. They addressed five areas: demographics, computer availability/access, computer activities use, attitudes and abilities. . . .

*Demographics.* The demographics section included name, class, school, grade, age, gender, land of birth (of self and parents) and language spoken at home.

*Computer availability, access and activity types.* . . . For school and at home, the computer activities section included the following categories of activities: practicing words/math; drawing; writing letters/stories; playing games; searching for information on Internet; reading/writing e-mail; and chatting (this last one was only asked for at home, as schools do not allow this practice). . . .

*Attitudes.* The attitude section was based on the computer importance and computer enjoyment subscales . . . designed for first through third graders. . . .

*Skills to use the computer independently.* . . . Children indicated how they used each computer activity: independently, with help, or neither (meaning, not at all). . . .

Except for the demographic information, black and white icons on colored cards were used to help the learners understand and stay focused on the interview questions. For example, children were shown the school icon card and then asked, "While at school, do you use the computer?" If they said yes, then a yellow set of cards was shown. . . . Children were then told what each one meant, then asked to turn face-down the ones that represent activities they did not do. For the remaining activities, children were asked if they did this often (daily or weekly) or sometimes (less than once a week). Children were first given practice questions on how often they watch television or go to the movies. . . .

The interviews were conducted with two trained interviewers. They used the icon cards when asking each question to a child and based on the child's answer completed the questionnaire. . . .

## Results

### Access to Computers Outside School

While both schools have computer facilities for use by the children, we were more interested in the availability of computers for children at home. The results . . . show that the penetration of computers at home is very high. It is notable that there is a relatively low presence of computers (computers with Internet access in particular) in the homes of Dutch native children in Southside. However, the overall picture is that most children do have access to a computer, often with Internet access, in their homes.

If you ask the children where, outside school, they mainly use the computer, most of them report that they use the computer at home. A few also use the computer mainly at a friend's house or at school (after school hours). Almost 10% of children in pre-K report not using the computer outside of school. Also, (relatively few) girls report more often than boys that they do not use the computer outside school.

### In and Out of School Computer Use: Activities

. . . The findings show that only a few children report never playing a computer game, but that many at this age level never search the Internet or read or write e-mail.

. . . Boys and girls do not differ a lot in the kind of use of the computer. Both boys and girls report that in school and outside the school they use the computer most often for 'playing a game.' This is followed by 'practicing words/math' (in school use) and 'searching the Internet' (out of school use). 'Reading and writing e-mail' is the least often mentioned use of the computer in this age range both in school and outside school. Although the majority of the children (both boys and girls) never chat on the computer, 'chatting' is fairly often mentioned by about 40% of the children as an activity they do on the computer.

. . . Medium–medium effect sizes in favor of boys were found for 'drawing' 'writing a letter/story', 'playing a game', indicating that boys use the computer in school for these activities more often than girls. With regard to out of school use, a medium⁺ effect size was found in favor of boys for 'searching the internet' and a medium effect size for 'drawing' in favor of girls.

. . . With regard to in school use, children report that 'playing games' is most often used in the lower grades (4–5 year olds), but in the middle grades (6–7 year olds) 'playing games' and 'practicing words/math' is about equally reported. The other activities are mentioned considerably less. A large effect size between pre-K and grade 2, in favor of the latter, is found for 'practicing words/ math', it indicates that in the middle grades compared to the lower grades the computer is more often used for school-based activities. Also 'writing a letter/story' is mentioned considerably more in grade 2 compared to pre-K, which makes sense, because pre-K students usually do not have formal writing skills. A medium⁺ effect size of 'playing a game' in favor of pre-K indicates that games are more often used in the lower grades.

. . . [O]utside school, an increase in use is found for all distinguished computer activities for grade 2 children compared to children in pre-K. 'Playing games' clearly is the most frequent use of the computer across grade levels. Followed by 'searching the Internet' (pre-K, grade 1 and grade 2) and 'drawing' (K).

. . . The overall picture is the same: both groups use the computer most often for playing games, both in school and outside school. Concerning the use of computers in school, differences be tween the two groups with medium to large effect sizes for writing letter/story and playing a game, suggesting that Dutch natives at Southside use the computer in school for these activities more often than their immigrant peers. For the other activities, no differences were found between the two groups. However, out of school computer use provides a very different picture. Immigrant children seem to use the computer more often for quite a number of activities. . . . The only activity for which Dutch native children report more frequent use than their immigrant peers, is 'writing a letter/story'.

. . . The picture that emerges throughout is the use of the computer for playing games, which seems the most favorite use for children from both schools. With regard to in school use, children attending Southside use the computer more, compared to Central children, for 'drawing', while children at Central use the computer more for searching the Internet, and reading/writing e-mail. It should be noted however that e-mail use does not happen very often in both schools. The picture for computer use outside school is different. Southside children use the computer more for chatting; drawing, writing letter/story and reading/writing email compared to their peers from Central, while Central children use the computer, more for playing games.

## Skills to Operate the Computer Independently

. . . The results . . . show that the majority of both boys and girls in this age range are able to play a computer game, start a computer game, make a drawing and search on the Internet alone or with some help. Differences in skills between boys and girls, with small⁺ effect sizes, were found for starting a computer game (in favor of boys), writing a letter/story (in favor of girls) and searching for information (in favor of boys).

With respect to grade level, the results show that the majority of the youngest children in pre-K are already able to start and play a game (with help or alone). However, it is striking that already at this age level (most pre-K children are 4 years old) so many children report being able—often with help—to handle the computer. It far less surprising that this has changed by grade 2 (most children are then 7 years old). In grade 2, the majority is able to use the computer (with help or alone) for all the different skills that were distinguished. . . .

. . . The results show that the majority of children in both ethnic groups (Dutch natives and immigrants) are able to start and play a computer game and to make a drawing. The majority of the immigrants at Southside are also able to search for information on the Internet. . . .

With regard to socio-economic status, we did find differences . . . in favor of Southside with regard to making a drawing, reading/writing e-mail and chatting. But, Central children report being more able to write a letter/story compared to their Southside peers.

## Attitudes

Overall, children express positive attitudes towards computers. Significant differences in attitudes towards computers were found for gender (in favor of boys), grade level (in favor of the older children in grade 2) and socio-economic status (in favor of the children from a lower socio-economic neighborhood, Southside).

## Discussion and Conclusions

Examining how young children perceive their use of computers provides information for educators and parents, many of whom are struggling to find practical, developmentally appropriate applications of technology in classrooms and at home. This study set out to explore young children's access to computers, their perceptions of what they do on the computer (in school and outside school), their abilities to operate the computer for specific activities, and their attitudes towards computers. . . .

The findings of this study showed that most young children had access to computers, regardless of gender, socio-economic background or ethic group. . . . The findings of this study suggest that the digital divide with regard to computer access is not so much an issue anymore in the Netherlands, but more large scale studies are needed to confirm this conclusion.

Regardless of gender, age, socio-economic status and ethic group, playing games is the computer activity young children most frequently do, both at home and at school. As playing games is the most common way for children of all ages to spend their free time, it is not surprising that children report playing games as the most frequent computer activity at home both in this study and in research with older children. Next to playing games, searching the Internet is the second most-frequently reported activity for out of school computer use. The other activities are carried out less often.

It is notable that children report that they also use the computer most for playing games while at school. Children in pre-K (4 year olds) play games in school more often than their peers from grade 2 (7 year olds). These results may imply that the computer in school is used as a bonus for children who are finished with their school tasks and are allowed to play a game on the computer. However, it is also possible that especially the younger children experience their activity as a game, even though their teachers might differently describe the same software, due to its affordances with regard to, for example, learning or practice in the area of (preparatory) literacy or numeracy. Further research is necessary to better understand this finding. Next to playing games, practicing words/math is the second reported use of the computer in school. This computer activity increases with grade level. Except for drawing on the computer, the other activities are carried out less often across grade levels. For in school computer use, not many differences were found between boys and girls, nor between Dutch natives and immigrants. However, at Southside the computer is used considerably more for drawing and at Central for searching the Internet. It is not clear whether this is due to the socio-economic background of the school population or if this has more to do with other factors, such as the educational view of the school team.

It is no surprise that outside school, older children (grade 2) use the computer more often and also are more able to operate the computer for a variety of activities than younger ones (pre-K). Literature has long suggested that pupil attitudes toward computers are favorable; this is consistent with the findings from this study. In addition, this study found that older children have a more positive attitude towards computers than younger children have.

Concern about girls' lack of interest in technology has been growing in the last decade. No big differences between boys and girls out of school computer use were found. Also no gender differences were found in the ability level of using various computer activities. These findings concur with those from a recent study in which young girls and young boys were equally likely to be using a home computer as well as another in which young girls now report using home computers as often, and with as much confidence as boys. While the findings of this study revealed that boys have a comparably more positive attitude towards computers than girls have, both groups remain generally positive. . . . Children's perceptions of computers are also influenced by the software they use. [A] gender-bias content analysis of educational software for preschoolers found significantly more male characters than female characters in preschool educational software, which . . . makes it difficult for teachers to address gender diversity and suggests that girls are not as valued as boys are. Subsequent research on gender differences in computing would benefit from a deeper look at the software being used.

Literature suggests that ethnic minority children may be disadvantaged by a lack of home experience with computers. The findings of this study suggest that immigrant children have more exposure to computers out of school than Dutch children from a low socio-economic background. In addition, immigrant children seem to be better able to operate the computer for a number of different activities, searching information on the Internet in particular. An explanation put forth by Southside teachers is that, often, computer use in immigrant families is focused on communication with family members still living in the country of origin. However, more research is necessary to fully understand this finding. No differences between immigrant children and Dutch children were found in attitude towards computers. The findings of this study also suggest that children from a lower socio-economic background use the computer slightly more often outside school compared to middle class children, and have a more positive attitude towards computers. . . . Further research is necessary to understand how crucial it is that schools take it upon themselves to ensure equal opportunity for less-advantaged children to access the benefits of the more intellectually powerful uses of computer technology. . . .

It is known that the benefits of using technology with young children vary with the kind of experiences offered and how frequently the children have access to computers. . . . As our picture of how children are spending their computer time sharpens, further research should be conducted into the quality and appropriateness of those experiences. . . . Understanding children's practices and attitudes can inform educators and parents in the search for developmentally appropriate uses of technology, as well as a healthy balance between computer use and other means for children to learn and explore the world around them.

SUSAN MCKENNEY is a professor at the University of Twente and the Open Universiteit in the Netherlands, specializing in curriculum design and educational innovation. Her work has emphasized the supportive role of technology in curriculum and teacher development, with a recent focus on early childhood literacy. She has consulted broadly in the Netherlands, India, and southern Africa, offering research expertise in the design, evaluation, and revision of educational improvement initiatives.

JOKE VOOGT, is an associate professor in the Department of Curriculum Design and Educational Innovation at the University of Twente, in the Netherlands. The primary focus of her research is on innovative uses of information and communication technologies in the curriculum, with a special interest in the demands on teachers when integrating technology into the classroom. She also serves as editor-in-chief of the *International Handbook of Information Technology in Primary and Secondary Education.*

# Article 18

## High-Tech Bullies

Prepared by: Claire N. Rubman, *Suffolk County Community College*

Suicides have made administrators aware that acts of aggression in the wireless, viral world of the Internet demand action to protect targeted students.

### Learning Outcomes

*After reading this issue, you will be able to:*
• Identify the most vulnerable members of our society who are most prone to bullying.
• Describe what colleges and universities are doing to combat cyberbullying.

Cases of cyberbullying have made headlines over the past decade, raising awareness about the number of young people who have committed suicide or otherwise been harmed as a result of being on the receiving end of constant Internet harassment or shaming.

Bullying that started in email and chat rooms in the early days of the Internet has evolved into other forms—mostly social networking sites and instant messaging, as well as video and pictures, Justin W. Patchin, PhD, co-director of the Cyberbullying Research Center at the University of Wisconsin-Eau Claire, agrees.

"It's constantly changing," he said. "The bullies are pretty creative. Now there is a level of permanence that is not evident in traditional bullying. Early adopters are most likely to use new technology. It's amazing how creative some can be to cause harm."

Patchin, author of *Words Wound: Delete Cyberbullying and Make Kindness Go Viral* (Free Spirit Publishing, December 2013), has been studying cyberbullying among secondary students for more than a decade, starting in 2001. He has surveyed nearly 15,000 students across the United States.

Most cases seem to involve middle school or high school students, whom experts say, are in the primary age group for such behavior.

However, as social media continues its pervasive intrusion into everyday lives, cyberbullying is trickling up to college campuses and even into the workplace. Researchers, law-enforcement lawyers, college officials, and students say there are more reported incidents of acts of cyberbullying cropping up on campus and a rise in incidents of teenage suicide has coincided with the rise in incidents of cyberbullying. In fact, the suicide of Rutgers University freshman Tyler Clementi in 2010, who was the target of a campaign of intimidation by his roommate, put universities on notice that what might have once been treated as a college prank could lead to suicide for vulnerable students. Clementi jumped off the George Washington Bridge after learning that his roommate spied on him during a romantic encounter with a man using a webcam. Clementi also learned that his roommate conspired to "out" him by alerting Twitter followers to a second viewing.

### Attacking the Vulnerable

Cyberbullies often target gays, women or people of color. Students who are different in some way (race, ethnicity, sexual orientation, religion, or appearance) or high-profile students (athletes, student government officers) are often the most vulnerable.

Jiyoon Yoon, associate professor and director of the elementary education program at University of Texas at Arlington, said via email that while nearly anyone can be a victim, most victims are targeted because of perceived differences from a group and weaknesses.

"Students who do not fit in may become the prime targets of cyberbullying," she said. "In many contexts, students of minority status and/or lower economic privilege may be more susceptible to the abuse."

Yoon said victims of such bullying are more likely to report feelings of depression than other groups of students, which interfere with their scholastic achievement, social skills, and sense of well-being. She has conducted research with Dr. Julie Smith on cyberbullying among college students and says it is increasing. According to survey responses conducted by Yoon and Smith within a Midwestern university system, 10.1 percent of the students said they experienced cyberbullying by another student; 2.9 percent of the students had been cyberbullied by instructors, and 27.5 percent of the students witnessed cyberbullying behavior by a student toward another student.

This is consistent with other studies on cyberbullying. In one study conducted at Indiana State University, 22 percent of college students reported being cyberbullied, and 9 percent reported cyberbullying someone.

"People thought cyberbullying happened mostly among teenagers who are familiar with and willingly use electronic technology," Yoon said. "However, as portability and accessibility of technology for distance learning increases daily in higher education, incidents of cyberbullying are rising on college campuses."

Dawn Harner, a training coordinator and counselor at Salisbury University, said a potent mix of 24/7, always-on communication lends itself to abuses. She cited the pervasive use of connected mobile devices, multiple social media profiles from Facebook to Twitter to Instagram, growth in text messaging and decline in phone conversations, the illusion of anonymity and the international reach of the Internet, coupled with students' immaturity and newly found freedom.

"It is much more common for students to be connected to social media," Harner said. "Now, as opposed to seven years ago, phones connect to Internet as well."

Researchers are just starting to examine the rise in university-level bullying. Today, universities are obligated to face the problem before another student is hurt. First, they must define cyberbullying.

"A lot of times as academics, we debate definitions," said Patchin. "What's the difference between hazing, bullying and harassing? All could be the same behaviors. We don't focus on it until something happens. We have to focus on behaviors that repeatedly cause harm to another person." Although definitions vary, cyberbullying can be defined as acts of aggression and subterfuge against someone that gain power through digital technology.

The problems can range from the use of gossip sites like JuicyCampus, College Anonymous Confessions Board or College Wall of Shame to "revenge porn sites," in which former lovers upload photos of ex-girl friends and to stalking by emails and text messages. Some of the most popular vehicles for cyberbullying, said Yoon, are Facebook texting, email, Twitter, and YouTube. Other technologies or applications and online gaming technologies, such as AOL Instant Messenger, MSN Messenger MySpace and League of Legends, as well as online forums, message boards, blogs, are also used. Researchers have identified several types of aggression, which include online stalking, flaming, fights, and arguments; posting embarrassing or incriminating photos of a victim; outing, revealing secrets; exclusion and masquerading as someone else.

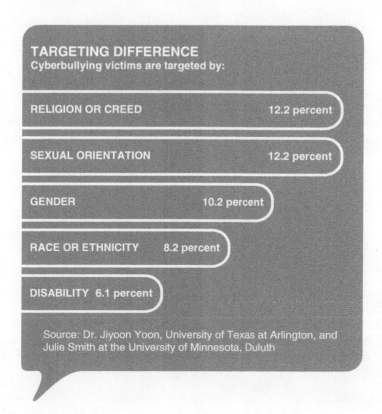

**TARGETING DIFFERENCE**
Cyberbullying victims are targeted by:

RELIGION OR CREED — 12.2 percent

SEXUAL ORIENTATION — 12.2 percent

GENDER — 10.2 percent

RACE OR ETHNICITY — 8.2 percent

DISABILITY — 6.1 percent

Source: Dr. Jiyoon Yoon, University of Texas at Arlington, and Julie Smith at the University of Minnesota, Duluth

Aggressors may send mean text messages or emails, spread rumors by email or social networking sites, and they may post videos, put up embarrassing websites, or create fake profiles of a victim. The use of technology means that victims can be exposed to an audience of millions and may be unable to escape scrutiny.

Students also face dangers from impersonation, fraud and trickery online. In one infamous incident, Manti Te'o, the Notre Dame star linebacker and a finalist for the Heisman Trophy, became a victim of "catfishing." He met someone online who pretended to become his "girlfriend" even though they had never met. The ruse was uncovered by a sports website after she was reported to have died. Similarly, MTV's reality TV show called "Catfish" focuses on deceptions in online dating and is popular among college students.

One of the main characteristics of the cyberbullying is that bullies believe they can act anonymously, said Yoon. "They can harass their victims without the victims ever knowing who or why they are being cyberbullied," she said. "The various forms of current professional technology on campus allow the victims to be continually victimized without identifying the perpetrators." Experts can determine the identities of the abusers, however. The pervasiveness of social media, said Elaine Heath, PhD, dean for Student Services at Howard University, and the fact that the reasoning capabilities in adolescents do not fully mature until age 25, makes students emotionally ill equipped to handle the consequences of being a bully or being bullied.

"They are not mature enough to pick up social cues to determine this is inappropriate behavior," Heath said. "They are shocked when you tell them. Young people don't understand the boundaries and the appropriateness of how to use it."

Heath said bullying often reveals a degree of anger and deepseated emotions. "It will start within the person and then triggers an outward manifestation," she said. "Anger or emotional problems will be acted out. They will continue the conversation with social media. It's a lack of impulse control."

When Heath asks students why they do it, she said many have given no thought to their actions. "Bottom line, people don't think about it," she said. "They are angry and want to get their story and their say out. These children live in reality TV."

"It's about power and control to instill fear," she said. "People don't fear the consequences. There is a lack of empathy, lack of control, and immaturity around relationships. A lot people don't know how to have healthy relationships."

## HANDLING THE CYBERBULLY

Colleges and universities are developing courses, starting anti-bully campaigns and offering mentoring relationships and other tools to deal with the emerging social issue of cyberbullying. Rutgers University opened the Tyler Clementi Center to help students adjust to college life. Other colleges and universities are developing anti-bullying policies and taking other actions to combat problems of cyberbullying and "online incivility."

In many states, schools are required to address cyberbullying in their anti-bullying policy. Some state laws also cover off-campus behavior that creates a hostile school environment. Some universities also address direct punishment of the cyberbullying and provide special reporting tools when cyberbullying is exhibited.

University instructors/faculty are also required to report cyberbullying incidents. University IT staffs record and track incidences and courses on college campuses contain "netiquette" rules in syllabi. As most colleges and universities realize the seriousness of cyberbullying on campus, said Dr. Jiyoon Yoon, associate professor and director of the elementary education program at University of Texas at Arlington, they start to incorporate anti-cyberbullying policies into the student handbook or student code of conduct and employment standards for faculty and staff. These policies are clear about what constitutes cyberbullying and what the penalties may be.

Dawn Harner, a training coordinator and counselor at Salisbury University, said the university has a program training first-year students as leaders and asking them to refer students to a counseling center if they are experiencing anxiety or depression as related to bullying.

Whitney Gibson, head of the Internet crises group for Vorys, Sater, Seymour, and Pease LLP, s said victims should tell someone at school or get help by talking to police or school officials or an expert to get screen shots of the offending posts, chats, messages, videos, or emails.

Yoon recommends that victims:

- Take immediate action but do not respond or forward cyberbullying messages.
- Keep evidence of cyberbullying.
- Learn how to use privacy settings to block the bully.
- Report cyberbullying to the social media site, law enforcement officials, the school and online service providers.
- Review the terms and conditions of service at social media sites and Internet service providers.

— Ingrid Sturgis

Patchin of the Cyberbullying Research Center said parents and teachers who may not use social media sometimes underestimate the seriousness of the issue. He said some adults ask cyberbullied students questions like, "Why can't you turn it off?"

"For high school and college students, it's a big part of their social lives," he said. "If you don't know anything about it, it's not a big problem."

Cyberbullying can have implications beyond the campus and maybe even have long-lasting legal ramifications for students. Whitney Gibson, a partner at Vorys, Sater, Seymour, and Pease LLP and head of the firm's Internet crises group, works with schools to help them educate students about the unintended consequences of Internet use.

"What I see is a lot of students using technology," he said. "A lot of students don't think what they are doing is a big deal . . . They don't understand how quickly that goes viral, and they can never get it down. There is a rise of serious damage being done to people on the Internet. People are dying. Kids are getting arrested for felony."

Gibson said students often don't realize that their online behavior, including posting pictures while drinking or using marijuana, as well as acts of bullying, can affect their scholarships or job prospects as more recruiters check social media sites. In addition, Gibson said, college students think they can conceal their identities with fake names.

"They don't realize that it is very hard to remain anonymous on the Internet," he said. "They end up getting in big trouble."

## Critical Thinking

1. How much supervision and monitoring is appropriate at the college level?
2. Where do we draw the line between teasing and cyberbullying?
3. How does technology like instagram, vine, and flikr contribute to cyberbullying?

## Create Central

www.mhhe.com/createcentral

## Internet References

**buzzfeed.com 9 Teenage Suicides In The Last Year Were Linked to Cyber-Bullying on Social Network Ask.fm**
http://www.buzzfeed.com/ryanhatesthis/a-ninth-teenager-since-last-september- has-committed-suicide
**cyberpsychology.eu Cyberbullying in Adolescent Victims: Perception and Coping**
http://www.cyberpsychology.eu/view.php?cisloclanku 5 2011121901
**Huffingtonpost.com 8 Scary Social Networking Sites Every Parent Should Know**
http://www.huffingtonpost.com/michael-gregg/8-scary-social-network-sites-every-parents-should-know_b_4178055.html
**thementalelf.net Bullying and Cyberbullying Increase the Risk of Suicidal Ideation and Suicide Attempts in Adolescents**
http://www.thementalelf.net/populations-and-settings/child-and-adolescent/bullying-and-cyberbullying-increase-the-risk-of-suicidal-ideation-and-suicideattempts-in-adolescents
**tylerclementi.org The Tyler Clementi Foundation**
http://www.tylerclementi.org/

**Ingrid Sturgis** is an author, journalist, and assistant professor specializing in new media in the Department of Media, Journalism and Film at Howard University.

Sturgis, Ingrid. "High-Tech Bullies." *Diverse: Issues in Higher Education, Convergence Supplement.* (February, 27, 2014): 19–23.

# Article 19

Allison A. Buskirk-Cohen

## Is Facebook Bad for College Students' Health?

Selected, Edited, and with Issue Framing Material by:
Allison A. Buskirk-Cohen, *Delaware Valley University*

**YES: Brian A. Feinstein, et al.,** from "Negative Social Comparison on Facebook and Depressive Symptoms: Rumination as a Mechanism," *Psychology of Popular Media Culture* (2013)

**NO: Amy L. Gonzales and Jeffrey T. Hancock,** from "Mirror, Mirror on My Facebook Wall: Effects of Exposure to Facebook on Self-esteem," *Cyberpsychology, Behavior, and Social Networking* (2011)

## Learning Outcomes

*After reading this issue, you will be able to:*
- Discuss how social networking experiences may put individuals at risk for depression and other mental health concerns.
- Understand that some research shows that social networking sites, such as Facebook, may increase likelihood of negative social comparisons which are associated with rumination, one pathway leading to depressive symptoms.
- Understand that other research indicates that Facebook enhances self-esteem through selective self-presentation which leads to intensified relationship formation.
- Recognize the nuances in how individuals use social networking sites may help explain differences in research findings.

## ISSUE SUMMARY

**YES:** Researchers Brian Feinstein and colleagues explore the link between use of social networking sites and depressive symptoms. Their study examined undergraduate students' use of Facebook. They argue that negatively comparing oneself with others is linked with rumination, which is linked with depression.

**NO:** The research from Amy Gonzales and Jeffrey Hancock presents a different view of the impact of social networking sites on mental health. Their research demonstrates how viewing one's Facebook profile actually enhances self-esteem through selective self-presentation.

## Where Do You Stand?

Social networking sites (SNS) are platforms that allow individuals to build social networks with others who share something in common—typically interests, activities, backgrounds, or other connections. SNS are web-based services that allow individuals to create a public profile, create a list of users to share connections with, and link with other users within the system. Most SNS allow users to interact using some type of messaging system. They offer social, informational and communication tools, such as the sharing of videos, photos, and links to other sources. SNS emerged in the 1990s, with many of the early communities, like Geocities and Tripod, using chat rooms to bring users together. In the late 1990s, user profiles became a popular feature that allows users to create lists of "friends" and search for others who share their interests. By the end of the decade, new developments provided more advanced features to find and manage "friend" lists. Friendster and MySpace became extremely popular, and SNS had become a part of mainstream society.

One of the most popular SNS today is Facebook. It launched in 2004 and had become the largest SNS in the world by 2009. Founded by college roommates Mark Zuckerberg and Eduardo Saverin, Facebook was originally limited to Harvard students as a way to connect with each other. It then expanded its membership options to other Ivy League colleges. Facebook grew in popularity, and was incorporated in the summer of 2004. By September 2006, everyone age thirteen and older was invited to join Facebook using a valid email address. By late 2007, Facebook had 100,000 business pages that allowed companies to attract users and communicate with them. By early 2011, Facebook had become the largest online photo host. By spring of 2014,

Facebook had over one billion monthly active users. (Active users are defined as those individuals who have logged in to Facebook during the past thirty days. This statistic means that Facebook actually has a greater number of total users than the number reported.)

SNS differ in terms of who their users are and how they behave online. According to the Pew Research Center, Facebook continues to dominate the SNS scene in terms of numbers of users. In the United States, women are more likely than men to use Facebook. It remains the top SNS for American adolescents; Facebook has more daily adolescent users than any other SNS. It is still considered a top site for college students. About one quarter of all Facebook users are college-aged individuals (ages 18 through 24). There are also differences in how users behave on Facebook compared with other SNS. The majority of Facebook users visit the site at least once a day, if not more.

Researchers have asked about potential consequences of Facebook use. Initially, people assumed that SNS would be beneficial, since there is a plethora of research showing the benefits of social contact. However, a study by University of Michigan psychologist Ethan Kross and his colleagues garnered the media's attention, with headlines warning readers about "Facebook depression." In the actual study, Kross and colleagues found that the more people used Facebook, the more their overall satisfaction declined. Past research has claimed that the Internet can be alienating, and tends to have negative socialization effects. The more people use the web, and Facebook in particular, the more lonely, depressed, and jealous they feel. However, some experts believe the opposite is true. Sebastián Valenzuela and his colleagues at the Pontificia Universidad Catolica de Chile found that using Facebook makes us happier. They also found that it increases social trust and engagement, and encourages political participation. The Pew Research Center's study of demographics also found that Facebook users are more politically engaged than other users.

In the YES selection of this issue, researchers Brian Feinstein and colleagues present findings from a study that help explain why Facebook use is linked with negative mental health outcomes. These researchers investigated two mechanisms that might explain this link by evaluating selfreport measures from a large group of undergraduate college students. The first mechanism explored was negative social comparisons. They believed that Facebook use might increase likelihood of negative social comparisons, since users can see frequent updates of their "friends" accomplishments. Negative social comparisons can maintain or exacerbate negative self-appraisals, which lead to poorer well-being. The other mechanism they considered was rumination. Rumination occurs when an individual repetitively focuses on his or her own distress, obsessing over potential causes and consequences. It has been linked with negative mental health, including depression. In fact, Feinstein and colleagues did find that individuals engaging in negative social comparisons while using Facebook placed themselves as risk for rumination, and, consequently, depressive symptoms.

However, might Facebook use involve behaviors other than negative social comparisons? Indeed, in the NO selection, Amy Gonzales and Jeffrey Hancock's study focuses on the consequences of viewing one's own Facebook profile. These researchers suggest that the ability to socialize may have important positive benefits. For example, having multiple "friends" comment positively about a post might increase the user's happiness, at least temporarily. Specifically, Gonzales and Hancock investigated whether Facebook would increase self-esteem among users. The mechanism they explored was selective self-presentation through the hyper-personal model. Joseph Walther developed the hyper-personal model in 1996; it suggests that computer mediated communication has a greater ability to develop and edit self-presentation than face-to-face communication, so it creates a selective and optimized presentation of one's self to others. In terms of Facebook, individuals can carefully select the aspects of themselves that they would like to present to other users in terms of both text and images. When Gonzales and Hancock surveyed undergraduate college students, they found that viewing one's Facebook profile did enhance self-esteem through selective self-presentation.

Thus, the question of whether Facebook and other SNS are bad for college students' health is quite complex. Upon reading the YES and NO selections, you might reflect on your own SNS usage. It appears that Facebook use on its own may not be detrimental, but how one spends that time could be advantageous or problematic. Do you believe the results from either study are significant enough to warrant education of college students on SNS? Colleges might offer courses teaching how to use Facebook and other SNS to increase emotional well-being and avoid negative mental health outcomes. What's your opinion?

Brian A. Feinstein et al.

# Negative Social Comparison on Facebook and Depressive Symptoms: Rumination as a Mechanism

As social networking sites such as Facebook have become more popular, researchers have become increasingly interested in understanding the potential consequences of their use. Initially, it was suggested that Internet use was associated with negative mental health outcomes such as depressive symptoms. However, as data accumulated, the results became increasingly mixed; some studies supported the associations between Internet use and mental health problems (Kraut et al., 1998; Selfhout, Branje, Delsing, ter Bogt, & Meeus, 2009; van den Eijnden, Meerkerk, Vermulst, Spijkerman, & Engels, 2008), whereas others demonstrated positive effects of Internet use (Bessière, Kiesler, Kraut, & Boneva, 2008; Morgan & Cotten, 2003; Valkenburg & Peter, 2007). To reconcile discrepant findings, Davila et al. (2012) examined the amount of time spent engaging in social networking activities as well as the quality of interactions people had while using social networking mediums. Consistent with the larger literature on mood and anxiety disorders and interpersonal functioning, the authors hypothesized that poorer quality interactions, rather than use alone, would be associated with negative mental health outcomes. As predicted, in cross-sectional and 3-week prospective analyses, more negative and less positive self-reported social networking interactions were associated with depressive symptoms, whereas time spent engaging in social networking was not (Davila et al., 2012).

As Facebook use becomes virtually ubiquitous, it is important to continue to identify the specific behaviors and processes that may be "risky." Previous research on Facebook use has garnered a great deal of media attention, particularly a clinical report claiming that researchers had documented a phenomenon called "Facebook depression," or depression that results from spending too much time on Facebook (O'Keeffe & Clarke-Pearson, 2011). In fact, no research supports this claim, and, although scholars have attempted to clarify this (Davila, 2011; Magid, 2011), such false claims emphasize the importance of testing hypothesis-driven research questions that shed light on specific mechanisms that may lead to poorer well-being in the context of social networking. As noted, Davila et al. (2012) suggest that it is the quality rather than the frequency of social networking experiences that predicts negative mental health outcomes, but it remains unclear what specifically takes place on social networking sites beyond poor quality interactions that may be pathogenic.

Social networking sites provide venues for people to engage in a variety of behaviors, such as actively interacting with others (e.g., instant messaging), passively interacting with others (e.g., posting a message on someone's profile), and obtaining information about others (e.g., looking at someone's profiles). Similar to traditional social activities, these online activities provide individuals with ample opportunity to compare themselves with others on numerous characteristics such as appearance, popularity, and success. When people are presented with information about others, they tend to relate that information to themselves (Mussweiler, Ruter, & Epstude, 2006), and this social comparison provides them with self-evaluative information that can be used to make positive or negative self-judgments (Festinger, 1954). For instance, if a person sees that many of his or her friends are getting jobs and he or she is unemployed and having a difficult time getting a job, then he or she might feel inadequate in that domain. In contrast, if a person sees that many of his or her friends are unemployed and he or she has just gotten a job, then he or she might feel especially adequate in that domain. Importantly, social comparison is a pervasive and automatic feature of relating to others on an individual and group level (Pratto, Sidanius, Stallworth, & Malle, 1994; Sidanius, Pratto, & Bobo, 1994; Wood, 1989), making it nearly impossible to circumvent.

Social comparison is not in itself problematic, and indeed, even negative1 social comparisons (i.e., comparisons with others who are perceived as superior) can have positive effects (e.g., self-improvement and self-enhancement; Wood, 1989). Still, negative social comparison can also maintain or exacerbate negative self-appraisals (for reviews, see Ahrens & Alloy, 1997; Suls & Wheeler, 2000; Swallow & Kuiper, 1988; Wood & Lockwood, 1999). Notably, individuals report increases in negative affect subsequent to negative social comparisons (Ahrens & Alloy, 1997; Antony, Rowa, Liss, Swallow, & Swinson, 2005; Giordano, Wood, & Michela, 2000; Wheeler & Miyake, 1992). Despite evidence that negative social comparison may lead to poorer well-being in general, little research exists on this process in the context of social networking. As an exception, a

Feinstein, B. A., Hershenberg, R., Bhatia, V., Latack, J. A., Meuwly, N., & Davila, J. (2013). Negative social comparison on Facebook and depressive symptoms: Rumination as a mechanism. *Psychology of Popular Media Culture,* 2(3), 161–170. Reprinted by permission of American Psychological Association.

qualitative study found that users of MySpace, another social networking site, reported engaging in social comparison on the site and reported negative self-views subsequent to such comparison (Manago, Graham, Greenfield, & Salimkhan, 2008). Chou and Edge (2012) also found that individuals who spent more time on Facebook were more likely to agree that others were "happier" and "had better lives." Finally, Haferkamp and Krämer (2011) found that individuals who looked at profile pictures of attractive members of the same-sex reported less positive affect than those who looked at nonattractive members of the same-sex. This emerging body of research provides preliminary support for a social networking site such as Facebook to provide a context for engaging in negative social comparison, which may be associated with negative consequences.

In addition to examining the relationship between specific processes taking place in the context of social networking and mental health outcomes, it is important to understand the mechanisms that may account for these associations. One possible factor that may account for the association between negative social comparison on Facebook and depressive symptoms is the tendency to engage in maladaptive emotion regulation strategies, such as rumination. Rumination refers to repetitively focusing on one's distress, including its potential causes and consequences (Nolen-Hoeksema, Wisco, & Lyubomirsky, 2008), and has been consistently linked to negative mental health outcomes, including depression (for a meta-analytic review, see Aldao, Nolen-Hoeksema, & Schweizer, 2010). Although there has been little research on social comparison and emotion regulation, one study found that social comparison was positively associated with rumination (Cheung, Gilbert, & Irons, 2004). Building on these cross-sectional findings, the present study tests the hypothesis that negative social comparison on Facebook will lead to increases in the use of rumination as an emotion regulation strategy. Given that negative social comparison may be associated with rumination, and that rumination has consistently been linked to depressive symptoms, it is likely that rumination may act as a mechanism through which negative social comparison increases depressive symptoms. Notably, Locatelli, Kluwe, and Bryant (2012) found that rumination mediated the association between negative status updates on Facebook and depressive symptoms. Although their study provides preliminary support for our meditation hypothesis, the current study extends this to social comparison and uses a prospective design to test changes over time.

In sum, to refine our understanding of the processes that render individuals at risk when using social networking sites, the current study used a 3-week prospective design to examine a mediation model, wherein it was hypothesized that negative social comparison on Facebook would be associated with increases in depressive symptoms 3 weeks later through its association with increases in rumination. We controlled for general social comparison tendencies (i.e., social comparison not specific to Facebook) to examine the specific effects of Facebook social comparison. Additionally, given that there are some data to suggest bidirectional associations between rumination and depressive symptoms (Nolen-Hoeksema, Larson, & Grayson, 1999; Nolen-Hoeksema, Stice, Wade, & Bohon, 2007; for an exception, see McLaughlin, Hatzenbuehler, Mennin, & Nolen-Hoeksema, 2011), we examined an alternate mediation model with depressive symptoms as the mediator and rumination as the outcome. By examining both models, we hoped to gain a better sense of the direction of the proposed mediation effect. The current study extended previous research in several ways, including examining a specific process that may put individuals at risk for depressive symptoms in the context of social networking, using path analysis to test mediation models to better understand mechanisms of action, and controlling for general social comparison tendencies to provide a more stringent test.

# Method

## Participants

Eligible participants were at least 18 years old and enrolled in a psychology course for which they earned research credits for study participation. The present study was posted on the online system used by the psychology department to advertise research projects and track student credit. Participants included 105 male and 181 female students from Stony Brook University. Nine participants did not complete the followup assessment (retention rate = 96%), and nine additional participants did not complete one or more of the measures. These 18 participants were excluded from analyses; they did not significantly differ from the rest of the sample on gender, race/ethnicity, age, Facebook social comparison, general social comparison, rumination, or depressive symptoms (ps range from .07 to .68). The final sample included 268 individuals (62% female), with an average age of 19.66 years ($SD = 2.29$) and a racial/ethnic distribution including Caucasian (40%), Asian (42%), Latino/a (5%), African American (4%), Middle-Eastern (3%), and other (6%).

# Procedure

Participants completed an online survey (Time 1; T1) consisting of questionnaires assessing social comparison (in general and specific to Facebook), rumination, and depressive symptoms. To assess change over time, a follow-up online survey was conducted 3 weeks later (Time 2; T2). Given that the surveys were administered online, respondents were able to participate from any location that had Internet access. Participants received course credit for their participation. This research was approved by the Stony Brook University Committee on Research Involving Human Subjects.

# Measures

**Social comparison on Facebook.** The tendency to engage in social comparison when using Facebook was assessed with the Social Comparison Rating Scale (SCR; Allan & Gilbert, 1995), an 11-item self-report measure that presents respondents with an incomplete sentence followed by a series of bipolar constructs. We modified the instructions so that participants endorsed items based on social comparison while using Facebook. Specifically, whereas the original scale began using the stem, "In relationship to others I generally feel. . ." we used the stem, "When I compare myself to others on Facebook, I feel. . ." Participants selected a number from 1 to 10 that best described their perceived position between two poles (e.g., inferior/ superior, incompetent/more competent, unlikeable/more likable, undesirable/more desirable). We reverse coded and summed all responses to compute a total score in which higher values indicated more negative selfperceptions compared with others. Possible total scores could range from 11 to 110, and in our sample, ranged from 13 to 110 at T1. Allan and Gilbert (1995) reported internal consistency (alpha) of .88 and significant correlations with measures of psychopathology, including depression. In the current sample, the alpha was .94 at T1.

      **General social comparison.** The general tendency to engage in social comparison was assessed with the Iowa-Netherlands Comparison Orientation Measure (INCOM; Gibbons & Buunk, 1999), which is an 11-item self-report measure. Participants were instructed to rate their degree of agreement with each statement, ranging from 1 (I disagree strongly) to 5 (I agree strongly). Sample items include, "I often compare how my loved ones are doing with how others are doing," "If I want to learn more about something, I try to find out what others think about it," and "If I want to find out how well I have done something, I compare what I have done with how others have done." Responses to all items were summed to create a total score, where higher scores reflected a greater tendency to compare oneself with others. Possible total scores could range from 11 to 55, and our sample had a large distribution (15–54 at T1). Gibbons and Buunk (1999) demonstrated internal consistencies (alphas) ranging from .78 to .84, 3 to 4 week test–retest reliability of .71, and significant convergent and divergent validity across numerous samples. The alpha was .85 at T1 in the current sample.

      **Rumination.** Rumination was assessed with the Ruminative Responses Scale (RRS; Nolen-Hoeksema & Morrow, 1991). The RRS is a 22-item self-report measure that assesses how frequently individuals experience or engage in various thoughts, feelings, and actions during a depressed mood. Sample items include "Think about how sad I feel" and "Analyze recent events to try to understand why I am depressed." Each item is rated on a 1 (almost never) to 4 (almost always) scale, and responses are summed to compute a total score, which could range from 22 to 88, with higher scores representing higher levels of rumination. At both time points in our sample, we had a full range of scores. Excellent internal consistency and a significant correlation with depressive symptom severity have been reported (Nolen-Hoeksema & Morrow, 1991). In this sample, the alpha was .94 at T1 and .96 at T2.

      **Depressive symptoms.** Depressive symptoms were assessed with the Center for Epidemiological Studies-Depression Scale (CES-D; Radloff, 1977). The CES-D was specifically designed for use with community samples and included 20 items assessing past week experience of depressive symptoms. Responses ranged from 0 (*rarely or none of the time*) to 3 (*most or all of the time*), with greater scores indicating greater depressive symptoms. Sample items included, "I was happy" (reverse scored), "I felt that I could not shake off the blues even with help from my family and friends," and "I felt hopeful about the future" (reverse scored). Construct validity, internal reliability, and other psychometric strengths of the CES-D have been widely supported (Radloff, 1977). Possible total scores could range from 0–60. In this sample, scores ranged from 1 to 44 at T1 and 0 to 51 at T2. The alpha was .88 at T1 and .89 at T2.

# Results

Table 1 presents the means, standard deviations, and zero-order correlations for all of the variables. As hypothesized, Facebook social comparison was significantly and positively associated with general social comparison, and both were significantly and positively associated with rumination and depressive symptoms at both time points. Rumination was also significantly and positively

**Table 1**
**Means, Standard Deviations, and Zero-Order Correlations**

| Variable | 1 | 2 | 3 | 4 | 5 | 6 | Mean (SD) |
|---|---|---|---|---|---|---|---|
| 1. T1 Facebook social comparison | — | — | — | — | — | — | 57.38 (16.95) |
| 2. T1 General social comparison | .18* | — | — | — | — | — | 35.68 (7.21) |
| 3. T1 Rumination | .42** | .37** | — | — | — | — | 49.63 (14.82) |
| 4. T1 Depressive symptoms | .38** | .19* | .57** | — | — | — | 12.89 (8.50) |
| 5. T2 Rumination | .42** | .26** | .66** | .43** | — | — | 48.07 (15.23) |
| 6. T2 Depressive symptoms | .35** | .16* | .49** | .69** | .54** | — | 13.07 (8.60) |

*p < .01. **p < .001.

associated with depressive symptoms at both time points. Notably, the correlation between Facebook social comparison and general social comparison was modest ($r = .18$), suggesting that they are distinct constructs.

Path analysis with measured variables was conducted using IBM SPSS Amos Version 20 to examine the primary hypothesized mediation model (see Figure 1). Path analysis has the advantage of being able to simultaneously test the associations among multiple predictor and outcome variables. The hypothesized model proposed that Facebook social comparison at T1 would lead to increases in depressive symptoms at T2 through increases in rumination at T2. Given the prospective design, we controlled for rumination and depressive symptoms at T1. Additionally, general social comparison was controlled for to test the specific effect of Facebook social comparison. To test the significance of the hypothesized indirect effect of Facebook social comparison on depressive symptoms mediated through rumination, we conducted bootstrapping analyses to estimate bias-corrected confidence intervals (cf. Mackinnon, Lockwood, & Williams, 2004). Less than 1% of the data from the final sample was missing, and it was handled by imputing a participant's mean score on a measure in place of a missing value on one of the measure's items. All paths included in the model were estimated freely, and two paths were not included, thus they were set to 0 (the path from T1 rumination to T2 depressive symptoms and the path from T1 depressive symptoms to T2 rumination). Model fit was assessed by the comparative fit index (CFI), the Tucker–Lewis index (TLI), and the root-mean-square error of approximation (RMSEA), with acceptable model fit indicated by a CFI and TLI > .90 and an RMSEA < .06 (Hu & Bentler, 1999; Kline, 2005).

Results indicated that the hypothesized model fit the data very well, $\chi^2 (2, N = 268) = 1.78, p = .41$, CFI = 1.00, TLI = 1.00, and RMSEA = .00 (90% CI = [.00–.12]). The model demonstrated that Facebook social comparison was significantly associated with increases in rumination, which, in turn, were significantly associated with depressive symptoms[2] (see Table 2). Bootstrapping analyses supported the significance of the indirect effect of Facebook social comparison on increases in depressive symptoms through increases in rumination, $\beta = .05$, bias-corrected 90% CI = [.02–.09], $SE = .02$. The direct effect of Facebook social comparison on increases in depressive symptoms was not significant in the model, but it was significant when the mediator (rumination) was not included in the model (standardized path coefficient = .11, $p = .03$). Together, these findings provide support for the hypothesized mediation effect. Further, the significance of the indirect effect of *general* social comparison on depressive symptoms through rumination was not significant, $\beta = .004$, bias-corrected 90% CI = [.02 to .03], $SE = .01$, suggesting that this effect may be specific to negative social comparison on Facebook.

Given that the mediator (rumination) and the outcome (depressive symptoms) were both measured at the T2 assessment, we also examined an alternate model with depressive symptoms as the mediator and rumination as the outcome. Results indicated that the alternate model did not fit the data well, $\chi^2(2, N = 268) = 9.36, p = .01$, CFI = .99, TLI = .90, and RMSEA = .12 (90% CI = [.05–.20]). Although bootstrapping analyses indicated that the indirect effect of Facebook social comparison on increases in rumination through increases in depressive symptoms was significant, $\beta = .03$, bias-corrected 90% CI = [.01–.06], $SE = .02$, this should be interpreted with caution because of the poor model fit. In sum, results provide stronger support for our primary model than our alternate model, suggesting that rumination mediates the association between negative social comparison on Facebook and depressive symptoms.

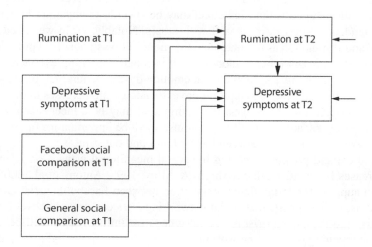

**Fig. 1.** Path model depicting the significant indirect effect of Facebook social comparison on increases in depressive symptoms *through* increases in rumination.

**Note.** Correlations among all T1 variables are included in the model, but not depicted for parsimony; paths representing the mediation component of the model are emphasized in bold.

**Table 2**
**Standardized Path Coefficients, Unstandardized Path Coefficients, and Standard Errors**

| Path | Standardized path coefficient | Unstandardized path coefficient | Standard error |
|---|---|---|---|
| T1 Facebook social comparison → T2 Rumination | .17* | .15* | .05 |
| T1 Facebook social comparison → T2 Depressive symptoms | .03 | .01 | .02 |
| T2 Rumination → T2 Depressive symptoms | .29* | .16* | .03 |
| T1 General social comparison → T2 Rumination | .01 | .03 | .10 |
| T1 General social comparison → T2 Depressive symptoms | −.02 | −.03 | .05 |
| T1 Rumination → T2 Rumination | .58* | .60* | .05 |
| T1 Depressive symptoms → T2 Depressive symptoms | .56* | .57* | .05 |
| T2 Depressive symptoms error term | — | 33.40* | 2.89 |
| T2 Rumination error term | — | 125.97* | 10.90 |

*Note.* → = predicting

*$p < .001$.

# Discussion

As the use of Facebook becomes increasingly commonplace, it is important to identify the behaviors and processes that may place users at risk for negative consequences. Given the inherently social nature of Facebook, we tested the hypothesis that negatively comparing oneself with others on Facebook leads to increases in depressive symptoms. Further, to better understand the mechanism underlying this association, we tested the hypothesis that negative social comparison would lead to increases in rumination, and this passive and repetitive focus on distress would in turn be associated with depressive symptoms. We review key findings below.

First, Facebook social comparison, rumination, and depressive symptoms were all positively and significantly associated with one another. As noted, the correlation between general social comparison and Facebook social comparison was modest at T1 and nonsignificant at T2, suggesting that these are distinct constructs. When we included all of the variables in the proposed path model, we found a strong fit to the data. Specifically, controlling for the general tendency to engage in social comparison, negatively comparing oneself with others while using Facebook predicted increases in rumination, which in turn was associated with increases in depressive symptoms. The significant indirect effect of Facebook social comparison on depressive symptoms through rumination coupled with the nonsignificant direct effect with the mediator in the model provides preliminary support for the possibility that rumination does indeed mediate the association in question. Further, the nonsignificant indirect effect of general social comparison on depressive symptoms through rumination suggests that this effect may be specific to engaging in negative social comparison on Facebook rather than the general tendency to compare oneself with others. Notably, when we tested an alternate model with depressive symptoms as the mediator and rumination as the outcome, the model fit was poor. This provides additional support for the proposed direction of the mediation effect in our primary model, and it is consistent with previous research that failed to find a significant association between depressive symptoms and increases in emotion dysregulation over time (McLaughlin et al., 2011). However, other studies *have* demonstrated that depressive symptoms are associated with increases in rumination over time (Nolen-Hoeksema et al., 1999, 2007). Thus, although findings suggest that rumination may be a mechanism underlying the association between negative social comparison on Facebook and depressive symptoms, it will be important for future research to collect at least three time points and include the *prospective* association between the mediator and outcome.

Findings are consistent with and expand previous research in several meaningful ways. Consistent with findings that link negative social comparison with increases in negative affect (Ahrens & Alloy, 1997; Antony et al., 2005; Giordano et al., 2000; Wheeler & Miyake, 1992), we found support for a significant association between Facebook social comparison and depressive symptoms in the zero-order correlations. This suggests that social networking sites can provide novel opportunities for individuals to compare themselves with others, and these comparisons can have negative influences on well-being. Further, this provides insight into what specifically may be happening on social networking sites that has the potential to be pathogenic—namely, comparing oneself with others who are perceived as superior. We also found that negative social comparison on Facebook predicted increases in rumination at a 3-week follow-up, which extends previous cross-sectional findings (Cheung et al., 2004). Why might this be the case? Some evidence suggests that individuals tend to self-disclose more positive information about themselves on Facebook compared with "real life" (Qiu, Lin, Leung, & Tov, 2012), and individuals who spend more time on Facebook are more likely to agree that others are "happier" and have "better lives" (Chou & Edge, 2012). As such, given that rumination involves passive and repetitive focus on one's distress, social comparison may provide ample opportunity to mull over causes and consequences of perceived inferiority.

Finally, consistent with the larger literature on risk factors for depression, we found that rumination was associated with depressive symptoms. If an individual ruminates on his or her perceived inferiority subsequent to negatively comparing oneself with others on Facebook, he or she is engaging in an emotion regulation strategy known to maintain and exacerbate distress. Nolen-Hoeksema et al. (2008) speculated that rumination may prolong and increase depression, in part, because it is associated with reduced interpersonal problem solving, less willingness to engage in pleasant activities to lift mood when given the chance, and more pessimistic views about positive events in the future. Thus, rather than problem solving (i.e., changing the situation that led to the negative social comparison) or switching the focus of attention to more positive or rewarding aspects of their environment, these individuals may continue to passively focus on distress (perhaps via increased time spent on the site) and/or seek out others in potentially problematic ways (e.g., corumination, excessive reassurance seeking). The significant indirect effect of Facebook social comparison on depressive symptoms through rumination is also consistent with a recent study that found that rumination mediated the association between negative status updates on Facebook and depressive symptoms (Locatelli et al., 2012). Together, these findings lend confidence to the notion that rumination may play a mechanistic role in the associations between negative social networking experiences and depressive symptoms, as two studies have now demonstrated similar meditational effects despite different predictor variables and methodological features.

It is useful to note that research on Facebook use and mental health has important public health implications. First, given the bidirectional and transactional nature of depression and problematic interpersonal functioning (see Joiner & Timmons, 2009), in order to continue to understand the bounds of their association it is incumbent upon researchers to examine interpersonal processes in the contexts in which they currently occur, which includes social networking sites. Next, the media has taken a particular interest in research on social networking, and has oft made large-scale claims about the "dangers" of Facebook use (e.g., "Facebook depression"). As scientists developing a programmatic line of research to test a priori hypotheses regarding Facebook use and mental health, we hope to shed light on the processes that may render individuals more vulnerable to negative effects of Facebook use.

The current study has several strengths, including a large and racially/ethnically diverse sample, a prospective design, and the use of path analysis to test the proposed mediation model. Nevertheless, it is important to keep in mind the following limitations that underscore the importance of replicating and extending these findings. We relied on a one-time selfreport assessment of social comparison tendencies, and findings would be strengthened by a laboratory manipulation of this process. Additionally, our sample was composed of nonclinical emerging adults and may not generalize to older or younger adults or a more clinically depressed sample. That said, that this effect was so robust in a nonclinical sample that commonly uses social networking sites is quite notable and suggests that this process may be especially relevant for those with elevated symptomatology. Consistent with current interventions designed to enhance adaptive emotion regulation (see Kring & Sloan, 2010), findings suggest that targeting rumination in a clinical context may minimize the negative consequences of engaging in negative social comparison. It will be useful for future research to test more complex models that account for the various types of maladaptive emotion regulation strategies that individuals may engage in to regulate their mood subsequent to negative social comparison on Facebook, as well as additional types of mental health outcomes that may be affected by these processes. Future research could also benefit from assessing specific behaviors related to rumination that may take place in the context of social networking (e.g., rereading posts on Facebook that contribute to one's dysphoria). Finally, our study focused on only one set of variables that may contribute to associations between Facebook use and depressive symptoms. Ongoing development of theory about the function of social networking, the contexts in which it occurs, and the ways in which it is related to self-concept and identity may provide new avenues of research that will allow for further understanding of its effect on people of all ages.

# Notes

1. Several different terms have been used throughout the literature to describe the process wherein an individual compares himself or herself with others who are perceived as superior. Although most studies refer to this process as upward social comparison, others have referred to it as downward social comparison or negative social comparison. We chose to use the term negative social comparison throughout this article, as it seems to be the least ambiguous.
2. Given that rumination and depressive symptoms were both measured at the T2 assessment, it is worth noting that, in a separate regression analysis, rumination at T1 was associated with depressive symptoms at T2, controlling for depressive symptoms at T1 ($\beta = .14$, $p = .01$). Thus, even though the model included a path from rumination at T2 to depressive symptoms at T2, it is likely that rumination does, in fact, predict increases in depressive symptoms over time (as demonstrated by our data and previous research).

# References

Ahrens, A. H., & Alloy, L. B. (1997). Social comparison processes in depression. In B. P. Buunk & F. X. Gibbons (Eds.), *Health, coping, and wellbeing: Perspectives from social comparison theory* (pp. 389–410). Mahwah, NJ: Erlbaum Publishers.

Aldao, A., Nolen-Hoeksema, S., & Schweizer, S. (2010). Emotion-regulation strategies across psychopathology: A meta-analytic review. *Clinical Psychology Review, 30,* 217–237. doi:10.1016/j.cpr.2009.11.004

Allan, S., & Gilbert, P. (1995). A social comparison scale: Psychometric properties and relationship to psychopathology. *Personality and Individual Differences, 19,* 293–299. doi:10.1016/0191-8869(95)00086-L

Antony, M. M., Rowa, K., Liss, A., Swallow, S. R., & Swinson, R. P. (2005). Social comparison processes in social phobia. *Behavior Therapy, 36,* 65–75. doi:10.1016/S0005-7894(05)80055-3

Bessière, K., Kiesler, S., Kraut, R., & Boneva, B. S. (2008). Effects of Internet use and social resources on changes in depression. *Information, Communication, & Society, 11,* 47–70. doi:10.1080/13691180701858851

Cheung, M. S., Gilbert, P., & Irons, C. (2004). An exploration of shame, rank, and rumination in relation to depression. *Personality and Individual Differences, 36,* 1143–1153. doi:10.1016/S0191-8869(03)00206-X

Chou, H., & Edge, N. (2012). 'They are happier and having better lives than I am': The impact of using Facebook on perceptions of others' lives. *Cyberpsychology, Behavior, and Social Networking, 15,* 117–121. doi:10.1089/cyber.2011.0324

Davila, J. (2011). The *"Facebook Depression"* controversy. Retrieved from http://www.psychology.sunysb.edu/jdavila-/webpage/facebook%20depression%20controversy.htm

Davila, J., Hershenberg, R., Feinstein, B. A., Gorman, K., Bhatia, V., & Starr, L. (2012). Frequency and quality of social networking experiences: Associations with depressive symptoms, rumination, and co-rumination. *Psychology of Popular Media Culture, 1,* 72–86. doi:10.1037/a0027512

Festinger, L. (1954). A theory of social comparison processes. *Human Relations, 7,* 117–140. doi: 10.1177/001872675400700202

Gibbons, F. X., & Buunk, B. P. (1999). Individual differences in social comparison: Development of a scale of social comparison orientation. *Journal of Personality and Social Psychology, 76,* 129–142. doi:10.1037/0022-3514.76.1.129

Giordano, C., Wood, J. V., & Michela, J. L. (2000). Depressive personality styles, dysphoria, and social comparisons in everyday life. *Journal of Personality and Social Psychology, 79,* 438–451. doi: 10.1037/0022-3514.79.3.438

Haferkamp, N., & Krämer, N. C. (2011). Social comparison 2.0: Examining the effects of online profiles on social-networking sites. *Cyberpsychology, Behavior, and Social Networking, 14,* 309–314. doi:10.1089/ cyber.2010.0120

Hu, L., & Bentler, P. M. (1999). Cutoff criteria for fit indexes in covariance structure analysis: Conventional criteria versus new alternatives. *Structural Equation Modeling, 6,* 1–55. doi:10.1080/10705519909540118

Joiner, T. E., & Timmons, K. A. (2009). Depression in its interpersonal context. In I. H. Gotlib & C. L. Hammen (Eds.), *Handbook of depression* (2nd ed., pp. 322–339). New York, NY: Guilford Press.

Kline, R. B. (2005). *Principles and practice of structural equation modeling* (2nd ed.). New York, NY: Guilford Press.

Kraut, R., Patterson, M., Lundmark, V., Kiesler, S., Mukopadhyay, T., & Scherlis, W. (1998). Internet paradox: A social technology that reduces social involvement and psychological well-being? *American Psychologist, 53,* 1017–1031. doi:10.1037/0003-066X.53.9.1017

Kring, A. M., & Sloan, D. M. (2010). *Emotion regulation and psychopathology: A transdiagnostic approach to etiology and treatment.* New York, NY: Guilford Press.

Locatelli, S. M., Kluwe, K., & Bryant, F. B. (2012). Facebook use and the tendency to ruminate among college students: Testing meditational hypotheses. *Journal of Educational Computing Research, 46,* 377–394. doi:10.2190/EC.46.4.d

Mackinnon, D. P., Lockwood, C. M., & Williams, J. (2004). Confidence limits for the indirect effect: Distribution of the product and resampling methods. *Multivariate Behavioral Research, 39,* 99–128. doi:10.1207/s15327906mbr3901_4

Magid, L. (2011). "Facebook Depression": A nonexistent condition. *The Huffington Post.* Retrieved from http://www.huffingtonpost.com/larry-magid/facebook-depression-nonexistent_b_842733.html

Manago, A. M., Graham, M. B., Greenfield, P. M., & Salimkhan, G. (2008). Self-presentation and gender on MySpace. *Journal of Applied Developmental Psychology, 29,* 446–458. doi:10.1016/j.appdev.2008.07.001

McLaughlin, K. A., Hatzenbuehler, M. L., Mennin, D. S., & Nolen-Hoeksema, S. (2011). Emotion dysregulation and adolescent psychopathology: A prospective study. *Behaviour Research and Therapy, 49,* 544–554. doi:10.1016/j.brat.2011.06.003

Morgan, C., & Cotten, S. R. (2003). The relationship between Internet activities and depressive symptoms in a sample of college freshmen. *CyberPsychology & Behavior, 6,* 133–142. doi:10.1089/109493103321640329

Mussweiler, T., Ruter, K., & Epstude, K. (2006). The why, who and how of social comparison: A socialcognition perspective. In S. Guimond (Ed.), *Social comparison processes and social psychology* (pp. 33–54). Cambridge, England: Cambridge University Press.

Nolen-Hoeksema, S., Larson, J., & Grayson, C. (1999). Explaining the gender difference in depressive symptoms. *Journal of Personality and Social Psychology, 77,* 1061–1072. doi:10.1037/0022-3514.77.5.1061

Nolen-Hoeksema, S., & Morrow, J. (1991). A prospective study of depression and distress following a natural disaster: The 1989 Loma Prieta earthquake. *Journal of Personality and Social Psychology, 61,* 115–121. doi:10.1037/0022-3514.61.1.115

Nolen-Hoeksema, S., Stice, E., Wade, E., & Bohon, C. (2007). Reciprocal relations between rumination and bulimic, substance abuse, and depressive symptoms in female adolescents. *Journal of Abnormal Psychology, 116,* 198–207. doi:10.1037/0021-843X.116.1.198

Nolen-Hoeksema, S., Wisco, B. E., & Lyubomirsky, S. (2008). Rethinking rumination. *Perspectives on Psychological Science, 3,* 400–424.

O'Keeffe, G. S., & Clarke-Pearson, K. (2011). The impact of social media on children, adolescents, and families. *Pediatrics, 127,* 800–804.

Pratto, F., Sidanius, J., Stallworth, L. M., & Malle, B. (1994). Social dominance orientation: A personality variable predicting social and political attitudes. *Journal of Personality and Social Psychology, 67,* 741–763. doi:10.1037/0022-3514.67.4.741

Qiu, L., Lin, H., Leung, A. K.-y., & Tov, W. (2012). Putting their best foot forward: emotional disclosure on facebook. *Cyberpsychology, Behavior, and Social Networking, 15,* 569–572. doi:10.1089/cyber.2012.0200

Radloff, L. S. (1977). The CES-D scale: A self-report depression scale for research in the general population. *Applied Psychological Measures, 1,* 385–401. doi:10.1177/014662167700100306

Selfhout, M. H., Branje, S. J., Delsing, M., ter Bogt, T. F., & Meeus, W. H. (2009). Different types of Internet use, depression, and social anxiety: The role of perceived friendship quality. *Journal of Adolescence, 32,* 819–833. doi:10.1016/j.adolescence.2008.10.011

Sidanius, J., Pratto, F., & Bobo, L. (1994). Social dominance orientation and the political psychology of gender: A case of invariance? *Journal of Personality and Social Psychology, 67,* 998–1011. doi:10.1037/0022-3514.67.6.998

Suls, J., & Wheeler, L. (2000). *A selective history of classic and neo-social comparison theory.* Handbook of Social Comparison. New York: Kluwer Academic/Plenum Press Publishers. doi:10.1007/978-1-4615-4237-7

Swallow, S. R., & Kuiper, N. A. (1988). Social comparison and negative self-evaluations: An application to depression. *Clinical Psychology Review, 8,* 55–76. doi:10.1016/0272-7358(88)90049-9

Valkenburg, P. M., & Peter, J. (2007). Preadolescents' and adolescents' online communication and their closeness to friends. *Developmental Psychology, 43,* 267–277. doi:10.1037/0012-1649.43.2.267

Van den Eijnden, R. M., Meerkerk, G., Vermulst, A. A., Spijkerman, R., & Engels, R. E. (2008). Online communication, compulsive Internet use, and psychosocial well-being among adolescents: A longitudinal study. *Developmental Psychology, 44,* 655–665. doi:10.1037/0012-1649.44.3.655

Wheeler, L., & Miyake, K. (1992). Social comparisons in everyday life. *Journal of Personality and Social Psychology, 62,* 760–773. doi:10.1037/0022-3514.62.5.760

Wood, J. V. (1989). Theory and research concerning social comparisons of personal attributes. *Psychological Bulletin, 106,* 231–248. doi:10.1037/0033-2909.106.2.231

Wood, J. V., & Lockwood, P. (1999). Social comparisons in dysphoric and low self-esteem people. In R. Kowalski & M. Leary (Eds.), *The social psychology of emotional and behavioral problems: Interfaces of social and clinical psychology* (pp. 97–135), Washington, DC: American Psychological Association. doi:10.1037/10320–004.

BRIAN A. FEINSTEIN is a doctoral candidate at SUNY Stony Brook. His research interests include ways in which psychopathology and interpersonal relationships affect one another, with an emphasis on the unique ways in which sexual orientation and other minority statuses (e.g., race, gender) influence these domains.

RACHEL HERSHENBERG is postdoctoral research fellow at the Philadelphia VA and University of Pennsylvania School of Medicine. Her research interests include depression, positive emotions, interpersonal behavior, behavioral activation, and evidence-based practice and clinical training.

VICKIE BHATIA is a doctoral candidate at SUNY Stony Brook. Her research focuses on examining the mechanisms involved in the bidirectional relationship between depression and romantic relationship dysfunction.

JESSICA A. LATACK is a doctoral candidate at SUNY Stony Brook. Her research focuses on the ways in which childhood sexual abuse and later sexual trauma may affect individuals' behavior in adult romantic relationships.

NATHALIE MEUWLY is a research fellow of the University of Fribourg, Switzerland. She is interested in what role intimate relationships play for our well-being and health, particularly within adolescent relationships.

JOANNE DAVILA is a psychology faculty member at SUNY Stony Brook. Her research focuses on the development and course of interpersonal functioning and psychopathology among adolescents and adults, with a particular emphasis on the interpersonal causes and consequences of depression and anxiety disorders, risk factors for the early development of romantic relationship dysfunction in adolescents, the role of attachment representations in interpersonal functioning, and well-being among LGBT individuals.

# Mirror, Mirror on My Facebook Wall:
# Effects of Exposure to Facebook on Self-Esteem

## Introduction

Over a decade ago, INTERNET USE WAS THOUGHT to promote negative psychosocial well-being, including depression and loneliness.[1] Having attracted attention in and out of the research community, these findings prompted researchers to take a more nuanced look at the relationship between Internet use and psychosocial health,[2,3] at times finding evidence that Internet use could be beneficial.[3,4] The present study extends this research by examining the effects of the social-networking site Facebook (http://facebook.com), which represents a popular new form of Internet communication, on self-esteem.

Previous work has addressed the role of Facebook and the ability to socialize, and the role that socializing online plays in supporting self-esteem and various forms of social capital.[5,6] For example, one recent study found that Facebook can enhance "social self-esteem," measured as perceptions of one's physical appearance, close relationships, and romantic appeal, especially when users received positive feedback from Facebook friends.[5] Also, individuals with low self-esteem may see particularly positive benefits from the social opportunities provided by Facebook.[6]

The effect of Facebook exposure on general self-esteem has not been explored. Yet Facebook, and other socialnetwork sites, have the potential to affect temporary states of self-esteem. Social-network sites are designed to share information about the self with others, including likes/dislikes, hobbies, and personal musings via "wall posts," and "status updates." This information could make people aware of their own limitations and shortcomings, which would lower self-esteem,[7] or it could be that this information represents selective and therefore positively biased aspects of the self, which might raise self-esteem.[8] Does Facebook operate on self-esteem in the same way non-digital information does, by decreasing self-esteem? Or does the opportunity to present more positive information about the self while filtering negative information mean that reviewing one's own Facebook site enhances self-esteem? The following piece examines these questions, by exploring the theoretical predictions of Objective Self- Awareness (OSA) theory[9] and the Hyperpersonal Model.[8]

## Objective Self-Awareness

One theoretical approach relevant to the effects of socialnetworking sites on self-esteem is OSA theory, one of the first experimentally tested psychological theories of the self. The theory assumes that humans experience the self as both subject and object.[9] For example, the self as subject is found in daily experiences of life (e.g., waiting for the bus, eating lunch, watching TV[10]). In those experiences the self is an active participant in life and is not self-conscious. However, people become the "object of [their] own consciousness" when they focus attention on the self,[9 (p2)] which can have both positive and negative effects.

In a state of objective self-awareness, Duval and Wicklund[9] claim that people are prone to self-evaluations based on broader social standards and norms. This usually results in a greater sense of humility, or downgraded ratings of self, and increased pro-social behavior. For example, people report feeling greater responsibility for social injustice,[11] or are less likely to take an extra helping of candy without being observed.[12] On the other hand, because most people often fall short of social standards when self-awareness is heightened, positive affect and self-esteem typically decrease when people are exposed to objective self-awareness stimuli.[13]

The stimuli used to evoke objective self-awareness is most commonly a mirror,[13] although other stimuli include images of the self,[14] audio feedback,[15] having a video camera pointed at participants,[16] or having participants write autobiographical information.[11] These stimuli cause people to view themselves as they believe others do, even if they are not immediately under observation. Exposure to these stimuli is what leads to pro-social behavior and decreases in self-esteem.

Given that social-networking profiles include information about the self similar to the type of information that is used to prompt objective self-awareness (e.g., photos, autobiographical information), viewing one's profile should prompt a downgrading of self-esteem according to OSA theory. That is, viewing one's Facebook profile should negatively affect one's self-esteem.

Gonzales, A. L., & Hancock, J. T. (2011). Mirror, mirror on my Facebook wall: Effects of exposure to Facebook on self-esteem. *Cyberpsychology, Behavior, and Social Networking*, 14(1–2), 79–83. Reprinted by permission of Mary Ann Liebert, Inc.

Furthermore, research in computer-mediated communication has found that information online is often over-interpreted relative to the same information provided offline,[17] leading to exaggerated or stereotyped impressions.[18] Is it possible that this same process could occur for impressions of the self? If Facebook acts on self-esteem in the same way as previous OSA stimuli, only to a more extreme degree, one prediction is:

> **H1: Exposure to one's Facebook site will have a more negative effect on self-esteem than traditional objective self-awareness stimuli (e.g., mirror).**

## Selective Self-Presentation

A second relevant theoretical approach to understanding effects of Facebook use is the Hyperpersonal Model.[8] Walther posits that affordances of the Internet allow users to *selectively self-present* themselves in asynchronous media. People can take their time when posting information about themselves, carefully selecting what aspects they would like to emphasize. Evidence of selective self-presentation is found in a variety of Internet spaces, including e-mails,[19] discussion boards,[20] and online dating Web sites.[21,22]

In addition to evidence that online self-presentations are especially positive presentations, recent research in computer-mediated communication (CMC) suggests that online self-presentations can become integrated into how we view ourselves, especially when the presentations take place in a public, digital space.[23] This phenomenon, known as *identity shift*, demonstrates that self-presentations enacted in online space can impact users' self-concepts.

Self-presentations online can be optimized through selective self-presentation, and online self-presentation affects attitudes about the self. Facebook profiles may provide sufficiently positively biased stimuli to counter the traditional effects of objective self-awareness, and instead prompt a positive change in self-esteem. From this perspective, the hyperpersonal prediction of exposure to Facebook is:

> **H2: Exposure to one's Facebook site will have a more positive effect on self-esteem than a control condition or traditional self-awareness stimuli (e.g., mirror).**

Furthermore, if exposure to one's own Facebook profile increases self-esteem due to selective self-presentation, then behaviors associated with selective self-presentation should correlate with changes in self-esteem. For example, because self-stimuli are most likely to be on one's own profile page, we would expect that participants who only view their own profile page would report higher selfesteem than participants who view other profiles within Facebook. Thus:

> **H3: Participants who exclusively examine only their own profile will report higher self-esteem than participants who view other profiles in addition to their own profiles.**

Finally, selective self-presentation should be reflected primarily in editing of one's online self-presentation, according to Walther.[8] That is, the ability to edit one's self-presentation after the fact is a unique attribute of asynchronous, textbased communication. Thus, according to the Hyperpersonal Model, we predict that:

> **H4: Participants who make changes to their profile during the experiment will report higher self-esteem than participants who do not.**

Each of these predictions is tested in the following study, comparing the effect of viewing one's Facebook site, viewing one's own image in a mirror, and being in a control condition on self-reported self-esteem.

# Methods

## Participants

A total of 63 students (16 males, 47 females) from a large, Northeastern university participated in this study for extra credit. The study consisted of three conditions: exposure to a mirror, exposure to one's own Facebook site, and a control condition in which participants used the same room without any treatment. Participants were randomly assigned to one of the three conditions, with a total of 21 participants taking part in each of the three conditions.

## Procedure

Each participant was told that the study was designed to examine "people's attitudes about themselves after exploring different Internet sites." People in both offline conditions were told that they were in a control condition, and thus would not be online. In the online condition, participants were asked to examine their own Facebook site.

In the Facebook stimulus condition, after logging on to Facebook, participants were instructed to click on the "Profile" tab after the experimenter left the room. The profile page contains the primary source of information on an individual user. Participants were told to look through any of the tabs on that page (Wall posts, Photos, Info, Boxes). Participants were given no specific instructions about making changes to their profile during the study. In addition to the main profile photo, the profile page has information on recent activity on Facebook sent to and from the site owner, personal demographic information, photos, and quizzes completed by the site owner. After being on Facebook for 3 minutes, the experimenter returned with a survey. Participants were instructed to keep the profile page open while completing the questionnaire.

Participants in the offline conditions were taken to the same small computer cubicle used in the online condition. In the objective self-awareness stimulus condition, a mirror was placed against the computer screen. To reduce suspicion of the mirror, they were also told that the cubicle was being used for another experiment and that they should not move anything. Other items were laid about the room in all conditions (e.g., intercoms, a television) in order to enhance the perception that the room was being used for another experiment. Participants were given a survey of questions, which were answered while being exposed to their own reflection in the mirror.

In the offline control condition, participants sat in the same room as participants in the previously mentioned two conditions, but without the mirror present and without the computer screen turned on. Participants were left with the survey and given instructions to buzz the experimenter when they had finished completing the survey. In all conditions, experimenters returned to collect the survey, and participants were then debriefed and probed for suspicion or failure to comply with instruction.

## Measures

### Self-esteem

Self-esteem was measured using the Rosenburg Self-Esteem scale,[24] in which 10 items were used to assess self-esteem ($\alpha = 0.82$). Half of the items were reverse coded. Responses were scored on a 4-point scale, ranging from "strongly agree" to "strongly disagree." Although this scale is generally used to measure trait self-esteem, as mentioned above, previous studies of objective self-awareness have used this measure to capture temporary changes in self-esteem due to awareness-enhancing stimuli.[7]

### Selective self-presentation

In order to examine behaviors predicted by the Hyperpersonal Model, we asked participants in the Facebook condition about their behavior while they were on Facebook. Questions included, "Did you leave your profile at any time during the study?" (1 = "yes," 2 = "no"), and "Did you change your profile while you were on the Web site?" (1 = "yes," 2 = "no").

## Results

To establish that the objective self-awareness stimuli had an effect on self-esteem, an analysis of variance (ANOVA) was first performed. Gender was also included in the model as a covariate, given previous research suggesting that gender may predict differences in self-esteem.[25] The following analyses all reflect significant differences using two-tailed tests of significance, unless otherwise noted. Indeed, the stimuli did have an effect on self-esteem, $F(1, 59) = 4.47$, $p = 0.02$, $n^2 = 0.13$. However, gender was not a significant predictor of self-esteem, $F(1, 60) = 0.94$, $p = 0.34$. This finding reveals that self-reported self-esteem did vary by condition.

To test the hypothesis that Facebook had a more negative effect on self-esteem than traditional objective self-awareness stimulus (H1), a linear contrast analysis was performed with a weight 0 assigned to the traditional objective self-awareness stimulus condition (i.e., mirror, $M = 2.97$, $SD = 0.51$), a weight of $-1$ assigned to the Facebook condition ($M = 3.35$, $SD = 0.37$), and a weight of 1 assigned to the control condition ($M = 3.23$, $SD = 0.40$). The results of this test were not significant, $F(1, 60) = 0.95$, $p = 0.33$.

To test the opposing hypothesis that Facebook has a positive impact on self-esteem (H2), a different linear contrast analysis was performed. A contrast weight of $-1$ was assigned to the traditional objective self-awareness stimuli condition, 0 was assigned to the control condition, and $+1$ was assigned to the Facebook condition. This contrast analysis was significant, $F(1, 59) = 8.60$, $p < 0.01$, $n^2 = 0.13$, demonstrating support for H2 and suggesting that Facebook has a positive effect on self-esteem relative to a traditional objective self-awareness stimulus.

Given that viewing Facebook enhanced self-esteem, is there additional evidence that the process of selective self presentation was responsible for influencing self-esteem? Our first method of testing this question included examining whether participants who exclusively viewed their own profile reported having higher self-esteem than participants who also viewed the profiles of others. An ordinary least squares (OLS) regression of self-esteem on viewing behavior (self-only profile vs. self and other profiles) and gender revealed a significant effect on viewing behavior, $b = 0.40$, $p = 0.03$ (one-tailed, 1 = "yes," 2 = "no"), indicating that participants who left their profile during the study reported lower self-esteem than those participants who exclusively viewed their own profile site, supporting H3. The relationship between gender and self-esteem was not significant, $b = 0.33$, $p = 0.12$ (1 = female, 2 = male).

Finally, we expected that changes to any part of the profile (i.e., status, photo, etc.) during the study would increase participant self-esteem (H4), as editing is a primary means of optimizing self-presentation, according to the Hyperpersonal Model.[8] We tested this hypothesis using OLS regression, and once again included gender in the analysis. In support of this hypothesis, participants who changed their profile during the study reported higher self-esteem than those who did not change their profile, $b = \_0.53$, $p = 0.01$, (1 = "yes," 2 = "no"). These data suggest that, because asynchronous social-network profiles allow for added time and energy to construct positive self-presentations, profiles contain information that prompts positive, rather than negative, effects on self-esteem. Men reported having greater self-esteem than women after controlling for the likelihood that participants changed their profile, $b = 0.45$, $p = 0.03$. However, this result cannot be fairly interpreted due to the very small number of men (17 women, 4 men).

# Discussion

This study was designed to test the effects of exposure to Facebook on self-esteem relative to traditional selfawareness enhancing stimuli, such as a mirror or photo of oneself. The study suggests that selective self-presentation, afforded by digitally mediated environments can have a positive influence on self-esteem.

These findings are in contrast to predictions from OSA theory, which posits that stimuli that prompt self-awareness (e.g., mirror, photo, autobiographical information) activate discrepancies between oneself and social standards,[9] and consequently lower self-esteem.[13,15] Instead, the results demonstrate that exposure to information presented on one's Facebook profile enhances self-esteem, especially when a person edits information about the self, or *selectively self-presents*. These findings are consistent with Walther's Hyperpersonal Model[8] and suggest that the process of *selective self-presentation*, which takes place in mediated spaces due to increased time for creating a self-presentation, makes Facebook a unique awareness-enhancing stimuli.

This study is a preliminary step toward understanding how selective self-presentation processes, which have been previously discussed in the context of interpersonal impression formation,[19,20,22] may also influence impressions of the self. Whereas a non-edited view of the self (i.e., mirror) is likely to decrease self-esteem, these findings suggest that the extra care involved in digital self-presentations may actually improve self-esteem. By allowing people to present preferred or positive information about the self, Facebook is a unique source of self-awareness stimuli in that it enhances awareness of the optimal self. This finding is consistent with previous work that has found that digital self-presentations can shape self-assessments.[23] In this case, however, the findings are striking because they contradict previous work on the negative effect of self-awareness enhancing information on self-assessments.

Previous work examining self-esteem suggests that consistency between the actual and the ideal self is an important factor in understanding how information can affect self-esteem.[26] Although participant perceptions between the actual and ideal self were not measured, it is possible that Facebook activates the ideal self. Future research on implications of self evaluations on self-esteem is needed to test this possibility.

Facebook may also be unique in that the public nature of the site may contribute to objective self-awareness. In previous work, autobiographical information or photos have prompted objective self-awareness.[11,14,15] We tested OSA in Facebook because these features are present there. However, Facebook is a public site, which should also remind users of self-evaluation. In this case, the same information that is prompting OSA is *actually* viewed and evaluated by others as well. Further work is necessary to determine whether public Internet audiences alone may stimulate OSA. In this case, we can only speculate that the high visibility of one's Facebook profile further adds to a sense of objective selfawareness. The difference is that that while Facebook may prime awareness of an audience and self-evaluation, it is a more optimal self that is being evaluated. Thus the effect of self-esteem is positive rather than negative.

# Limitations

An important limitation of this study was our failure to account for the effect of the number of Facebook friends on self-esteem. As previous research has demonstrated, the social opportunities in Facebook contribute to an enhanced feeling of social competence.[5,6] We cannot rule out the possibility that reminders of one's social connections are partially responsible for the increase in self-esteem. On the other hand, social connection does not seem to be completely responsible for this effect. Changes to one's profile and attention to one's profile (vs. others' profiles) have a positive effect on self-esteem, which suggests that selective self-presentation is a factor in shaping the resultant self reports of self-esteem.

Another limitation is that we cannot know the longterm implications of using Facebook on self-esteem from a single study. The measure of self-esteem used in this study is generally used as a measure of stable self-esteem, but has been used on other occasions to measure temporary shifts in self-esteem.[7,13,15] Though difficult to perform in an experimental setting, research that examines long-term effects of social network sites, such as Facebook, would be valuable. Also, incorporating pre- and post-test measures of self-esteem and other relevant psychological measures would be useful in future work.

The focus in the present study is on Facebook, although we make arguments about social-network sites in general regarding their effect on self-esteem. While future research will be required to extend these findings beyond Facebook, the Facebook interface has several advantages over other sites, such as MySpace (http:// myspace.com), including a more uniform layout and the sheer popularity of the site. Given that every person must view their own site, the increased uniformity and popularity of Facebook made it a useful starting point for examining digital self-awareness stimuli and self-esteem.

Finally, participants in the offline conditions did not have the same 3-minute lapse between coming into the room and completing the questionnaire as participants in the Facebook condition. We were concerned, however, that including a filler task would potentially introduce an additional and unintended manipulation into the study. It seems unlikely that the time lapse alone was part of the reason for the different ratings of self-esteem, but to be sure, future research will need to account for this effect by providing an appropriate filler task for participants in the non-digital environments.

## Conclusion

The Internet has not created new motivation for self presentation, but provides new tools to implement such motives. The negative effects of objective self-awareness on self-esteem originated from work in the early 1970s.[9,13–15] Social-networking sites, a product of the 21st century, provide new access to the self as an object. By providing multiple opportunities for selective self-presentation— through photos, personal details, and witty comments— social-networking sites exemplify how modern technology sometimes forces us to reconsider previously understood psychological processes. Theoretical development can benefit from expanding on previous "offline" theories by incorporating an understanding of how media may alter social processes.

## References

1. Kraut R, Patterson M, Lundmark V, et al. Internet paradox: A social technology that reduces social involvement and psychological well-being? American Psychologist 1998; 53:1017–31.
2. Bessière K, Kiesler S, Kraut R, et al. Effects of Internet use and social resources on changes in depression. Information, Communication & Society 2008; 11:47–70.
3. McKenna KYA, Bargh JA. Plan 9 from cyberspace: The implications of the Internet for personality and social psychology. Personality & Social Psychology Review 2000; 4:57–75.
4. Shaw LH, Gant LM. In defense of the Internet: The relationship between Internet communication and depression, loneliness, self-esteem, and perceived social support. CyberPsychology & Behavior 2002; 5:157–71.
5. Valkenburg PM, Peter J, Schouten AP. Friend networking sites and their relationship to adolescents' well-being and social self-esteem. CyberPsychology & Behavior 2006; 9:484–590.
6. Ellison NB, Steinfield C, Lampe C. The benefits of Facebook "friends": Social capital and college students' use of online social network sites. Journal of Computer- Mediated Communication 2007; 12: 1. jcmc. indiana.edu/vol12/issue4/ellison.html (Accessed Jan. 27, 2009).
7. Heine SJ, Takemoto T, Moskalenko S, et al. Mirrors in the head: Cultural variation in objective self-awareness. Personality & Social Psychology Bulletin 2008; 34:879–87.
8. Walther JB. Computer-mediated communication: Impersonal, interpersonal, and hyperpersonal interaction. Communication Research 1996; 23:3–43.
9. Duval S, Wicklund RA. (1972) *A theory of objective self awareness*. New York: Academic Press.
10. Moskalenko S, Heine SJ. Watching your troubles away: Television viewing as a stimulus for a subjective self-awareness. Personality & Social Psychology Bulletin 2003; 29:76–85.
11. Duval S, Duval VH, Neely, R. Self-focus, felt responsibility, and helping behavior. Journal of Personality & Social Psychology 1979; 37:1769–78.
12. Beaman AL, Klentz B, Diener E, et al. Self-awareness and transgression in children: Two field studies. Journal of Personality & Social Psychology 1979; 37:1835–46.
13. Fejfar MC, Hoyle RH. Effect of private self-awareness on negative affect and self-referent attribution: A quantitative review. Personality & Social Psychology Review 2000; 4:132–42.
14. Storms MD. Videotape and the attribution process: Reversing actors' and observers' points of view. Journal of Personality & Social Psychology 1973; 27:165–75.
15. Ickes WJ, Wicklund RA, Ferris CB. Objective selfawareness and self-esteem. Journal of Experimental Social Psychology 1973; 9:202–19.
16. Duval T, Duval V, Mulilis J. Effects of self-focus, discrepancy between self and standard, and outcome expectancy favorability on the tendency to match self to standard and withdraw. Journal of Personality & Social Psychology 1992; 62:340–8.
17. Hancock JT, Dunham PJ. Impression formation in computermediated communication. Communication Research 2001; 28:325–47.

18. Epley N, Kruger J. When what you type isn't what they read: The perseverance of stereotypes and expectancies over e-mail. Journal of Experimental Social Psychology 2005; 41:414–22.
19. Duthler KW. The politeness of requests made via email and voicemail: Support for the hyperpersonal model. Journal of Computer-Mediated Communication 2006; 11. jcmc.indiana.edu/vol11/issue2/duthler.html (accessed Jan. 13, 2009).
20. Walther JB. Selective self-presentation in computermediated communication: Hyperpersonal dimensions of technology, language, and cognition. Computers in Human Behavior 2007; 23:2538–57.
21. Ellison N, Heino R, Gibbs J. Managing impressions online: Self-presentation processes in the online dating environment. Journal of Computer-Mediated Communication 2006; 11.//jcmc.indiana.edu/vol11/issue2/ellison.html (Accessed Sept. 12, 2007).
22. Toma CL, Hancock JT, Ellison NB. Separating fact from fiction: An examination of deceptive self-presentation in online dating profiles. Personality & Social Psychology Bulletin 2008; 4:1023–36.
23. Gonzales AL, Hancock JT. Identity shift in computermediated environments. Media Psychology 2008; 11:167–85.
24. Rosenberg M. (1965) *Society and the adolescent self-image.* Princeton, NJ: Princeton University Press.
25. Josephs RA, Markus HR, Tafarodi RW. Gender and self-esteem. Journal of Personality & Social Psychology 1992; 63:391–402.

**Amy L. Gonzales** is a faculty member in the department of telecommunications at Indiana University Bloomington. Her research examines the effects that communication technologies have on individual identity, social support, and well-being.

**JEFFREY T. HANCOCK** is a professor in the Communications and Information Science departments at Cornell University and is the Chair of the Information Science department. He is interested in social interactions mediated by information and communication technology, with an emphasis on how people produce and understand language in these contexts.

# Technology and Work

Technology has changed the entire landscape of work with the development and disappearance of certain occupations, how we meet and discuss ideas with coworkers and supervisors, and how and where products get manufactured and produced. On the one hand, technological developments have severely affected the manufacturing industry with the replacement of human workers with machines. Newer technological advancements may create confusion and tension for workers who may not know how to change or develop a compatible skill set. Technology has also allowed companies to outsource more aspects of their businesses, impacting manufacturing, service, and professional occupations around the world. Yet, on the other hand, technology has provided opportunities for groups who may have been prohibited from performing certain jobs. For example, women can work in factories with machinery that has been adapted to their smaller frames. The information economy has created a surge in telecommuting and working from home (via computer) which has allowed flexibility for parents to participate in both the world of paid employment and parenting work. Voice recognition software and other technological advancements have allowed more opportunities for the employment of disabled persons. Thus, the impact of technology on the changing workplace has benefits and drawbacks, issues to be explored through the readings in this section.

## Objectives

1. Identify the role of technology in the workplace.
2. Describe how the changing or expanding use of technology has affected human workers.
3. Identify how workers adapt to changing technology.

# Article 20

Theodore Lewis

## Studying the Impact of Technology on Work and Jobs

It can be compellingly argued that understanding technology has become as important for vocational educators as it has been for technology educators. Indeed, because of shared interests and concerns, technology has the potential for uniting aspects of the discourse of technology educators and vocationalists. Placing it at the center of vocationalism, authors of the SCANS report (Secretary's Commission on Achieving Necessary Skills [SCANS], 1991) set forth mastery of technology as a core competency that schools should provide their graduates to make them workplace ready. Correspondingly, technology educators (Deal, 1994; Johnson, 1991) have suggested that their subject ought to be fashioned to improve the career choices of students in today's workplace.

Vocational institutions have traditionally relied upon labor market information derived from graduate follow-ups and the counsel of advisory committees to make curriculum and planning decisions. While data thus derived are still of value, it is imperative that these approaches be expanded to include proactive, workplace-based inquiry that provides first hand insight and multiple perspectives regarding technological impact. To this end, Lewis and Konare (1993) found that "changing workplace" characterized the highest priority information needed by vocational planners.

In adjusting to new workplace realities it would be a mistake for vocationalists to accept technological determinism as an inevitable fate, requiring meek acceptance that curricula be altered to keep up with the pace of change. There is need instead for a critical disposition that interrogates technology, examines the intentions of those who introduce it, and weighs its desirable as well as undesirable effects.

We are indeed witnessing a revolution in the workplace, wrought substantially by the introduction of technology, the consequence of which is that the very nature of work is changing, with jobs either being transformed or made obsolete (Danziger, 1985; Ducatel, 1994; Fearfull, 1992; Form, 1987; Freeman & Soete, 1994; McLoughlin & Clark, 1994; Spenner, 1983, 1985; Wallace, 1989; Zuboff, 1988) and with skill being redefined and its measurement the object of contestation (Attewell, 1990; Carnevale, Gainer, & Meltzer, 1988; SCANS, 1991; Spenner, 1990; Vallas, 1990). These changes have important human and societal consequences. At the human level, while some workers may find that technology makes their jobs more complex and satisfying, others may find themselves bewildered and suddenly incompetent. Still others may find that their work has become less challenging and that the expertise and artistry they had acquired over the years no longer matter. Some may pay the ultimate price of job loss. At the societal level, balancing productivity gains due to technology with its undesirable side effects (e.g., technological unemployment, lower wage jobs, or worker alienation) has become a challenge.

Workplace changes as described above have had reform consequences for all of education (Johnston, 1993), leading to conjecture as to how much schooling the new jobs will demand (Bailey, 1991). While all of education must respond to the changes, vocational education especially ought to do so because work is central to its basic claims (see Lewis, 1992). Where the issue of the impact of technology is concerned, vocational education has substantially defaulted on its claims that it is at the center of discourse on work. Instead, the locus of such discourse lies with sociologists and other social scientists, who for two decades or so (taking the publication of Braverman's [1974] *Labor and Monopoly Capital* as a starting point) have been framing and testing hypotheses regarding consequences of technological change on work and jobs, using actual workplaces as their laboratory. One reason why this rich area of discourse has not been influenced by vocationalists might be that vocational education scholarship has been driven more by legislative and policy dictates (e.g., the Perkins Act, or SCANS prescriptions) than by workplace-related theory. The field has paid insufficient attention to the sociology, psychology, and politics of work and workplaces.

Vocational education (and indeed technology education) researchers must come to view the workplace as a laboratory for the study of technology and its impact. How workers fare therein, and the skills they need to survive amidst constant change, must become a core area of inquiry. Three recent studies invite brief comment here. Custer and Claiborne (1992, 1995) found alignment when they juxtaposed the perceptions of vocational instructors and employers on the kinds of employability skills that are needed in the workplace. Similarly, Thomas and Gray (1991) examined the skill priorities of employers. Taken together, these studies were seeking answers to the question, "What skills do workplaces really call for?" In this regard, they could be foundational to further inquiry, located in actual workplaces and based upon worker interviews and direct observation of work. The discourse on skill change has to be expanded to include the voices of workers and move beyond perceptions to workplace reality.

To establish a tradition of inquiry among vocational educators (and technology educators who include career possibilities in their teaching) on changing skill needs, changing work, changing jobs, and the role that technology plays in such change, there is need for an ongoing related discourse. This article is intended to act as a catalyst for such a discourse by focusing on issues, challenges, and approaches that must be considered when studying the impact of technology on work and jobs. It examines relevant theory, possible research hypotheses and questions, appropriate conceptual frameworks, appropriate methodologies, and the problem of operationalizing and measuring skill. One consequence of the ideas explored here is that the inquiry terrain would become more easily navigable for vocational education (and technology education) scholars who might be contemplating study of the new workplace and the role of technology, as a way to test or formulate theory, or as the basis for curricular and instructional decisions.

## Theoretical Underpinnings

Discourse on the impact of technology on work pivots around labor process theory as articulated by Braverman (1974). The theory, roughly, states that the basic purpose of introducing technology into workplaces is to foster transference of skill from labor to capital, thereby affording management greater control of the labor process. With the transference of skill comes a loss of worker efficacy. In other words, technology engenders a dialectic between labor and management, mediated by the location of skill, with the stakes being workplace power.

Labor process theory has had to withstand vigorous challenge over time by analysts offering their own conceptions of the nature of the interplay between management and labor when technology is introduced (Burawoy, 1979; Edwards, 1979; McLoughlin & Clark, 1994). Burawoy contended that when technology is introduced, workers invariably find ways to make shop-floor compromises. With the tacit agreement of management, they find ways to compensate for the degree of skill or control they now must yield. Thus worker consent is integral to the introduction of technology. Edwards asserted that the introduction of technology does not automatically lead to workers' yielding their shop-floor power to management. The workplace constitutes *contested terrain* where each new salvo by management aimed at wresting shop floor control from labor can be expected to be countered. Consistent with Edwards (1979) and E. G. Burawoy (1979), McLoughlin and Clark (1994) offer a stage theory of the introduction of technology. At each stage there is opportunity for negotiation where managers, workers, and their representatives can seek out common ground as they decide on the efficacy of the proposed change.

Challenges notwithstanding, labor process theory remains the predominant explanation of the motivation behind the introduction of technology into work places. If we agree with the theory, then hypotheses of the following order suggest themselves: With the introduction of technology into workplaces (a) there will be net loss of traditional skills, (b) craft knowledge will be devalued or made anachronistic, (c) the power of unions will diminish, and (d) the autonomy and discretionary power of workers will diminish. These hypotheses would be in keeping with the idea of the *deskilling* of jobs.

Labor process theory has appeal as an explanation of the decline of craft, a phenomenon that is observable across an array of occupations. For example, in the machining trades Computerized Numerical Control (CNC) has replaced traditional setups and processes. Computer Assisted Drafting (CAD) has replaced much of traditional hand drawing. In the printing trades, computers are replacing light tables and artists' knives. Trends such as these provide raw material for the idea of deskilling (Kalleberg, Wallace, Loscocco, Leicht, & Ehm, 1987; Wallace & Kalleberg, 1982; Wilson & Buchannan, 1988). The theory is useful not just in manufacturing settings. For example, it can explain skill change among clerical workers (Fearfull, 1992), and although the teaching profession has remained relatively impervious to technological change thus far, with the prospect of a computer in most homes, will it be long before the job of teacher becomes substantially redefined?

At the opposite pole of deskilling is upgrading, the idea that the introduction of technology enhances skill (Bell, 1973; Grayson, 1993; Hirschhorn, 1984; Piore & Sabel, 1984; Zuboff, 1988). Zuboff (1988) speaks of new *informating* work environments that are conducive to workplace democracy. Workers have more information about work processes at their command and rely more on their cognitive abilities and less on their bodies. Hirschhorn (1984) views technology as consuming much of the drudgery of work, freeing the worker for contemplative thought. Piore and Sabel (1984) advance the idea of *flexible specialization*, which is the antithesis of mass production and calls for workers who can combine formal education, practical skill, and experience. This theory sees a role still for craft knowledge.

If we agree that technology engenders skill upgrading, then countervailing hypotheses are suggested: With the introduction of technology (a) the complexity of work is increased, (b) worker autonomy is enhanced, and (c) tasks become more complex.

Between the poles of deskilling and upgrading are theoretical explanations asserting gradations of the effects of technology. One position is that the introduction of technology leads to *mixed* or *contingent* outcomes that are context dependent (Form, 1987; Spenner, 1985). A related conception is *skill polarization* (Gallie, 1991; Milkman & Pullman, 1991), that is, with the introduction of technology there are winners and losers in the workplace. While the job complexity of some may increase, that of others might decrease. Another conception is that the new workplace calls for *functional flexibility* (O'Reilly, 1992). With the introduction of technology, companies may resort to fewer workers, who are then asked to perform a variety of jobs.

Theoretical explanations relating to this line of inquiry revolve around the *intentions* of those who make the decision to introduce technology, and the *consequences* of their actions. Because intentions are at issue, the balance of workplace power comes into question. Consequences must also be discussed in terms of power, but must also extend to manifestations of shifts in power, such as impact on craft, weakening of trade unions, boredom, and alienation. In the discourse on the impact of technology on work and jobs, intentions and consequences become encapsulated in the concept of *skill*. Skill is the capital with which workers negotiate. Technology invariably calls the value of that capital into question.

# Resolving The Problem Of Skill

Consistent with labor process theory, skill is the variable that is the primary measure of technology's effects. Recall that the heart of Braverman's (1974) argument is that technology leads to deskilling. To come to terms with the theory, we must agree on what *skill* is. There is still disagreement about its nature, and hence, how it ought to be operationalized, observed, and measured. Since the conception, operationalization, and measurement of skill are requisite to the study of technology's impact on work and jobs, it is important that the central tensions be examined.

Whether skill is an empirical or social construct is a source of debate. Positivists may be inclined to an empirical conception, allowing for its exact measurement. Those inclined to critical or interpretative perspectives may be partial to a constructivist explanation. Beyond such concerns, there is the problem of resolving what may be called the *politics* of skill. For example, unions may be inclined to rate the skill level of a given job more highly than would management. Or, there may be a gender variant in the distribution of skill in the workplace. This section of the article explores many-sided dimensions of skill such as these, and the inquiry challenges they pose to those investigating the impact of technology on work and jobs.

## Emerging Meanings of Skill

The question "What is skill?" currently yields varied answers. In everyday life, skill has a commonplace meaning. Within vocational and technology education, skill has been a valued currency and is perceived as being demonstrable, empirically verifiable, and transferable. The mechanism of transfer is instruction, requiring that tasks be decomposed (via task analyses) and taught. The quality of skill one possesses can be measured via predetermined competency standards.

This conception of skill is being contested. Spenner has raised the question of whether skills reside in people or in jobs. Expressing the view that "workplaces and jobs are imperfect translators of human abilities and capacities" (1985, p. 132), he contends (as did Berg in 1970) that schooling and training have more to do with screening available labor market entrants than with real demand for skill. He proposed two conceptions of skill: (a) skill as *substantive complexity*, referring to "the level, scope, and integration of mental, interpersonal, and manipulative tasks in a job" (p. 135); and (b) skill as *autonomy-control*, referring to "the discretion available in a job to initiate and conclude action, to control the content, manner, and speed with which tasks are done" (p. 135).

The first of these two measures of skill has been supported empirically. In a factor analysis study of *Dictionary of Occupational Titles* occupational characteristics, Cain and Treiman (1981) found that the factor *substantive complexity* explained half of the shared variance. Items that loaded on this factor reflected education and training, intelligence, quantitative and verbal ability, and ability to interact with people, data and things. Spenner's second measure-skill as autonomy-control-has been challenged. In his study of the impact of technology on the jobs of Canadian workers, Grayson (1993) concluded that it was conceptually inappropriate to link skill and autonomy.

At the very least, Spenner's schema suggests that skill goes beyond measurable competence. There *must* be a difference between a skilled machine and a skilled human being. Power and self efficacy add the uniquely human dimension to the equation of skill and must on that account be factored into our observation and measurement of it.

Offering a schema that subsumes but goes beyond Spenner's, Atwell (1990) has identified four schools of thought relating to skill. The first is *positivism*, which treats skill complexity as being quantifiable and measurable. Adherents are likely to rely on aggregate skill data published in the *Dictionary of Occupational Titles* in making determinations about job complexity. The second is *ethnomethodology*, which is at odds with the positivist school, deems *all* human activity to be complex, and cautions against the danger of assuming that everyday actions are simple. According to Atwell, the observer's reference point becomes of great importance here. Tasks that the observer can perform may appear to be mundane while more distant esoteric skills may be perceived to be complex. Again, workers may tend to undervalue their day to day skill, assuming the disposition that there is "nothing to it." Zuboff (1988) discusses this phenomenon in her methodology, highlighting it as a possible pitfall. The difficulties here are evident. Both self-report of skill and observer estimates of it could be subject to error.

A third view of skill, set forth by Atwell, is a *neo-Weberian* or *constructionist school*, which looks at skill as a contrivance that could be fashioned by strategies such as "social closure." This view is evident in the ways of the Medieval guilds and in the restricted entry practices of trade unions or professional groups. The aura of restricted entry and long apprenticeships conveys complexity and assures monopoly power and control for the groups in question. Under this conception, skill correlates with control over the supply of labor, the training of labor, and importantly, over wage rates.

A final view of skills is *Marxist*, which also views skill in terms of control-control this time resting not with labor but with capital. This view of skill can be seen to be in a dialectical relationship with the neo-Weberian school. Technology becomes the instrument of workplace power because management can use it to demystify worker-centered skill, and indeed to replace human-based processes. This latter view of skill essentially is the conception around which labor process theory is formulated.

Vallas (1990) has suggested that many issues relating to skill and its manifestations remain unexplored. One such issue surrounds the direction of causality between technology and skill, suggesting the need for research on their possible reciprocal effects. A second issue is the hypothesized link between skill and worker consciousness. The question here is whether the content of their jobs shapes the political attitudes of workers. Vallas speaks of the need for "nuanced, multidimensional conceptions of skill" (p. 384).

Darrah (1994) cautions that to understand skill, we must view workplaces as being variable, along lines dictated in part by technology. What constitutes important skill lies in the eyes of the beholder. In other words, skill is a social construction. He found that while supervisors rate oral communication and working in teams as high level skills, operators contrarily viewed these merely as necessities to get the job done. In this vein, critical tacit knowledge of workers might go unrewarded. Darrah suggests that "the appropriate analytical unit in the study of skills may be the workplace and not the individual job" (1994, p. 82). His counsel might be better understood if we consider how different a unionized work environment might be from a non-unionized one, or the cultural differences that might exist between a large corporation and a small firm. The experience of the introduction of technology can be expected to vary across settings.

## Skill and Gender

Social (and political) dimensions of skill are further illuminated when gender is taken into account. Issues here spring from the segmented nature of labor markets, with gender being a basis of difference. For example, men are more likely to be carpenters or electricians while women are more likely to be nurses or secretaries. Is there a skill differential in the jobs that men and women typically perform? This is a complex question, because women have not traditionally had much choice in determining their work, instead relying on what society has deemed to be suitable for them. Steinberg (1990) speaks of the invisibility of women's work-important skill characteristics of women's jobs are overlooked. Horrell, Rubery, and Burchell (1990) found that the jobs typically held by women involved attributes and skills that were different from the jobs of men. Likewise, Myles and Fawcett (1990) found that fewer women than men have skilled jobs. Grayson (1993) found that a majority of women in clerical jobs reported high skill and high autonomy; women were poorly represented in the high skill/high autonomy category among electrical, machining workers, and among engineers. Wajcman (1991) laments the absence of a gender dimension in the sociology of technology. She expresses concern that women may be disadvantaged in technology-oriented workplaces because technology essentially is a manifestation of masculine culture.

Caution would dictate that gender be considered a mediating variable when studying the impact of technology in workplaces. The interrelationships among technology, gender, and skill remain a promising line of workplace inquiry, with particular reference to the circumstances of women. Gender, technology, and skill are certainly issues within formal schooling, particularly within vocational and technology education. Within the K-12 system, boys are more likely to have taken technology as a school subject and to pursue manufacturing related vocational course work (e.g., machining, welding, electrical, construction) than girls.

Awareness of the possibility of a gender effect should influence how firms, occupations, and individuals are to be selected for study. Researchers should enter inquiry with the assumption that men and women may have very different stories to relate, and that their insights, observations, and experiences might be colored by their respective circumstances.

## Skills Employers Want

In many practical respects, the frontier of the definition of skill is now occupied by employers, whose need for *necessary skills* in terms of the imperative to compete in the global economy, have reached the ear of policy-makers and vocationalists. Skill in this realm attends *workplaces*, not occupations. It manifests itself in a set of attributes, or *basics*, that are criteria for labor market entry. This employer-driven discourse on skill is inherently problematic because at the rhetorical level, employers often down play the technical skills and tacit knowledge that workers draw upon to establish their worth and value, while they highlight attitudinal attributes. Skill and competence thereby become mediated by value questions. In a recent national report, employers rated having "a good work ethic" ahead of other workplace attributes (Commission on Skills of the American Workforce, 1990). How literally to take such a finding is difficult to determine. If conformity with workplace norms is skill, as employers tacitly claim, then there would be an abundance of such skill in workplaces, since it could be cultivated merely by the imposition of workplace rules and sanctions-such as the prospect of job loss. Skills derived through years of formal schooling, on-the-job training, and experience clearly are much scarcer, and theoretically (as trade unionists would argue) should be of greater value.

A central work on employer needs is Carnevale, Gainer, and Meltzer's (1988) taxonomy of workplace basics. The skills employers are said to want are independent of jobs. They include learning how to learn, the 3Rs, communication, creative thinking, problem solving, self esteem, and interpersonal skills. These aspects of skill intersect substantially with those set forth in the SCANS report (1991). Despite their widespread acceptance, these now popular conceptions of workplace basics are essentially points of view, requiring validation. As discussed elsewhere in this article, studies within vocational education (Custer & Claiborne, 1992, 1995; Thomas & Gray, 1991) have been seeking to corroborate them, mainly by asking stakeholders such as employers and vocational instructors to identify the necessary workplace skills. One important outcome of these studies is that they have reclaimed space in the discourse for technical skills as an integral part of needed workplace basics.

Often the skills employers want are discussed in terms of workplace literacy, central to which is the ability to read in the context of one's job. Workplace literacy is also a contested view of skill, because the instrumental is accorded primacy over the intrinsic. For example, reading is not assumed to be a general skill, but rather a context-bound one. This is the reason behind the separation Sticht (1978) makes between reading-to-learn, reading-to do, and reading-to-assess. By this conception, one may be able to follow steps from an electronics manual, but be unable to read the daily newspaper. (See Diehl and Mikulecky [1980] for a workplace-based account).

The skills employers want must be accounted for in studying the impact of technology on work and jobs. But employers cannot have the last word on needed skills. Skills have a cost, which employers must pay. It might therefore be natural for them to understate or undervalue their worth. Hence possible differences between employer perceptions and that of workers must be reconciled, as should any differences between perceived worker skill needs and skills actually needed to get work done.

## Measuring Skill

Just as the meaning of skill is contested, how to measure it is also at issue. Spenner (1985, 1990) has identified three tendencies here, *nonmeasures, indirect measures, and direct measures*. Nonmeasurement assumes that skill levels correlate with occupational class. Thus, white collar skills are tacitly assumed to be of greater complexity than blue collar ones. Indirect measures utilize skill proxies, such as wage rates or level of education. Direct measures require "explicit assessment of specific dimensions of skills for jobs or workers in jobs" (Spenner, 1985, p. 133). Spenner asserts that with direct measures, issues relating to validity and reliability are more easily examined. In his view, the shortage of direct measures has hampered inquiry into skill changes in the workplace. An example of a direct measure approach can be seen in Milkman and Pullman's (1991) study of the introduction of technology into an auto assembly plant in which jobs were decomposed and the impact of technology on job facets examined.

As Spenner points out, the *Dictionary of Occupational Titles* is the most frequently used source of direct measurement data in studies of skill change. He finds it to be a flawed but still unparalleled source of data. Each occupation in the *Dictionary of Occupational Titles* is classified and coded in terms of *worker functions*, *physical demands*, and *environmental conditions*. From the standpoint of skill measurement, the "worker functions" segment of the code is of greatest interest. It catalogs capacities required to perform jobs, in terms of one's relative involvement with data, people, and things, each represented by a taxonomy of behaviors.

Because the *Dictionary of Occupational Titles* provides time series data, it is possible to track skill changes, or compositional shifts (the mix of job titles), within occupations or industries. This capability is of great value when one is inquiring into the impact of technology. Whether upgrading or deskilling occurs can be assessed, though one must bear in mind that these are aggregated data. In a study of the impact of technology on work and jobs in the printing industry of a mid-Western state (Lewis, 1995), the *Dictionary of Occupational Titles* was utilized to study temporal changes. Changes in the occupation of study could be tracked at two points in time, 1977 and 1991. The temporal shift in skill revealed by the *Dictionary of Occupational Titles* suggested that within the last decade or so, traditional pre-press skills would have been in retreat as companies scrambled to become proficient in the new technologies. The practical details of this retreat were then probed through study of actual cases.

## Advantages and Disadvantages of the Dictionary of Occupational Titles

While the *Dictionary of Occupational Titles* is heavily relied upon by researchers studying skill change, its advantages must be tempered by its disadvantages. Advantages include the opportunity it affords to study the same jobs over time, opportunity to study compositional shifts within occupations and industries, and the comprehensiveness of its database. Disadvantages include the unrepresentativeness of the sample of occupations listed (manufacturing jobs are overrepresented, while service and clerical jobs are under represented); the tendency to undervalue jobs that typically are held by women; classifying a majority of the listed occupations on the basis of fewer than three jobs; aggregating the data so they are not necessarily representative of the reality within individual firms; and the unstable reliabilities of the job characteristics. (See especially Cain & Green, 1983; Cain & Treiman, 1981; Miller et al., 1980; Spenner, 1985).

Spenner cautions that the *Dictionary of Occupational Titles* "probably underestimates the true level of skill change" (1985, p. 134), but adds that studies that do not use the *Dictionary of Occupational Titles* reach conclusions that are comparable to those that do use it. Vallas (1990) asserts that the *Dictionary of Occupational Titles* tends to be partial to the upgrading explanation of skill change. He further observes that despite the clear need for multiple dimensions of skill, the *Dictionary of Occupational*

*Titles* is restricted to a single dimension-complexity-while ignoring autonomy-control. This observation is consistent with Cain and Treiman's (1981) finding that substantive complexity was the dominant factor reflected by *Dictionary of Occupational Titles* skill estimates, explaining half of shared variance. Autonomy did not emerge as a factor.

Many of the basic criticisms of the *Dictionary of Occupational Titles* are now embodied in proposals to overhaul and replace it with a new database of occupational titles that can serve the needs of employers, trainers, educators, and others better (Advisory Panel for the *Dictionary of Occupational Titles*, 1993).

## Studying Workplaces

The issues discussed here (e.g., contested meanings of skill and difficulties of measuring it) must eventually be distilled to be of practical utility in the inquiry process. Such a distillation must come to inform conceptual frameworks, instrumentation, design, and methodology. This section seeks to move the discussion closer to practice by dwelling first upon suggested frameworks for inquiry, then upon methodologies utilized in selected studies on the impact of technology on work.

### Research Frameworks

Frameworks for the study of technology's impact on work and jobs must provide opportunity for the testing of hypotheses relating to upgrading and deskilling. They must also reflect sensitivity to the subtle and multidimensional nature of skill. Setting forth one such framework, Form, Kaufman, Parcel, and Wallace (1988) asserted that when studying the impact of technology on work the *establishment* ought to be the most important unit of analysis because it allows individuals, departments, or work units to be studied simultaneously. This assertion is in keeping with that of Darrah (1994). Hypotheses would reflect upgrading or deskilling propositions. Research questions would vary as the focus shifted from worker to department to establishment. The dependent variables of interest would shift from skill/autonomy, to job satisfaction, to market characteristics, or type of technology.

Hampson, Ewer, and Smith (1994) posit a research framework that would critically interrogate the idea of post-Fordism (production beyond the rigidities of the assembly line and beyond mass production). They probe whether the new workplace culture allows or precludes common action to be taken by workers, and whether practices such as out-sourcing (contracting out components) affect the career possibilities of many workers. Consistent with the critical posture of this framework, they include issues of technology and gender.

## Research Methodologies

The thought processes embodied in research frameworks become operationalized in the actual approach to inquiry. What questions are asked, to whom, about what, and to what end, are all manifestations of stances and ideologies that underlie the research framework. Examination of the methodologies of selected studies can be instructive in making one a better consumer and ultimately a better producer of such work.

An illustrative study from the standpoint of design and methodology is Milkman and Pullman's (1991) examination of the impact of the introduction of robotics and programmable automation on work and jobs in an auto-assembly plant. This study utilized multiple sources of data. The methodology included document inspection, which provided background data on the company, such as its profile of layoffs and hires across departments. It was thereby possible to examine specific labor force census changes wrought by the introduction of the technologies. Also included were on-site observations of workers on the job. The authors conducted extensive interviews of workers, managers, and union officials, both individually and in groups. Further, they conducted an in-plant survey of the impact of the introduction of technology on the workforce. Data were retrospective; workers were asked to recall pre- and post-changeover memories pertaining to their jobs and to compare the two. While questionnaires were used, they were completed during face to face interviews with respondents.

Workers were further asked how much the technology had affected their work, and their responses were measured by a Likert-type scale, ranging from *a lot* to *not at all*. They were also asked if any of the work they performed previously was now automated. The researchers checked for changes in *job content*. They picked out specific job-tasks and tried to find out if these were more important now than before. They compared results across classes of workers. For production workers, tasks used for comparisons included tool use, inspection, machine monitoring, and repair. For skilled trades workers, tasks included troubleshooting, repairing equipment, programming, training new workers, diagnostic work, and making parts. The authors were also interested in changes in *skill levels*. They did this by asking workers to compare the importance of certain skills before and after the changeover. Skills included reading, spelling, math, and creativity. Overall, they found "an unmistakable deskilling tendency" in all four production departments. Conversely they found "marked upgrading" in the case of skill workers, more so for high-tech than traditional ones. This case supported the contingency explanation of the impact of technology (Form, 1987). There was also evidence of skill polarization.

A possible shortcoming of the approach here was that the data were aggregated, resulting in the suppression of individual perspectives. It is the human drama attending the introduction of technology that makes this such an important and interesting problem area.

Zuboff (1988) studied eight organizations that had introduced technology in ways that had substantially altered work processes and jobs. In her methodology, she explained that "timing" was an important factor in collecting data. There was a "window of opportunity" during which people working with the technology for the first time were at peak interest, and keenly reflective. Beyond this window, they would seek to "accommodate their understanding to the altered conditions of work, making it more difficult to extract fresh insights from beneath a new crust of familiarity" (p. 13). This ethnomethodological stance is consistent with Atwell (1990). Like Milkman and Pullman (1991), Zuboff searched out subjects who had worked at the same tasks under old conditions and new, requiring them to compare both conditions.

An intriguing methodological strategy employed in this study was to have some subjects draw pictures that portrayed the felt sense of their job experience before and after the conversion to the new computer system (Zuboff, 1988). These renderings were said to provide an avenue for the expression of feelings that workers had difficulty converting into words. The illustrations were then grouped into thematic categories, which became the basis of analysis.

Wilson and Buchanan (1988) examined the impact of computerized numerical control (CNC) on skill in three engineering companies. The method was a combination of structured and unstructured interviews, and a questionnaire. With the introduction of CNC, the machines were now programmed by computer programmers away from the shop floor. The technology brought clear workplace advantages, including reduced need for maintenance persons, since "self-diagnostics" were integral to the design of the machines. The old job was compared with the new. Workers were asked to rate their extent of agreement or disagreement with statements about the effects of technology on their work. The researchers concluded that the introduction of CNC and the division of labor it engendered had given managers greater control over the labor process, but that much shop floor intelligence still resided with the workers. There was still opportunity for the exercise of skill and discretion.

In a study cited previously, Grayson (1993) examined the relationship among skill, autonomy, and technological change, by using data from the General Social Survey conducted by Statistics Canada in 1989. The sample consisted of 9,338 Canadian workers, who were asked the following questions as part of the survey:

- Do you agree or disagree that your job requires a high level of skill?
- Do you agree or disagree that there is a lot of freedom to decide how to do your work?
- In the last 5 years, how much has your work been affected by the introduction of computers or automated technology? Would you say greatly, somewhat, hardly or not at all? (p. 26)

Grayson was testing Spenner's (1985) conception of skill as autonomy/control. The responses of subjects with respect to skill were compared with those with respect to freedom (autonomy). The responses were analyzed by gender, industrial sector, and occupations, using the chi square statistic. Frequencies of instances of high skill/high autonomy, high skill/low autonomy, low skill/high autonomy, and low skill/low autonomy were determined. The results indicated that gender, occupation, and industrial sector all made a difference in skill and autonomy.

As to the impact of technology, Grayson further found that those who characterized their jobs as high skill/high autonomy were more likely to report that technology had greatly influenced their work. This trend was in keeping with upgrading theory. But Grayson noted also that the impact of technology varied across occupations, industrial sectors, and gender.

In another study cited previously, Lewis (1995) customized interview protocols according to the status of key informants (e.g., workers, managers, supervisors, union representatives). Skill was treated as a many-sided construct. Following Spenner (1985), aspects of skill built into the interview protocol included *autonomy/control* (e.g., "Can you use your own judgment?" or "Can you make adjustments on your own?") and *substantive complexity* (e.g., "Do you troubleshoot if there is a problem?" or "Are there new things to be learned all the time?"). These notions were complemented by questions reflective of skills employers want. Sample protocol items here included "Do you work in a team?" or "Do you have to read and work from manuals?" Preliminary findings are suggesting mixed effects, both the erosion of craft and upgrading of aspects of prepress work.

## Summary

The studies discussed here, while not exhaustive, illustrate a variety of methodological possibilities. There is the option of case methodology (Lewis, 1995; Milkman & Pullman, 1991; Wilson & Buchanan, 1988; , 1988), or the use of aggregate data (such as the *Dictionary of Occupational Titles*) or existing databases of workers (Grayson, 1993; Lewis, 1995). Within these options one sees a variety of data gathering approaches including worker self report, document inspection, individual interviews, group interviews, face to face completion of structured surveys, on site observation of work, and use of drawings as a proxy for opinion. There are also a variety of inquiry approaches-positivistic, critical, or interpretative.

# Discussion and Conclusion

This article has addressed important issues, challenges, and approaches that must be considered when studying the impact of technology on work and jobs. Braverman's (1974) labor process theory, the dominant explanation of technology's introduction, was examined, along with important challenges such as the role of consent, and the view of the shop floor as contested terrain. Deskilling and upgrading arguments were explored. Since skill is at the heart of labor process theory, a discussion of conceptual and methodological issues was set forth that examined emerging meanings of skill, the problem of skill and gender, and skills employers want. Issues involved in the measurement of skill were then addressed, featuring an examination of uses of the *Dictionary of Occupational Titles*. A discussion of protocols for studying workplaces followed, featuring illustrative examples from exemplary studies.

Technology's hold on the modern workplace cannot be seriously disputed. Since work stands at the core of vocationalism, few issues are as important to vocational educators as technology (Lewis, 1992). As indicated earlier, technology might be a unifying theme in the convergence of technology education and vocational education.

Despite the many obvious ways in which technology has improved our world, it is necessary to adopt a critical stance towards it. In workplaces, employing technology is an imperative, and could be a blessing for the owners of capital, if they can afford it. Technology engenders productivity. The jury remains out for workers, especially in these times of "re-engineering" when companies are finding it possible, mainly because of enabling technologies, to lay off experienced workers (Rifkin, 1995). As companies become more reliant on technology, long term mutual loyalties that were the basis of job security erode.

This article was intended to provoke the scholars of our field to enter into a discourse on the nature of inquiry on the impact of the introduction of technology into workplaces, so that we can all become better at framing questions and embarking upon inquiry of this order. The new workplace remains a mysterious black box into which we send graduates and hope for the best. Providing them with technological acumen would appear to be a responsible course of action. Much ambiguity and confusion pervade the rhetoric as to what skills are needed out there. Sometimes it appears that no skills are needed, beyond a good attitude or the ability to be flexible. Other times it appears that one needs merely to be literate.

Computerized environments are now the order of the day. What do students really need to exist in these environments? What should the curricular and instructional response be within vocational education and technology education with the life cycle of specific technologies becoming ever shorter? Inquiry into the new workplace can provide some answers. What is needed now is that others join in the conversation.

# Author

Lewis is Associate Professor, Department of Vocational and Technical Education, University of Minnesota, St. Paul, Minnesota. The author thanks doctoral student Stephan Flister for conducting part of the library research that supported this article.

# References

Advisory Panel for the *Dictionary of Occupational Titles* (1993). *The New DOT: A Database of Occupational Titles for the Twenty-First Century*, Washington DC: U.S. Department of Labor.

Attewell, P. (1990). What is skill? *Work and Occupations*, 17(4), 422-447.

Bailey, T. (1991). Jobs of the future and the education they will require: Evidence from occupational forecasts. *Educational Researcher*, 20(2), 11-20.

Braverman, H. (1974). *Labor and monopoly capital-The degradation of work in the twentieth century*. New York: Monthly Press Review.

Bell, D. (1973). *The coming of post-industrial society-A venture in social forecasting*. New York: Basic Books.

Berg, I. (1970). *Education and jobs*. New York: Praeger.

Burawoy, M. (1979). *Manufacturing consent-Changes in the labor process under capitalism*. Chicago: University of Chicago Press.

Cain, P. S., & Green, B. F. (1983). Reliabilities of selected ratings available from the dictionary of occupational titles, *Journal of Applied Psychology*, 68(1), 155-165.

Cain, P. S., & Treiman, D. J. (1981). The dictionary of occupational titles as a source of occupational data. *American Sociological Review*, 46, 253-258.

Carnevale, A. P., Gainer, L. J., & Meltzer, A. S. (1988). *Workplace basics: The skills employers want*. Washington, DC: U.S. Department of Labor and the American Society for Training and Development.

Commission on Skills of the American Workforce. *America's choice: High skills or low wages*. Rochester, NY: National Center on Education and the Economy.

Custer, R. L., & Claiborne, D. M. (1992). Critical skill clusters for vocational education. *Journal of Vocational Education Research*, 17(4), 15-40.

Custer, R. L., & Claiborne, D. M. (1995). Critical skill clusters for vocational education: The employers' perspective-A replication study. *Journal of Vocational Education Research*, 20(1), 7-33.

Danziger, J. N. (1985). Social science and the impact of computer technology. *Social Science Quarterly*, 66, 3-21.

Darrah, C. (1994). Skill requirements at work. *Work and Occupations*, 21(1), 64-84.

Deal, W. F. (1994). Spotlight on careers! Science, engineering & technology. *The Technology Teacher*, 54(2), 13-24.

Diehl, W. A., & Mikulecky, L. (1980). *Journal of Reading*, 24(3), 221-227.

Ducatel, K. (Ed.) (1994). *Employment and technical change in Europe*. Cambridge, England: Cambridge University Press.

Edwards, R. (1979). *Contested terrain: The transformation of the workplace in the twentieth century*. New York: Basic Books.

Fearfull, A. (1992). The introduction of information and office technologies: The great divide. *Work, Employment & Society*, 6(3), 423-442.

Form, W. (1987). On the degradation of skills. *Annual Review of Sociology*, 13, 29-47.

Form, W., Kaufman, R. L., Parcel, T. L., Wallace, M. (1988). The impact of technology on work organization and work outcomes. In G. Farkas & P. England (Eds.), *Industry, firms, and jobs: Sociological and economic approaches* (pp. 303-328). New York: Plenum.

Freeman, C., & Soete, L. (1994). *Work for all or mass unemployment?* New York: Pinter.

Gallie, D. (1991). Patterns of skill change: Upskilling, deskilling or the polarization of skills? *Work, Employment & Society*, 5(3), 319-351.

Grayson, J. P. (1993). Skill, autonomy, and technological change in Canada. *Work and Occupations*, 20(1), 23-45.

Hampson, I., Ewer, P., & Smith, M. (1994). Post-Fordism and workplace change: Towards a critical research agenda. *The Journal of Industrial Relations*, 36(2), 231-257.

Hirschhorn, L. (1984). *Beyond mechanization: Work and technology in a postindustrial age*. Cambridge, MA: MIT Press.

Horrell, S., Rubery, J., & Burchell, B. (1990). *Work, Employment & Society*, 4(2), 189-216.

Johnson, S. D. (1991). Productivity, the workforce, and technology education. *Journal of Technology Education*, 2(2), 32-49.

Johnston, B. J. (1993). The transformation of work and educational reform policy. *American Educational Research Journal*, 30(1), 39-63.

Kalleberg, A. L., Wallace, M., Loscocco, K. A., Leicht, K. T., & Ehm, H. (1987). The eclipse of craft: The changing face of labour in the newspaper industry. In D. B. Cornfield & R. Marshall (Eds.), *Workers, managers, and technological change: Emerging patterns of relations* (pp. 47-72). New York: Plenum Press.

Lewis, T. (1992). Technology and work-Issues. *Journal of Vocational Education Research*. 17(2), 13-44.

Lewis, T., & Konare, A. (1993). Labor market dispositions of technical college personnel in Minnesota and Wisconsin. Journal of Vocational Education Research, 18(3), 15-47.

Lewis, T. (1995, December). *Impact of technology on work and jobs in the printing industry-implications for vocational institutions*. Paper presented at the annual conference of the American Vocational Association, Denver, CO.

McLoughlin, I., & Clark, J. (1994). *Technological change and work*. Philadelphia: Open University Press.

Milkman, R., & Pullman, C. (1991). Technological change in an auto assembly plant: The impact on workers' tasks and skills. *Work and Occupations*, 18(2), 123-147.

Miller, A. R., Treiman, D. J., Cain, P. S., & Roos, P. A. (1980). *Work, jobs and occupations: A critical review of the dictionary of occupational titles*. Washington, DC: National Academy Press.

Myles, J., & Fawcett, G. (1990). *Job skills and the service economy*. Ottawa: Economic Council of Canada.

O'Reilly, J. (1992). Where do you draw the line? Functional flexibility, training and skill in Britain and France. *Work, Employment & Society*, 6(3), 369-396.

Piore, M. J., & Sabel, C. F. (1984). *The second industrial divide: Possibilities for prosperity*. New York: Basic Books.

Rifkin, J. (1995). *The end of work: The decline of the global labor force and the dawn of the post-market Era*. New York: G. P. Putnam's Sons.

Secretary's Commission on Achieving Necessary Skills. (1991). *What work requires of schools: A SCANS report for America*. Washington DC: U.S. Department of Labor.

Spenner, K. I. (1983). Deciphering Prometheus: Temporal change in the skill level of work. *American Sociological Review*, 48, 824-837.

Spenner, K. I. (1985). The upgrading and downgrading of occupations: Issues, evidence, and implications for education. *Review of Educational Research*, 55(2), 125-154.

Spenner, K. I. (1990). Skill-meanings, methods, and meanings. *Work and Occupations*, 17(4), 399-421.

Steinberg, R. J. (1990). Social construction of skill. *Work and Occupations*, 17(4), 449-482.

Sticht, T. (1978). *Literacy and vocational competence-Occasional Paper No. 39.* Columbus: The Ohio State University, National Center for Research in Vocational Education.

Thomas, D., & Gray, K. C. (1991). An analysis of entry-level skill requirements for blue-collar technicians in electronics firms. *Journal of Vocational Education Research*, 16(3), 59-77.

U.S. Department of Labor (1977). *Dictionary of occupational titles.* Washington DC: U.S. Government Printing Office.

U.S. Department of Labor (1991). *Dictionary of occupational titles.* Washington DC: U.S. Government Printing Office.

Vallas, S. P. (1990). The concept of skill. *Work and Occupations*, 17(4), 379-397.

Wajcman, J. (1991). *Feminism confronts technology*, University Park: The Pennsylvania State University Press.

Wallace, M. (1989). Brave new workplace: Technology and work in the new economy. *Work and Occupations*, 16(4), 363-392.

Wallace, M., & Kalleberg, A. L. (1982). Industrial transformation and the decline of craft: The decomposition of skill in the printing industry, 1931-1978. *American Sociological Review*, 47, 307-324.

Wilson, F. M., & Buchanan, D. A. (1988). The effect of new technology in the engineering industry: Cases of control and constraint. *Work, Employment and Society*, 2(3) 366-380.

Zuboff, S. (1988). *In the age of the smart machine.* New York: Basic Books.

*Reference Citation:* Lewis, T. (1996). Studying the impact of technology on work and jobs. *Journal of Industrial Teacher Education, 33*(3), 44-65.

# Article 21

Brian Hayes

## Automation on the Job

Computers were supposed to be labor-saving devices. How come we're still working so hard?

Automation was a hot topic in the 1950s and '60s—a subject for congressional hearings, blue-ribbon panels, newspaper editorials, think-tank studies, scholarly symposia, documentary films, World's Fair exhibits, even comic strips and protest songs. There was interest in the technology itself—everybody wanted to know about "the factory of the future"—but the editorials and white papers focused mainly on the social and economic consequences of automation. Nearly everyone agreed that people would be working less once computers and other kinds of automatic machinery became wide-spread. For optimists, this was a promise of liberation: At last humanity would be freed from constant toil, and we could all devote our days to more refined pursuits. But others saw a threat: Millions of people would be thrown out of work, and desperate masses would roam the streets.

Looking back from 50 years hence, the controversy over automation seems a quaint and curious episode. The dispute was never resolved; it just faded away. The factory of the future did indeed evolve; but at the same time the future evolved away from the factory, which is no longer such a central institution in the economic scheme of things, at least in the United States. As predicted, computers guide machine tools and run assembly lines, but that's a minor part of their role in society. The computer is far more pervasive in everyday life than even the boldest technophiles dared to dream back in the days of punch cards and mainframes.

As for economic consequences, worries about unemployment have certainly not gone away—not with job losses in the current recession approaching 2 million workers in the U.S. alone. But recent job losses are commonly attributed to causes other than automation, such as competition from overseas or a roller-coaster financial system. In any case, the vision of a world where machines do all the work and people stand idly by has simply not come to pass.

## The Problem of Leisure

In 1930 the British economist John Maynard Keynes published a short essay titled "Economic Possibilities for Our Grandchildren." At the time, the economic possibilities looked pretty grim, but Keynes was implacably cheerful. By 2030, he predicted, average income would increase by a factor of between four and eight. This prosperity would be brought about by gains in productivity: Aided by new technology, workers would produce more with less effort.

Keynes did not mention *automation*—the word would not be introduced until some years later—but he did refer to *technological unemployment,* a term that goes back to Karl Marx. For Keynes, a drop in the demand for labor was a problem with an easy solution: Just work less. A 3-hour shift and a 15-hour workweek would become the norm for the grandchildren of the children of 1930, he said. This would be a momentous development in human history. After millennia of struggle, we would have finally solved "the economic problem": How to get enough to eat. The new challenge would be the problem of leisure: How to fill the idle hours.

Decades later, when automation became a contentious issue, there were other optimists. The conservative economist Yale Brozen wrote in 1963:

> Perhaps the gains of the automation revolution will carry us on from a mass democracy to a mass aristocracy. . . .
> The common man will become a university-educated world traveler with a summer place in the country, enjoying such leisure-time activities as sailing and concert going.

Other measures of how hard people are working tell a similar story. The total labor force in the U.S. has increased by a factor of 2.5 since 1950, growing substantially faster than the working-age population. Thus labor-force participation (the percentage of people who hold jobs, among all those who could in principle be working) has risen from 59 percent to 66 percent.

These trends contradict almost all the expectations of early writers on automation, both optimists and pessimists. So far, automation has neither liberated us from the need to work nor deprived us of the opportunity to work. Instead, we're working more than ever.

Economists reflecting on Keynes's essay suggest he erred in supposing that people would willingly trade income for leisure. Instead, the commentators say, people work overtime to buy the new wide-screen TV even if they then have no time to enjoy it. Perhaps so. I would merely add that many who are working long hours (post-docs, say, or parents of young children) do not see their behavior as a product of conscious choice. And they do not think society has "solved the economic problem."

## On the Factory Floor

Perhaps the most thoughtful and knowledgeable of the early writers on automation was John Diebold, a consultant and author. It was Diebold who introduced the word *automation* in its broad, modern sense. He clearly understood that there was more to it than reducing labor costs in factories. He foresaw applications to many other kinds of work, including clerical tasks, warehousing and even retailing. Nevertheless, when he chose examples for detailed description, they almost always came from manufacturing.

Automatic control first took hold in continuous-process industries such as oil refining. A closed-loop control mechanism could regulate the temperature of a distilling tower, eliminating the need for a worker to monitor a gauge and adjust valve settings. As such instruments proliferated, a refinery became a depopulated industrial landscape. An entire plant could be run by a few technicians, huddled together in a glass-walled control room. This hands-off mode of operation became the model that other industries strove to emulate.

In the automation literature of the 1950s and '60s, attention focuses mainly on manufacturing, and especially on the machining of metal. A celebrated example was the Ford Motor Company's Cleveland Engine Plant No. 1, built in 1951, where a series of interconnected machines took in raw castings at one end and disgorged finished engine blocks at the other. The various tools within this complex performed several hundred boring and milling operations on each engine, with little manual intervention.

A drawback of the Ford approach to automation was inflexibility. Any change to the product would require an extensive overhaul of the machinery. But this problem was overcome with the introduction of programmable metalworking tools, which eventually became computer-controlled devices.

Other kinds of manufacturing also shifted to automated methods, although the result was not always exactly what had been expected. In the early years, it was easy to imagine a straightforward substitution of machines for labor: Shove aside a worker and install a machine in his or her place. The task to be performed would not change, only the agent performing it. The ultimate expression of this idea was the robot—a one-for-one replacement for the factory worker. But automation has seldom gone this way.

Consider the manufacture of electronic devices. At the outset, this was a labor-intensive process of placing components on a chassis, stringing wires between them and soldering the connections one by one. Attempts to build automatic equipment to perform the same operations proved impractical. Instead, the underlying technology was changed by introducing printed circuit boards, with all the connections laid out in advance. Eventually, machines were developed for automatically placing the parts on the boards and for soldering the connections all at once.

The further evolution of this process takes us to the integrated circuit, a technology that was automated from birth. The manufacture of microprocessor chips could not possibly be carried out as a handicraft business; no sharp-eyed artisan could draw the minuscule circuit patterns on silicon wafers. For many other businesses as well, manual methods are simply unthinkable. Google could not operate by hiring thousands of clerks to read Web pages and type out the answers to queries.

The automation of factories has gone very much according to the script written by Diebold and other early advocates. Computer control is all but universal. Whole sections of automobile assembly plants are now walled off to exclude all workers. A computer screen and a key-board are the main interface to most factory equipment.

Meanwhile, though, manufacturing as a whole has become a smaller part of the U.S. economy—12 percent of gross domestic product in 2005, down from more than double that in the 1950s. And because of the very success of industrial automation, employment on production lines has fallen even faster than the share of GDP. Thus, for most Americans, the factory automation that was so much the focus of early commentary is all but invisible. Few of us ever get a chance to see it at work.

But automation and computer technology have infiltrated other areas of the economy and daily life—office work, logistics, commerce, finance, household tasks. When you look for the impact of computers on society, barcodes are probably more important than machine tools.

## The Do-It-Yourself Economy

In the 1950s, digital computers were exotic, expensive, unapproachable and mysterious. It was far easier to see such a machine becoming the nexus of control in a vast industrial enterprise than to imagine the computer transformed into a household object, comparable to a telephone or a typewriter—or even a toy for the children to play with. Donald Michael wrote:

> Most of our citizens will be unable to understand the cybernated world in which they live. . . . There will be a small, almost separate, society of people in rapport with the advanced computers. . . . Those with the talent for the work probably will have to develop it from childhood and will be trained as intensively as the classical ballerina.

If this attitude of awestruck reverence had persisted, most of the computer's productive potential would have been wasted. Computers became powerful when they became ubiquitous—not inscrutable oracles guarded by a priestly elite but familiar appliances found on every desk. These days, we are all expected to have rapport with computers.

The spread of automation outside of the factory has altered its social and economic impact in some curious ways. In many cases, the net effect of automation is not that machines are doing work that people used to do. Instead we've dispensed with the people who used to be paid to run the machines, and we've learned to run them ourselves. When you withdraw money from the bank via an ATM, buy an airline ticket online, ride an elevator or fill up the gas tank at a self-service pump, you are interacting directly with a machine to carry out a task that once required the intercession of an employee.

The dial telephone is the archetypal example. My grand-mother's telephone had no dial; she placed calls by asking a switchboard operator to make the connection. The dial (and the various other mechanisms that have since replaced it) empowers you to set up the communications channel without human assistance. Thus it's not quite accurate to say that the operator has been replaced by a machine. A version of the circuit-switching machine was there all along; the dial merely provided a convenient interface to it.

The process of making travel arrangements has been transformed in a similar way. It was once the custom to telephone a travel agent, who would search an airline database for a suitable flight with seats available. Through the Web, most of us now access that database directly; we even print our own boarding passes. Again, what has happened here is not exactly the substitution of machines for people; it is a matter of putting the customer in control of the machines.

Other Internet technologies are taking this process one more dizzy step forward. Because many Web sites have published interface specifications, I now have the option of writing a program to access them. Having already removed the travel agent, I can now automate myself out of the loop as well.

## The Full-Employment Paradox

Enabling people to place their own phone calls and make their own travel reservations has put whole categories of jobs on the brink of extinction. U.S. telephone companies once employed more than 250,000 telephone operators; the number remaining is a tenth of that, and falling fast. It's the same story for gas-station attendants, elevator operators and dozens of other occupations. And yet we have not seen the great contraction of the workforce that seemed inevitable 50 years ago.

One oft-heard explanation holds that automation brings a net increase in employment by creating jobs for people who design, build and maintain machines. A strong version of this thesis is scarcely plausible. It implies that the total labor requirement per unit of output is higher in the automated process than in the manual one; if that were the case, it would be hard to see the economic incentive for adopting automation. A weaker but likelier version concedes that labor per unit of output declines under automation, but total output increases enough to compensate. Even for this weaker prediction, however, there is no guarantee of such a rosy outcome. The relation may well be supported by historical evidence, but it has no theoretical underpinning in economic principles.

For a theoretical analysis we can turn to Herbert A. Simon, who was both an economist and a computer scientist and would thus seem to be the ideal analyst. In a 1965 essay, Simon noted that economies seek equilibrium, and so "both men and machines can be fully employed regardless of their relative productivity." It's just a matter of adjusting the worker's wage until it balances the cost of machinery. Of course there's no guarantee that the equilibrium wage will be above the subsistence level. But Simon then offered a more complex argument showing that any increase in productivity, whatever the underlying cause, should increase wages as well as the return on capital investment. Do these two results add up to perpetual full employment at a living wage in an automated world? I don't believe they offer any such guarantee, but perhaps the calculations are reassuring nonetheless.

Another kind of economic equilibrium also offers a measure of cheer. The premise is that whatever you earn, you eventually spend. (Or else your heirs spend it for you.) If technological progress makes some commodity cheaper, then the money that used to go that product will have to be spent on something else. The flow of funds toward the alternative sectors will drive up prices there and create new economic opportunities. This mode of reasoning offers an answer to questions such as, "Why has health care become so expensive in recent years?" The answer is: Because everything else has gotten so cheap.

I can't say that any of these formulations puts my mind at ease. On the other hand, I do have faith in the resilience of people and societies. The demographic history of agriculture offers a precedent that is both sobering and reassuring. It's not too much of an exaggeration to say that before 1800 everyone in North America was a farmer, and now no one is. In other words, productivity gains in agriculture put an entire population out of work. This was a wrenching experience for those forced to leave the farm, but the fact remains that they survived and found other ways of life. The occupational shifts caused by computers and automation cannot possibly match the magnitude of that great upheaval.

## The Future of the Future

What comes next in the march of progress? Have we reached the end point in the evolution of computerized society?

Since I have poked fun at the predictions of an earlier generation, it's only fair that I put some of my own silly notions on the record, giving some future pundit a chance to mock me in turn. I think the main folly of my predecessors was not being reckless enough. I'll probably make the same mistake myself. So here are three insufficiently outrageous predictions.

1. We'll automate medicine. I don't mean robot surgeons, although they're in the works too. What I have in mind is Internet-enabled, do-it-yourself diagnostics. Google is already the primary-care physician for many of us; that role can be expanded in various directions. Furthermore, as mentioned above, medical care is where the money is going, and so that's where investment in cost-saving technologies has the most leverage.
2. We'll automate driving. The car that drives itself is a perennial on lists of future marvels, mentioned by a number of the automation prophets of the 50s and 60s. A fully autonomous vehicle, able to navigate ordinary streets and roads, is not much closer now than it was then, but a combination of smarter cars and smarter roads could be made to work. Building those roads would require a major infrastructure project, which might help make up for all the disemployed truckers and taxi drivers. I admit to a certain boyish fascination with the idea of a car that drops me at the office and then goes to fetch the dry cleaning and fill up its own gas tank.
3. We'll automate warfare. I take no pleasure in this one, but I see no escaping it either. The most horrific weapons of the 20th century had the redeeming quality that they are difficult and expensive to build, and this has limited their proliferation. When it comes to the most fashionable weapons of the present day—pilotless aircraft, cruise missiles, precision-guided munitions—the key technology is available on the shelf at Radio Shack.

What about trades closer to my own vital interests? Will science be automated? Technology already has a central role in many areas of research; for example, genome sequences could not be read by traditional lab-bench methods. Replacing the scientist will presumably be a little harder that replacing the lab technician, but when a machine exhibits enough curiosity and tenacity, I think we'll just have to welcome it as a companion in zealous research.

And if the scientist is elbowed aside by an automaton, then surely the science writer can't hold out either. I'm ready for my 15-hour workweek.

## Bibliography

Buckingham, Walter S. 1961. *Automation: Its Impact on Business and People.* New York: Harper and Row.

Cortada, James W. 2004. *The Digital Hand: How Computers Changed the Work of American Manufacturing, Transportation, and Retail Industries.* Oxford: Oxford University Press.

Diebold, John. 1952. *Automation: The Advent of the Automatic Factory.* New York: D. Van Nostrand Company.

Einzig, Paul. 1956. *The Economic Consequences of Automation.* London: Secker and Warburg.

Hayes, A. J. 1964. Automation: A real "H" bomb. In *Jobs, Men, and Machines: Problems of Automation,* ed. Charles Markham, New York: Frederick A. Praeger, pp. 48–57.

Keynes, John Maynard. 1930. Economic possibilities for our grandchildren. Reprinted in *Revisiting Keynes: Economic Possibilities for Our Grandchildren,* ed. Lorenzo Pecchi and Gustavo Piga, Cambridge, Mass.: The MIT Press.

Leontief, Wassily. 1952. Machines and man. *Scientific American* 187(3):150–160.

Lilley, S. 1957. *Automation and Social Progress.* New York: International Publishers.

Michael, Donald N. 1962. *Cybernation: The Silent Conquest.* Santa Barbara, Calif.: Center for the Study of Democratic Institutions.

Pecchi, Lorenzo, and Gustavo Piga. 2008. *Revisiting Keynes: Economic Possibilities for Our Grandchildren.* Cambridge, Mass.: The MIT Press.

Philipson, Morris. 1962. *Automation: Implications for the Future.* New York: Vintage Books.

Pollock, Frederick. 1957. *Automation: A Study of Its Economic and Social Consequences.* Translated by W. O. Henderson and W. H. Chaloner. New York: Frederick A. Praeger.

Simon, Herbert A. 1965. *The Shape of Automation for Men and Management.* New York: Harper and Row.

Whaples, Robert. 2001. Hours of work in U.S. history. *EH.Net Encyclopedia,* Economic History Association. eh.net/encyclopedia/article/whaples.work.hours.us.

Wiener, Norbert. 1954. *The Human Use of Human Beings: Cybernetics and Society.* New York: Avon Books.

## Critical Thinking

1. Who was John Maynard Keynes? His name is associated with a particular way of stimulating a sluggish economy. Use the Internet to find out more about it. Would he be more closely aligned with the modern democratic or republican parties?
2. Hayes says that labor force participation has risen from 59 percent to 66 percent since 1950. That is, more and more of us are working. What change in cultural mores allowed this shift to happen?

3. The decline in manufacturing employment parallels a decline in union membership since the 1950s. Are they related? Use the Internet (and a reference librarian) to try to untangle them.

4. What is the "full-employment paradox"? What are some of the explanations that Hayes offers?

5. Hayes has very little to say about a globalized labor force. Investigate labor productivity in Chinese factories. How has the cost of labor in China affected the incentive to automate?

6. Hayes sometimes writes of technological progress as if it were a force of nature (e.g., "If technological progress makes some commodity cheaper . . ."). Does he slip on Postman's fifth big idea, that is, the tendency to think of technology as a force of its own rather than a specific response to a specific set of circumstances?

# Overload!

## Journalism's Battle for Relevance in an Age of Too Much Information

In 2007, as part of the third round of strategic planning for its digital transformation, The Associated Press decided to do something a little different. It hired a research company called Context to conduct an in-depth study of young-adult news consumption around the world. Jim Kennedy, the AP's director of strategic planning, initially agreed to the project because he thought it would make for a "fun and entertaining" presentation at the annual meeting. It turned out to be more than that; the AP believed that the results held fundamental implications for the role of the news media in the digital age. Chief among the findings was that many young consumers craved more in-depth news but were unable or unwilling to get it. "The abundance of news and ubiquity of choice do not necessarily translate into a better news environment for consumers," concluded the researchers in their final report. "Participants in this study showed signs of news fatigue; that is, they appeared debilitated by information overload and unsatisfying news experiences. . . . Ultimately news fatigue brought many of the participants to a learned helplessness response. The more overwhelmed or unsatisfied they were, the less effort they were willing to put in."

The idea that news consumers, even young ones, are overloaded should hardly come as a surprise. The information age is defined by output: we produce far more information than we can possibly manage, let alone absorb. Before the digital era, information was limited by our means to contain it. Publishing was restricted by paper and delivery costs; broadcasting was circumscribed by available frequencies and airtime. The Internet, on the other hand, has unlimited capacity at near-zero cost. There are more than 70 million blogs and 150 million websites today—a number that is expanding at a rate of approximately ten thousand an *hour.* Two hundred and ten billion e-mails are sent each day. Say goodbye to the gigabyte and hello to the exabyte, five of which are worth 37,000 Libraries of Congress. In 2006 alone, the world produced 161 exabytes of digital data, the equivalent of three million times the information contained in all the books ever written. By 2010, it is estimated that this number will increase to 988. Pick your metaphor: we're drowning, buried, snowed under.

The information age's effect on news production and consumption has been profound. For all its benefits—increased transparency, accessibility, and democratization—the Internet has upended the business model of advertising-supported journalism.

This, in turn, has led news outlets to a ferocious focus on profitability. Over the past decade, they have cut staff, closed bureaus, and shrunk the newshole. Yet despite these reductions, the average citizen is unlikely to complain of a lack of news. Anyone with access to the Internet has thousands of free news sources at his fingertips. In a matter of seconds, we can browse *The New York Times* and *The Guardian, Newsweek* and *The Economist,* CNN and the BBC.

News is part of the atmosphere now, as pervasive—and in some ways as invasive—as advertising. It finds us in airport lounges and taxicabs, on our smart phones and PDAS, through e-mail providers and Internet search engines. Much of the time, it arrives unpackaged: headlines, updates, and articles are snatched from their original sources—often as soon as they're published—and excerpted or aggregated on blogs, portals, social-networking sites, RSS readers, and customizable homepages like My MSN, My Yahoo, myAOL, and iGoogle. These days, news comes at us in a flood of unrelated snippets. As Clay Shirky, author of *Here Comes Everybody: The Power of Organizing without Organizations,* explains, "The economic logic of the age is unbundling." But information without context is meaningless. It is incapable of informing and can make consumers feel lost. As the AP noted in its research report, "The irony in news fatigue is that these consumers felt helpless to change their news consumption at a time when they have more control and choice than ever before. When the news wore them down, participants in the study showed a tendency to passively receive versus actively seek news."

There has always been a large swath of the population that is not interested in news, of course, just as there has always been a portion that actively seeks it out. What's interesting about the current environment is that despite an enormous increase in available news and information, the American public is no better informed now than it has been during less information-rich times. "The basic pattern from the forties to today is that the amount of information that people have and their knowledge about politics is no worse or no better than it's been over that sixty-year period," explains Michael X. Delli Carpini, dean of the Annenberg School for Communication at the University of Pennsylvania. For example, a 2007 survey conducted by the Pew Research Center for the People & the Press found that 69 percent of Americans could correctly name the vice president, only a slight decrease from the 74 percent who could in 1989.

This phenomenon can be partially explained by our tendency to become passive in the face of too much information. It can also be attributed to the fact that the sheer number of specialized publications, the preponderance of television channels, the wide array of entertainment options, and the personalization and customization encouraged by digital technologies have made it far easier to avoid public-affairs content. "As choice goes up, people who are motivated to be politically informed take advantage of these choices, but people who are not move away from politics," explains Delli Carpini. "In the 1960s, if you wanted to watch television you were going to watch news. And today you can avoid news. So choice can be a mixed blessing."

Markus Prior writes in his book, *Post-Broadcast Democracy: How Media Choice Increases Inequality in Political Involvement and Polarizes Elections,* "Political information in the current media environment comes mostly to those who want it." In other words, in our supersaturated media environment, serendipitous exposure to political-affairs content is far less common than it used to be. Passive news consumers are less informed and less likely to become informed than ever before.

The tragedy of the news media in the information age is that in their struggle to find a financial foothold, they have neglected to look hard enough at the larger implications of the new information landscape—and more generally, of modern life. How do people process information? How has media saturation affected news consumption? What must the news media do in order to fulfill their critical role of informing the public, as well as survive? If they were to address these questions head on, many news outlets would discover that their actions thus far—to increase the volume and frequency of production, sometimes frantically and mindlessly—have only made things more difficult for the consumer.

**To win the war for our attention, news organizations must make themselves indispensable by producing journalism that helps make sense of the flood of information that inundates us all.**

While it is naïve to assume that news organizations will reduce their output—advertising dollars are involved, after all—they would be wise to be more mindful of the content they produce. The greatest hope for a healthy news media rests as much on their ability to filter and interpret information as it does on their ability to gather and disseminate it. If they make snippets and sound bites the priority, they will fail. Attention—our most precious resource—is in increasingly short supply. To win the war for our attention, news organizations must make themselves indispensable by producing journalism that helps make sense of the flood of information that inundates us all.

## The Limits of Human Attention

Ours is a culture of multitasking, of cramming as many activities as possible into as short a period of time as possible. We drive and talk on our cell phones, check e-mail during meetings and presentations, eat dinner while watching TV. In part, says Maggie Jackson, author of *Distracted: The Erosion of Attention and the Coming Dark Age,* such multitasking "is part of a wider value system that venerates speed, frenetic activity, hyper-mobility, etcetera, as the paths to success. That's why we're willing to drive like drunks or work in frenzied ways, although it literally might kill us."

Many young people multitask to the extreme, particularly when it comes to media consumption. I've witnessed my twenty-two-year-old brother watch television while talking on the phone, IMing with several friends, composing an e-mail, and updating his Facebook page. A widely cited 2006 study by the Henry J. Kaiser Family Foundation found that 81 percent of young people engage in some form of media multitasking during a given week. But as cognitive psychologists have long known, human attention is quite limited. Despite our best efforts, when we try to do more than one thing at once, we are less efficient and more prone to error. This is because multitasking is actually a process of dividing attention, of toggling back and forth between tasks.

Acquiring new information requires particularly focused attention, which includes the ability to ignore distractions. In order to absorb the information contained in a CNN newscast, for example, we must not only direct our attention to the person talking, but also filter out the running headlines, news updates, and financial ticker on the lower part of the screen. Torkel Klingberg, a professor of cognitive neuroscience at Karolinska Institute in Sweden and author of *The Overflowing Brain,* puts it simply: "If we do not focus our attention on something, we will not remember it." In other words, attention is a critical component of learning.

Michael Posner, a researcher who has dedicated his career to studying attention and a professor emeritus of psychology at the University of Oregon, explains attention as a system of three networks—alerting, orienting, and executive. Alerting refers to the state of wakefulness necessary to attend to information, while orienting is the process by which we respond to stimuli, such as movement, sound, or noise. Executive attention is the highest-order network, the one that we have conscious control over. If we are trying to study for a test or read a novel, we use it to direct and maintain our focus, as well as to suppress our reaction to competing stimuli like the din of a nearby conversation or television.

The information-saturated environment that we live in is, unsurprisingly, extremely demanding of our attention. Modern life—both at work and at home—has become so information-rich that Edward Hallowell, a Boston-area psychiatrist, believes many of us suffer from what he calls an attention-deficit trait, a culturally induced form of attention-deficit disorder. As he pointed out in a 2005 interview with CNET News, "We've been able to overload manual labor. But never before have we so routinely been able to overload brain labor." According to Hallowell and other psychiatrists, all these competing inputs prevent us from assimilating information. "What your brain is best equipped to do is to think, to analyze, to dissect, and create," he explains. "And if you're simply responding to bits of stimulation, you won't ever go deep." Journalist John Lorinc noted as much in an elegant article on distraction in the April 2007 issue of *The Walrus:*

> It often seems as though the sheer glut of data itself has supplanted the kind of focused, reflective attention that might make this information useful in the first place. The dysfunction of our information environment is an outgrowth of its extraordinary fecundity. Digital communications technology

has demonstrated a striking capacity to subdivide our attention into smaller and smaller increments; increasingly, it seems as if the day's work has become a matter of interrupting the interruptions.

In a recent report, *Information Overload: We Have Met the Enemy and He Is Us,* the research firm Basex concluded that interruptions take up nearly 30 percent of a knowledge worker's day and end up costing American businesses $650 billion annually. Other studies show that interruptions cause significant impairments in performance on IQ tests.

In many ways, the modern age—and the Internet, in particular—is a veritable minefield of distractions. This poses a central challenge to news organizations whose mandate is to inform the public. Research by Pablo Boczkowski, who teaches communication studies at Northwestern University, has revealed that when we consume news online we do so for significantly less time than in print and that we do it while we're working. Further complicating matters is the disruptive nature of online advertising. Intrusive Web advertisements—washingtonpost.com recently featured one in which a Boeing helicopter flies right across the text of a news story—exploit our orienting network, which evolved to respond quickly to novel stimuli. Could we train ourselves to suppress our tendency to be distracted by such advertising? "You can get somewhat better, but it's hard to resist because it'll produce orienting," Posner explains. "The way you resist it is you bring your attention back as quickly as you can." Yet even if we were somehow able to eliminate ads, the sheer number of articles, headlines, and video and audio feeds on news websites makes focused attention difficult. Having to decide where to direct our attention and then maintain it makes reading and retaining news online a formidable task.

## The Attention Economy

One of the most useful frameworks for understanding journalism's challenges and behavior in the information age is the notion of the attention economy. Economics is the study of the allocation of resources and the basic principles of supply and demand, after all, and about a decade ago a handful of economists and scholars came up with the concept of the attention economy as a way of wrestling with the problem of having too much information—an oversupply, if you will—and not enough time or people to absorb it all.

The dynamics of the attention economy have created a complicated and hypercompetitive arena for news production and consumption. News media must not only compete with one another, as well as with an ever-increasing assortment of information and entertainment options, but also with the very thing that supports their endeavors—advertising. In fact, the advertising industry has been struggling with the dynamics of the attention economy for a couple of decades now. As the advertising landscape becomes more saturated, advertisers must work harder to get their messages to the consumer. But as Mark Crispin Miller, professor of media ecology at New York University, notes in the *Frontline* documentary *The Persuaders:*

> Every effort to break through the clutter is just more clutter. Ultimately, if you don't have clean, plain borders and backdrops for your ads, if you don't have that blank space, that commons, that virgin territory, you have a very hard time

making yourself heard. The most obvious metaphor is a room full of people, all screaming to be heard. What this really means, finally, is that advertising is asphyxiating itself.

The news media also run the risk of self-asphyxiation in an information landscape crowded with headlines, updates, and news feeds. In order to garner audience attention and maintain financial viability, media outlets are increasingly concerned with the "stickiness" of their content. According to Douglas Rushkoff, host of *The Persuaders* and author of the forthcoming book *Life Incorporated,* the question for these organizations has become, "How do we stick the eyeballs onto our content and ultimately deliver the eyeballs to our sponsors?" As he dryly points out, "That's a very different mandate than how do we make information—real information—available to people. The information economy, then, is a competitive space. So as more people who are information providers think of themselves as competing for eyeballs rather than competing for a good story, then journalism's backwards." The rise of sound bites, headlines, snippets, infotainment, and celebrity gossip are all outgrowths of this attempt to grab audience attention—and advertising money. Visit a cable-news website most any day for an example along the lines of POLICE: WOMAN IN COW SUIT CHASED KIDS (CNN); or MAN BEATS TEEN GIRL WAITING IN MCDONALD'S LINE (Fox News). As Northwestern's Boczkowski points out, "Unlike when most of the media were organized in monopolistic or oligopolistic markets, now they are far more competitive; the cost of ignoring customer preferences is much higher."

Meanwhile, the massive increase in information production and the negligible cost of distributing and storing information online have caused it to lose value. Eli Noam, director of the Columbia Institute for Tele-Information, explains that this price deflation is only partly offset by an increase in demand in the digital age, since the time we have to consume information is finite. "On the whole—on the per-minute, per-line, per-word basis—information has continuously declined in price," says Noam. "The deflation makes it very difficult for many companies to stay in business for a long time."

Thus, we come to the heart of journalism's challenge in an attention economy: in order to preserve their vital public-service function—not to mention survive—news organizations need to reevaluate their role in the information landscape and reinvent themselves to better serve their consumers. They need to raise the value of the information they present, rather than diminish it. As it stands now, they often do the opposite.

## More-Faster-Better

"Living and working in the midst of information resources like the Internet and the World Wide Web can resemble watching a firefighter attempt to extinguish a fire with napalm," write Paul Duguid and John Seely Brown, information scientists, in *The Social Life of Information.* "If your Web page is hard to understand, link to another. If a 'help' system gets overburdened, add a 'help on using help.' If your answer isn't here, then click on through another 1,000 pages. Problems with information? Add more."

Like many businesses in the information age, news outlets have been steadily increasing the volume and speed of their output. As the proliferation of information sources on the Web continues at a breakneck pace, news media compete for attention by adding content and features—blogs, live chat sessions with journalists, video and audio streams, and slideshows. Much of this is of excellent quality. But taken together, these features present a quandary: Do we persevere or retreat in the face of too much information? And as the AP study showed, even young news consumers get fatigued.

In psychology, passivity resulting from a lack of control is referred to as "learned helplessness." Though logic would suggest that an increase in available news would give consumers more control, this is not actually the case. As Barry Schwartz, the Dorwin Cartwright Professor of Social Theory and Social Action at Swarthmore College, argues in his book *The Paradox of Choice: Why More is Less,* too many choices can be burdensome. "Instead of feeling in control, we feel unable to cope," he writes. "Freedom of choice eventually becomes a tyranny of choice."

**Too many choices can be burdensome: 'Instead of feeling in control, we feel unable to cope. Freedom of choice becomes a tyranny of choice.'**

A recent study by Northwestern University's Media Management Center supports this phenomenon. It found that despite their interest in the 2008 election, young adults avoid political news online "because they feel too much information is coming at them all at once and too many different things are competing for their attention." The study participants said they wanted news organizations to display *less* content in order to highlight the essential information. "Young people want the site design to signal to them what's really important . . . instead of being confronted by a bewildering array of choices," write the researchers in their final report, *From "Too Much" to "Just Right": Engaging Millennials in Election News on the Web.*

The instinct that more is better is deeply ingrained in the modern psyche. David Levy, a professor at The Information School of the University of Washington, uses the phrase "more-better-faster" to describe the acceleration of society that began with the Industrial Revolution. According to Levy, we tend to define productivity in terms of speed and volume rather than quality of thought and ideas. "We are all now expected to complete more tasks in a smaller amount of time," writes Levy in a 2007 journal article. "And while the new technologies do make it remarkably efficient and easy to search for information and to collect masses of potentially relevant sources on a huge variety of topics, they can't, in and of themselves, clear the space and time needed to absorb and to reflect on what has been collected." In the case of news production, Swarthmore's Schwartz agrees. "The rhythm of the news cycle has changed so dramatically that what's really been excluded," he says, "is the time that it takes to think."

## Implications for Democracy

Our access to digital information, as well as our ability to instantly publish, share, and improve upon it at negligible cost, hold extraordinary promise for realizing the democratic ideals of journalism. Yet as we've seen, many news consumers are unable or unwilling to navigate what Michael Delli Carpini refers to as the "chaotic and gateless information environment that we live in today."

When people had fewer information and entertainment options, journalistic outlets were able to produce public-affairs content without having to worry excessively about audience share. As the Internet and the 24/7 news cycle splinter readership and attention

spans, this is no longer the case. "Real journalism is a kind of physician-patient relationship where you don't pander to readers," says Bob Garfield, a columnist for *Advertising Age* and co-host of NPR's *On the Media.* "You give them some of what they want and some of what you as the doctor-journalist think they ought to have." Unfortunately, many news outlets feel they can no longer afford to strike the right balance.

As information proliferates, meanwhile, people inevitably become more specialized both in their careers and their interests. This nichification—the basis for *Wired* editor Chris Anderson's breakthrough concept of the Long Tail—means that shared public knowledge is receding, as is the likelihood that we come in contact with beliefs that contradict our own. Personalized home pages, newsfeeds, and e-mail alerts, as well as special-interest publications lead us to create what sociologist Todd Gitlin disparagingly referred to as "my news, my world." Serendipitous news—accidentally encountered information—is far less frequent in a world of TiVo and online customization tools.

Viewed in this light, the role of the journalist is more important than ever. "As society becomes splintered," writes journalist and author David Shenk in *Data Smog,* "it is journalists who provide the vital social glue to keep us at least partly intact as a common unit." Journalists work to deliver the big picture at a time when the overload of information makes it hard to piece it together ourselves. "The journalist's job isn't to pay attention simply to one particular field," explains Paul Duguid. "The job is to say, 'Well, what are all the different fields that bear on this particular story?' They give us the breadth that none of us can have because we're all specialists in our own particular area." In other words, the best journalism does not merely report and deliver information, it places it in its full and proper context.

## Journalism's New Role

The primacy placed on speed and volume in the information age has led to an uneven news landscape. "There is an over-allocation of resources on breaking and developing news production and constant updates," observes Boczkowski. "I think many news organizations are overdoing it." While headlines and updates are undoubtedly important, their accumulation is problematic. "Increasingly, as the abundance of information overwhelms us all, we need not simply more information, but people to assimilate, understand, and make sense of it," write Duguid and Seely Brown.

The question, then, is how?

As David Shenk presciently noted more than a decade ago, "In a world with vastly more information than we can process, journalists are the most important processors we have." The researchers who conducted the study for the AP concluded that the news fatigue they observed among young adults resulted from "an overload of basic staples in the news diet—the facts and updates that tend to dominate the digital news environment." In other words, the news they were encountering was underprocessed.

**"In a world with vastly more information than we can process, journalists are the most important processors we have."**

—David Shenk

In order to address the problem, the AP has made a number of changes in the way it approaches news production. For starters, it instituted a procedure it calls 1-2-3 filing, which attempts to reduce news clutter and repetition (the days of endless write-throughs are over) while also acknowledging the unpackaged and real-time nature of news in the digital world. With 1-2-3 filing, reporters produce news content in three discrete parts, which they file separately: a headline, a short present-tense story, and, when appropriate, a longer in-depth account. By breaking down the news in this way, the AP hopes to eliminate the redundancy and confusion caused by filing a full-length article for every new story development. In 1-2-3 filing, each component replaces the previous component: the headline is replaced by the present-tense story, which is then replaced by the in-depth account.

The AP has also launched a series of initiatives aimed at providing consumers with deeper, more analytical content. It has created a Top Stories Desk at its New York headquarters to identify and "consider the big-picture significance" of the most important stories of the day. It has also begun developing interactive Web graphics to help explain complicated and ongoing stories like Hurricane Katrina and the Minnesota bridge collapse. And for 2008, the AP launched "Measure of a Nation," a multimedia series dedicated to examining the election "through the prism of American culture, rather than simply the candidates and the horse race." "Measure of a Nation" packages take a historical approach to covering such notions as myth, elitism, and celebrity in American presidential politics. In one article published in late August, for example, journalist Ted Anthony explains the powerful political influence of the Kennedy family over the past fifty years, drawing parallels between the campaigns of JFK and RFK and that of Barack Obama. As the AP writes in its report, these changes in approach represent "a concerted effort to think about the news from an end-user's perspective, re-emphasizing a dimension to news gathering and editing that can get lost in the relentless rush of the daily news cycle."

Much like educational institutions, the best news organizations help people convert information into the knowledge they need to understand the world. As Richard Lanham explains in *The Economics of Attention,* "Universities have never been simply data-mining and storage operations. They have always taken as their central activity the conversion of data into useful knowledge and into wisdom. They do this by creating attention structures that we call curricula, courses of study." Institutions of journalism do it by crafting thoughtful and illuminating stories. "Journalists who limit their role to news flashes are absolving themselves of any overarching obligation to the audience," writes Shenk in *The End of Patience.* "Mere telling focuses on the mechanics of transmitting information of the moment, while education assumes a responsibility for making sure that knowledge sticks." The most valuable journalism is the kind that *explains.* "The first and foremost role that a journalist plays is to provide the information in a context that we wouldn't be able to get as amateurs," says Delli Carpini. "And I think that's where journalism should be focusing."

As it turns out, explanatory journalism may have a promising future in the market for news. On May 9, in partnership with NPR News, *This American Life* dedicated its hour-long program to explaining the housing crisis. "The Giant Pool of Money" quickly became the most popular episode in the show's thirteen-year history. *CJR* praised the piece (in "Boiler Room," the essay by Dean Starkman in our September/October issue) as "the most comprehensive and insightful look at the system that produced the credit crisis." And on his blog, *PressThink,* Jay Rosen, a journalism professor at New York University, wrote that the program was "probably the best work of explanatory journalism I have ever heard." Rosen went on to note that by helping people understand an issue, explanatory journalism actually creates a market for news. It gives people a reason to tune in. "There are some stories—and the mortgage crisis is a great example—where until I grasp the *whole,* I am unable to make sense of *any* part," he writes. "Not only am I not a customer for news reports prior to that moment, but the very frequency of the updates alienates me from the providers of those updates because the news stream is adding daily to my feeling of being ill-informed, overwhelmed, out of the loop."

> **"There are some stories—and the mortgage crisis is a great example—where until I grasp the *whole,* I am unable to make sense of *any* part."**
>
> —Jay Rosen

Rather than simply contributing to the noise of the unending torrent of headlines, sound bites, and snippets, NPR and *This American Life* took the time to step back, report the issue in depth, and then explain it in a way that illuminated one of the biggest and most complicated stories of the year. As a result of the program's success, *NPR News* formed a multimedia team in late August to explain the global economy through a blog and podcast, both of which are called "Planet Money." And on October 3, *This American Life* and NPR aired a valuable follow-up episode, "Another Frightening Show About the Economy," which examined the deepening credit crisis, including how it might have been prevented and Washington's attempts at a bailout.

Along with supplying depth and context, another function of the modern news organization is to act as an information filter. No news outlet better embodies this aim than *The Week,* a magazine dedicated to determining the top news stories of the week and then synthesizing them. As the traditional newsweeklies are struggling to remain relevant and financially viable, *The Week* has experienced steady circulation growth over the past several years. "The purpose of *The Week* is not to tell people the news but to make sense of the news for people," explains editor William Falk. "Ironically, in this intensive information age, it's in some ways harder than ever to know what's important and what's not. And so I often say to people, 'With *The Week,* you're hiring this group of really smart, well-versed people that read for you fifty hours a week and then sit down and basically give you a report on what they learned that week.' "

Rather than merely excerpting and reprinting content, this slim magazine takes facts, text, and opinions from a variety of sources—approximately a hundred per issue—to create its own articles, columns, reviews, and obituaries. As Falk explains, there's a certain "alchemy" that occurs when you synthesize multiple accounts of a news story. And *The Week*'s success suggests that consumers are willing to pay for this. "We're a service magazine as much as we are a journalism magazine," says Falk. "People work ten, eleven hours a day. They're very busy. There are tremendous demands on their time. There are other things competing for your leisure time—you can go online, you can watch television or a DVD. So what we do is deliver to you, in a one-hour package or less, is a smart distillation of what happened last week that you need to pay attention to."

One ally in journalism's struggle to deal with information overload, meanwhile, may be the digital machinery that brought it about in the first place. While digital archiving and data tagging cannot replace human interpretation and editorial judgment, they have an important role to play in helping us navigate the informational sea. As any news consumer knows, searching for or following a story can be frustrating on the Internet, where information is both pervasive and transient. In its study, the AP observed that young consumers struggled to find relevant in-depth news. So the wire service stepped up an effort begun in 2005 to tag all its articles, images, and videos according to a classification system of major news topics and important people, places, and things. These tags allow consumers, as well as news organizations and aggregators, to more effectively find and link to AP content. A number of other organizations, including *The New York Times* (check out the Times Topics tab on nytimes.com), *The Washington Post,* and CNN have similar projects under way, promising an opportunity to rapidly—and often automatically—provide consumers with a high level of detail, context, and graphical means of explanation.

The website for BBC News may be the best example of how journalistic organizations can deliver context in the digital environment. A news story about the Russia-Georgia crisis, for example, is displayed alongside a list of links to a map of the region, a country profile, an explanation of the crisis, a summary of Russian foreign policy, and related news articles and video footage. All online BBC News stories are presented in this manner, giving consumers multiple ways to learn about and understand an issue. While no American site is this comprehensive, a handful of major news outlets, from CNN to NPR to the *National Journal,* have used this approach in creating special election 2008 Web pages. By linking stories to one another and to background information and analysis, news organizations help news consumers find their way through a flood of information that without such mediation could be overwhelming and nearly meaningless.

## Why Journalism Won't Disappear

While it's true that the Web allows the average individual to create and disseminate information without the help of a publishing house or a news organization, this does not mean journalism institutions are no longer relevant. "Oddly enough, information is one of the things that in the end needs brands almost more than anything else," explains Paul Duguid. "It needs a recommendation, a seal of approval, something that says this is reliable or true or whatever. And so journalists, but also the institutions of journalism as one aspect of this, become very important."

Moreover, the flood of news created by the production bias of the Internet could, in the end, point to a new role for journalistic institutions. "We're expecting people who are not librarians, who are not knowledge engineers to do the work of knowledge engineers and librarians," says Jonathan Spira, CEO and chief analyst for the business research firm Basex and an expert in information overload.

In other words, most of us lack the skills—not to mention the time, attention, and motivation—to make sense of an unrelenting torrent of information. This is where journalists and news organizations come in. The fact that there is more information than there are people or time to consume it—the classic economy-of-attention problem—represents a financial opportunity for news organizations. "I think that the consumers, being subjects to this flood, need help, and they know it," says Eli Noam. "And so therefore they want to have publications that will be selecting along the lines of quality and credibility in order to make their lives easier. For that, people will be willing to pay." A challenge could become an opportunity.

In fact, journalism that makes sense of the news may even increase news consumption. As Jay Rosen points out on his blog, explanatory journalism creates a "scaffold of understanding in the users that future reports can attach to, thus driving demand for the updates that today are more easily delivered." In a similar fashion—by providing links to background information and analysis alongside every news story—the BBC gives consumers frameworks for understanding that generate an appetite for more information.

The future of news depends on the willingness of journalistic organizations to adjust to the new ecology and new economy of information in the digital age. "I think in some ways, we need a better metaphor," says Delli Carpini. "The gatekeeping metaphor worked pretty well in the twentieth century, but maybe what news organizations should be now is not gatekeepers so much as guides. You don't want gatekeepers that can say you can get this and you can't get that. You want people who can guide you through all this stuff."

> **"Maybe what news organizations should be now is not gatekeepers so much as guides. You want people who can guide you through all this stuff."**
>
> —Delli Carpini

Ironically, if out of desperation for advertising dollars, news organizations continue to chase eyeballs with snippets and sound bites, they will ultimately lose the war for consumer attention. Readers and viewers will go elsewhere, and so will advertisers. But if news organizations decide to rethink their role and give consumers the context and coherence they want and need in an age of overload, they may just achieve the financial stability they've been scrambling for, even as they recapture their public-service mission before it slips away.

## Critical Thinking

1. To what degree do you want news media to filter and interpret information you receive?
2. Describe the media implications of *the attention economy.*

**BREE NORDENSON** is a freelance writer.

From *Columbia Journalism Review,* November/December 2008, pp. 30–42. Copyright © 2008 by Columbia Journalism Review. Reprinted by permission.

# Article 23

Tim Brown

# Design Thinking

Design Thinking by Tim Brown
*harvard business review* • june 2008

Thinking like a designer can transform the way you develop products, services, processes—and even strategy.

Thomas Edison created the electric lightbulb and then wrapped an entire industry around it. The lightbulb is most often thought of as his signature invention, but Edison understood that the bulb was little more than a parlor trick without a system of electric power generation and transmission to make it truly useful. So he created that, too.

Thus Edison's genius lay in his ability to conceive of a fully developed marketplace, not simply a discrete device. He was able to envision how people would want to use what he made, and he engineered toward that insight. He wasn't always prescient (he originally believed the phonograph would be used mainly as a business machine for recording and replaying dictation), but he invariably gave great consideration to users' needs and preferences.

Edison's approach was an early example of what is now called "design thinking"—a methodology that imbues the full spectrum of innovation activities with a human-centered design ethos. By this I mean that innovation is powered by a thorough understanding, through direct observation, of what people want and need in their lives and what they like or dislike about the way particular products are made, packaged, marketed, sold, and supported.

Many people believe that Edison's greatest invention was the modern R&D laboratory and methods of experimental investigation. Edison wasn't a narrowly specialized scientist but a broad generalist with a shrewd business sense. In his Menlo Park, New Jersey, laboratory he surrounded himself with gifted tinkerers, improvisers, and experimenters. Indeed, he broke the mold of the "lone genius inventor" by creating a team-based approach to innovation. Although Edison biographers write of the camaraderie enjoyed by this merry band, the process also featured endless rounds of trial and error—the "99% perspiration" in Edison's famous definition of genius. His approach was intended not to validate preconceived hypotheses but to help experimenters learn something new from each iterative stab. Innovation is hard work; Edison made it a profession that blended art, craft, science, business savvy, and an astute understanding of customers and markets.

Design thinking is a lineal descendant of that tradition. Put simply, it is a discipline that uses the designer's sensibility and methods to match people's needs with what is technologically feasible and what a viable business strategy can convert into customer value and market opportunity. Like Edison's painstaking innovation process, it often entails a great deal of perspiration.

I believe that design thinking has much to offer a business world in which most management ideas and best practices are freely available to be copied and exploited. Leaders now look to innovation as a principal source of differentiation and competitive advantage; they would do well to incorporate design thinking into all phases of the process.

## Getting Beneath the Surface

Historically, design has been treated as a downstream step in the development process—the point where designers, who have played no earlier role in the substantive work of innovation, come along and put a beautiful wrapper around the idea. To be sure, this approach has stimulated market growth in many areas by making new products and technologies aesthetically attractive and therefore more desirable to consumers or by enhancing brand perception through smart, evocative advertising and communication strategies. During the latter half of the twentieth century design became an increasingly valuable competitive asset in, for example, the consumer electronics, automotive, and consumer packaged goods industries. But in most others it remained a late-stage add-on.

Now, however, rather than asking designers to make an already developed idea more attractive to consumers, companies are asking them to create ideas that better meet consumers' needs and desires. The former role is tactical, and results in limited value creation; the latter is strategic, and leads to dramatic new forms of value.

Moreover, as economies in the developed world shift from industrial manufacturing to knowledge work and service delivery, innovation's terrain is expanding. Its objectives are no longer just physical products; they are new sorts of processes, services, IT-powered interactions, entertainments, and ways of communicating and collaborating—exactly the kinds of human-centered activities in which design thinking can make a decisive difference. (See the sidebar "A Design Thinker's Personality Profile.")

Consider the large health care provider Kaiser Permanente, which sought to improve the overall quality of both patients' and medical practitioners' experiences. Businesses in the service sector can often make significant innovations on the front lines of service creation and delivery. By teaching design thinking techniques to nurses, doctors, and administrators, Kaiser hoped to inspire its practitioners to contribute new ideas. Over the course of several months Kaiser teams participated in workshops with the help of my firm, IDEO, and a group of Kaiser coaches. These workshops led to a portfolio of innovations, many of which are being rolled out across the company.

One of them—a project to reengineer nursing-staff shift changes at four Kaiser hospitals—perfectly illustrates both the broader nature of innovation "products" and the value of a holistic design approach. The core project team included a strategist (formerly a nurse), an organizational-development specialist, a technology expert, a process designer, a union representative, and designers from IDEO. This group worked with innovation teams of frontline practitioners in each of the four hospitals.

During the earliest phase of the project, the core team collaborated with nurses to identify a number of problems in the way shift changes occurred. Chief among these was the fact that nurses routinely spent the first 45 minutes of each shift at the nurses' station debriefing the departing shift about the status of patients. Their methods of information exchange were different in every hospital, ranging from recorded dictation to face-to-face conversations. And they compiled the information they needed to serve patients in a variety of ways—scrawling quick notes on the back of any available scrap of paper, for example, or even on their scrubs. Despite a significant investment of time, the nurses often failed to learn some of the things that mattered most to patients, such as how they had fared during the previous shift, which family members were with them, and whether or not certain tests or therapies had been administered. For many patients, the team learned, each shift change felt like a hole in their care. Using the insights gleaned from observing these important times of transition, the innovation teams explored potential solutions through brainstorming and rapid prototyping. (Prototypes of a service innovation will of course not be physical, but they must be tangible. Because pictures help us understand what is learned through prototyping, we often videotape the performance of prototyped services, as we did at Kaiser.)

**Tim Brown** (tbrown@ideo.com) is the CEO and president of IDEO, an innovation and design firm with headquarters in Palo Alto, California. His designs have won numerous awards and been exhibited at the Museum of Modern Art in New York, the Axis Gallery in Tokyo, and the Design Museum in London.

---

## A DESIGN THINKER'S PERSONALITY PROFILE

Contrary to popular opinion, you don't need weird shoes or a black turtleneck to be a design thinker. Nor are design thinkers necessarily created only by design schools, even though most professionals have had some kind of design training. My experience is that many people outside professional design have a natural aptitude for design thinking, which the right development and experiences can unlock. Here, as a starting point, are some of the characteristics to look for in design thinkers:

**Empathy.** They can imagine the world from multiple perspectives—those of colleagues, clients, end users, and customers (current and prospective). By taking a "people first" approach, design thinkers can imagine solutions that are inherently desirable and meet explicit or latent needs. Great design thinkers observe the world in minute detail. They notice things that others do not and use their insights to inspire innovation.

**Integrative thinking**. They not only rely on analytical processes (those that produce either/or choices) but also exhibit the ability to see all of the salient—and sometimes contradictory— aspects of a confounding problem and create novel solutions that go beyond and dramatically improve on existing alternatives. (See Roger Martin's *The Opposable Mind: How Successful Leaders Win Through Integrative Thinking.*)

**Optimism.** They assume that no matter how challenging the constraints of a given problem, at least one potential solution is better than the existing alternatives.

**Experimentalism.** Significant innovations don't come from incremental tweaks. Design thinkers pose questions and explore constraints in creative ways that proceed in entirely new directions.

**Collaboration.** The increasing complexity of products, services, and experiences has replaced the myth of the lone creative genius with the reality of the enthusiastic interdisciplinary collaborator. The best design thinkers don't simply work alongside other disciplines; many of them have significant experience in more than one. At IDEO we employ people who are engineers *and* marketers, anthropologists *and* industrial designers, architects and psychologists.

Prototyping doesn't have to be complex and expensive. In another health care project, IDEO helped a group of surgeons develop a new device for sinus surgery. As the surgeons described the ideal physical characteristics of the instrument, one of the designers grabbed a whiteboard marker, a film canister, and a clothespin and taped them together. "Do you mean like this?" he asked. With his rudimentary prototype in hand, the surgeons were able to be much more precise about what the ultimate design should accomplish.

Prototypes should command only as much time, effort, and investment as are needed to generate useful feedback and evolve an idea. The more "finished" a prototype seems, the less likely its creators will be to pay attention to and profit from feedback. The goal of prototyping isn't to finish. It is to learn about the strengths and weaknesses of the idea and to identify new directions that further prototypes might take.

The design that emerged for shift changes had nurses passing on information in front of the patient rather than at the nurses' station. In only a week the team built a working prototype that included new procedures and some simple software with which nurses could call up previous shift-change notes and add new ones. They could input patient information throughout a shift rather than scrambling at the end to pass it on. The software collated the data in a simple format customized for each nurse at the start of a shift. The result was both higher-quality knowledge transfer and reduced prep time, permitting much earlier and betterinformed contact with patients.

As Kaiser measured the impact of this change over time, it learned that the mean interval between a nurse's arrival and first interaction with a patient had been more than halved, adding a huge amount of nursing time across the four hospitals. Perhaps just as important was the effect on the quality of the nurses' work experience. One nurse commented, "I'm an hour ahead, and I've only been here 45 minutes." Another said, "[This is the] first time I've ever made it out of here at the end of my shift."

Thus did a group of nurses significantly improve their patients' experience while also improving their own job satisfaction and productivity. By applying a human-centered design methodology, they were able to create a relatively small process innovation that produced an outsize impact. The new shift changes are being rolled out across the Kaiser system, and the capacity to reliably record critical patient information is being integrated into an electronic medical records initiative at the company.

What might happen at Kaiser if every nurse, doctor, and administrator in every hospital felt empowered to tackle problems the way this group did? To find out, Kaiser has created the Garfield Innovation Center, which is run by Kaiser's original core team and acts as a consultancy to the entire organization. The center's mission is to pursue innovation that enhances the patient experience and, more broadly, to envision Kaiser's "hospital of the future." It is introducing tools for design thinking across the Kaiser system.

## How Design Thinking Happens

The myth of creative genius is resilient: We believe that great ideas pop fully formed out of brilliant minds, in feats of imagination well beyond the abilities of mere mortals. But what the Kaiser nursing team accomplished was neither a sudden breakthrough nor the lightning strike of genius; it was the result of hard work augmented by a creative human-centered discovery process and followed by iterative cycles of prototyping, testing, and refinement.

The design process is best described metaphorically as a system of spaces rather than a predefined series of orderly steps. The spaces demarcate different sorts of related activities that together form the continuum of innovation. Design thinking can feel chaotic to those experiencing it for the first time. But over the life of a project participants come to see—as they did at Kaiser—that the process makes sense and achieves results, even though its architecture differs from the linear, milestonebased processes typical of other kinds of business activities.

Design projects must ultimately pass through three spaces (see the exhibit "Inspiration, Ideation, Implementation"). We label these "inspiration," for the circumstances (be they a problem, an opportunity, or both) that motivate the search for solutions; "ideation," for the process of generating, developing, and testing ideas that may lead to solutions; and "implementation," for the charting of a path to market. Projects will loop back through these spaces—particularly the first two— more than once as ideas are refined and new directions taken.

Sometimes the trigger for a project is leadership's recognition of a serious change in business fortunes. In 2004 Shimano, a Japanese manufacturer of bicycle components, faced flattening growth in its traditional high-end road-racing and mountain-bike segments in the United States. The company had always relied on technology innovations to drive its growth and naturally tried to predict where the next one might come from. This time Shimano thought a high-end casual bike that appealed to boomers would be an interesting area to explore. IDEO was invited to collaborate on the project.

During the inspiration phase, an interdisciplinary team of IDEO and Shimano people— designers, behavioral scientists, marketers, and engineers—worked to identify appropriate constraints for the project. The team began with a hunch that it should focus more broadly than on the high-end market, which might prove to be neither the only nor even the best source of new growth. So it set out to learn why 90% of American adults don't ride bikes. Looking for new ways to think about the problem, the team members spent time with all kinds of consumers. They discovered that nearly everyone they met rode a bike as a child and had happy memories of doing so. They also discovered that many Americans are intimidated by cycling today—by the retail experience (including the young, Lycraclad athletes who serve as sales staff in most independent bike stores); by the complexity and cost of the bikes,

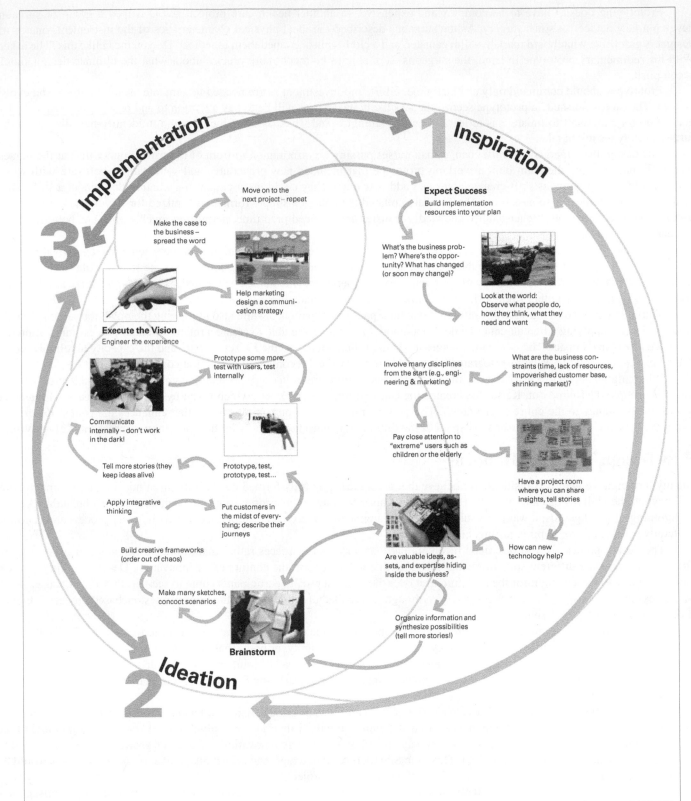

**Implementation**

**3**

**1 Inspiration**

Move on to the next project – repeat

Make the case to the business – spread the word

Help marketing design a communication strategy

**Execute the Vision**
Engineer the experience

Prototype some more, test with users, test internally

Communicate internally – don't work in the dark!

Prototype, test, prototype, test...

Tell more stories (they keep ideas alive)

Apply integrative thinking

Put customers in the midst of everything; describe their journeys

Build creative frameworks (order out of chaos)

Make many sketches, concoct scenarios

**Brainstorm**

**2 Ideation**

**Expect Success**
Build implementation resources into your plan

What's the business problem? Where's the opportunity? What has changed (or soon may change)?

Look at the world: Observe what people do, how they think, what they need and want

What are the business constraints (time, lack of resources, impoverished customer base, shrinking market)?

Involve many disciplines from the start (e.g., engineering & marketing)

Pay close attention to "extreme" users such as children or the elderly

Have a project room where you can share insights, tell stories

Are valuable ideas, assets, and expertise hiding inside the business?

How can new technology help?

Organize information and synthesize possibilities (tell more stories!)

Images copyright © IDEO

COASTING
A **sketch** (left, seat plus helmet storage) and a **prototype** (middle) show elements of coasting bicycles. Shimano's coasting **website** (right) points users to safe bike paths.

accessories, and specialized clothing; by the danger of cycling on roads not designed for bicycles; and by the demands of maintaining a technically sophisticated bike that is ridden infrequently.

This human-centered exploration—which took its insights from people outside Shimano's core customer base—led to the realization that a whole new category of bicycling might be able to reconnect American consumers to their experiences as children while also dealing with the root causes of their feelings of intimidation—thus revealing a large untapped market.

The design team, responsible for every aspect of what was envisioned as a holistic experience, came up with the concept of "Coasting." Coasting would aim to entice lapsed bikers into an activity that was simple, straightforward, and fun. Coasting bikes, built more for pleasure than for sport, would have no controls on the handlebars, no cables snaking along the frame. As on the earliest bikes many of us rode, the brakes would be applied by backpedaling. With the help of an onboard computer, a minimalist three gears would shift automatically as the bicycle gained speed or slowed. The bikes would feature comfortably padded seats, be easy to operate, and require relatively little maintenance.

Three major manufacturers—Trek, Raleigh, and Giant—developed new bikes incorporating innovative components from Shimano. But the design team didn't stop with the bike itself. In-store retailing strategies were created for independent bike dealers, in part to alleviate the discomfort that biking novices felt in stores designed to serve enthusiasts. The team developed a brand that identified Coasting as a way to enjoy life. ("Chill. Explore. Dawdle. Lollygag. First one there's a rotten egg.") And it designed a public relations campaign—in collaboration with local governments and cycling organizations—that identified safe places to ride.

Although many others became involved in the project when it reached the implementation phase, the application of design thinking in the earliest stages of innovation is what led to this complete solution. Indeed, the single thing one would have expected the design team to be responsible for—the look of the bikes—was intentionally deferred to later in the development process, when the team created a reference design to inspire the bike companies' own design teams. After a successful launch in 2007, seven more bicycle manufacturers signed up to produce Coasting bikes in 2008.

## Taking a Systems View

Many of the world's most successful brands create breakthrough ideas that are inspired by a deep understanding of consumers' lives and use the principles of design to innovate and build value. Sometimes innovation has to account for vast differences in cultural and socioeconomic conditions. In such cases design thinking can suggest creative alternatives to the assumptions made in developed societies.

India's Aravind Eye Care System is probably the world's largest provider of eye care. From April 2006 to March 2007 Aravind served more than 2.3 million patients and performed more than 270,000 surgeries. Founded in 1976 by Dr. G. Venkataswamy, Aravind has as its mission nothing less than the eradication of needless blindness among India's population, including the rural poor, through the effective delivery of superior ophthalmic care. (One of the company's slogans is "Quality is for everyone.") From 11 beds in Dr. Venkataswamy's home, Aravind has grown to encompass five hospitals (three others are under Aravind management), a plant that manufactures ophthalmic products, a research foundation, and a training center.

Aravind's execution of its mission and model is in some respects reminiscent of Edison's holistic concept of electric power delivery. The challenge the company faces is logistic: how best to deliver eye care to populations far removed from the urban centers where Aravind's hospitals are located. Aravind calls itself an "eye care system" for a reason: Its business goes beyond ophthalmic care per se to transmit expert practice to populations that have historically lacked access. The company saw its network of hospitals as a beginning rather than an end.

Much of its innovative energy has focused on bringing both preventive care and diagnostic screening to the countryside. Since 1990 Aravind has held "eye camps" in India's rural areas, in an effort to register patients, administer eye exams, teach eye care, and identify people who may require surgery or advanced diagnostic services or who have conditions that warrant monitoring.

In 2006 and early 2007 Aravind eye camps screened more than 500,000 patients, of whom nearly 113,000 required surgery. Access to transportation is a common problem in rural areas, so the company provides buses that take patients needing further treatment to one of its urban facilities and then home again. Over the years it has bolstered its diagnostic capabilities in the field with telemedicine trucks, which enable doctors back at Aravind's hospitals to participate in care decisions. In recent years Aravind's analysis of its screening data has led to specialized eye camps for certain demographic groups, such as school-age children and industrial and government workers; the company also holds camps specifically to screen for eye diseases associated with diabetes. All these services are free for the roughly 60% of patients who cannot afford to pay.

In developing its system of care, Aravind has consistently exhibited many characteristics of design thinking. It has used as a creative springboard two constraints: the poverty and remoteness of its clientele and its own lack of access to expensive solutions. For example, a pair of intraocular lenses made in the West costs $200, which severely limited the number of patients Aravind could help. Rather than try to persuade suppliers to change the way they did things, Aravind built its own solution: a manufacturing plant in the basement of one of its hospitals. It eventually discovered that it could use relatively inexpensive technology to produce lenses for $4 a pair.

Throughout its history—defined by the constraints of poverty, ignorance, and an enormous unmet need—Aravind has built a systemic solution to a complex social and medical problem.

## Getting Back to the Surface

I argued earlier that design thinking can lead to innovation that goes beyond aesthetics, but that doesn't mean that form and aesthetics are unimportant. Magazines like to publish photographs of the newest, coolest products for a reason: They are sexy and appeal to our emotions. Great design satisfies both our needs and our desires. Often the emotional connection to a product or an image is what engages us in the first place. Time and again we see successful products that were not necessarily the first to market but were the first to appeal to us emotionally and functionally. In other words, they do the job and we love them. The iPod was not the first MP3 player, but it was the first to be delightful. Target's products appeal emotionally through design and functionally through price—simultaneously.

This idea will grow ever more important in the future. As Daniel Pink writes in his book A Whole New Mind , "Abundance has satisfied, and even over-satisfied, the material needs of millions—boosting the significance of beauty and emotion and accelerating individuals' search for meaning." As more of our basic needs are met, we increasingly expect sophisticated experiences that are emotionally satisfying and meaningful. These experiences will not be simple products. They will be complex combinations of products, services, spaces, and information. They will be the ways we get educated, the ways we are entertained, the ways we stay healthy, the ways we share and communicate. Design thinking is a tool for imagining these experiences as well as giving them a desirable form.

One example of experiential innovation comes from a financial services company. In late 2005 Bank of America launched a new savings account service called "Keep the Change." IDEO, working with a team from the bank, helped identify a consumer behavior that many people will recognize: After paying cash for something, we put the coins we received in change into a jar at

---

ARAVIND

**Aravind's** outreach to rural patients frequently brings basic **diagnostic tools** (left and center) and an advanced satellite-linked **telemedicine truck** (right) to remote areas of India.

---

**HOW TO MAKE DESIGN THINKING PART OF THE INNOVATION DRILL**

**Begin at the beginning.**    Involve design thinkers at the very start of the innovation process, before any direction has been set. Design thinking will help you explore more ideas more quickly than you could otherwise.

**Take a human-centered approach.**    Along with business and technology considerations, innovation should factor in human behavior, needs, and preferences. Human-centered design thinking—especially when it includes research based on direct observation—will capture unexpected insights and produce innovation that more precisely reflects what consumers want.

**Try early and often.**    Create an expectation of rapid experimentation and prototyping. Encourage teams to create a prototype in the first week of a project. Measure progress with a metric such as average time to first prototype or number of consumers exposed to prototypes during the life of a program.

**Seek outside help.**    Expand the innovation ecosystem by looking for opportunities to cocreate with customers and consumers. Exploit Web 2.0 networks to enlarge the effective scale of your innovation team.

**Blend big and small projects.**    Manage a portfolio of innovation that stretches from shorter-term incremental ideas to longer-term revolutionary ones. Expect business units to drive and fund incremental innovation, but be willing to initiate revolutionary innovation from the top.

**Budget to the pace of innovation.**    Design thinking happens quickly, yet the route to market can be unpredictable. Don't constrain the pace at which you can innovate by relying on cumbersome budgeting cycles. Be prepared to rethink your funding approach as projects proceed and teams learn more about opportunities.

**Find talent any way you can.**    Look to hire from interdisciplinary programs like the new Institute of Design at Stanford and progressive business schools like Rotman, in Toronto. People with more-conventional design backgrounds can push solutions far beyond your expectations. You may even be able to train nondesigners with the right attributes to excel in design-thinking roles.

**Design for the cycle.**    In many businesses people move every 12 to 18 months. But design projects may take longer than that to get from day one through implementation. Plan assignments so that design thinkers go from inspiration to ideation to implementation. Experiencing the full cycle builds better judgment and creates great long-term benefits for the organization.

---

home. Once the jar is full, we take the coins to the bank and deposit them in a savings account. For many people, it's an easy way of saving. Bank of America's innovation was to build this behavior into a debit card account. Customers who use their debit cards to make purchases can now choose to have the total rounded up to the nearest dollar and the difference deposited in their savings accounts.

The success of this innovation lay in its appeal to an instinctive desire we have to put money aside in a painless and invisible way. Keep the Change creates an experience that feels natural because it models behavior that many of us already exhibit. To be sure, Bank of America sweetens the deal by matching 100% of the change saved in the first three months and 5% of annual totals (up to $250) thereafter. This encourages customers to try it out. But the real payoff is emotional: the gratification that comes with monthly statements showing customers they've saved money without even trying.

In less than a year the program attracted 2.5 million customers. It is credited with 700,000 new checking accounts and a million new savings accounts. Enrollment now totals more than 5 million people who together have saved more than $500 million. Keep the Change demonstrates that design thinking can identify an aspect of human behavior and then convert it into both a customer benefit and a business value.

Thomas Edison represents what many of us think of as a golden age of American innovation—a time when new ideas transformed every aspect of our lives. The need for transformation is, if anything, greater now than ever before. No matter where we look, we see problems that can be solved only through innovation: unaffordable or unavailable health care, billions of people trying to live on just a few dollars a day, energy usage that outpaces the planet's ability to support it, education systems that fail many students, companies whose traditional markets are disrupted by new technologies or demographic shifts. These problems all have people at their heart. They require a human-centered, creative, iterative, and practical approach to finding the best ideas and ultimate solutions. Design thinking is just such an approach to innovation.

Reprint R0806E
To order, see the next page
or call 800-988-0886 or 617-783-7500
or go to www.hbr.org

# Further Reading

### The Harvard Business Review

*Paperback Series*

Here are the landmark ideas—both contemporary and classic—that have established Harvard Business Review as required reading for businesspeople around the globe. Each paperback includes eight of the leading articles on a particular business topic. The series includes over thirty titles, including the following best-sellers:

**Harvard Business Review on Brand Management**
    Product no. 1445
**Harvard Business Review on Change**
    Product no. 8842
**Harvard Business Review on Leadership**
    Product no. 8834
**Harvard Business Review on Managing People**
    Product no. 9075
**Harvard Business Review on Measuring Corporate Performance**
    Product no. 8826

For a complete list of the *Harvard Business Review* paperback series, go to www.hbr.org.

To Order

For *Harvard Business Review*
reprints and subscriptions, call 800-988-0886 or
617-783-7500. Go to www.hbr.org

For customized and quantity orders of
*Harvard Business Review* article reprints,
call 617-783-7626, or e-mail
customizations@hbsp.harvard.edu

*Harvard Business Review*
U.S. and Canada
800-988-0886
617-783-7500
617-783-7555 fax

# Article 24

## 4 Reasons Why the Internet of Everything
## Will Require a New Breed of IT Pros

### Learning Outcomes

*After reading this article, you will be able to:*
• Give a fundamental description of the Internet of Everything (IoE).
• Appreciate the crucially heightened role of data analysis as the IoE grows.
• Identify the many emerging roles in the future for the IoE.

Like many products and services we enjoy today, the Internet's origins rest within the halls of government.

The Advanced Research Projects Agency Network, which laid the technology foundation for how the Internet works, was originally funded by the Defense Department. Just a few decades later, that foundation has been built upon to create an entity only the most visionary thinkers could have imagined: the Internet of Everything.

IoE is an interconnected web of systems that brings together people, processes, data and things. There are currently over 20 billion connected devices, representing less than 1 percent of physical objects. Cisco predicts that by 2020, 50 billion devices will be connected.

IoE's ubiquity and scale are even now producing data-derived insights that promise gains in productivity, new revenue streams and cost savings.

However, these changes cannot occur without a new breed of trained IT professionals.

### 1. Analysis is Key

With IoE, the network will play a more crucial role than ever. It will need to be more secure, agile, context-aware, automated, dynamic, and programmable. The realms of mobile, cloud, apps, and big data and analytics will all be interconnected in IoE. Security will be of particular concern; with so many devices all connected, the attack surface will increase exponentially, and security breaches could become even costlier.

The amount of data generated by and exchanged among this ever-growing number of devices will require analysis. The role of the data scientist will therefore be crucial in terms of converting this data into usable information.

Government agencies stand to gain dramatically from the improvements in data gathering and streamlined workflows. In short, IoE is about connecting people, process, data, and things; ensuring the connections are secure; and making the network programmable so information gathered from data can be more intelligently applied to devices rather than having to configure and manage them manually.

### 2. The Network is Expanding

IoE makes important connections that reveal actionable insights, but it also will create significant challenges for the workforce—in terms of both security and data handling issues and adequate training. Getting prepared for IoE will require the existing workforce—especially in areas such as manufacturing, safety and security, utilities and transportation—to understand IT networking to a greater degree.

At the same time, IT networking professionals need to better understand manufacturing-control systems and industrial networks as IoE will cause these operational technologies to converge with IT. And lastly, it will be vital for the current generation of students coming out of college to have the networking skills that will enable them to address this convergence.

The traditional networker's view is expanding to include many new technologies, and the networker's responsibilities are expanding to include many new duties. For example, the increase in connected things requires network professionals to maintain a strong security posture across the expanded attack surface.

Also, the ability to analyze big data and turn it into actionable information is needed to drive business outcomes. There are many emerging roles in the future for IoE: business transformation specialists, cloud brokers, network programmers, and data scientists. Cybersecurity becomes more pervasive and the networking career becomes much more specialized.

## 3. Training Is Only Half the Battle

The transition to IoE is not only desirable but inevitable, and the people best suited to lead that transition are those with fundamental networking experience. That is because they are equipped with the knowledge to build the bridge from network infrastructure to the application environment. Agencies will need to work with industries throughout the world to create the pathway for IT networking skills and talent development. Continued efficiency and productivity gains will depend upon it.

Training current IT employees is half of the battle. The other half of the educational battle is to prepare youth from the beginning to understand the network and its underlying connection to everything. It is incumbent on IT companies to work with universities, secondary schools, networking academies, and learning partners to develop curricula to ensure rising talent is well prepared to understand the functioning of the network and how it makes IoE work.

Because IoE will eventually affect all government entities, employees of those entities must be properly trained in managing the network as IoE's basic platform. The evolution is already well under way, and the demand for networking talent is already being felt. Beyond understanding network deployment and operation, those at the forefront of the change will be taking the network in new directions, using 21st-century skills in the process: critical thinking, complex problem solving, data analysis, and communication and collaboration.

## 4. New Workers Ditch the Traditional

Students' needs and preferences regarding where and when they will get training are changing, along with what they are learning, because of new bring your own device policies, and ubiquitous access models of education. Students no longer prefer traditional delivery modalities. Instead, they want mobile, video-based, game-based learning that not only is an evolution of traditional delivery but also helps remove barriers to education by making it easy, fun, accessible, and effective. A 2013 survey of Cisco-certified professionals revealed a strong preference for hands-on practice labs, simulations, and video-based training. Rather than attending a class on each of these subjects, this core knowledge set will be available in real time on an as-needed basis to aid in decision-making.

It is incumbent upon government agencies to strategically forecast the needs of their constituents and develop plans to best meet those needs. The network demands of IoE require a shift in how the current and future workforces are educated to fill critical gaps. With a properly equipped staff of network professionals, agencies will be able to fully realize the benefits of IoE: faster and more efficient services, greater productivity and cost savings.

## Critical Thinking

1. Why does the IoE's expanded attack surface present a particularly serious concern?
2. In what ways will government agencies gain dramatically from the improvements in data gathering and streamlined workflows?
3. For the upcoming generation, how early in their education should IT instruction begin? Explain.

## Create Central

www.mhhe.com/createcentral

## Internet References

**Goldman Sachs: "The Internet of Things: The Next Mega-Trend"**
   http://www.goldmansachs.com/our-thinking/outlook/internet-of-things/index.html
**InformationWeek: "Cisco Futurists Plan For Internet Of Everything"**
   http://www.informationweek.com/big-data/big-data-analytics/cisco-futurists-plan-for-internet-of-everything/d/d-id/1108286
**Yahoo! Finance: "What the 'Internet of Things' Means for Enterprising Entrepreneurs"**
   http://finance.yahoo.com/news/internet-things-means-enterprising-entrepreneurs-234500396.html

# Article 25 ↵

## Will Robots Take Your Job?

Selected, Edited, and with Issue Framing Material by:
Thomas A. Easton, *Thomas College*

**YES: Kevin Drum,** from "Welcome, Robot Overlords. Please Don't Fire Us?" *Mother Jones* (2013)

**NO: Peter Gorle and Andrew Clive,** from "Positive Impact of Industrial Robots on Employment," Metra Martech (2011)

## Learning Outcomes

**After reading this issue, you will be able to:**
- Explain what kinds of jobs are now and may soon be suitable for robots.
- Discuss the impact of robotics on their future job prospects.
- Apply their understanding of how robots will affect future jobs in a discussion of career choices.
- Discuss how, if robots indeed do cause widespread unemployment, the world's economies will have to change.

## ISSUE SUMMARY

**YES:** Kevin Drum argues that we are about to make very rapid progress in artificial intelligence, and by about 2040, robots will be replacing people in a great many jobs. On the way to that "robot paradise," corporate managers and investors will expand their share of national wealth, at the expense of labor's share, even more than they have in recent years. That trend, however, depends on an ample supply of consumers—workers with enough money to buy the products the machines are making. It is thus already time to start rethinking how the nation ensures that its citizens have enough money to be consumers and keep the economy going.

**NO:** Peter Gorle and Andrew Clive argue that robots are not a threat to human employment. Historically, increases in the use of automation almost always increase both productivity and employment. Over the next few years, the use of robotics will generate 700,000–1,000,000 new jobs.

## Where Do You Stand?

The idea that technology threatens jobs is not new. In the early 1800s, the "Luddites" were textile workers who destroyed new weaving machinery that could be operated by unskilled labor. The movement faded away with the end of the Napoleonic Wars, but its name has continued to be applied to those who oppose industrialization, automation, computerization, and even any new technology. See, for example, Steven E. Jones, *Against Technology: From the Luddites to Neo-Luddism* (CRC Press, 2006).

Not surprisingly, modern computer technology arouses many job-related fears, for computers seem to be growing ever more capable. When IBM's "Watson" won a dramatic victory in the game of *Jeopardy,* many wondered if we were finally seeing true artificial intelligence. Kirk L. Kroeker, "Weighing Watson's Impact," *Communications of the ACM* (July 2011), notes that despite many dismissive comments, Watson is an excellent demonstration of the power of machine learning. Future applications of the technology will soon play important roles in medicine (extracting information from vast numbers of medical books and journals), law, education, and the financial industry. Many of these applications do not require that a robot look and act like a human being, but researchers are working on that, too; see Alex Wright, "Robots Like Us," *Communications of the ACM* (May 2012); and Dennis Normile, "In Our Own Image," *Science* (October 10, 2014).

"Robocars"—cars that drive themselves, with no human hand at the wheel—have already been demonstrated and their capabilities are improving rapidly; see Sebastian Thrun, "Toward Robotic Cars," *Communications of the ACM* (April 2010), and Alex Wright, "Automotive Autonomy," *Communications of the ACM* (July 2011). Before they can be broadly used, there must be changes in legislation (can you be guilty of OUI if the car drives itself?) and insurance, among other things; see "The Future of the Self-Driving Automobile," *Trends E-Magazine* (December 2010), and John Markoff, "Collision in the Making Between Self-Driving Cars and How the World Works," *New York Times* (January 23, 2012). Given such changes, we can expect to see job losses among taxi drivers and truckers, among others.

Robots may also cost other people their jobs. Jason Borenstein, "Robots and the Changing Workforce," *AI & Society* (2011), notes that robotic workers are going to become ever more common, and though new job opportunities are bound to arise from this, many jobs will disappear and the human workforce will change in many ways—including necessary education and worker income. Judith Aquino, "Nine Jobs that Humans May Lose to Robots," *Business Insider* (March 22, 2011), says the endangered list includes drivers, but also pharmacists, lawyers and paralegals, astronauts, store clerks, soldiers, babysitters, rescuers, and sports-writers and other reporters. John Sepulvado asks "Could a Computer Write This Story?" (CNN, May 11, 2012) (http://edition.cnn.com/2012/05/11/tech/innovation/computer-assisted-writing/index.html). By 2014, robowriters from the company, Narrative Science (http://www.narrativescience.com/), were already being deployed; see Francie Diep, "Associated Press Will Use Robots to Write Articles," *Popular Science* (July 1, 2014) (http://www.popsci.com/article/technology/associated-press-will-use-robots-write-articles). Farhad Manjoo asks (and answers) "Will Robots Steal Your Job? If You're Highly Educated, You Should Still Be Afraid," *Slate* (September 26, 2011) (http://www.slate.com/articles/technology/robot_invasion/2011/09/will_robots_steal_your_job.html). "Robots to Take 500,000 Human Jobs . . . for Now," *The Fiscal Times* (December 29, 2011), notes that every industry, from agriculture to the military, will be affected. Martin Ford, "Google's Cloud Robotics Strategy— and How It Could Soon Threaten Jobs," *Huffington Post* (January 3, 2012), says that "nearly any type of work that is on some level routine in nature—regardless of the skill level or educational requirements—is likely to someday be impacted by [robotic] technologies. The only real question is how soon it will happen." This foreboding thought is echoed by Dan Lyons, "Who Needs Humans?" Newsweek (July 25, 2011). David J. Lynch is more optimistic in "It's a Man vs. Machine Recovery," *Bloomberg Businessweek* (January 5, 2012), he notes that businesses are buying machines more than hiring people, but "there's nothing wrong with the labor market that resurgent demand wouldn't fix." There may also be a need to consider the ethics involved, for as more robots enter the workplace, they will bring with them changed expectations (robots are tireless, and they don't need health insurance, retirement plans, vacations, and even pay; will employers expect the same of humans?); this may even mean restricting the use of robots; see Jason Borenstein, "Computing Ethics: Work Life in the Robotic Age," *Communications of the ACM* (July 2010).

Not everyone agrees on the degree of the threat. In "Will Work for Machines" (August 2014), *Scientific American's* editors note that it is actually hard to tell whether there is a threat at all, for there is a serious shortage of data. David Bourne, "My Boss the Robot," Scientific American (May 2013), sees a future in which humans and robots collaborate to get jobs done more rapidly and efficiently than either could do alone. See also John Bohannon, "Meet Your New Co-Worker," *Science* (October 10, 2014). David H. Autor, "Polanyi's Paradox and the Shape of Employment Growth," report prepared for the Federal Reserve Bank of Kansas City symposium on "Re-Evaluating Labor Market Dynamics" (August 21–13, 2014) (http://www.kansascityfed.org/publicat/sympos/2014/093014.pdf), concludes that most "commentators overstate the extent of machine substitution for human labor and ignore the strong complementarities." Neil Irwin, "Why the Robots Might Not Take Our Jobs After All: They Lack Common Sense," *New York Times* (August 22, 2014), thinks robots aren't going to replace humans any time soon, except in very limited ways. See also John Tamny, "Why Robots Will Be the Biggest Job Creators in World History," Forbes (March 1, 2015 @ 9 AM) (http://www.forbes.com/sites/johntamny/2015/03/01/why-robots-will-be-the-biggest-job-creators-in-history/).

How bad might it get? Stuart Elliott, in "An tici pating a Luddite Revival," *Issues in Science and Technology* (Spring 2014), compares the capabilities of computers as reflected in the literature with job skills as defined in the Department of Labor's O*NET system. He finds that computers are already close to being able to meet skills requirements of 75 percent of jobs. "Safe" jobs that demand more skills are in education, health care, science, engineering, and law, but even those may be matched within a few decades. "In principle," he says, "there is no problem with imagining a transformation in the labor market that substitutes technology for workers for 80 percent of current jobs and then expands in the remaining 20 percent to absorb the entire labor force. [But} We do not know how successful the nation can be in trying to prepare everyone in the labor force for jobs that require these higher skill levels. It is hard to imagine, for example, that most of the labor force will move into jobs in health care, education, science, engineering, and law. . . . At some point it will be too difficult for large numbers of displaced workers to move into jobs requiring capabilities that are difficult for most of them to carry out even if they have the time and resources for retraining. When that time comes, the nation will be forced to reconsider the role that paid employment plays in distributing economic goods and services and in providing a meaningful focus for many people's daily lives." Marcus Wohlsen, in "When Robots Take All the Work, What'll Be Left for Us to Do?" Wired (August 8, 2014) (http://www.wired.com/2014/08/when-robots-take-all-the-work-whatll-be-left-for-us-to-do/), says that "The scariest possibility of all is that [the loss of jobs means that] only then do we figure out what really makes us human is work." William H. Davidow and Michael S. Malone, "What Happens to Society When Robots Replace Workers?" *Harvard Business Review* (December 10, 2014) (https://hbr.org/2014/12/what-happens-to-society-when-robots-replace-workers), reach a similar con clu sion: "Ultimately, we need a new, individualized, *cultural,* approach to the meaning of work and the purpose of life."

In the YES selection, Kevin Drum argues that we are about to make very rapid progress in artificial intelligence, and by about 2040, robots will be replacing people in a great many jobs. On the way to that "robot paradise," corporate managers and investors will expand their share of national wealth, at the expense of labor's share, even more than they have in recent years. That trend, however, depends on an ample supply of consumers—workers with enough money to buy the products the machines are making. It is thus already time to start rethinking how the nation ensures that its citizens have enough money to be consumers and keep the economy going. In the NO selection, Peter Gorle and Andrew Clive argue that robots are not a threat to human employment. Historically, increases in the use of automation almost always increase both productivity and employment. Over the next few years, the use of robotics will generate 700,000 to 1,000,000 new jobs.

# Welcome, Robot Overlords. Please Don't Fire Us?

This is a story about the future. Not the unhappy future, the one where climate change turns the planet into a cinder or we all die in a global nuclear war. This is the *happy* version. It's the one where computers keep getting smarter and smarter, and clever engineers keep building better and better robots. By 2040, computers the size of a softball are as smart as human beings. Smarter, in fact. Plus they're *computers*: They never get tired, they're never ill-tempered, they never make mistakes, and they have instant access to all of human knowledge.

The result is paradise. Global warming is a problem of the past because computers have figured out how to generate limitless amounts of green energy and intelligent robots have tirelessly built the infrastructure to deliver it to our homes. No one needs to work anymore. Robots can do everything humans can do, and they do it uncomplainingly, 24 hours a day. Some things remain scarce—beachfront property in Malibu, original Rembrandts—but thanks to super-efficient use of natural resources and massive recycling, scarcity of ordinary consumer goods is a thing of the past. Our days are spent however we please, perhaps in study, perhaps playing video games. It's up to us.

Maybe you think I'm pulling your leg here. Or being archly ironic. After all, this does have a bit of a rose-colored tint to it, doesn't it? Like something from *The Jetsons* or the cover of *Wired*. That would hardly be a surprising reaction. Computer scientists have been predicting the imminent rise of machine intelligence since at least 1956, when the Dartmouth Summer Research Project on Artificial Intelligence gave the field its name, and there are only so many times you can cry wolf. Today, a full seven decades after the birth of the computer, all we have are iPhones, Microsoft Word, and in-dash navigation. You could be excused for thinking that computers that truly match the human brain are a ridiculous pipe dream.

But they're not. It's true that we've made far slower progress toward real artificial intelligence than we once thought, but that's for a very simple and very human reason: Early computer scientists grossly underestimated the power of the human brain and the difficulty of emulating one. It turns out that this is a very, very hard problem, sort of like filling up Lake Michigan one drop at a time. In fact, not just *sort of* like. It's *exactly* like filling up Lake Michigan one drop at a time. If you want to understand the future of computing, it's essential to understand this.

What do we do over the next few decades as robots become steadily more capable and steadily begin taking away all our jobs?

Suppose it's 1940 and Lake Michigan has (somehow) been emptied. Your job is to fill it up using the following rule: To start off, you can add one fluid ounce of water to the lake bed. Eighteen months later, you can add two. In another 18 months, you can add four ounces. And so on. Obviously this is going to take a while.

By 1950, you have added around a gallon of water. But you keep soldiering on. By 1960, you have a bit more than 150 gallons. By 1970, you have 16,000 gallons, about as much as an average suburban swimming pool.

At this point it's been 30 years, and even though 16,000 gallons is a fair amount of water, it's nothing compared to the size of Lake Michigan. To the naked eye you've made no progress at all.

So let's skip all the way ahead to 2000. Still nothing. You have—maybe—a slight sheen on the lake floor. How about 2010? You have a few inches of water here and there. This is ridiculous. It's now been *70 years* and you still don't have enough water to float a goldfish. Surely this task is futile?

But wait. Just as you're about to give up, things suddenly change. By 2020, you have about 40 feet of water. And by 2025 you're done. After 70 years you had nothing. Fifteen years later, the job was finished.

If you have any kind of background in computers, you've already figured out that I didn't pick these numbers out of a hat. I started in 1940 because that's about when the first programmable computer was invented. I chose a doubling time of 18 months because of a cornerstone of computer history called Moore's Law, which famously estimates that computing power doubles approximately every 18 months. And I chose Lake Michigan because its size, in fluid ounces, is roughly the same as the computing power of the human brain measured in calculations per second.

In other words, just as it took us until 2025 to fill up Lake Michigan, the simple exponential curve of Moore's Law suggests it's going to take us until 2025 to build a computer with the processing power of the human brain. And it's going to happen the same way: For the first 70 years, it will seem as if nothing is happening, even though we're doubling our progress every 18 months. Then, in the final 15 years, seemingly out of nowhere, we'll finish the job.

True artificial intelligence really is around the corner, and it really will make life easier. But first we face vast economic upheaval.

And that's exactly where we are. We've moved from computers with a trillionth of the power of a human brain to computers with a billionth of the power. Then a millionth. And now a thousandth. Along the way, computers progressed from ballistics to accounting to word processing to speech recognition, and none of that really seemed like progress toward artificial intelligence. That's because even a thousandth of the power of a human brain is—let's be honest—a bit of a joke. Sure, it's a billion times more than the first computer had, but it's still not much more than the computing power of a hamster.

This is why, even with the IT industry barreling forward relentlessly, it has never seemed like we were making any real progress on the AI front. But there's another reason as well: Every time computers break some new barrier, we decide—or maybe just finally get it through our thick skulls—that we set the bar too low. At one point, for example, we thought that playing chess at a high level would be a mark of human-level intelligence. Then, in 1997, IBM's Deep Blue supercomputer beat world champion Garry Kasparov, and suddenly we decided that playing grandmaster-level chess didn't imply high intelligence after all.

So maybe translating human languages would be a fair test? Google Translate does a passable job of that these days. Recognizing human voices and responding appropriately? Siri mostly does that, and better systems are on the near horizon. Understanding the world well enough to win a round of *Jeopardy!* against human competition? A few years ago IBM's Watson supercomputer beat the two best human *Jeopardy!* champions of all time. Driving a car? Google has already logged more than 300,000 miles in its driverless cars, and in another decade they may be commercially available.

The truth is that all this represents more progress toward true AI than most of us realize. We've just been limited by the fact that computers still aren't quite muscular enough to finish the job. That's changing rapidly, though. Computing power is measured in calculations per second—a.k.a. floating-point operations per second, or "flops"—and the best estimates of the human brain suggest that our own processing power is about equivalent to 10 petaflops. ("Peta" comes after giga and tera.) That's a lot of flops, but last year an IBM Blue Gene/Q supercomputer at Lawrence Livermore National Laboratory was clocked at 16.3 petaflops.

Of course, raw speed isn't everything. Livermore's Blue Gene/Q fills a room, requires eight megawatts of power to run, and costs about $250 million. What's more, it achieves its speed not with a single superfast processor, but with 1.6 million ordinary processor cores running simultaneously. While that kind of massive parallel processing is ideally suited for nuclear-weapons testing, we don't know yet if it will be effective for producing AI.

But plenty of people are trying to figure it out. Earlier this year, the European Commission chose two big research endeavors to receive a half billion euros each, and one of them was the Human Brain Project led by Henry Markram, a neuroscientist at the Swiss Federal Institute of Technology in Lausanne. He uses another IBM supercomputer in a project aimed at modeling the entire human brain. Markram figures he can do this by 2020.

The Luddites weren't wrong. They were just 200 years too early.

That might be optimistic. At the same time, it also might turn out that we don't need to model a human brain in the first place. After all, when the Wright brothers built the first airplane, they didn't model it after a bird with flapping wings. Just as there's more than one way to fly, there's probably more than one way to think, too.

Google's driverless car, for example, doesn't navigate the road the way humans do. It uses four radars, a 64-beam laser range finder, a camera, GPS, and extremely detailed high-res maps. What's more, Google engineers drive along test routes to record data before they let the self-driving cars loose.

Is this disappointing? In a way, yes: Google *has* to do all this to make up for the fact that the car can't do what any human can do while also singing along to the radio, chugging a venti, and making a mental note to pick up the laundry. But that's a cramped view. Even when processing power and software get better, there's no reason to think that a driverless car should replicate the way humans drive. They will have access to far more information than we do, and unlike us they'll have the power to make use of it in real time. And they'll never get distracted when the phone rings.

True artificial intelligence will very likely be here within a couple of decades. By about 2040 our robot paradise awaits.

In other words, you should still be impressed. When we think of human cognition, we usually think about things like composing music or writing a novel. But a big part of the human brain is dedicated to more prosaic functions, like taking in a chaotic visual field and recognizing the thousands of separate objects it contains. We do that so automatically we hardly even think of it as intelligence. But it is, and the fact that Google's car can do it at all is a real breakthrough.

The exact pace of future progress remains uncertain. For example, some physicists think that Moore's Law may break down in the near future and constrain the growth of computing power. We also probably have to break lots of barriers in our knowledge of neuroscience before we can write the software that does all the things a human brain can do. We have to figure out how to make petaflop computers smaller and cheaper. And it's possible that the 10-petaflop estimate of human computing power is too low in the first place.

Nonetheless, in Lake Michigan terms, we finally have a few inches of water in the lake bed, and we can see it rising. All those milestones along the way—playing chess, translating web pages, winning at *Jeopardy!,* driving a car—aren't just stunts. They're precisely the kinds of things you'd expect as we struggle along with platforms that aren't quite powerful enough—yet. True artificial intelligence will very likely be here within a couple of decades. Making it small, cheap, and ubiquitous might take a decade more.

In other words, by about 2040 our robot paradise awaits.

AND NOW FOR THE BAIT and switch. I promised you this would be a happy story, and in the long run it is.

But first we have to get there. And at this point our tale takes a darker turn. What do we do over the next few decades as robots become steadily more capable and steadily begin taking away all our jobs? This is the kind of thing that futurologists write about frequently, but when I started looking for answers from mainstream economists, it turned out there wasn't much to choose from. The economics community just hasn't spent much time over the past couple of decades focusing on the effect that machine intelligence is likely to have on the labor market. Now is a particularly appropriate time to think about this question, because it was two centuries ago this year that 64 men were brought to trial in York, England. Their crime? They were skilled weavers who fought back against the rising tide of power looms they feared would put them out of work. The Luddites spent two years burning mills and destroying factory machinery, and the British government was not amused. Of the 64 men charged in 1813, 25 were transported to Australia and 17 were led to the gallows.

Since then, Luddite has become a derisive term for anyone afraid of new technology. After all, the weavers turned out to be wrong. Power looms put them out of work, but in the long run automation made the entire workforce more productive. Everyone still had jobs—just different ones. Some ran the new power looms, others found work no one could have imagined just a few decades before, in steel mills, automobile factories, and railroad lines. In the end, this produced wealth for everyone, because, after all, someone still had to make, run, and maintain the machines.

But that was then. During the Industrial Revolution, machines were limited to performing physical tasks. The Digital Revolution is different because computers can perform cognitive tasks too, and that means machines will eventually be able to run themselves. When that happens, they won't just put individuals out of work temporarily. Entire classes of workers will be out of work permanently.

In other words, the Luddites weren't wrong. They were just 200 years too early.

This isn't something that will happen overnight. It will happen slowly, as machines grow increasingly capable. We've already seen it in factories, where robots do work that used to be done by semiskilled assembly line workers. In a decade, driverless cars will start to put taxi hacks and truck drivers out of a job. And while it's easy to believe that some jobs can never be done by machines—do the elderly really want to be tended by robots?—that may not be true. Nearly 50 years ago, when MIT computer scientist Joseph Weizenbaum created a therapy simulation program named Eliza, he was astonished to discover just how addictive it was. Even though Eliza was almost laughably crude, it was endlessly patient and seemed interested in your problems. People *liked* talking to Eliza.

Robots will take over more and more jobs. As this happens, capital will become ever more powerful and labor will become ever more worthless.

And that was 50 years ago, using only a keyboard and an old Teletype terminal. Add a billion times more processing power and you start to get something much closer to real social interaction. Robotic pets are growing so popular that Sherry Turkle, an MIT professor who studies the way we interact with technology, is uneasy about it: "The idea of some kind of artificial companionship," she says, "is already becoming the new normal."

It's not hard to see why. Unlike humans, an intelligent machine does whatever you want it to do, for as long as you want it to. You want to gossip? It'll gossip. You want to complain for hours on end about how your children never call? No problem. And as the technology of robotics advances—the Pentagon has developed a fully functional robotic arm that can be controlled by a human mind— they'll be able to perform ordinary human physical tasks too. They'll clean the floor, do your nails, diagnose your ailments, and cook your food.

Increasingly, then, robots will take over more and more jobs. And guess who will own all these robots? People with money, of course. As this happens, capital will become ever more powerful and labor will become ever more worthless. Those without money—most of us—will live on whatever crumbs the owners of capital allow us.

This is a grim prediction. But it's not nearly as farfetched as it sounds. Economist Paul Krugman recently remarked that our long-standing belief in skills and education as the keys to financial success may well be outdated. In a blog post titled "Rise of the Robots," he reviewed some recent economic data and predicted that we're entering an era where the prime cause of income inequality will be something else entirely: capital vs. labor.

Until a decade ago, the share of total national income going to workers was pretty stable at around 70 percent, while the share going to capital—mainly corporate profits and returns on financial investments—made up the other 30 percent. More recently, though, those shares have started to change. Slowly but steadily, labor's share of total national income has gone down, while the share going to capital owners has gone up. The most obvious effect of this is the skyrocketing wealth of the top 1 percent, due mostly to huge increases in capital gains and investment income.

In the economics literature, the increase in the share of income going to capital owners is known as capitalbiased technological change. Let's take a layman's look at what that means.

The question we want to answer is simple: If CBTC is already happening—not a lot, but just a little bit—what trends would we expect to see? What are the signs of a computer-driven economy? First and most obviously, if automation were displacing labor, we'd expect to see a steady decline in the share of the population that's employed.

Second, we'd expect to see fewer job openings than in the past. Third, as more people compete for fewer jobs, we'd expect to see middle-class incomes flatten in a race to the bottom. Fourth, with consumption stagnant, we'd expect to see corporations stockpile more cash and, fearing weaker sales, invest less in new products and new factories. Fifth, as a result of all this, we'd expect to see labor's share of national income decline and capital's share rise.

These trends are the five horsemen of the robotic apocalypse, and guess what? We're already seeing them, and not just because of the crash of 2008. They started showing up in the statistics more than a decade ago. For a while, though, they were masked by the dot-com and housing bubbles, so when the financial crisis hit, years' worth of decline was compressed into 24 months. The trend lines dropped off the cliff.

How alarmed should we be by this? In one sense, a bit of circumspection is in order. The modern economy is complex, and most of these trends have multiple causes. The decline in the share of workers who are employed, for example, is partly caused by the aging of the population. What's more, the financial crisis has magnified many of these trends. Labor's share of income will probably recover a bit once the economy finally turns up.

Doctors should probably be worried as well. Remember Watson, the *Jeopardy!*-playing computer? In another decade, there's a good chance that Watson will be able to do this without any human help at all.

But in another sense, we should be *very* alarmed. It's one thing to suggest that robots are going to cause mass unemployment starting in 2030 or so. We'd have some time to come to grips with that. But the evidence suggests that—slowly, haltingly—it's happening already, and we're simply not prepared for it.

How exactly will this play out? Economist David Autor has suggested that the first jobs to go will be middleskill jobs. Despite impressive advances, robots still don't have the dexterity to perform many common kinds of manual labor that are simple for humans—digging ditches, changing bedpans. Nor are they any good at jobs that require a lot of cognitive skill—teaching classes, writing magazine articles. But in the middle you have jobs that are both fairly routine and require no manual dexterity. So that may be where the hollowing out starts: with desk jobs in places like accounting or customer support.

That hasn't yet happened in earnest because AI is still in its infancy. But it's not hard to see which direction the wind is blowing. The US Postal Service, for example, used to employ humans to sort letters, but for some time now, that's been done largely by machines that can recognize human handwriting. Netflix does a better job picking movies you might like than a bored video-store clerk. Facial recognition software is improving rapidly, and *that's* a job so human there's an entire module in the human brain, the fusiform gyrus, solely dedicated to this task.

In fact, there's even a digital sports writer. It's true that a human being wrote this story—ask my mother if you're not sure—but in a decade or two I might be out of a job too. Doctors should probably be worried as well. Remember Watson, the *Jeopardy!*-playing computer? It's now being fed millions of pages of medical information so that it can help physicians do a better job of diagnosing diseases. In another decade, there's a good chance that Watson will be able to do this without any human help at all.

This is, admittedly, pretty speculative. Still, even if it's hard to find concrete examples of computers doing human work today, it's going to get easier before long.

Take driverless cars. My newspaper is delivered every day by a human being. But because humans are fallible, sometimes I don't get a paper, or I get the wrong one. This would be a terrific task for a driverless car in its early stages of development. There are no passengers to worry about. The route is fixed. Delivery is mostly done in the early morning, when traffic is light. And the car's abundance of mapping and GPS data would ensure that it always knows which house is which.

The next step might be passenger vehicles on fixed routes, like airport shuttles. Then long-haul trucks. Then buses and taxis. There are 2.5 million workers who drive trucks, buses, and taxis for a living, and there's a good chance that, one by one, all of them will be displaced by driverless vehicles within the next decade or two. What will they do when that happens? Machines will be putting everyone else with modest skill levels out of work too. There will be no place to go but the unemployment line.

WHAT CAN WE DO about this? First and foremost, we should be carefully watching those five economic trends linked to capital-biased technological change to see if they rebound when the economy picks up. If, instead, they continue their long, downward slide, it means we've already entered a new era.

Next, we'll need to let go of some familiar convictions. Left-leaning observers may continue to think that stagnating incomes can be improved with better education and equality of opportunity. Conservatives will continue to insist that people without jobs are lazy bums who shouldn't be coddled. They'll both be wrong.

Corporate executives should worry too. For a while, everything will seem great for them: Falling labor costs will produce heftier profits and bigger bonuses. But then it will all come crashing down. After all, robots might be able to *produce* goods and services, but they can't consume them. And eventually computers will become pretty good CEOs as well.

Solutions to this will remain elusive as long as we resist facing the real change in the way our economy works. When we finally do, we'll probably have only a few options open to us. The simplest, because it's relatively familiar, is to tax capital at high rates and use the money to support displaced workers. In other words, as The *Economist's* Ryan Avent puts it, "redistribution, and a lot of it."

There's not much question that this could work, but would we be happy in a society that offers real work to a dwindling few and bread and circuses for the rest? Most likely, owners of capital would strongly resist higher taxes, as they always have, while workers would be unhappy with their enforced idleness. Still, the ancient Romans managed to get used to it—with slave labor playing the role of robots—and we might have to, as well.

Alternatively, economist Noah Smith suggests that we might have to fundamentally change the way we think about how we share economic growth. Right now, he points out, everyone is born with an endowment of labor by virtue of having a body and a brain that can be traded for income. But what to do when that endowment is worth a fraction of what it is today? Smith's suggestion: "Why not also an endowment of capital? What if, when each citizen turns 18, the government bought him or her a diversified portfolio of equity?"

In simple terms, if owners of capital are capturing an increasing fraction of national income, then that capital needs to be shared more widely if we want to maintain a middle-class society. Somehow—and I'm afraid a bit of vagueness is inevitable here— an increasing share of corporate equity will need to be divvied up among the entire population as workers are slowly but surely stripped of their human capital. Perhaps everyone will be guaranteed ownership of a few robots, or some share of robot production of goods and services.

But whatever the answer—and it might turn out to be something we can't even imagine right now—it's time to start thinking about our automated future in earnest. The history of mass economic displacement isn't encouraging—fascists in the '20s, Nazis in the '30s—and recent high levels of unemployment in Greece and Italy have already produced rioting in the streets and larger followings for right-wing populist parties. And that's after only a few years of misery.

So far, though, the topic has gotten surprisingly little attention among economists. At MIT, Autor has written about the elimination of middle-class jobs thanks to encroaching technology, and his colleagues, Erik Brynjolfsson and Andrew McAfee of MIT's Center for Digital Business, got a lot of attention a couple of years ago for their e-book *Race Against the Machine,* probably the best short introduction to the subject of automation and jobs. (Though a little too optimistic about the future of humans, I think.) The fact that Paul Krugman is starting to think about this deeply is also good news.

But it's not enough. When the robot revolution finally starts to happen, it's going to happen fast, and it's going to turn our world upside down. It's easy to joke about our future robot overlords—R2-D2 or the Terminator?—but the challenge that machine intelligence presents really isn't science fiction anymore. Like Lake Michigan with an inch of water in it, it's happening around us right now even if it's hard to see. A robotic paradise of leisure and contemplation eventually awaits us, but we have a long and dimly lit tunnel to navigate before we get there.

**Kevin Drum** is a political blogger for *Mother Jones* magazine. He was a blogosphere pioneer when, after a stint in marketing, he went online as Calpundit in 2003. Prior to joining *Mother Jones,* he blogged at the *Washington Monthly's Political Animal.*

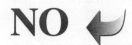
# Positive Impact of Industrial Robots on Employment

## Introduction

### Study Aim

The study analyses the impact of the use of robots in the industrialized production of goods on employment. The study covers years 2000 to 2016.

### Project Scope

The sectors considered are:

1. The large automotive players as well as the component suppliers.
2. Electronics and its interface with specialist plastics [solar cells, photovoltaics etc or other advanced materials], particularly clean rooms [but not the very specialised microchip manufacturing application].
3. Food and beverage, [health, cleanliness and safety*]
4. Plastics [and Rubber] Industry as such, not only in combination with Electronics, Chemicals and Pharmaceuticals, . . .

**Other than the automotive sector, the brief specified that SMEs** (Small and Medium Enterprises) up to 250 employees were specified as the target where possible. By agreement, this has been given less emphasis in the project as there is little available information on the use of robots specifically by smaller companies.

### Industrial Robots Are the Target

Global markets are covered by the economic background data. The study then focused on six key countries. Brazil, China, Germany, Japan, Republic of Korea and USA.

### Method

The project is based largely on analyses of economic data on the six selected countries. This has been combined with the data on Robot use provided by IFR [International Federation of Robotics].

Conclusions were drawn by the Metra Martech team based on economic and industry knowledge. There are considerable gaps in the information available and the main quantifications show orders of magnitude rather than precise numbers. These conclusions have been tested on IFR members in the countries. The testing process involved a two stage set of questions which were responded to by eighteen of these experts. The first question set established the validity of the main assumptions made by Metra Martech; the second was a more detailed set of questions, sent by IFR to selected experts. . . .

## The Economic Factors: And Their Effects on the Use of Robotics

### Displacement and Re-Employment

Where automation displaces people in manufacturing it almost always increases output. In some cases it allows such an increase in production and related decrease in unit price that it creates a whole new market and generates the need for downstream jobs to get the product to the consumer. It releases employees for other, often new jobs outside manufacturing. Historically, this has always been the case.

An alternative view is that this displacement in the future will be more difficult to place, as service robotics may take over many of the new job opportunities in human tasks such as in banking, fast food chains, and retailing petrol forecourts.

What is likely is that the growth of the production, marketing, selling and maintaining of service robots will create the next wave of employment.

The USA has provided a good example, where the total number of people in employment has grown, driven by increase in population, increased participation by women and increased immigrant labour. The long downward trend in manufacturing as a proportion of total employment has been caused by failure to remain competitive in manufacturing as the industrialising countries have grown capacity. . . .

What is driving this trend to fewer employees in manufacturing is that manufacturers have steadily improved manufacturing productivity, largely by increasing the size of production units, automating tasks and sourcing components globally.

. . . [D]oubling use of robots in the past ten years in USA has not affected the trend. By contrast, Germany, which has proportionately many more robots, also doubled the number of robots and has achieved slightly higher growth with almost no reduction in manufacturing employment.

Pressure to increase productivity in the developed countries, has been precipitated by greatly increased competition from overseas manufacturers, and passing of high labour content production to the low labour cost areas.

Pressure to use robotics in the developing countries has been that, despite availability of low cost labour, consistency and accuracy required to compete with or meet the requirements of the developed markets, can sometimes only be achieved by robotics.

Five other economic factors have to be considered:

- Globalisation
- Increasing speed of technology development
- Age and skills profiles
- Wage levels
- Health and safety legislation levels

## Globalisation of the Market

There has been very rapid growth of the very large developing markets of China and India.

These are low labour cost countries and while labour costs can be expected to level up around the world, these two countries are likely to be relatively low cost areas for at least 20 years. The markets are so large that they encourage the development of locally grown research and technology. This means the phase when China, for example, largely produced goods to western specifications is passing.

Two defences that the developed countries have to maintain their wealth creating production capacity [without putting up trade barriers] are:

1. To put more money into research and development. The success of the Frauenhofer Institutes in Germany, and the new 150bn Yen FIRST projects [Funding program for world leading Innovative R&D on Science and Technology] in Japan are examples of this.
2. To reduce dependence on high cost labour by introducing automation when it offers an economic alternative.

## Increasing Speed of Technology Development

This is about the pace of technological development, and the opportunity which this provides for those who can introduce the new technologies. It results in the shortening of product life cycles. Shorter cycles call for more flexible robotics. The product sectors which are the target for this report are not all affected to the same degree by shortening life cycles. Length of production run is an allied factor. Increasing customisation of products, and the flexibility needed by smaller companies are likely to be met by the next generation of robots.

## Age and Skills Profiles

The ageing populations in, for example China, Japan and Germany are often cited as an added reason for adoption of robotics. USA is also affected but to a lesser degree.

A very significant ageing is forecast, but if we consider the workforce, within the timescale of the survey, only Japan is significantly affected, with a projected 5% loss of people of employable age. The German situation will become critical in the following years, but is projected to be less than 2% loss in workforce because of ageing, between now and 2016. Our discussions with robotics experts identify specific problems with ageing workforce in the aerospace sector in USA, but this is outside the scope of the present study.

The existence of skills gaps is reported to be a problem, but this is more a question of education and training regimes than the effect of population ageing.

Several factors are involved in addition to age, the change in population as a whole, the change in people of [currently] employable age, the overall number of people employed and the success of skills training in the country. . . .

## Skills Gaps

Even with increasing levels of technology training around the world, reports on the subject show that skills gaps are occurring. The recession has accelerated this. The idea of a jobless recovery [see extract below] favours investment in productivity rather than people. There is another factor connected to this which is the much greater computer and electronic interface skills of the up and coming generation. They also have higher expectations about the type of work they would like to do.

The problem is more of skills mismatch than overall skills availability. This is a structural training problem rather than a consequence of the ageing population.

- jobs are changing
- educational attainment is lagging. . . .

## Wage Costs and Availability of Low Cost Labour

One of the arguments against robots, contested by the suppliers, is that they are less flexible in operation and demand more up-front investment than the employment of low cost [often immigrant in the developed countries] labour.

The high labour cost sectors are more likely to use robots.

The differences between the countries are large too, although the interpretation of comparative data is often difficult. . . .

## Low Cost Labour

China, and to some extent Brazil, have had access to low cost indigenous labour.

Japan and to a lesser extent Korea have restricted incoming workers.

USA and parts of Europe have until recently allowed this inflow, and both areas have used fewer robots proportionately as a partial result of this, with the exception of Germany. The table shows very large differences in immigration. . . .

## Health, Safety [H&S] and Environment

The increasing attention to these factors adds impetus to the employment of robotics in hazardous environments, or those involving great monotony. In the developed countries, H&S is a steadily advancing area; in the developing countries, progress is very sporadic.

According to the International Labor Organization (ILO), 270 million workers fall victim to occupational injuries and illnesses, leading to 2.3 million deaths annually, showing that the problem is significant.

There is pressure from consumer groups to force manufacturers in developing countries to look after their workers to a standard approaching that achieved by the developed world manufacturers, but progress is slow.

However, no specific new initiatives have been identified in the study so far, which would cause a *step change* in the current trend to gradual improvement of health and safety practices in the six countries being studied. . . .

# Summary

## Overall Rise in Employment

**Overall paid employment has risen in most countries. In the six considered here, only Japan has seen a decline.**

This is driven by increasing participation of women, and increases in population, including immigration in some cases. It is also caused by the increasing demand for services, and the creation of completely new products and markets, often related to the application of electronics to communication.

**The statistics mainly point to reduction in employment in manufacturing in the developed countries, but this is often a small reduction. It coincides with an increase in output and an increase in robotics use except in the case of Japan.**

**The extra number that have gained employment in the years 2000 to 2008 is far greater than the small numbers losing their jobs in manufacturing.**

The new jobs have been in:

1. distribution and services, some of the distribution jobs are the result of manufacturers outsourcing their distribution. In the past these jobs would have been classified as part of manufacturing.
2. and also in new manufacturing applications, particularly using technology advances to create new consumer products [mobile phones, computers, games etc].

**In the industrialising countries, as could be expected, there has been a sharp rise in employment in manufacturing, as well as increase in output.**

Productivity increases are not just caused by automation and robotics, but it is one of three main factors, along with increased size of manufacturing plants and the globalisation of sourcing. *Note: while the IFR numbers provide a clear basis from which to work, it has not always been possible to separate robotics from automation in our analyses.*

**Individual countries differ greatly, the importance of manufacturing is only 11% of employment in USA . . . but 24% in Germany and as high as 27% in more recently industrialising countries such as the Republic of Korea.**

**The level of robotics use has almost always doubled, in all of the six countries [except Japan] in the eight years covered by the study. The proportion of the workforce that is unemployed has hardly changed in this period. . . .**

## Employment *Directly* Due to the Use of Robotics [World]

The robot industry itself generates on the order of 150,000 jobs worldwide, to which can be added the support staff and operators, another 150,000 people.

There are three other types of application where robotics create or preserve jobs. These are jobs which can only be done by robots.

I Where the product cannot be made to satisfactory precision, consistency and cost, without robotics.

II Where the conditions under which the current work is done are unsatisfactory [may be illegal in the developed countries], but where a robot will operate.

III Where [particularly] a developed country manufacturing unit with high labour costs is threatened by a unit in a low labour cost area.

## Employment *Indirectly* Due to the Use of Robotics

A much larger source of employment, at least partly due to robotics, is the newly created downstream activity necessary to support manufacturing which can only be done by robots. We have been conservative in what we have chosen to include here. Some of the people we have spoken to, for example, would have liked us to have included large parts of the automotive sector sales and distribution employment. Our conclusion was that much of this infrastructure was in place before robots were widely used, and so not resulting from the use of robots.

The best example is the communication and leisure equipment business, from distribution to retailing. In the USA, this part of retailing is of the order of 1 million. In world terms this accounts for 3 to 5 million of jobs which would not exist if automation and robotics had not been developed to allow production of millions of electronic products, from phones to Playstations. . . .

*Note that China now produces more cars than USA, but the number of robots used in vehicle manufacture in China is estimated at 28,000 compared with 77,000 in USA.*

*Robot density in a sector only provides a partial view of employment which is dependent on robotics. For example, use of robotics in the automotive sector does not cover all parts of the industry. However, large parts of the motor vehicle assembly sector would be lost to a country if it did not employ robotics. Probably not the components side, this is often highly automated but less likely to depend on robotics.*

*In the electronics sector some components could not be made without robotics, or could not be made at a cost which would sell, which would cause job losses not just in manufacture but downstream as well.*

## Potential for New Job Creation in the Years up to 2016

There are five main areas where new jobs may be created in the next five years by the use of robotics.

I. Continued development of new products based on the development of electronics and communication technology. One of the new areas identified, for example, is the manufacture of service robots. Another is the development and mass adoption of renewable energy technologies.

II. Expansion of existing economies and industries, notably automotive.

III. Greater use of robotics in the SME [small and medium enterprises] sectors, particularly in the developed countries, to protect or win back manufacture from the low cost countries, or to win back production which had been seen as hazardous, but which had been taken up by the developing countries.

IV. Greater use of robotics in the food sector [where current use is low] as processed meals develop, to meet more stringent hygiene conditions.

V. Expansion of the robotics sector itself, to cope with the growth in demand. We have assumed a 15% growth which adds 45,000 people.

## Overall Effect

**Direct employment due to robotics:**

2 to 3 million jobs created in world manufacturing.
Considering the world population of industrial robots at just over 1 million, **that is 2 to 3 jobs per robot in use.**
Indirect employment downstream of this more than doubles this number.
**For the future, 700,000 to 1 million new jobs to be created by robots in the next five years.**

**Peter Gorle** is the managing director of Metra Martech, a firm specializing in industrial and economic analysis for governments and international organizations.

**ANDREW CLIVE** is a senior consultant with Metra Martech, a firm specializing in industrial and economic analysis for governments and international organizations.

# SECTION 5

## Technology and Health

Technological developments and innovation are used in healthcare from birth to preserving life to ending life. The medical process spanning conception to birth may include anything from genetic testing, cesarean section delivery, or sustaining the life of a new baby born too soon or too small. Scientific breakthroughs have allowed people to survive debilitating diseases and defects, providing opportunities for living normal lives, and in some cases prolonging death. Certainly, technology can provide the opportunity to maximize human beings' capabilities. Yet, ethical dilemmas arise from the available medical technologies such as in-vitro fertilization, genetic modifications (designer babies), and euthanasia. Patients can now have more control of their medical care even seeking treatments and medical assistance in other countries, or using telemedicine for appointments. Has this changed the doctor/patient relationship? While new health developments can be beneficial, much controversy surrounds these emerging medical technologies and the possible negative impact on our health. The degree to which technology has changed our healthcare system, our relationships with our bodies, family members, and doctors causes us to contemplate the very complex relationship between man-made advancements and natural systems. The readings in this section raise questions about the direction of our health and healthcare system.

### Learning Objectives

1.  Identify the benefits and drawbacks of technological development on health.
2.  Understand how healthcare has been changed by new technological developments.
3.  Consider the ethical dilemmas presented by medical technological developments.

# Article 26

Carol Gorga Williams

## Virtual Health Care Gaining Ground

Prepared by: Sudip Ghosh, *Penn State University—Berks*

### Learning Outcomes

*After reading this article, you will be able to:*
• Explain how multimedia technology is changing the healthcare industry.
• See the advent of multimedia replacing face-to-face meetings with virtual meetings.

Technology is going to radically change your office visit to the doctor in the years ahead. An "office" may not even be associated with your visit.

You may already have seen the changes: Your doctor allows you to make your next appointment online or when you arrive at your doctor's office, you sign in on an iPad instead of a clipboard. In some states, physicians already conduct office visits via personal communication devices, using Skype, FaceTime, email or text. Eventually, your doctor's visit will go something like this:

Your doctor reviews your test results on his laptop or handheld device in the examining room. As he listens to your concerns, he can access laboratory results from a facility five states away. Then, instead of reaching for that little blue pad to write a prescription, he quickly taps his computer and it is filed digitally to your pharmacy. As you drive home, your cellphone beeps: The pharmacy has alerted you that your prescription is ready. No matter how far technology advances, however, you are still going to wait on line there.

Larry Downs, the chief executive officer of the Medical Society of New Jersey, was just one of many who likened the end result of the electronic revolution in health care to the way the practice of medicine was portrayed on the original "Star Trek" series where Dr. McCoy often worked alone, aided largely by a single small device that could not only diagnose but also treat the patient.

The more radical applications of telemedicine are probably 10 years or more away here, experts say. Telemedicine has evolved more quickly in states and regions that are largely rural where finding a medical specialist is difficult and often involves a lengthy wait for an appointment.

"Some of my patients are already asking, 'Can I have a copy of my blood test today?' and I can print it right out for them," said Dr. John D. Gumina, founding member of the Jersey Shore Monmouth Family Medicine Group and chairman of Jersey Shore University Medical Center's Family Practice department. "I like it because patients are becoming more involved in their care. This is especially true of seniors who like to be kept updated."

The technology will mature very quickly, said those who are on the front lines now.

"We can take into account every patient at risk, and we will have the tools available to tell patients how they are doing," said Dr. Anthony D. Slonim, chief medical officer of Barnabas Health. "They are in the game now."

There are pilot programs that health systems can join. Some pilot programs use special computers that allow physicians in remote locations to take vital signs, have real-time conversations with patients and potentially improve outcomes by having specialists see patients promptly, even over long distances. That, in turn, means a faster, more accurate diagnosis for which treatment can begin more rapidly. Less waiting and fewer duplicate medical tests may mean more economical and less physically intrusive practice of medicine.

Nine states require a special license for the practice of telemedicine. Thirteen states have some form of telemedicine legislation under consideration.

"I think it is timely now," said Mishael Azam, senior manager for legislative services at the Medical Society of New Jersey. "I think people in health care are starting to talk about it. We have the technology now."

## Electronic Data

According to 2012 data from an annual survey by the federal Centers for Disease Control and Prevention, 72 percent of office-based physicians used electronic medical record or electronic health record systems, up from 48 percent in 2009. Such record-keeping use ranged from 54 percent in New Jersey to 89 percent in Massachusetts.

Electronic record-keeping will become almost universally available within the next few years. Physicians face monetary penalties from the federal government if they don't comply. The same is true of electronic prescriptions. Physicians will have no choice. The little blue pads will be history.

With more accessible health care information, physicians will be able to detect health care patterns. Carol Nering, a registered nurse from Toms River, N.J., who has been a longtime patient of Dr. Diane G. Verga, said the electronic medical record has its pluses and minuses.

"I personally am a little uncomfortable with it because I know anyone can hack into a computer," said Nering, 78. "I don't think you are really secure with" the way the information is stored and protected.

Still, Nering said, "in the computer, the information is easily read and that saves time, and unfortunately, in some instances, time is of the essence."

## What About Malpractice?

While many physicians say it will probably reduce costs over the long term, one component of telemedicine practice still is the focus of debate and study. With telemedicine crossing state lines and with medical licenses still very much up to the states, how will questions of malpractice be handled?

"As the use of telemedicine grows, malpractice claims relating to telemedicine services may increase and, if so, these complications are likely to create a new body of law," the University of Maryland School of Law concluded in 2010. "As the specter of telemedicine-related claims grows, the professional liability industry is studying how to write and price medical malpractice policies for telemedicine practitioners."

The issue is complex. Telemedicine crosses state lines. Which state would have jurisdiction? Should a physician be held to the same standard of care as in face-to-face appointments? If a case goes bad, is the physician responsible or is it a failure of the technology as in the case of a lost Internet connection? Should telemedicine be its own category of malpractice law? What about informed consent from patients?

At this intersection of the age-old practice of medicine and the rapid development of technology, how malpractice and negligence questions will shake out is anyone's guess, the law school study summarized.

## Technology's Help

But what does not seem to be in question is whether telemedicine can help make sick people better. The federal Department of Health and Human Services Office of Health Information Technology—which is overseeing the digital transformation of health care—says the medical applications of telemedicine helps patients, especially those who prefer to stay in their homes as they battle chronic conditions. And the government says the evidence demonstrates the quality of telemedicine.

Technology appears to help mitigate human error, which kills about 98,000 people every year, according to the American Association for Justice, a trial-lawyers' consumer group. The U.S. Department of Health and Human Services said 64 percent of physicians using electronic health record software properly were alerted to potential medication errors while 62 percent of physicians were informed of a critical laboratory test finding, thanks to the software.

Telemedicine, digital doctoring, telehealth, e-health, cybermedicine—whatever it'll be called—is appealing to physicians and their patients as insurers become more supportive. When Medicare pays, private insurers typically follow suit, and Medicare is authorizing reimbursement of telemedicine in limited ways, officials said.

"People are going to be seen by their doctor, either there or through a digital application," said Dr. Paul Katz, founding dean of Cooper Medical School of Rowan University in Camden, N.J. "Now we must figure out a way to manage it, a way that is not excessive and unnecessary."

## Critical Thinking

1. How does virtual meeting allow for reducing costs?
2. Is telemedicine the way to go for remote and rural areas?
3. How can we engage the consumer in telemedicine?

## Create Central

www.mhhe.com/createcentral

## Internet References

www.news-medical.net/health/What-is-Telemedicine.aspx
www.healthcareitnews.com/news/st-louis-virtual-care-center-expand-telehealth-jobs
www.modernhealthcare.com/article/20130410/NEWS/304109960
http://usatoday30.usatoday.com/money/industries/health/story/2012-04-27/virtual-doctors-telemedicine/54791506/1
http://health.usnews.com/health-news/articles/2012/07/24/pros-and-cons-of-telemedicine-for-todays-workers

# Why We Need Innovation to Prepare
# for the Global Aging Society

A startling new United Nations Population Fund report projects that in 2050 there will be more people over the age of 60 than those under 15. Put another way, there will be more pensioners than children by 2050. In just 10 years from today, there will be 1 billion people in this age group. These numbers suggest that the elderly will soon become a major burden on society. The challenge, however, is finding ways that turn the elderly into an asset by seeing them as sources of innovation.

According to *Ageing in the Twenty-first Century: A Celebration and a Challenge,* governments will need to adopt a wide range of policies and laws aimed at supporting the elderly and protecting them against discrimination. Japan is currently the only nation in the world where people aged 60 or over represent more than 30% of the population. The report says that by "2050, there will be 64 countries where older people make up more than 30 per cent of their population."

So far much of the policy debate on aging has focused on developed countries. But according to the report, today almost "two in three people aged 60 or over live in developing countries, and by 2050, nearly four in five will live in the developing world."

United Nations Secretary-General Ban Ki-moon notes that "the social and economic implications of this phenomenon are profound, extending far beyond the individual older person and the immediate family, touching broader society and the global community in unprecedented ways."

The report stresses the importance of adopting policies that provide income security, access to quality health care, and a supporting legal environment for the elderly.

Advances in science and technology play an important part in addressing the challenges of aging. However, the report acknowledges that "the application of advances in medical technology to support older persons is often uneven across age groups." For example, a "study in Sweden found that the use of such technology is initially restricted to the younger old and is gradually extended to older age groups."

The role of innovation in addressing the aging challenge is already attracting the attention of governments. Denmark, for example, has embarked on an aggressive program to develop what it calls "welfare technologies" partly in response to the challenges of its aging population. The Southern Denmark region, which accounts for 22% of the national population and 20% of GDP, is the home of a new Welfare Tech Region (WTR). The region is currently promoting pioneering medical technology that enables hospitals to move medical care to homes while providing quality care.

A start-up company, Medisat, has developed a briefcase that allows doctors to discharge patients early and monitor them from their homes. The Patient Briefcase "is a laptop-sized device with a built-in screen and microphone but no keys except a single call button. The device allowed the patient and doctor to see and talk with each other in real time over an Internet or satellite connection," according to a Harvard Kennedy School (HKS) case written on the initiative. Furthermore, the HKS case explains that the Patient Briefcase "was designed so that medical devices such as spirometers and scales could be plugged into it, allowing a doctor, working from a specially modified telemedicine workstation, to remotely read and monitor patients' blood pressure, lung function, heart electrical activity."

By 2012, "the Patient Briefcase had been used to treat 933 Odense and Svendborg hospital COPD patients in their own home that the company said corresponded to 9,317 acute telemedicine treatments. Because doctors at the hospitals were able to monitor patients at home, their patients' hospital stays were reduced from 7 days to 24 hours," according to the HKS study. In 2010, the Patient Briefcase was introduced in Norway and in the UK in 2012. The WTR is now looking into marketing the technology worldwide.

The case of Southern Denmark demonstrates that hospitals, universities, and municipal authorities can work together to develop new technologies that directly respond to the needs of elderly populations. This will require a confluence of a wide range of approaches from engineering (electronics, robotics and ergonomics) and medical fields.

Technologies such as the Patient Briefcase could also be deployed in regions without adequate medical care. In fact, mobile technologies are being adapted to support medical needs in developing countries. Hand-held ultra-sound devices and other diagnostic techniques are being developed for use in remote areas.

Deployment of broadband technology in developing countries also provides new avenues for telemedicine. With additional support from robotic surgery, new technologies offer the prospects of designing new health care systems that address the needs of the elderly while lowering costs.

Technology alone will not be adequate to address the needs of the elderly. But policy proposals that fail to take into account advances in medicine and engineering are unlikely to take advantage of human creativity. In fact, strategies that put the elderly at the center of the innovation process could significantly increase the prospects of turning the elderly from being a burden on society to being an asset.

**Calestous Juma** is professor of the practice of international development and director of the Science, Technology, and Globalization Project at the Harvard Kennedy School of Government. He formerly served as executive secretary of the UN Convention on Biological Diversity.

Julian Savulescu

## Genetic Interventions and the Ethics
## of Enhancement of Human Beings

Should we use science and medical technology not just to prevent or treat disease, but to intervene at the most basic biological levels to improve biology and enhance people's lives? By 'enhance', I mean help them to live a longer and/or better life than normal. There are various ways in which we can enhance people but I want to focus on biological enhancement, especially genetic enhancement.

There has been considerable recent debate on the ethics of human enhancement. A number of prominent authors have been concerned about or critical of the use of technology to alter or enhance human beings, citing threats to human nature and dignity as one basis for these concerns. The President's Council Report entitled *Beyond Therapy* was strongly critical of human enhancement. Michael Sandel, in a widely discussed article, has suggested that the problem with genetic enhancement

> is in the hubris of the designing parents, in their drive to master the mystery of birth . . . it would disfigure the
> relation between parent and child, and deprive the parent of the humility and enlarged human sympathies that
> an openness to the unbidden can cultivate. . . . [T]he promise of mastery is flawed. It threatens to banish our
> appreciation of life as a gift, and to leave us with nothing to affirm or behold outside our own will. (Sandel 2004)

Frances Kamm has given a detailed rebuttal of Sandel's arguments, arguing that human enhancement is permissible. Nicholas Agar, in his book *Liberal Eugenics*, argues that enhancement should be permissible but not obligatory. He argues that what distinguishes liberal eugenics from the objectionable eugenic practices of the Nazis is that it is not based on a single conception of a desirable genome and that it is voluntary and not obligatory.

In this chapter I will take a more provocative position. I want to argue that, far from its being merely permissible, we have a moral obligation or moral reason to enhance ourselves and our children. Indeed, we have the same kind of obligation as we have to treat and prevent disease. Not only *can* we enhance, we *should* enhance.

I will begin by considering the current interests in and possibilities of enhancement. I will then offer three arguments that we have very strong reasons to seek to enhance.

Tom Murray concludes 'Enhancement' by arguing that 'the ethics of enhancement must take into account the meaning and purpose of the activities being enhanced, their social context, and the other persons and institutions affected by them' (Murray, 2007: 514). Such caution is no doubt well grounded. But it should not blind us to the very large array of cases in which biological modification will improve the opportunities of an individual to lead a better life. In such cases, we have strong reasons to modify ourselves and our children. Indeed, to fail to do so would be wrong. Discussion of enhancement can be muddied by groundless fears and excessive caution and qualification. I will outline some ethical constraints on the pursuit of enhancement.

## CURRENT INTEREST IN ENHANCEMENT

There is great public interest in enhancement of people. Women employ cosmetic surgery to make their noses smaller, their breasts larger, their teeth straighter and whiter, to make their cheekbones higher, their lips fuller, and to remove wrinkles and fat. Men, too, employ many of these measures, as well as pumping their bodies with steroids to increase muscle bulk. The beauty industry is testimony to the attraction of enhancement. Body art, such as painting and tattooing, and body modification, such as piercing, have, since time began, represented ways in which humans have attempted to express their creativity, values, and symbolic attachments through changing their bodies.

Modern professional sport is often said to be corrupted by widespread use of performance-enhancing drugs, such as human erythropoietin, anabolic steroids, and growth hormone. However, some effective performance enhancements are

From *The Oxford Handbook of Bioethics*, edited by Bonnie Steinbock (2007), Ch. 22: 516–535. Reprinted with permission of the author and Oxford University Press.
*Editors' note*: Most references have been cut. Students who want to follow up on sources should consult the original article.

permitted in sport, such as the use of caffeine, glutamine, and creatine in diets, salbutamol, hypoxic air tents, and altitude training. Many people attempt to improve their cognitive powers through the use of nicotine, caffeine, and drugs like Ritalin and Modavigil.

Mood enhancement typifies modern society. People use psychological 'self-help', Prozac, recreational drugs, and alcohol to feel more relaxed, socialize better, and feel happier.

Even in the most private area of sexual relations, many want to be better. Around 34 percent of all men aged 40–70—around 20 million in the United States—have some erectile dysfunction, which is a part of normal ageing. There is a 12 percent decline in erectile function every decade normally. As a result, 20 million men worldwide use Viagra (Cheitlin *et al.* 1999).

More radical forms of biological enhancement appear possible. Even if all disease (heart disease, cancer, etc.) were cured, the average human lifespan would only be extended by twelve years. However, stem cell science has the potential to extend human lifespan radically further than this, by replacing ageing tissue with healthy tissue. We could live longer than the current maximum of 120 years.

But instead of the radical prolongation of length of life, I want to focus on the radical improvement in quality of life through biological manipulation. Some sceptics believe that this is not possible. They claim that it is our environment, or culture, that defines us, not genetics. But a quiet walk in the park demonstrates the power of a great genetic experiment: dogbreeding. It is obvious that different breeds of dog differ in temperament, intelligence, physical ability, and appearance. No matter what the turf, a Dobermann will tear a corgi to pieces. You can debilitate a Dobermann through neglect and abuse. And you can make him prettier with a bow. But you will never turn a chihuahua into a Dobermann through grooming, training, and affection. Dog breeds are all genetic—for over 10,000 years we have bred some 300–400 breeds of dog from early canids and wolves. The St Bernard is known for its size, the greyhound for its speed, the bloodhound for its sense of smell. There are freaks, hard workers, vicious aggressors, docile pets, and ornamental varieties. These characteristics have been developed by a crude form of genetic selection—selective mating or breeding.

Today we have powerful scientific tools in animal husbandry: genetic testing, artificial reproduction, and cloning are all routinely used in the farming industry to create the best stock. Scientists are now starting to look at a wider range of complex behaviours. Changing the brain's reward centre genetically may be the key to changing behaviour.

Gene therapy has been used to turn lazy monkeys into workaholics by altering the reward centre in the brain. In another experiment, researchers used gene therapy to introduce a gene from the monogamous male prairie vole, a rodent that forms lifelong bonds with one mate, into the brain of the closely related but polygamous meadow vole. Genetically modified meadow voles became monogamous, behaving like prairie voles. This gene, which controls a part of the brain's reward centre different from that altered in the monkeys, is known as the vasopressin receptor gene. It may also be involved in human drug addiction.

Radical enhancements may come on the back of very respected research to prevent and treat disease. Scientists have created a rat model of the genetic disease Huntington's Chorea. This disease results in progressive rapid dementia at the age of about 40. Scientists found that rats engineered to develop Huntington's Chorea who were placed in a highly stimulating environment (of mazes, coloured rings, and balls) did not go on to develop the disease—their neurons remained intact. Remotivation therapy improves functioning in humans, suggesting that environmental stimulation in this genetic disease may affect brain biology at the molecular level (by altering neurotrophins). Prozac has also been shown to produce a beneficial effect in humans suffering from Huntington's Chorea. Neural stem cells have also been identified that could potentially be induced to proliferate and differentiate, mediated through nerve growth factors and other factors. We now know that a stimulating environment, drugs like Prozac, and nerve growth factors can affect nerve proliferation and connections—that is our brain's biology. These same interventions could, at least in theory, be used to increase the neuronal complement of normal brains and increase cognitive performance in normal individuals.

IQ has been steadily increasing since first measured, about twenty points per decade. This has been called the Flynn effect. Large environmental effects have been postulated to account for this effect. The capacity to increase IQ is significant. Direct biological enhancement could have an equal if not greater effect on increase in IQ.

But could biological enhancement of human beings really be possible? Selective mating has been occurring in humans ever since time began. Facial asymmetry can reflect genetic disorder. Smell can tell us whether our mate will produce the child with the best resistance to disease. We compete for partners in elaborate mating games and rituals of display that sort the best matches from the worst. As products of evolution, we select our mates, both rationally and instinctively, on the basis of their genetic fitness—their ability to survive and reproduce. Our (subconscious) goal is the success of our offspring.

With the tools of genetics, we can select offspring in a more reliable way. The power of genetics is growing. Embryos can now be tested not only for the presence of genetic disorder (including some forms of bowel and breast cancer), but also for less serious genetic abnormalities, such as dental abnormalities. Sex can be tested for too. Adult athletes have been genetically tested for the presence of the ACTN3 gene to identify potential for either sprint or endurance events. Research is going on in the field of behavioural genetics to understand the genetic basis of aggression and criminal behaviour, alcoholism, anxiety, antisocial personality disorder, maternal behaviour, homosexuality, and neuroticism.

While at present there are no genetic tests for these complex behaviours, if the results of recent animal studies into hard work and monogamy apply to humans, it may be possible in the future to change genetically how we are predisposed to behave. This raises a new question: Should we try to engineer better, happier people? While at present genetic technology is most efficient at selecting among different embryos, in the future it will be possible to genetically alter existing embryos, with considerable progress already being made to the use of this technology for permanent gene therapy for disease. There is no reason why such technology could not be used to alter non-disease genes in the future.

# THE ETHICS OF ENHANCEMENT

We want to be happy people, not just healthy people.

I will now give three arguments in favour of enhancement and then consider several objections.

## First Argument for Enhancement: Choosing Not to Enhance Is Wrong

Consider the case of the Neglectful Parents. The Neglectful Parents give birth to a child with a special condition. The child has a stunning intellect but requires a simple, readily available, cheap dietary supplement to sustain his intellect. But they neglect the diet of this child and this results in a child with a stunning intellect becoming normal. This is clearly wrong.

But now consider the case of the Lazy Parents. They have a child who has a normal intellect but if they introduced the same dietary supplement, the child's intellect would rise to the same level as the child of the Neglectful Parent. They can't be bothered with improving the child's diet so the child remains with a normal intellect. Failure to institute dietary supplementation means a normal child fails to achieve a stunning intellect. The inaction of the Lazy Parents is as wrong as the inaction of the Neglectful Parents. It has exactly the same consequence: a child exists who could have had a stunning intellect but is instead normal.

Some argue that it is not wrong to fail to bring about the best state of affairs. This may or may not be the case. But in these kinds of case, when there are no other relevant moral considerations, the failure to introduce a diet that sustains a more desirable state is as wrong as the failure to introduce a diet that brings about a more desirable state. The costs of inaction are the same, as are the parental obligations.

If we substitute 'biological intervention' for 'diet', we see that in order not to wrong our children, we should enhance them. Unless there is something special and optimal about our children's physical, psychological, or cognitive abilities, or something different about other biological interventions, it would be wrong not to enhance them.

## Second Argument: Consiste

Some will object that, while we do have an obligation to institute better diets, biological interventions like genetic interventions are different from dietary supplementation. I will argue that there is no difference between these interventions.

In general, we accept environmental interventions to improve our children. Education, diet, and training are all used to make our children better people and increase their opportunities in life. We train children to be well behaved, cooperative, and intelligent. Indeed, researchers are looking at ways to make the environment more stimulating for young children to maximize their intellectual development. But in the study of the rat model of Huntington's Chorea, the stimulating environment acted to change the brain structure of the rats. The drug Prozac acted in just the same way. These environmental manipulations do not act mysteriously. They alter our biology.

The most striking example of this is a study of rats that were extensively mothered and rats that were not mothered. The mothered rats showed genetic changes (changes in the methylation of the DNA) that were passed on to the next generation. As Michael Meaney has observed, 'Early experience can actually modify protein–DNA interactions that regulate gene expression' (Society for Neuroscience 2004). More generally, environmental manipulations can profoundly affect biology. Maternal care and stress have been associated with abnormal brain (hippocampal) development, involving altered nerve growth factors and cognitive, psychological, and immune deficits later in life.

Some argue that genetic manipulations are different because they are irreversible. But environmental interventions can equally be irreversible. Child neglect or abuse can scar a person for life. It may be impossible to unlearn the skill of playing the piano or riding a bike, once learnt. One may be wobbly, but one is a novice only once. Just as the example of mothering of rats shows that environmental interventions can cause biological changes that are passed onto the next generation, so too can environmental interventions be irreversible, or very difficult to reverse, within one generation.

Why should we allow environmental manipulations that alter our biology but not direct biological manipulations? What is the moral difference between producing a smarter child by immersing that child in a stimulating environment, giving the child a drug, or directly altering the child's brain or genes?

One example of a drug that alters brain chemistry is Prozac, which is a serotonin reuptake inhibitor. Early in life it acts as a nerve growth factor, but it may also alter the brain early in life to make it more prone to stress and anxiety later in life by altering receptor development. People with a polymorphism that reduced their serotonin activity were more likely than others to become depressed in response to stressful experiences. Drugs like Prozac and maternal deprivation may have the same biological effects.

If the outcome is the same, why treat biological manipulation differently from environmental manipulation? Not only may a favourable environment improve a child's biology and increase a child's opportunities, so too may direct biological interventions. Couples should maximize the genetic opportunity of their children to lead a good life and a productive, cooperative social existence. There is no relevant moral difference between environmental and genetic intervention.

## Third Argument: No Difference from Treating Disease

If we accept the treatment and prevention of disease, we should accept enhancement. The goodness of health is what drives a moral obligation to treat or prevent disease. But health is not what ultimately matters—health enables us to live well; disease prevents us from doing what we want and what is good. Health is instrumentally valuable—valuable as a resource that allows us to do what really matters, that is, lead a good life.

What constitutes a good life is a deep philosophical question. According to hedonistic theories, what is good is having pleasant experiences and being happy. According to desire fulfilment theories, and economics, what matters is having our preferences satisfied. According to objective theories, certain activities are good for people: developing deep personal relationships, developing talents, understanding oneself and the world, gaining knowledge, being a part of a family, and so on. We need not decide on which of these theories is correct in order to understand what is bad about ill health. Disease is important because it causes pain, is not what we want, and stops us engaging in those activities that giving meaning to life. Sometimes people trade health for well-being: mountain climbers take on risk to achieve, smokers sometimes believe that the pleasures outweigh the risks of smoking, and so on. Life is about managing risk to health and life to promote well-being.

Beneficence—the moral obligation to benefit people—provides a strong reason to enhance people in so far as the biological enhancement increases their chance of having a better life. But can biological enhancements increase people's opportunities for well-being? There are reasons to believe that they might.

Many of our biological and psychological characteristics profoundly affect how well our lives go. In the 1960s Walter Mischel conducted impulse control experiments in which 4-year-old children were left in a room with one marshmallow, after being told that if they did not eat the marshmallow, they could later have two. Some children would eat it as soon as the researcher left; others would use a variety of strategies to help control their behaviour and ignore the temptation of the single marshmallow. A decade later they reinterviewed the children and found that those who were better at delaying gratification had more friends, better academic performance, and more motivation to succeed. Whether the child had grabbed for the marshmallow had a much stronger bearing on their SAT scores than did their IQ.

Impulse control has also been linked to socioeconomic control and avoiding conflict with the law. The problems of a hot and uncontrollable temper can be profound. Shyness too can greatly restrict a life. I remember one newspaper story about a woman who blushed violet every time she went into a social situation. This led her to a hermitic, miserable existence. She eventually had the autonomic nerves to her face surgically cut. This revolutionized her life and had a greater effect on her well-being than the treatment of many diseases.

Buchanan and colleagues have discussed the value of 'all purpose goods'. These are traits that are valuable regardless of the kind of life a person chooses to live. They give us greater all-round capacities to live a vast array of lives. Examples include intelligence, memory, self-discipline, patience, empathy, a sense of humour, optimism, and just having a sunny temperament. All of these characteristics—sometimes described as virtues—may have some biological and psychological basis capable of manipulation using technology.

Technology might even be used to improve our moral character. We certainly seek through good instruction and example, discipline, and other methods to make better children. It may be possible to alter biology to make people predisposed to be more moral by promoting empathy, imagination, sympathy, fairness, honesty, etc. In so far as these characteristics have some genetic basis, genetic manipulation could benefit us. There is reason to believe that complex virtues like fair-mindedness may have a biological basis. In one famous experiment a monkey was trained to perform a task and rewarded with either a grape or a piece of cucumber. He preferred the grape. On one occasion he performed the task successfully and was given a piece of cucumber. He watched as another monkey who had not performed the task was given a grape and he became very angry. This shows that even monkeys have a sense of fairness and desert—or at least self-interest!

At the other end, there are characteristics that we believe do not make for a good and happy life. One Dutch family illustrates the extreme end of the spectrum. For over thirty years this family recognized that there were a disproportionate number of male family members who exhibited aggressive and criminal behaviour. This was characterized by aggressive outbursts resulting in arson, attempted rape, and exhibitionism. The behaviour was documented for almost forty years by an unaffected maternal grandfather, who could not understand why some of the men in his family appeared to be prone to this type of behaviour. Male relatives who did not display this aggressive behaviour did not express *any* type of abnormal behaviour. Unaffected males reported difficulty in understanding the behaviour of their brothers and cousins. Sisters of the males who demonstrated these extremely aggressive outbursts reported intense fear of their brothers. The behaviour did not appear to be related to environment and appeared consistently in different parts of the family, regardless of social context and degree of social contact. All affected males were also found to be mildly mentally retarded, with a typical IQ of about 85 (females had normal intelligence) (Brunner 1993*a*). When a family tree was constructed, the pattern of inheritance was clearly X-linked recessive. This means, roughly, that women can carry the gene without being affected; 50 percent of men at risk of inheriting the gene get the gene and are affected by the disease.

Genetic analysis suggested that the likely defective gene was a part of the X chromosome known as the monoamine oxidase region. This region codes for two enzymes that assist in the breakdown of neurotransmitters. Neurotransmitters are substances that play a key role in the conduction of nerve impulses in our brain. Enzymes like the monoamine oxidases are required to degrade the neurotransmitters after they have performed their desired task. It was suggested that the monoamine oxidase activity might be disturbed in the affected individuals. Urine analysis showed a higher than normal amount of neurotransmitters being excreted in the urine of affected males. These results were consistent with a reduction in the functioning of one of the enzymes (monoamine oxidase A).

How can such a mutation result in violent and antisocial behaviour? A deficiency of the enzyme results in a build-up of neurotransmitters. These abnormal levels of neurotransmitters result in excessive, and even violent, reactions to stress. This hypothesis was further supported by the finding that genetically modified mice that lack this enzyme are more aggressive.

This family is an extreme example of how genes can influence behaviour: it is the only family in which this mutation has been isolated. Most genetic contributions to behaviour will be weaker predispositions, but there may be some association between genes and behaviour that results in criminal and other antisocial behaviour.

How could information such as this be used? Some criminals have attempted a 'genetic defence' in the United States, stating that their genes caused them to commit the crime, but this has never succeeded. However, it is clear that couples should be allowed to test to select offspring who do not have the mutation that predisposes them to act in this way, and if interventions were available, it might be rational to correct it since children without the mutation have a good chance of a better life.

'Genes, Not Men, May Hold the Key to Female Pleasure' ran the title of one recent newspaper article (*The Age* 2005), which reported the results of a large study of female identical twins in Britain and Australia. It found that 'genes accounted for 31 percent of the chance of having an orgasm during intercourse and 51 percent during masturbation'. It concluded that the 'ability to gain sexual satisfaction is largely inherited' and went on to speculate that 'The genes involved could be linked to physical differences in sex organs and hormone levels or factors such as mood and anxiety.'

Our biology profoundly affects how our lives go. If we can increase sexual satisfaction by modifying biology, we should. Indeed, vast numbers of men attempt to do this already through the use of Viagra.

## Summary: The Case for Enhancement

What matters is human well-being, not just treatment and prevention of disease. Our biology affects our opportunities to live well. The biological route to improvement is no different from the environmental. Biological manipulation to increase opportunity is ethical. If we have an obligation to treat and prevent disease, we have an obligation to try to manipulate these characteristics to give an individual the best opportunity of the best life.

# How do we decide?

If we are to enhance certain qualities, how should we decide which to choose? Eugenics was the movement early in the last century that aimed to use selective breeding to prevent degeneration of the gene pool by weeding out criminals, those with mental illness, and the poor, on the false belief that these conditions were simple genetic disorders. The eugenics movement had its inglorious peak when the Nazis moved beyond sterilization to extermination of the genetically unfit.

What was objectionable about the eugenics movement, besides its shoddy scientific basis, was that it involved the imposition of a state vision for a healthy population and aimed to achieve this through coercion. The movement was aimed not at what was good for individuals, but rather at what benefited society. Modern eugenics in the form of testing for disorders, such as Down syndrome, occurs very commonly but is acceptable because it is voluntary, gives couples a choice of what kind of child to have, and enables them to have a child with the greatest opportunity for a good life.

There are four possible ways in which our genes and biology will be decided:

1. nature or God;
2. 'experts' (philosophers, bioethicists, psychologists, scientists);
3. 'authorities' (government, doctors);
4. people themselves: liberty and autonomy.

It is a basic principle of liberal states like the United Kingdom that the state be 'neutral' to different conceptions of the good life. This means that we allow individuals to lead the life that they believe is best for themselves, implying respect for their personal autonomy or capacity for self-rule. The sole ground for interference is when that individual choice may harm others. Advice, persuasion, information, dialogue are permissible. But coercion and infringement of liberty are impermissible.

There are limits to what a liberal state should provide:

1. safety: the intervention should be reasonably safe;
2. harm to others: the intervention (like some manipulation that increases uncontrollable aggressiveness) should not result in harm. Such harm should not be direct or indirect, for example, by causing some unfair competitive advantage;
3. distributive justice: the interventions should be distributed according to principles of justice.

The situation is more complex with young children, embryos, and fetuses, who are incompetent. These human beings are not autonomous and cannot make choices themselves about whether a putative enhancement is a benefit or a harm. If a proposed intervention can be delayed until that human reaches maturity and can decide for himself or herself, then the intervention should be delayed. However, many genetic interventions will have to be performed very early in life if they are to have an effect. Decisions about such interventions should be left to parents, according to a principle of procreative liberty and autonomy. This states that parents have the freedom to choose when to have children, how many children to have, and arguably what kind of children to have.

Just as parents have wide scope to decide on the conditions of the upbringing of their children, including schooling and religious education, they should have similar freedom over their children's genes. Procreative autonomy or liberty should be extended to enhancement for two reasons. Firstly, reproduction: bearing and raising children is a very private matter. Parents must bear much of the burden of having children, and they have a legitimate stake in the nature of the child they must invest so much of their lives raising.

But there is a second reason. John Stuart Mill argued that when our actions only affect ourselves, we should be free to construct and act on our own conception of what is the best life for us. Mill was not a libertarian. He did not believe that such freedom is valuable solely for its own sake. He believed that freedom is important in order for people to discover for themselves what kind of life is best for themselves. It is only through 'experiments in living' that people discover what works for them and others come to see the richness and variety of lives that can be good. Mill strongly praised 'originality' and variety in choice as being essential to discovering which lives are best for human beings.

Importantly, Mill believed that some lives are worse than others. Famously, he said that it is better to be Socrates dissatisfied than a fool satisfied. He distinguished between 'higher pleasures' of 'feelings and imagination' and 'lower pleasures' of 'mere sensation' (Mill 1910: 7). He criticized 'apelike imitation', subjugation of oneself to custom and fashion, indifference to individuality, and lack of originality (1910: 119–20, 123). Nonetheless, he was the champion of people's right to live their lives as they choose.

I have said that it is important to give the freest rein possible to things that are not customary, in order that it may in time transpire which of them are fit to become customary. But independence of action and disregard of custom are not deserving of encouragement solely for the chance they afford for better modes of action, and customs more worthy of general adoption, to be discovered; nor is it only people of decided mental superiority who have a just claim to carry on their lives in their own way. There is no reason for all human existence to be constructed on some single or small number of patterns. If a person possesses a tolerable amount of common sense and experience, his own mode of designing his existence is the best, not because it is the best in itself, but because it is his own mode.

I believe that reproduction should be about having children with the best prospects. But to discover what are the best prospects, we must give individual couples the freedom to act on their own judgment of what constitutes a life with good prospects. 'Experiments in reproduction' are as important as 'experiments in living' (as long as they don't harm the children who are produced). For this reason, procreative freedom is important.

There is one important limit to procreative autonomy that is different from the limits to personal autonomy. The limits to procreative autonomy should be:

1. safety;
2. harm to others;
3. distributive justice;
4. *such that the parent's choices are based on a plausible conception of well-being and a better life for the child;*
5. *consistent with development of autonomy in the child and a reasonable range of future life plans.*

These last two limits are important. It makes for a higher standard of 'proof' that an intervention will be an enhancement because the parents are making choices for their child, not themselves. The critical question to ask in considering whether to alter some gene related to complex behaviour is: Would the change be better for the individual? Is it better for the individual to have a tendency to be lazy or hardworking, monogamous or polygamous? These questions are difficult to answer. While we might let adults choose to be monogamous or polygamous, we would not let parents decide on their child's predispositions unless we were reasonably clear that some trait was better for the child.

There will be cases where some intervention is plausibly in a child's interests: increased empathy with other people, better capacity to understand oneself and the world around, or improved memory. One quality is especially associated with socio-economic success and staying out of prison: impulse control. If it were possible to correct poor impulse control, we should correct it. Whether we should remove impulsiveness altogether is another question.

Joel Feinberg has described a child's right to an open future (Feinberg 1980). An open future is one in which a child has a reasonable range of possible lives to choose from and an opportunity to choose what kind of person to be; that is, to develop autonomy. Some critics of enhancement have argued that genetic interventions are inconsistent with a child's right to an open future. Far from restricting a child's future, however, some biological interventions may increase the possible futures or at least their quality. It is hard to see how improved memory or empathy would restrict a child's future. Many worthwhile possibilities would be open. But it is true that parental choice should not restrict the development of autonomy or reasonable range of possible futures open to a child. In general, fewer enhancements will be permitted in children than in adults. Some interventions, however, may still be clearly enhancements for our children, and so just like vaccinations or other preventative health care.

# Objections

## Playing God or Against Nature

This objection has various forms. Some people in society believe that children are a gift, of God or of nature, and that we should not interfere in human nature. Most people implicitly reject this view: we screen embryos and fetuses for diseases, even mild correctable disease. We interfere in nature or God's will when we vaccinate, provide pain relief to women in labour (despite objections of some earlier Christians that these practices thwarted God's will), and treat cancer. No one would object to the treatment of disability in a child if it were possible. Why, then, not treat the embryo with genetic therapy if that intervention is safe? This is no more thwarting God's will than giving antibiotics.

Another variant of this objection is that we are arrogant if we assume we could have sufficient knowledge to meddle with human nature. Some people object that we cannot know the complexity of the human system, which is like an unknowable magnificent symphony. To attempt to enhance one characteristic may have other unknown, unforeseen effects elsewhere in the system. We should not play God since, unlike God, we are not omnipotent or omniscient. We should be humble and recognize the limitations of our knowledge.

A related objection is that genes are pleiotropic—which means they have different effects in different environments. The gene or genes that predispose to manic depression may also be responsible for heightened creativity and productivity.

One response to both of these objections is to limit intervention, until our knowledge grows, to selecting between different embryos, and not intervening to enhance particular embryos or people. Since we would be choosing between complete systems on the basis of their type, we would not be interfering with the internal machinery. In this way, selection is less risky than enhancement.

But such a precaution could also be misplaced when considering biological interventions. When benefits are on offer, such objections remind us to refrain from hubris and over-confidence. We must do adequate research before intervening. And because the benefits may be fewer than when we treat or prevent disease, we may require the standards of safety to be higher than for medical interventions. But we must weigh the risks against the benefits. If confidence is justifiably high, and benefits outweigh harms, we should enhance.

Once technology affords us the power to enhance our own and our children's lives, to fail to do so would be to be responsible for the consequences. To fail to treat our children's diseases is to wrong them. To fail to prevent them from getting depression is to wrong them. To fail to improve their physical, musical, psychological, and other capacities is to wrong them, just as it would be to harm them if we gave them a toxic substance that stunted or reduced these capacities.

Another variant of the 'Playing God' objection is that there is a special value in the balance and diversity that natural variation affords, and enhancement will reduce this. But in so far as we are products of evolution, we are merely random chance variations of genetic traits selected for our capacity to survive long enough to reproduce. There is no design to evolution. Evolution selects genes, according to environment, that confer the greatest chance of survival and reproduction. Evolution would select a tribe that was highly fertile but suffered great pain the whole of their lives over another tribe that was less fertile but suffered less pain. Medicine has changed evolution: we can now select individuals who experience less pain and disease. The next stage of human evolution will be rational evolution, according to which we select children who not only have the greatest chance of surviving, reproducing, and being free of disease, but who have the greatest opportunities to have the best lives in their likely environment. Evolution was indifferent to how well our lives went; we are not. We want to retire, play golf, read, and watch our grandchildren have children.

'Enhancement' is a misnomer. It suggests luxury. But enhancement is no luxury. In so far as it promotes well-being, it is the very essence of what is necessary for a good human life. There is no moral reason to preserve some traits—such as uncontrollable aggressiveness, a sociopathic personality, or extreme deviousness. Tell the victim of rape and murder that we must preserve diversity and the natural balance.

## Genetic Discrimination

Some people fear the creation of a two-tier society of the enhanced and the unenhanced, where the inferior, unenhanced are discriminated against and disadvantaged all through life. We must remember that nature allots advantage and disadvantage with no gesture to fairness. Some are born terribly disadvantaged, destined to die after short and miserable lives. Some suffer great genetic disadvantage while others are born gifted, physically, musically, or intellectually. There is no secret that there are 'gifted' children naturally. Allowing choice to change our biology will, if anything, be more egalitarian, allowing the ungifted to approach the gifted. There is nothing fair about the natural lottery: allowing enhancement may be fairer.

But more importantly, how well the lives of those who are disadvantaged go depends not on whether enhancement is permitted, but on the social institutions we have in place to protect the least well off and provide everyone with a fair chance. People have disease and disability: egalitarian social institutions and laws against discrimination are designed to make sure everyone, regardless of natural inequality, has a decent chance of a decent life. This would be no different if enhancement were permitted. There is no necessary connection between enhancement and discrimination, just as there is no necessary connection between curing disability and discrimination against people with disability.

## The Perfect Child, Sterility, and Loss of the Mystery of Life

If we engineered perfect children, this objection goes, the world would be a sterile, monotonous place where everyone was the same, and the mystery and surprise of life would be gone.

It is impossible to create perfect children. We can only attempt to create children with better opportunities of a better life. There will necessarily be difference. Even in the case of screening for disability, like Down syndrome, 10 percent of people choose not to abort a pregnancy known to be affected by Down syndrome. People value different things. There will never be complete convergence. Moreover, there will remain massive challenges for individuals to meet in their personal relationships and in the hurdles our unpredictable environment presents. There will remain much mystery and challenge—we will just be better able to deal with these. We will still have to work to achieve, but our achievements may have greater value.

## Against Human Nature

One of the major objections to enhancement is that it is against human nature. Common alternative phrasings are that enhancement is tampering with our nature or an affront to human dignity. I believe that what separates us from other animals is our rationality, our capacity to make normative judgements and act on the basis of reasons. When we make decisions to improve our lives by biological and other manipulations, we express our rationality and express what is fundamentally important about our nature. And if those manipulations improve our capacity to make rational and normative judgements, they further improve what is fundamentally human. Far from being against the human spirit, such improvements express the human spirit. To be human is to be better.

## Enhancements Are Self-Defeating

Another familiar objection to enhancement is that enhancements will have self-defeating or other adverse social effects. A typical example is increase in height. If height is socially desired, then everyone will try to enhance the height of their children at great cost to themselves and the environment (as taller people consume more resources), with no advantage in the end since there will be no relative gain.

If a purported manipulation does not improve well-being or opportunity, there is no argument in favour of it. In this case, the manipulation is not an enhancement. In other cases, such as enhancement of intelligence, the enhancement of one individual may increase that individual's opportunities only at the expense of another. So-called positional goods are goods only in a relative sense.

But many enhancements will have both positional and non-positional qualities. Intelligence is good not just because it allows an individual to be more competitive for complex jobs, but because it allows an individual to process information more rapidly in her own life, and to develop greater understanding of herself and others. These non-positional effects should not be ignored. Moreover, even in the case of so-called purely positional goods, such as height, there may be important non-positional values. It is better to be taller if you are a basketball player, but being tall is a disadvantage in balance sports such as gymnastics, skiing, and surfing.

Nonetheless, if there are significant social consequences of enhancement, this is of course a valid objection. But it is not particular to enhancement: there is an old question about how far individuals in society can pursue their own self-interest at a cost to others. It applies to education, health care, and virtually all areas of life.

Not all enhancements will be ethical. The critical issue is that the intervention is expected to bring about more benefits than harms to the individual. It must be safe and there must be a reasonable expectation of improvement. Some of the other features of ethical enhancements are summarized below.

## What Is an Ethical Enhancement?

An ethical enhancement:

1.   is in the person's interests;
2.   is reasonably safe;
3.   increases the opportunity to have the best life;
4.   promotes or does not unreasonably restrict the range of possible lives open to that person;
5.   does not unreasonably harm others directly through excessive costs in making it freely available;
6.   does not place that individual at an unfair competitive advantage with respect to others, e.g. mind-reading;
7.   is such that the person retains significant control or responsibility for her achievements and self that cannot be wholly or directly attributed to the enhancement;
8.   does not unreasonably reinforce or increase unjust inequality and discrimination—economic inequality, racism.

## What Is an Ethical Enhancement for a Child or Incompetent Human Being?

Such an ethical enhancement is all the above, but in addition:

1.   the intervention cannot be delayed until the child can make its own decision;
2.   the intervention is plausibly in the child's interests;
3.   the intervention is compatible with the development of autonomy.

# Conclusion

Enhancement is already occurring. In sport, human erythropoietin boosts red blood cells. Steroids and growth hormone improve muscle strength. Many people seek cognitive enhancement through nicotine, Ritalin, Modavigil, or caffeine. Prozac, recreational drugs, and alcohol all enhance mood. Viagra is used to improve sexual performance.

And of course mobile phones and aeroplanes are examples of external enhancing technologies. In the future, genetic technology, nanotechnology, and artificial intelligence may profoundly affect our capacities.

Will the future be better or just disease-free? We need to shift our frame of reference from health to life enhancement. What matters is how we live. Technology can now improve that. We have two options:

1.   Intervention:
     * treating disease;
     * preventing disease;
     * supra-prevention of disease—preventing disease in a radically unprecedented way;
     * protection of well-being;
     * enhancement of well-being.

2.   No intervention, and to remain in a state of nature—no treatment or prevention of disease, no technological enhancement.

I believe that to be human is to be better. Or, at least, to strive to be better. We should be here for a *good* time, not just a *long* time. Enhancement, far from being merely permissible, is something we should aspire to achieve.

# References

*The Age* (2005), 'Genes, Not Men, May Hold the Key to Female Pleasure', 9 June.

Brunner, H. G., Nelen, M., *et al.* (1993*a*), 'Abnormal Behaviour Associated with a Point Mutation in the Structural Gene for Monoamine Oxidase A', Science, 262/5133: 578–80.

Cheitlin, M. D., Hutter, A. M., *et al.* (1999), 'ACC/AHA Expert Consensus Document JACC: Use of Sildenafil (Viagra) in Patients with Cardiovascular Disease', *Journal of the American College of Cardiology,* 33/1: 273–82.

Feinberg, J. (1980), 'The Child's Right to an Open Future,' in W. Aiken and H. LaFollette (eds.), *Whose Child? Parental Rights, Parental Authority and State Power* (Totowa, NJ: Rowman and Littlefield), 124–53.

Mill, J. S. (1910), *On Liberty* (London: J. M. Dent).

Murray, T. (2007), 'Enhancement', in B. Steinbock (ed.), *The Oxford Handbook of Bioethics* (Oxford: Oxford University Press), 491–515.

Sandel, M. (2004), 'The Case Against Perfection,' *Atlantic Monthly* (Apr. 2004), 51–62.

Society for Neuroscience (2004), 'Early Life Stress Harms Mental Function and Immune System in Later Years According to New Research,' 26 Oct., <http://apu.sfn.org/content/AboutSFN1/NewsReleases/am2004_early.html>, accessed Feb. 2006.

# Article 29

Mark A. Bedau

# The Intrinsic Scientific Value
# of Reprogramming Life

The general public's attention to synthetic biology has been accelerated by the achievement a year ago of a so-called synthetic cell by a team of scientists at the J. Craig Venter Institute, and also by the helpful and timely report on the ethics of synthetic biologyfrom the Presidential Commission for the Study of Bioethical Issues. Most attention has focused on synthetic biology's practical implications, such as he need for safeguards in the laboratory and the environment and security procedures to prevent malicious use. But we should give more attention to some of synthetic biology's less practical implications. In particular, I urge us not to overlook theintrinsic scientific value of making synthetic cells.

First, let us be clear about what the JCVI team actually accomplished. Although their achievement is often called a "synthetic cell," it is a *partly* synthetic cell. They were working with normal bacteria, the simplest known cellular forms of life. They first sequenced the entire genome of one natural bacterial species (*Mycoplasma mycoides*). They next synthesized copies of the entire *M.mycoides* genome—atechnical tour de force that involved making newcopies of the *mycoides* genome out of nonliving rawmaterials that can be ordered from chemical supplyhouses. Next, they inserted their synthetic genomesinto bacteria from *Mycoplasma capricolum*, a closely related species, and got the *capricolum* bacteria toexpress the synthetic *mycoides* genome. This in effect changed the *capricolum* bacterium into a *mycoides* bacterium. However, 99 percent of the dry weight of the resulting bacterium is simply a normal living *M.capricolum* bacterium used as the genome transplant recipient. So, the JCVI synthetic cell isonly partly synthetic. Furthermore, the resulting construct is not a new *kind* of bacterium, but merely (a slightly modified version of) an old, familiar bacterium produced by artificial means.

Because the JCVI cell is only partly synthetic, and because the resulting cell is merely an artificially produced example of a natural life form, the commission's report can correctly deny that the JCVI has "created life." However, there is an active scientific research program aimed at making *fully* synthetic cells being carried out today by a number of different laboratory teams in the United States, Europe, and Japan. The commission report downplays these efforts, claiming that creating a fully synthetic cell "remains remote for the foreseeable future."[1]Yet many—including me—are convinced that fully synthetic cells might very well be created within our lifetimes, perhaps even within the next decade. The reason for this optimism is that most of the components of such cells have already been synthesized, and many of them have already been combined in the laboratory. Fully synthetic cells will in all likelihood be a form of life that is rather new and perhaps very unnatural. There is no reason why a fully synthetic cell must closely mimic any natural form of life; novel molecular mechanisms might make the project much more feasible. Furthermore, it will be easier to create fully synthetic cells if they are much simpler than any natural form of life. So making a fully synthetic cell would be creating genuinely new forms of life from wholly non-living materials. (Of course, human scientists are needed to create the laboratory conditions in which nonliving materials will assemble into a synthetic cell. Nobody supposes that any synthetic cell will arise without the intentional efforts of intelligent, living beings.)

The commission report warns against using "sensationalist buzzwords" and phrases such as "creating life" because "ultimately such words impede ongoing understanding of both the scientific and ethical issues at the core of public debateson these topics."[2] I disagree. When synthetic biologists do create fully synthetic cells—and they will, at some point—then we *should* describe it as creating life, for that would be true. Similarly, those who are trying to make fully synthetic cells should be forthright about the fact that they aim to create life. This will encourage us all to face squarely the resulting social and ethical issues.

The main point of making synthetic cells is to make new kinds of cells—cells that perform useful and desired functions beyond the capability of any existing form of life. The JCVI achievement opens the door to this possibility. This is one of the reasons why the JCVI achievement is game changing. To make a synthetic genome, one needs a supply of the nucleotides out of which a genome is constructed, and one needs the information describing the entire genetic sequence of the genome. While the JCVI team used the sequence of *M. mycoides*, they could have started with a different genetic sequence. In fact, in principle they could have started with virtually *any* genetic sequence; they could have invented an entirely new sequence and created an entirely new genome. If you think of the genome as a kind of software that drives a cell's development and behavior, you

From *Hastings Center Report* 41, no. 4 (2011): 29–31.Reprinted with permission of the author and The Hastings Center.

could say that the JCVI team demonstrated they could *arbitrarily reprogram* simple forms of life. Fully synthetic cells will take full advantage of life's programmability. This point is often unappreciated, and it is largely ignored in the commission report. But it is precisely this arbitrary programmability that opens the door to synthetic biology's great intrinsic scientific value.

Arbitrarily reprogrammable synthetic cells are a fantastic new tool for illuminating the complex molecular mechanisms that can give rise to simple forms of life. Even the simplest forms of life are enormously complex biomolecular complexes, about which there are a multitude of unanswered questions. The ability to reprogram simple lifeforms however we wish enables us to make vast arrays of precise experimental modifications of the cells' molecular conditions. The JCVI achievement enables us to construct any new genome we want and observe what happens when we put them inside donor cells. The eventual achievement of fully synthetic cells will expand this reprogrammability to include modifications of every aspect of a cell's molecular constituents. A molecular biologist could hardly dream of a more powerful and flexible experimental methodology. For this reason, arbitrarily reprogrammable synthetic cells can propel a basic scientific research program to reveal all the molecular mechanisms underlying simple life forms.

In addition, efforts to make fully synthetic cells will also help us better understand exactly what it is for a simple molecular aggregate to be alive. At the time of his death, the blackboard of Nobel laureate Richard Feynman contained the sentence, "What I cannot create, I do not understand." Feynman's dictum succinctly captures why our ability to make synthetic cells has such great intrinsic scientific value. The nature of life remains one of the deepest fundamental mysteries about our world. Once we finally figure out how to make wholly new forms of life entirely from nonliving materials, we will be able to design research programs to probe what kinds of radically novel chemical systems deserve to be considered as alive. We can test radically different genetic programs, with new kinds of metabolic systems, new kinds of containers, and new kinds of interactions among them. Making just one kind of synthetic cell will not tell us very much about the nature of life. But experimenting with a great variety of different synthetic cells is exactly what will eventually enable us to learn what is and what is not required to turn a collection of inert molecules into a living organism.

Make no mistake. It is one thing to conduct a research program to unlock the remaining molecular secrets of life. It is quite another thing to program synthetic cells to do whatever we want. There is nothing stopping us from embarking on the research program. But today nobody has any idea how to program a partly or fully synthetic cell to do whatever we want—neither the JCVI team nor anybody else. If we could, then we already would have reprogrammed bacteria to produce inexpensive fuels, foods, building materials, pharmaceuticals, you name it. People are actively working on these tasks, and no doubt many will eventually succeed. But today we can program only pretty trivial traits, and only one synthetic biology reprogramming project has had notable commercial success (making cheaper malaria drugs). Synthetic biology has reprogrammed bacteria to do many things, but progress is painstaking and each achievement requires surmounting many challenges. Furthermore, the dificulty increases by leaps and bounds as we try to reprogram much more complex traits. The JCVI team unlocked the door to arbitrarily reprogramming simple life forms, but figuring out how to go through that door and end up where we want remains a largely unsolved scientific challenge.

Here is one way to get some sense of the dificulty. It has been estimated that it would take about $10^{80}$ hydrogen atoms to fill the entire known universe. The number $10^{80}$ can be written as a one followed by eighty zeros, and typing this number on an ordinary piece of paper would take one to two lines of text. The genome that the JCVI team synthesized consists of a little over one million base pairs. Since there are four nucleotides, there are about $4^{1,000,000}$, or about $10^{600,000}$, different genomes of the same length that the JCVI team could have synthesized instead. To get a feel for the size of this number, bear in mind that written out, it would be a one followed by 600,000 zeros, which would fill about two hundred pages. In other words, the number of different genomes of the size of *M. mycoides*'s genome (which is uncommonly small, as genomes go) that could be synthesized is many, many, many times larger than the number of hydrogen atoms that would fill the entire known universe. So, choosing which genome will produce a specific kind of synthetic cell is like finding the proverbial needle in a haystack. Although the JCVI team has unlocked the door to reprogramming life, we need further research on programming different kinds of synthetic cells before we can take advantage of this new ability.

Of course, any such research program must be conducted in a socially responsible manner. Most of the public commentary on synthetic biology so far has focused on concerns about safety and security, and such concerns must be adequately met. Furthermore, addressing them can be difficult, because life forms can adapt and evolve in unanticipated and unintended directions. So there is good reason for synthetic biology to exercise all due caution—and the synthetic biology community should be commended for making serious and sensible efforts to do just that.

The awareness of life's arbitrary reprogrammability will no doubt shock and disturb some people. In particular, constructing synthetic cells entirely from nonliving materials will provide overwhelming evidence that simple life forms are nothing more than very complex molecular mechanisms. Overwhelming evidence is not absolutely conclusive proof; one could still consistently believe that simple life forms are more than complex molecular mechanisms, just as one could consistently hold the belief that everything in the universe, including everyone's memories and beliefs about past experiences, was created only five minutes ago. But both beliefs would be equally desperate attempts to deny the obvious. Now, if the simplest life forms are just complex molecular mechanisms, then there is good reason to conclude that the same holds for more complex life forms—even human beings. Humans are vastly more complex than bacteria, of course, and humans have conscious mental states and complex moral attitudes that are worlds beyond anything true of any bacterium. Nevertheless, since the simplest and original life forms are just complex chemical machinery, and since humans evolved from those simple life forms by along series of evolutionary transitions and innovations, it stands to reason that something like the same conclusion will apply to human life, too. That is, synthetic biology drives us to acknowledge that we, too, are complex chemical mechanisms.

Rather than ignoring this conclusion, or being frightened or embarrassed by it, we should face it squarely. What consequences follow? Does it undermine respect for humans and other life forms? Does it debunk the pretensions of conventional morality? Does it imply that life is not a legitimate source of awe and wonder? All of these questions remain open. Debate on these issues will be provoked by, and should be informed by, the new scientific insights that result from our efforts to make and reprogram synthetic cells.

---

[1] Presidential Commission for the Study of Bioethical Issues, New Directions: The Ethics of Synthetic Biologyand Emerging Technologies (Washington, D.C.: Government Printing Office, 2010), 3.

[2] Ibid., 15.

# Article 30

## Is the Use of Medical Tools to Enhance Human Beings Morally Troubling?

Selected, Edited, and with Issue Framing Material by:
Gregory E. Kaebnick, *The Hastings Center*

**YES: President's Council on Bioethics**, from *Beyond Therapy: Biotechnology and the Pursuit of Happiness*, U.S. Government Printing Office (2003)

**NO: Ronald Bailey**, from "The Case for Enhancing People" *The New Atlantis* (2011)

## Learning Outcomes

*After reading this issue, you will be able to:*

• Discuss a range of arguments for and against using medical technologies to enhance human bodies and behavior.
• Identify some claims commonly made about human nature in the debate about enhancement.

### ISSUE SUMMARY

**YES:** The President's Council on Bioethics, a presidential body formed by President Bush, argues that biotechnological interventions for making people better than normal raise profound concerns about the relationship between humans and nature, human identity, and human happiness.

**NO:** The libertarian science writer Ronald Bailey maintains that enhancements will only help people live better lives.

## Where Do You Stand?

Perhaps more than any other people, Americans seem to be obsessed with self-improvement. Each year there is a flood of new books and television commercials promoting ways to be richer, thinner, smarter, happier, healthier, more successful, attractive, or all of the above. Whatever one's presumed character or bodily flaw, there is a remedy. And for parents, there is an additional opportunity (sometimes presented as an obligation) to make one's children richer, thinner, smarter, happier, or all of the above.

Traditionally, most of these strategies for improving ourselves or our children are activities or experiences—education, exercise, summer camps, yoga, and so on. But what if we could change that? What if the self-improvement could be achieved with much less work, or without real work at all—in effect dropping the kinds of activities that the term "self-improvement" brings to mind and more directly *enhancing* ourselves or our children? The most obvious targets for enhancement include physical form and functioning, cognitive functioning, and mood or temperament, but conceivably we could even go beyond the traditional targets of self-improvement and enhance such seeming givens of human life as lifespan, so that we lived hundreds of years or more.

Increasingly, if incrementally, biotechnologies seem to offer this promise. A biotechnological enhancement strategy that is by now relatively familiar is the use of pharmaceuticals, such as performance-enhancing drugs in sports (discussed in issue 13) or cognitive enhancers, such as Ritalin, in the classroom. Certain antidepressants are thought to have the ability to enhance mood. Surgery sometimes offers another familiar though limited route to enhancement, at least of bodily form.

Foreseeable sometime in the future is enhancement through genetic manipulation. This could happen by identifying genes that confer improved capabilities (which is much more difficult than news stories usually suggest, but may for at least some traits prove feasible) and transferring them into a person's somatic cells—into muscles to produce superior physical performance, for example—or into germline cells—that is, the cells that produce gametes—so that the changes would be passed from generation to generation. The first method would allow individuals to seek genetic enhancements for themselves or for their children, if the genes were transferred into their children's bodies, and the second would be a way of enhancing both one's children and subsequent generations.

The basic idea of genetic enhancement is arguably not new. Germline genetic enhancement has been practiced for centuries in animal husbandry and agriculture. By breeding for certain characteristics, animals and plants have been created to better meet human purposes. The largest Great Dane and the smallest Pekinese, and all the dog breeds in between, are descended from a handful of wolves tamed by humans in Asia nearly 15,000 years ago. Over the last 500 years, humans have practiced breeding techniques that account for vastly different appearances and characteristics of modern dogs.

Applying these techniques to humans—the theory of eugenics or "better genes"—also has a long but disastrous history. Its advocates, many of them in the United States in the twentieth century, advocated the elimination of "undesirable" people by preventing them from reproducing through involuntary sterilization. In the most malevolent form of eugenics, of course, the Nazi regime in Germany in the 1930s wanted to create a "master race" by encouraging reproduction among blonde, blue-eyed, tall Aryan types and eliminating from the gene pool—through murder—those other population groups, such as Jews and gypsies.

While these eugenics methods are not only barbarous and morally corrupt, the idea of enhancing one's capacities and those of future generations has been given new life by scientific advances in genetics. Being able to manipulate genes—the very core of human inheritance—opens up a new world of possibilities. Already animals like sheep and cows have been cloned, that is, their genomes were transferred into eggs to create animals that are genetically identical (although the animals are never entirely identical because of uterine and environmental differences). In principle, if the genetic contributions to traits can be identified, it might eventually be possible to use genetic enhancement to conduct a new eugenics—a "liberal eugenics"—in which the birth of people with desirable traits is promoted although people with undesirable traits are not targeted or suppressed.

Enhancement raises an assortment of ethical questions. Even if it is possible to enhance an individual's height, beauty, intelligence, or capacity for happiness, is it desirable? If these techniques proved to be safe and effective, would they be distributed fairly throughout society?

These questions are at the core of the following selections. The President's Council on Bioethics, a presidential commission during the administration of George W. Bush that was chaired by the physician and philosopher Leon Kass, argues that there are a number of moral problems with enhancement, whether it is undertaken for one's own benefit or to benefit one's children. Ronald Bailey, a libertarian science writer, is dismissive of the PCB's concerns.

# Beyond Therapy: Biotechnology and the
# Pursuit of Happiness

Before proceeding, we wish to reiterate our intention in this inquiry, so as to avoid misunderstanding. In offering our synopsis of concerns, we are not making predictions; we are merely pointing to possible hazards, hazards that become visible only when one looks at "the big picture." More important, we are not condemning either biotechnological power or the pursuit of happiness, excellence, or self-perfection. Far from it. We eagerly embrace biotechnologies as aids for preventing or correcting bodily or mental ills and for restoring health and fitness. We even more eagerly embrace the pursuits of happiness, excellence, and self-improvement, for ourselves, our children, and our society. Desires for these goals are the source of much that is good in human life. Yet, as has long been known, these desires can be excessive. Worse, they can be badly educated regarding the nature of their object, sometimes with tragic result: we get what we ask for only to discover that it is very far from what we really wanted. Finally, they can be pursued in harmful ways and with improper means, often at the price of deforming the very goals being sought. To guard against such outcomes, we need to be alert in advance to the more likely risks and the more serious concerns. We begin with those that are more obvious and familiar.

## Familiar Sources of Concern

The first concerns commonly expressed regarding any uses of biotechnology beyond therapy reflect, not surprisingly, the dominant values of modern America: health and safety, fairness and equality, and freedom. The following thumbnail sketches of the issues should suffice to open the questions—though of course not to settle them.

### A. Health: Issues of Safety and Bodily Harm

In our health-conscious culture, the first reason people worry about any biotechnical intervention, whatever its intended purpose, is safety. This will surely be true regarding "elective" uses of biotechnology that aim beyond therapy. Athletes who take steroids to boost their strength may later suffer premature heart disease. College students who snort Ritalin to increase their concentration may become addicted. Melancholics taking mood-brighteners to change their outlook may experience impotence or apathy. To generalize: no biological agent used for purposes of self-perfection or self-satisfaction is likely to be entirely safe. This is good medical common sense: anything powerful enough to enhance system A is likely to be powerful enough to harm system B (or even system A itself), the body being a highly complex yet integrated whole in which one intervenes partially only at one's peril. And it surely makes sense, ethically speaking, that one should not risk basic health pursuing a condition of "better than well."

Yet some of the interventions that might aim beyond therapy—for example, genetic enhancement of muscle strength, retardation of aging, or pharmacologic blunting of horrible memories or increasing self-esteem—may, indirectly, lead also to improvements in general health. More important, many good things in life are filled with risks, and free people—even if properly informed about the magnitude of those risks—may choose to run them if they care enough about what they might gain thereby. . . .

### B. Unfairness

An obvious objection to the use of enhancement technologies, especially by participants in competitive activities, is that they give those who use them an unfair advantage: blood doping or steroids in athletes, stimulants in students taking the SATs, and so on. This issue . . . has been well aired by the International Olympic Committee and the many other athletic organizations

From the President's Council on Bioethics, October 2003.

who continue to try to formulate rules that can be enforced, even as the athletes and their pharmacists continue to devise ways to violate those rules and escape detection. Yet as we saw, the fairness question can be turned on its head, and some people see in biotechnical intervention a way to compensate for the "unfairness" of natural inequalities—say, in size, strength, drive, or native talent. Still, even if everyone had equal access to genetic improvement of muscle strength or mind-enhancing drugs, or even if these gifts of technology would be used only to rectify the inequalities produced by the unequal gifts of nature, an additional disquiet would still perhaps remain: The disquiet of using such new powers in the first place or at all, even were they fairly distributed. . . .

## C. Equality of Access

A related question concerns inequality of access to the benefits of biotechnology, a matter of great interest to many Members of this Council. . . . The issue of distributive justice is more important than the issue of unfairness in competitive activities, especially if there are systemic disparities between those who will and those who won't have access to the powers of biotechnical "improvement." Should these capabilities arrive, we may face severe aggravations of existing "unfairnesses" in the "game of life," especially if people who need certain agents to treat serious illness cannot get them while other people can enjoy them for less urgent or even dubious purposes. If, as is now often the case with expensive medical care, only the wealthy and privileged will be able to gain easy access to costly enhancing technologies, we might expect to see an everwidening gap between "the best and the brightest" and the rest. The emergence of a biotechnologically improved "aristocracy"—augmenting the already cognitively stratified structure of American society—is indeed a worrisome possibility, and there is nothing in our current way of doing business that works against it. Indeed, unless something new intervenes, it would seem to be a natural outcome of mixing these elements of American society: our existing inequalities in wealth and status, the continued use of free markets to develop and obtain the new technologies, and our libertarian attitudes favoring unrestricted personal freedom for all choices in private life.

Yet the situation regarding rich and poor is more complex, especially if one considers actual benefits rather than equality or relative well-being. The advent of new technologies often brings great benefits to the less well off, if not at first, then after they come to be mass-produced and massmarketed and the prices come down. (Consider, over the past half-century, the spread in the United States of refrigerators and radios, automobiles and washing machines, televisions and VCRs, cell phones and personal computers, and, in the domain of medicine, antibiotics, vaccines, and many expensive diagnostic and therapeutic procedures.) To be sure, the gap between the richest and the poorest may increase, but in absolute terms the poor may benefit more, when compared not to the rich but to where they were before. . . .

## D. Liberty: Issues of Freedom and Coercion, Overt and Subtle

A concern for threats to freedom comes to the fore whenever biotechnical powers are exercised by some people upon other people. We encountered it in our discussion of "better children" (the choice of a child's sex or the drugmediated alteration of his or her behavior . . .), as well as in the coerced use of anabolic steroids by the East German Olympic swimmers. . . . This problem will of course be worse in tyrannical regimes. But there are always dangers of despotism within families, as many parents already work their wills on their children with insufficient regard to a child's independence or long-term needs, jeopardizing even the "freedom to be a child." To the extent that even partial control over genotype—say, to take a relatively innocent example, musician parents selecting a child with genes for perfect pitch—would add to existing social instruments of parental control and its risks of despotic rule, this matter will need to be attended to. Leaving aside the special case of children, the risk of overt coercion does not loom large in a free society. On the contrary, many enthusiasts for using technology for personal enhancement are libertarian in outlook; they see here mainly the enlargement of human powers and possibilities and the multiplication of options for private choice, both of which they see as steps to greater human freedom. They look forward to growing opportunities for more people to earn more, learn more, see more, and do more, and to choose—perhaps several times in one lifetime—interesting new careers or avocations. And they look with suspicion at critics who they fear might want to limit their private freedom to develop and use new technologies for personal advancement or, indeed, for any purpose whatsoever. The coercion they fear comes not from advances in technology but from the state, acting to deny them their right to pursue happiness or self-improvement by the means they privately choose.

Yet no one can deny that people living in free societies, and even their most empowered citizens, already experience more subtle impingements on freedom and choice, operating, for example, through peer pressure. What is freely permitted and widely used may, under certain circumstances, become practically mandatory. If most children are receiving memory enhancement or stimulant drugs, failure to provide them for your child might be seen as a form of child neglect. If all the defensive linemen are on steroids, you risk mayhem if you go against them chemically pure. And, a point subtler still, some critics complain that, as with cosmetic surgery, Botox, and breast implants, many of the enhancement technologies of the future will very likely be used in slavish adherence to certain socially defined and merely fashionable notions of "excellence" or improvement, very likely shallow and conformist. If these fears are realized, such exercises of individual freedom, suitably multiplied, might compromise the freedom to be an individual.

This special kind of reduction of freedom—let's call it the problem of conformity or homogenization—is of more than individual concern. In an era of mass culture, itself the by product of previous advances in communication, manufacture, and marketing techniques, the exercise of uncoerced private choices may produce untoward consequences for society as a whole. Trends in popular culture lead some critics to worry that the self-selected nontherapeutic uses of the new biotechnical powers, should they become widespread, will be put in the service of the most common human desires, moving us toward still greater homogenization of human society—perhaps raising the floor but also lowering the ceiling of human possibility, and reducing the likelihood of genuine freedom, individuality, and greatness. . . .

## Essential Sources of Concern

Our familiar worries about issues of safety, equality, and freedom, albeit very important, do not exhaust the sources of reasonable concern. When richly considered, they invite us to think about the deeper purposes for the sake of which we want to live safely, justly, and freely. And they enable us to recognize that even the safe, equally available, noncoerced and non-faddish uses of biomedical technologies to pursue happiness or self-improvement raise ethical and social questions, questions more directly connected with the essence of the activity itself: the use of technological means to intervene into the human body and mind, not to ameliorate their diseases but to change and improve their normal workings. Why, if at all, are we bothered by the voluntary self-administration of agents that would change our bodies or alter our minds? What is disquieting about our attempts to improve upon human nature, or even our own particular instance of it?

The subject being relatively novel, it is difficult to put this worry into words. We are in an area where initial revulsions are hard to translate into sound moral arguments. Many people are probably repelled by the idea of drugs that erase memories or that change personalities, or of interventions that enable seventy-year-olds to bear children or play professional sports, or, to engage in some wilder imaginings, of mechanical implants that would enable men to nurse infants or computer-brain hookups that would enable us to download the Oxford English Dictionary. But can our disquiet at such prospects withstand rational, anthropological, or ethical scrutiny? Taken one person at a time, with a properly prepared set of conditions and qualifications, it will be hard to say what is wrong with any biotechnical intervention that could improve our performances, give us (more) ageless bodies, or make it possible for us to have happier souls. Indeed, in many cases, we ought to be thankful for or pleased with the improvements our biotechnical ingenuity is making possible. . . .

### A. Hubris or Humility: Respect for "the Given"

A common, man-on-the-street reaction to the prospects of biotechnological engineering beyond therapy is the complaint of "man playing God." If properly unpacked, this worry is in fact shared by people holding various theological beliefs and by people holding none at all. Sometimes the charge means the sheer prideful presumption of trying to alter what God has ordained or nature has produced, or what should, for whatever reason, not be fiddled with. Sometimes the charge means not so much usurping Godlike powers, but doing so in the absence of God-like knowledge: the mere playing at being God, the hubris of acting with insufficient wisdom. . . .

One revealing way to formulate the problem of hubris is what one of our Council Members has called the temptation to "hyper-agency," a Promethean aspiration to remake nature, including human nature, to serve our purposes and to satisfy our desires. This attitude is to be faulted not only because it can lead to bad, unintended consequences; more fundamentally, it also represents a false understanding of, and an improper disposition toward, the naturally given world. The root of the difficulty seems to be both cognitive and moral: the failure properly to appreciate and respect the "giftedness" of the world. Acknowledging the giftedness of life means recognizing that our talents and powers are not wholly our own doing, nor even fully ours, despite the efforts we expend to develop and to exercise them. It also means recognizing that not everything in the world is open to any use we may desire or devise. Such an appreciation of the giftedness of life would constrain the Promethean project and conduce to a much-needed humility. Although it is in part a religious sensibility, its resonance reaches beyond religion.

Human beings have long manifested both wondering appreciation for nature's beauty and grandeur and reverent awe before nature's sublime and mysterious power. . . . [A]ppreciating that the given world—including our natural powers to alter it—is not of our own making could induce a welcome attitude of modesty, restraint, and humility. Such a posture is surely recommended for anyone inclined to modify human beings or human nature for purposes beyond therapy.

Yet the respectful attitude toward the "given," while both necessary and desirable as a restraint, is not by itself sufficient as a guide. The "giftedness of nature" also includes smallpox and malaria, cancer and Alzheimer disease, decline and decay. Moreover, nature is not equally generous with her gifts, even to man, the most gifted of her creatures. Modesty born of gratitude for the world's "givenness" may enable us to recognize that not everything in the world is open to any use we may desire or devise, but it will not by itself teach us which things can be tinkered with and which should be left inviolate. Respect for the "giftedness" of things cannot tell us which gifts are to be accepted as is, which are to be improved through use or training, which are to be housebroken through self-command or medication, and which opposed like the plague. . . .

## B. "Unnatural" Means: The Dignity of Human Activity

Until only yesterday, teaching and learning or practice and training exhausted the alternatives for acquiring human excellence, perfecting our natural gifts through our own efforts. But perhaps no longer: biotechnology may be able to do nature one better, even to the point of requiring less teaching, training, or practice to permit an improved nature to shine forth. As we noted earlier, the insertion of the growth-factor gene into the muscles of rats and mice bulks them up and keeps them strong and sound without the need for nearly as much exertion. Drugs to improve alertness (today) or memory and amiability (tomorrow) could greatly relieve the need for exertion to acquire these powers, leaving time and effort for better things. What, if anything, is disquieting about such means of gaining improvement?

The problem cannot be that they are "artificial," in the sense of having man-made origins. Beginning with the needle and the fig leaf, man has from the start been the animal that uses art to improve his lot by altering or adding to what nature alone provides. Ordinary medicine makes extensive use of similar artificial means, from drugs to surgery to mechanical implants, in order to treat disease. If the use of artificial means is absolutely welcome in the activity of healing, it cannot be their unnaturalness alone that disquiets us when they are used to make people "better than well."

Still, in those areas of human life in which excellence has until now been achieved only by discipline and effort, the attainment of similar results by means of drugs, genetic engineering, or implanted devices looks to many people (including some Members of this Council) to be "cheating" or "cheap." Many people believe that each person should work hard for his achievements. Even if we prefer the grace of the natural athlete or the quickness of the natural mathematician—people whose performances deceptively appear to be effortless—we admire also those who overcome obstacles and struggle to try to achieve the excellence of the former. This matter of character—the merit of disciplined and dedicated striving—is surely pertinent. For character is not only the source of our deeds, but also their product. As we have already noted, healthy people whose disruptive behavior is "remedied" by pacifying drugs rather than by their own efforts are not learning self-control; if anything, they may be learning to think it unnecessary. People who take pills to block out from memory the painful or hateful aspects of a new experience will not learn how to deal with suffering or sorrow. A drug that induces fearlessness does not produce courage.

Yet things are not so simple. Some biotechnical interventions may assist in the pursuit of excellence without in the least cheapening its attainment. And many of life's excellences have nothing to do with competition or overcoming adversity. Drugs to decrease drowsiness, increase alertness, sharpen memory, or reduce distraction may actually help people interested in their natural pursuits of learning or painting or performing their civic duty. Drugs to steady the hand of a neurosurgeon or to prevent sweaty palms in a concert pianist cannot be regarded as "cheating," for they are in no sense the source of the excellent activity or achievement. And, for people dealt a meager hand in the dispensing of nature's gifts, it should not be called cheating or cheap if biotechnology could assist them in becoming better equipped—whether in body or in mind.

Nevertheless, . . . there remains a sense that the "naturalness" of means matters. It lies not in the fact that the assisting drugs and devices are artifacts, but in the danger of violating or deforming the nature of human agency and the dignity of the naturally human way of activity. In most of our ordinary efforts at self-improvement, whether by practice, training, or study, we sense the relation between our doings and the resulting improvement, between the means used and the end sought. . . . In contrast, biotechnical interventions act directly on the human body and mind to bring about their effects on a passive subject, who plays little or no role at all.

## C. Identity and Individuality

With biotechnical interventions that skip the realm of intelligible meaning, we cannot really own the transformations nor can we experience them as genuinely ours. And we will be at a loss to attest whether the resulting conditions and activities of our bodies and our minds are, in the fullest sense, our own as human. But our interest in identity is also more personal. For we do not live in a generic human way; we desire, act, flourish, and decline as ourselves, as individuals. To be human is to be someone, not anyone—with a given nature (male or female), given natural abilities (superior wit or musical talent), and—most important—a real history of attachments, memories, and experiences, acquired largely by living with others.

In myriad ways, new biotechnical powers promise (or threaten) to transform what it means to be an individual: giving increased control over our identity to others, as in the case of genetic screening or sex selection of offspring by parents; inducing psychic states divorced from real life and lived experience; blunting or numbing the memories we wish to escape; and achieving the results we could never achieve unaided, by acting as ourselves alone.

To be sure, in many cases, biomedical technology can restore or preserve a real identity that is slipping away: keeping our memory intact by holding off the scourge of Alzheimer disease; restoring our capacity to love and work by holding at bay the demons of self-destroying depression. In other cases, the effect of biotechnology on identity is much more ambiguous. By taking psychotropic drugs to reduce anxiety or overcome melancholy, we may become the person we always wished to be—more cheerful, ambitious, relaxed, content. But we also become a different person in the eyes of others, and in many cases we become dependent on the continued use of psychotropic drugs to remain the new person we now are. . . .

## D. Partial Ends, Full Flourishing

Beyond the perils of achieving our desired goals in a "less-than-human way" or in ways "not fully our own," we must consider the meaning of the ends themselves: better children, superior performance, ageless bodies, and happy souls. Would their attainment in fact improve or perfect our lives as human beings? Are they—always or ever—reasonable and attainable goals?. . .

In many cases, biotechnologies can surely help us cultivate what is best in ourselves and in our children, providing new tools for realizing good ends, wisely pursued. But it is also possible that the new technological means may deform the ends themselves. In pursuit of better children, biotechnical powers risk making us "tyrants"; in pursuit of superior performance, they risk making us "artifacts." In both cases, the problem is not the ends themselves but our misguided idea of their attainment or our false way of seeking to attain them. And in both cases, there is the ubiquitous problem that "good" or "superior" will be reconceived to fit the sorts of goals that the technological interventions can help us attain. We may come to believe that genetic predisposition or brain chemistry holds the key to helping our children develop and improve, or that stimulant drugs or bulkier muscles hold the key to excellent human activity. If we are equipped with hammers, we will see only those things that can be improved by pounding.

The goals of ageless bodies and happy souls—and especially the ways biotechnology might shape our pursuit of these ends—are perhaps more complicated. The case for ageless bodies seems at first glance to look pretty good. The prevention of decay, decline, and disability, the avoidance of blindness, deafness, and debility, the elimination of feebleness, frailty, and fatigue, all seem to be conducive to living fully as a human being at the top of one's powers—of having, as they say, a "good quality of life" from beginning to end. . . . And, should aging research deliver on its promise of adding not only extra life to years but also extra years to life, who would refuse it?

But . . . there may in fact be many human goods that are inseparable from our aging bodies, from our living in time, and especially from the natural human life cycle by which each generation gives way to the one that follows it. Because this argument is so counterintuitive, we need to begin not with the individual choice for an ageless body, but with what the individual's life might look like in a world in which everyone made the same choice. We need to make the choice universal, and see the meaning of that choice in the mirror of its becoming the norm.

What if everybody lived life to the hilt, even as they approached an ever-receding age of death in a body that looked and functioned—let's not be too greedy—like that of a thirty-year-old? Would it be good if each and all of us lived like light bulbs, burning as brightly from beginning to end, then popping off without warning, leaving those around us suddenly in the dark? Or is it perhaps better that there be a shape to life, everything in its due season, the shape also written, as it were, into the wrinkles of our bodies that live it—provided, of course, that we do not suffer years of painful or degraded old age and that we do not lose our wits?. . .

Going against both common intuition and native human desire, some commentators have argued that living with full awareness and acceptance of our finitude may be the condition of many of the best things in human life: engagement, seriousness, a taste for beauty, the possibility of virtue, the ties born of procreation, the quest for meaning. . . .

What about the pursuit of [happiness], and especially of the sort that we might better attain with pharmacological assistance? Painful and shameful memories are disturbing; guilty consciences trouble sleep; low self esteem, melancholy, and world-weariness besmirch the waking hours. Why not memory-blockers for the former, mood-brighteners for the latter, and a good euphoriant—without risks of hangovers or cirrhosis—when celebratory occasions fail to be jolly? For let us be clear: If it is imbalances of neurotransmitters that are largely responsible for our state of soul, would it not be sheer priggishness to refuse the help of pharmacology for our happiness, when we accept it guiltlessly to correct for an absence of insulin or thyroid hormone?

And yet, . . . there seems to be something misguided about the pursuit of utter and unbroken psychic tranquility or the attempt to eliminate all shame, guilt, and painful memories. Traumatic memories, shame, and guilt, are, it is true, psychic pains. In extreme doses, they can be crippling. Yet, short of the extreme, they can also be helpful and fitting. They are appropriate responses to horror, disgraceful conduct, injustice, and sin, and, as such, help teach us to avoid them or fight against them in the future. Witnessing a murder should be remembered as horrible; doing a beastly deed should trouble one's soul. Righteous indignation at injustice depends on being able to feel injustice's sting. And to deprive oneself of one's memory—including and especially its truthfulness of feeling—is to deprive oneself of one's own life and identity. . . .

Looking into the future at goals pursuable with the aid of new biotechnologies enables us to turn a reflective glance at our own version of the human condition and the prospects now available to us (in principle) for a flourishing human life. For us today, assuming that we are blessed with good health and a sound mind, a flourishing human life is not a life lived with an ageless body or an untroubled soul, but rather a life lived in rhythmed time, mindful of time's limits, appreciative of each season and filled first of all with those intimate human relations that are ours only because we are born, age, replace ourselves, decline, and die—and know it. It is a life of aspiration, made possible by and born of experienced lack, of the disproportion between the transcendent longings of the soul and the limited capacities of our bodies and minds. It is a life that stretches toward some fulfillment to which our natural human soul has been oriented, and, unless we extirpate the source, will always be oriented. It is a life not of better genes and enhancing chemicals but of love and friendship, song and dance, speech and deed, working and learning, revering and worshipping. If this is true, then the pursuit of an ageless body may prove finally to be a distraction and a deformation. And the pursuit of an untroubled and self satisfied soul may prove to be deadly to desire, if finitude recognized spurs aspiration and fine aspiration acted upon is itself the core of happiness. Not the agelessness of the body, nor the contentment of the soul, nor even the list of external achievements and accomplishments of life, but the engaged and energetic being-at-work of what nature uniquely gave to us is what we need to treasure and defend.

---

PRESIDENT'S COUNCIL ON BIOETHICS is a presidential advisory body formed by President George W. Bush.

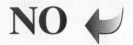
# The Case for Enhancing People

$D$oes the enhancement of human physical and intellectual capacities undermine virtue?

In answering this question, we must first make a distinction between therapy and enhancement. Therapeutic technologies are meant to restore impaired or degraded human capacities to some more normal level. By contrast, any enhancements would alter human functioning beyond the normal.

We must also keep in mind that, whatever we think about them, enhancements are going to happen. Age retardation or even age-reversal are prime targets for research, but other techniques aimed at preventing disease and boosting memory, intelligence, and physical strength will also be developed.

Much worried attention is focused particularly on the possibility of achieving these and other enhancements through genetic engineering; that will indeed one day happen. But the fastest advances in enhancement will occur using pharmaceutical and biomedical interventions to modulate and direct the activity of existing genes in the bodies of people who are already alive. These will happen alongside the development of human-machine interfaces that will extend and boost human capacities.

Contrary to oft-expressed concerns, we will find, first, that enhancements will better enable people to flourish; second, that enhancements will not dissolve whatever existential worries people have; third, that enhancements will enable people to become more virtuous; fourth, that people who don't want enhancement for themselves should allow those of us who do to go forward without hindrance; fifth, that concerns over an "enhancement divide" are largely illusory; and sixth, that we already have at hand the social "technology," in the form of protective social and political institutions, that will enable the enhanced and the unenhanced to dwell together in peace.

## Strengthening Virtue

What is an enhancement? A good definition is offered by Sarah Chan and John Harris in a 2007 article in the journal *Studies in Ethics, Law, and Technology*: an enhancement is "a procedure that improves our functioning: any intervention which increases our general capabilities for human flourishing." People will choose enhancements that they believe are likely to help them or their children to flourish. Of course, their knowledge of a benefit will be likely rather than certain because people choosing enhancements will recognize that there is always the risk that they are wrong about the benefit, or that the attempt at enhancement will go awry, such as with a treatment failure. After all, most medical and technological advances are riskier in their early stages.

Just as Dante found it easier to conjure the pains of Hell than to evoke the joys of Heaven, so too do bioethicists find it easier to concoct the possible perils of a biotech-nanotech-infotech future than to appreciate how enhancements will contribute to flourishing lives. One of the chief goals of this symposium is to think about the indispensable role that virtue plays in human life. The chief motivating concern seems to be the fear that biotechnologies and other human enhancement technologies will somehow undermine human virtue. As we will see, far from undermining virtue, biotech, nanotech, and infotech enhancements will tend to support virtue; that is, they will help enable people to be actually good.

Peter Lawler, in *Stuck With Virtue* (2005), agrees that "the unprecedented health, longevity, and other indispensable means for human flourishing will deserve our gratitude." So far, so good. Then he goes on to claim, "But the victories that will be won [over nature]—like most of the victories won on behalf of the modern individual—will also probably be, in part, at the expense of the distinctively human goods: love, family, friends, country, virtue, art, spiritual life, and, most generally, living responsibly in light of what we really know about what we have been given." In fact, according to Lawler, we don't have to wait for future enhancements; modern technology is already making people less virtuous: as he has argued in the pages of this journal, "one of the downsides of living in an increasingly high-tech society is that both virtue and opportunities to act virtuously seem to be in short supply" [*"Restless Souls,"* Winter 2004].

Really? Thanks to modern technology, sanitation, better nutrition, and medical care, Americans are living much longer and healthier lives than people did just a century ago. Do longer lives mean that people today are less virtuous? Or, inversely, does this mean that when people lived shorter lives they were *more* virtuous? Harvard political philosopher Michael Sandel offered a tart and persuasive response to suggestions that enhancing life spans might result in a less virtuous world:

> Are the background conditions in human self-understandings for the virtues just about right now at 78 years of the average life span, or such that they would be eroded and diminished if we extend it to 120 or 150, or 180? . . . Is it the suggestion that back when it was 48, rather than 78, a century ago . . . that the virtues we prize were on greater display or more available to us? And if so, would that be reason to aim for, or at least to wish for or long for, a shorter life span, rather than a longer one? . . .

Further, on what grounds do Lawler and others suggest that smarter, stronger, healthier, longer-lived people will care less about human goods like friendship, art, and the pursuit of virtue? As Elizabeth Fenton argued in a 2008 article in the journal *Bioethics,* "none of these capabilities (bodily health, imagination, emotion, practical reason, friendship, etc.) are in fact threatened by, for example, enhanced intelligence or athleticism." Being stronger, healthier, and smarter would more likely aid a person in his pursuit of virtue and moral excellence. And the unspoken implication that the state should somehow aim at inculcating collective virtue is incoherent: the pursuit of virtue is what *individuals* do.

## The Dangers of Immortality?

Age-retardation technologies are the "killer app" (so to speak) of enhancements—so deeply and self-evidently appealing that they would seem to sell the whole project of enhancement on their own. Nonetheless, there are those who oppose them. For example, Leon Kass, the former chairman of the President's Council on Bioethics (PCBE) under President Bush, has asserted, "the finitude of human life is a blessing for every individual, whether he knows it or not." And Daniel Callahan, co-founder of the Hastings Center, has declared, "There is no known social good coming from the conquest of death." Callahan added, "The worst possible way to resolve [the question of life extension] is to leave it up to individual choice." When asked if the government has a right to tell its citizens that they have to die, Johns Hopkins University political scientist Francis Fukuyama answered, "Absolutely."

The PCBE's 2003 report *Beyond Therapy* raised concerns that a society of people with "ageless bodies" might have significant downsides. Much longer lives would weaken our "commitment and engagement," the Council fretted: Today, we live with the knowledge that we will soon die, and thus "aspire to *spend* our lives in the ways we deem most important and vital"; but this "aspiration and urgency" might flag because we would ask, "Why not leave for tomorrow what you might do today, if there are endless tomorrows before you?" Further, our "attitudes toward death and mortality" might shift dramatically because "an individual committed to the technological struggle against aging and decline would be less prepared for . . . death, and the least willing to acknowledge its inevitability." Finally, age-retardation might undermine "the meaning of the life cycle" so that we would not be able "to make sense of what time, age, and change should mean to us." The Council does admit that as "powerful as some of these concerns are, however, from the point of view of the individual considered in isolation, the advantages of age-retardation may well be deemed to outweigh the dangers." Indeed.

But what about the consequences of longer human life spans to society as a whole? *Beyond Therapy* highlights three areas of societal concern. Significant age-retardation would disrupt the succession of "generations and families." This succession "could be obstructed by a glut of the able," the report suggests, since cohorts of healthy geezers would have no intention of shuffling off this mortal coil to be replaced by younger people. Longer lives could also slow down "innovation, change, and renewal" since "innovation . . . is . . . often the function of a new generation of leaders." Finally, even if we are not aging individually, we will need to worry about "the aging of society" that would then result. Societies composed of people whose bodies do not age significantly might "experience their own sort of senescence—a hardening of the vital social pathways."

Let us address each of these concerns in turn. First, we must deal with the notion of a nursing-home world. The point of anti-aging research is not to make people older longer, but to make them younger longer. So what about the concerns raised by the PCBE? Political scientist Diana Schaub, who also served on the Council, has made similar points. For instance, in an article in *Cato Unbound,* she asked, if people lived for a thousand years, "how would human relations be affected? How would monogamy fare? . . . Would there be enough psychic energy for ever-renewed love?"

As we age today, our declining psychic energy correlates pretty well with our declining physical energy. Who is to say, then, that with renewed physical energy we would not have more psychic energy as well? Actually, a pressing current question is: why has monogamy already begun to fall apart in developed societies? The rise in life expectancy over the last century may have had a bit to do with it; but surely the advent of truly effective contraception and the entrance of women fully into the paid workforce are far more significant factors. Marriage based on romantic love is a relatively modern notion, after all. As some commentators have noted, marriage before the twentieth century was not often based on romantic love, but could well be described as an alliance in which a man and woman stood together back to back fending off attacks on their family. As the modern world became less economically and socially threatening, marriage partners began to turn toward each other seeking more emotional support and often found it lacking.

Schaub next asks, "What would the tally of disappointments, betrayals, and losses be over a millennium?" Try turning that question around: what would the tally of satisfactions, affections, and triumphs be over a millennium? Modern material and intellectual abundance has already offered many of us a way out of the lives of quiet desperation suffered by our impoverished ancestors. The twenty-first century will provide an ever-increasing menu of life plans and choices. Surely, exhausting the coming possibilities for intellectual, artistic, and even spiritual growth will take more time than a typical life span today.

Schaub also queries, "Would we love other people more or less than at present? Would we be better partners, parents, friends, and neighbors?" She does not offer any evidence that shorter-lived people in past centuries and societies loved more deeply or were better neighbors, friends, and parents. But as Steven Pinker has argued in *The New Republic,* it is very suggestive that as life expectancies increased over the past century, levels of domestic and international violence also declined: "When pain and early death are everyday features of one's own life, one feels fewer compunctions about inflicting them on others. As technology and economic efficiency lengthen and improve our lives, we place a higher value on life in general." More simply, perhaps empathy has more of an opportunity to flourish when we are not constantly in danger of our lives.

"What would it be like to experience the continued vitality of the body in conjunction with the aging of the spirit?" continues Schaub. She initially suggests that longer, healthier lives might happily unite the vitality of youth with the wisdom of maturity. But she then worries that, instead, longer lives would combine the "characteristic vices of age with the strength of will to impose them on others." What is meant by the phrase "aging of the spirit," and just what are the "characteristic vices of age" that trouble her? Which of the traditional vices—gluttony, anger, greed, envy, pride, lust, indifference, melancholy—does she expect will increase among hale near-immortals? As Georges Minois notes in his *History of Old Age,* avarice is among the vices of old age most commonly depicted in classical literature. Roman playwright Terence wrote, "A vice common to all mankind is that of being too keen after money when we are old." In Gulliver's Travels, Jonathan Swift warned, "avarice is the necessary consequence of old age." Swift was describing the immortal, but not ageless, people known as the Struldbrugs. There is little reason to doubt that material comfort and security grow in importance as physical vitality ebbs and mental acuity withers. But perpetually vital oldsters would have no need for such security, because they could count on having the mental and physical powers necessary to pursue new goals and possibilities. No failures would be permanent; they would instead become learning experiences.

In addition to these concerns, Schaub suggests that "a nation of ageless individuals could well produce a sclerotic society, petrified in its ways and views." Daniel Callahan makes a similar argument in a debate with life-extension advocate Gregory Stock, in which he claims, "I doubt that if you give most people longer lives, even in better health, they are going to find new opportunities and make new initiatives." Stock goes so far as to help his interlocutor with the hoary example of brain-dead old professors blocking the progress of vibrant young researchers by holding onto tenure. But that seems more of a problem for medieval institutional holdovers like universities than for modern social institutions like corporations. Assuming it turns out that even with healthy long-lived oldsters there is still an advantage in turnover in top management, then institutions that adopt that model will thrive and those that do not will be out-competed. Besides, even today youngsters don't simply wait around for their elders to die. They go out and found their own companies and other institutions. Bill Gates didn't wait to take over IBM; he launched Microsoft at age 19. Scott Harrison started a nonprofit to supply clean drinking water to poor people in developing countries at age 31. Larry Page and Sergey Brin were both 25 when they founded Google. Nor did human genome sequencer Craig Venter loiter about until the top slot at the National Institutes of Health opened up. In politics, we already solve the problem of entrenched oldsters by term-limiting the presidency, as well as many state and local offices.

In fact, the available evidence cuts against concerns about "a hardening of the vital social pathways." Social and technological innovation has been most rapid in those societies with the highest average life expectancies. Yale economist William D. Nordhaus estimates that increases in longevity in the West account for 40 percent of the growth in gross national product for the period 1975–1995. Why? Not only do people work longer, but they work smarter—long lives allow for the accumulation of human capital. Economists Kevin M. Murphy and Robert H. Topel have analyzed how much human capital was gained by over-coming the vagaries of nature, to the tune of $1.2 million in value per person over the course of the twentieth century, during which time life expectancy at birth for a representative American increased by roughly thirty years. In 1900, they note, "nearly 18 percent of males born in the United States died before their first birthday: today, cumulative mortality does not reach 18 percent until age 62." The economic and social dynamism of societies that already enjoy longer average life expectancies (such as ours) also cuts against fears that "urgency" and "engagement" might flag with increased life spans.

Schaub further conjures the possibility of near-immortal dictators—Stalin and Hitler, alive forever. The implied argument that everyone must continue to die before age 100 to avoid the possibility of thousand-year tyrants is not persuasive. Must we really surrender to the tyranny of aging and death in order to prevent human despotism? Wouldn't a better strategy be to focus on pre-venting the emergence of tyrants, either of the short- or long-lived variety?

Like the PCBE, Schaub also worries about decreased fertility—that healthy oldsters would be less interested in reproducing. The facts seem to support this view: already, countries with the highest life expectancies have the lowest levels of fertility. In a recent study published in the journal *Human Nature,* University of Connecticut anthropologists Nicola L. Bulled and Richard Sosis reported that total fertility rates (the number of children a woman will have over the course of her lifetime) drop by half in reaching a life expectancy threshold of 60. For example, they found that women who live in countries where life expectancy is below 50 years bear an average of 5.5 children. When life expectancy is between 50 and 60, they bear an average of 4.8 children. The big drop occurs when they can expect to live between 60 and 70 years, in which case women have about 2.5 children on average.

But so what? A lack of interest in progeny could have the happy side effect of addressing the possibility that radically increased human life spans might lead to overpopulation. On the other hand, it might turn out that bearing and rearing children would eventually interest long-lived oldsters who would come to feel that they had the time and the resources to do it right. Since assisted reproductive techniques will extend procreation over many decades, perhaps centuries, people who can look forward to living and working for hundreds of years will be able to delay and stretch out the period in which they can choose to become parents.

And again, what about love? Do people today love their children, their spouses, and their friends less than shorter-lived people did a century ago? Were our forebears who lived thirty fewer years on average more committed to their children than are twenty-first-century American parents? Do people today love their children less than nineteenth-century Americans did because, as Michael Haines of Colgate University reports, instead of having a one-in-five chance of dying in their first year of life, most American kids now face a roughly one-in-200 chance?

Then there is the allegedly special case of "manufactured children." Along with many other opponents of enhancement technologies, Peter Lawler darkly speculates in *Stuck With Virtue* that enhanced children will be less loved than those produced the old-fashioned way: "A world in which children are manufactured and sex and procreation are totally disconnected would surely be one without much love, one where one manufactured being would have little natural or real connection to other manufactured beings."

But Lawler and his *confrères* need not speculate on what happens to parental love in such cases, for we have actual data. As physician Sally Satel notes in the journal Policy Review, "For all the deference that conservative bioethics pays to the implicit wisdom of the ages, it rarely mines the recent past for lessons. Instead of concentrating on the ancients, why not also study the history of in vitro fertilization, paid egg donation, and surrogate motherhood to learn about cultural resistance and adaptation to such practices?" Indeed. Fears about waning parental love and loosening generational ties were expressed by many bioethicists when in vitro fertilization began to be used in the 1970s and 1980s. Forty years later, the evidence is that their worries were overblown. A recent study in the journal *Human Reproduction* finds that IVF children and their parents are as well-adjusted as those born in the conven-tional way. There are no good reasons to doubt that this will not be the case for enhanced children in the future as well. As Harvard philosopher Frances Kamm argues in an essay in the 2009 collection *Human Enhancement:* not accepting whatever characteristics nature will bring but altering them ex-ante does not show lack of love. . . . This is because no conscious being yet exists who has to work hard to achieve new traits or suffer fears of rejection at the idea that they should be changed. Importantly, it is rational and acceptable to seek good characteristics in a new person, even though we know that when the child comes to be and we love him or her, many of these characteristics may come and go and we will continue to love the particular person.

In fact, so many infertile people have wanted to have children to love that more than 4 million have been brought into the world using various reproductive technologies since the birth of the first test-tube baby back in 1978.

What about the PCBE's fears that age-retardation technologies would undermine "the meaning of the life cycle" so that we would not be able "to make sense of what time, age, and change should mean to us"? Left-leaning environmental writer Bill McKibben has also expressed this concern. "Without mortality, no time," he writes in *Enough: Staying Human in an Engineered Age* (2003). "All moments would be equal; the deep, sad, human wisdom of Ecclesiastes would vanish. If for everything there is an endless season, then there is also no right season. . . . The future stretches before you, endlessly flat." But that deep, sad wisdom of Ecclesiastes is a powerful human response of existential dread to the oblivion that stretches endlessly before the dead: "For the living know that they shall die: but the dead know not any thing, neither have they any more a reward; for the memory of them is forgotten. Also their love, and their hatred, and their envy, is now perished; neither have they any more a portion for ever in any thing that is done under the sun" (Ecclesiastes 9:5-6). Is there not in this an argument against death? If wisdom is lost in death, does it not follow that longer lives could lead to greater wisdom? And this is not to mention love and all the other good things that are snuffed out in that oblivion.

On the other hand, if the endless future turns out to be as horrible as McKibben imagines it to be, then people can still simply choose to give up their empty, meaningless lives. So if people did opt to live yet longer, would that not mean they had found sufficient pleasure, joy, love, and even meaning to keep them going? McKibben is right: We do not know what immortality would be like. But should that happy choice become available, we can still decide whether or not we want to enjoy it. Besides, even if the ultimate goal of this technological quest is immortality, what will be immediately available is only longevity. The experience of longer lives will give the human race an opportunity to see how it works out. If immortality is a problem, it is a correctable one. Death always remains an option. Let us turn on its head the notorious argument by Leon Kass that our initial repugnance to biotechnological advances should make us wary of them. Put the other way around, the near-universal human *yearning* for longer, healthier lives should serve as a preliminary warrant for pursuing age-retardation as a moral good.

# Inviolable Characteristics?

What other features of human life might ethically be altered by enhancements? Almost any, according to the argument of George Washington University philosophy professor David DeGrazia. Writing in the *Journal of Medicine and Philosophy,* he systematically examines several core human traits—internal psychological style, personality, general intelligence and memory, sleep, normal aging, gender, and being a member of the species *Homo sapiens*—that might be considered so fundamental that they cannot be ethically altered, but concludes that *"characteristics likely to be targeted or otherwise affected by enhancement technologies* are not plausibly regarded as [ethically] inviolable."

Regarding psychological style, there is no ethical reason to require that a particular person remain worried, suspicious, or downbeat if he wants to change. As DeGrazia points out, psychotherapy already aims at such self-transformation. And what about the impact of education? Many people who come back from college or the military seem unrecognizable to their old friends. If a pill will make a person more confident and upbeat, then there is no reason for him not to use it if he so wishes. Personality is perhaps the external manifestation of one's internal psychological style, and here, too, it's hard to think of any ethical basis for requiring someone to remain, for example, cynical or excessively shy.

But what about boosting intelligence and memory? Of course, from childhood on, we are constantly exhorted to improve ourselves by taking more classes, participating in more job training, and reading good books. Opponents of biotech enhancements might counter that all of these methods of improvement manipulate our environments and do not reach to the genetic cores of our beings. But DeGrazia points out that the wiring of our brains is the result of the interaction between our genes and our environment. For example, our intellectual capacities depend on proper nutrition as well as on our genetic endowments. One's genome is not fundamentally more important than environmental factors, he concludes; rather, "they are equally important, so we should bear in mind that no one objects to deliberately introducing environmental factors [such as schools or diet] that promote intelligence." It does not matter ethically whether one's intellectual capacities are boosted by schooling, a pill, or a set of genes.

As for sleep: all vertebrates sleep. Sleep, unlike cynicism, does seem biologically fundamental—but again, so what? Nature is not a reliable source for ethical norms. If a person could safely reduce his need for sleep and enjoy more waking life, that wouldn't be at all ethically problematic. Our ancestors who lacked artificial light probably got a lot more sleep than we moderns do, yet history doesn't suggest that they were morally superior to us.

Then, again, there is the argument about normal aging. As everyone knows, the only inevitabilities are death and taxes. Death, however, used to come far more frequently at younger ages, but global average life expectancy has doubled in the past century. DeGrazia asks whether "normal aging" is "an essential part of any recognizable human life," and falters here, admitting, "frankly, I do not know how to determine whether aging is an inviolable characteristic." The question, then, is whether someone who does try to "violate" this characteristic by biotechnological means is acting unethically. It is hard to see why the answer would be yes. Such would-be immortals are not forcing other people to live or die, nor are they infringing on the rights or dignities of others. DeGrazia finally recognizes that biotech methods aimed at slowing or delaying aging significantly are not morally different from technologies that would boost intelligence or reduce the need for sleep. He concludes, "even if aging is an inviolable core trait of human beings, living no more than some specified number of years is not." . . .

DeGrazia convincingly argues that whatever it is that makes us fundamentally us is not captured by the set of characteristics he considers. The inviolable core of our identities is the narrative of our lives—the sum of our experiences, enhanced or not. If we lose that core (say, through dementia), we truly do lose ourselves. But whoever we are persists and perhaps even flourishes if we choose to use biotech to brighten our moods, improve our personalities, boost our intelligence, sleep less, live longer and healthier lives, change our gender, or even change species. . . .

# Enhancement Wars?

Those who favor restricting human enhancements often argue that human equality will fall victim to differential access to enhancement technologies, resulting in conflicts between the enhanced and the unenhanced. For example, at a 2006 meeting called by the American Association for the Advancement of Science, Richard Hayes, the executive director of the left-leaning Center for Genetics and Society, testified that "enhancement technologies would quickly be adopted by the most privileged, with the clear intent of widening the divisions that separate them and their progeny from the rest of the human species." Deploying such enhancement technologies would "deepen genetic and biological inequality among individuals," exacerbating "tendencies towards xenophobia, racism and warfare." Hayes concluded that allowing people to use genetic engineering for enhancement "could be a mistake of world-historical proportions." . . .

In the same vein, George J. Annas, Lori B. Andrews, and Rosario M. Isasi have laid out a rather apocalyptic scenario in the *American Journal of Law and Medicine:*

> The new species, or "posthuman," will likely view the old "normal" humans as inferior, even savages, and fit for slavery or slaughter. The normals, on the other hand, may see the posthumans as a threat and if they can, may engage in a preemptive strike by killing the posthumans before they themselves are killed or enslaved by them. It is ultimately this predictable potential for genocide that makes species-altering experiments potential weapons of mass destruction, and makes the unaccountable genetic engineer a potential bioterrorist.

Let's take their over-the-top scenario down a notch or two. The enhancements that are likely to be available in the relatively near term to people now living will be pharmacological—pills and shots to increase strength, lighten moods, and improve memory. Consequently, such interventions could be distributed to nearly everyone who wanted them. Later in this century, when safe genetic engineering becomes possible, it will likely be deployed gradually and will enable parents to give their children beneficial genes for improved health and intelligence that other children already get naturally. Thus, safe genetic engineering in the long run is more likely to ameliorate than to exacerbate human inequality. . . .

## The Necessity of Moral Toleration

People should not be forced to use medicines and technologies that they find morally objectionable. Take the case of the Amish. Amish individuals live in an open society—ours—and can opt out of our society or theirs whenever they want. As followers of a reasonable comprehensive doctrine, they have a system for voluntarily deciding among themselves what new technologies they will embrace. (For instance, despite their generally anti-technology stance, Amish practicality has caused them to embrace modern medicine when it comes to treating genetic maladies that plague their community.) The situation of the Amish demonstrates that technological choices don't have to involve everyone in a given society.

One can imagine that, eventually, different treatment and enhancement regimens will be available to accommodate the different values and beliefs held by citizens. Christian Scientists would perhaps reject most of modern biotechnology outright; Jehovah's Witnesses might remain leery of treatments that they consider akin to using blood products or blood transfusions; Catholics might refuse to use regenerative treatments derived from destroyed human embryos; and still others may wish to take the fullest advantage of all biomedical enhancements and treatments. In this way, members of a pluralistic society respect the reasonable comprehensive doctrines of their fellow citizens, thus enabling social peace among moral strangers.

Daniel Callahan, in an essay in *Cato Unbound,* writes: "I really wish we would be told, when the great day arrives and we have dozens, maybe hundreds of years ahead of us, exactly how it would all work." Well, I wish I knew too, but the fact of the matter is that humanity advances by trial and error. Even the smartest people cannot figure out how scientific and technological advances will play out over the next few decades, much less centuries. In 1960, the optical laser was reputedly described as an invention looking for a job. In 2011, ubiquitous lasers routinely cut metal, play CDs, reshape corneas, carry billions of Internet messages, remove tattoos, and guide bombs. As age-retardation and other enhancement technologies are likely to develop incrementally, humanity will have lots of opportunities for course corrections as we go along.

The very good news is that the history of the last two centuries has shown that technological advance has been far more beneficial than harmful for humanity. The development of age-retardation and other enhancement technologies will be further steps along that encouraging progressive path. We should all have the right to choose to use or not use new technologies to help us and our families flourish. Is humanity ready for enhancements like radically longer life spans? We're about as ready as we'll ever be. In other words: yes. . . .

---

RONALD BAILEY is the science correspondent for *Reason* magazine and Reason.com.

# Global and Political Issues

The question of whether society helps to shape technological advancement and innovation or whether technology shapes social systems and relationships was posed in the section, Theories of Technology and Society. However the question is answered, the relationship between technology and society involves the values, beliefs, and norms of entire social systems. For example, one groups' beliefs can be promoted through the use of specific technology while diminishing the beliefs of another group. On a grand scale, technology can be used to improve the quality of life for entire communities, or it might be used to destroy them. Technology may be used to subdue the voices of marginalized individuals but it may also be used to draw attention to inhumane or unethical practices affecting certain groups. Our world has become ever more interconnected, no longer can governments turn a blind eye to injustices occurring in other parts of the world. While we may be presented with more opportunities to gather information on individuals and social systems around the world, is it quality information? How do we make decisions or process information when we are overwhelmed with it on a daily basis? Our information society has exposed us to other communities, issues, and problems. Will it be up to technology to help us cognitively organize the information as well? The readings presented in this section elucidate the politics surrounding technological development and its implementation in different parts of the world.

## Learning Objectives

1. Identify the role of individual and group values in the development and implementation of technology.
2. Identify the ways in which technology has changed, shaped, and influenced the political climate of our world.
3. Identify the ways we promote the needs of the poor, or ways in which we disenfranchise them through technology.

# Do Artifacts Have Politics?

No idea is more provocative in controversies about technology and society than the notion that technical things have political qualities. At issue is the claim that the machines, structures, and systems of modern material culture can be accurately judged not only for their contributions to efficiency and productivity and their positive and negative environmental side effects, but also for the ways in which they can embody specific forms of power and authority. Since ideas of this kind are a persistent and troubling presence in discussions about the meaning of technology, they deserve explicit attention.

Writing in the early 1960s, Lewis Mumford gave classic statement to one version of the theme, arguing that "from late neolithic times in the Near East, right down to our own day, two technologies have recurrently existed side by side: one authoritarian, the other democratic, the first system-centered, immensely powerful, but inherently unstable, the other man-centered, relatively weak, but resourceful and durable."[1] This thesis stands at the heart of Mumford's studies of the city, architecture, and history of technics, and mirrors concerns voiced earlier in the works of Peter Kropotkin, William Morris, and other nineteenth-century critics of industrialism. During the 1970s, antinuclear and pro-solar energy movements in Europe and the United States adopted a similar notion as the centerpiece of their arguments. According to environmentalist Denis Hayes, "The increased deployment of nuclear power facilities must lead society toward authoritarianism. Indeed, safe reliance upon nuclear power as the principal source of energy may be possible only in a totalitarian state." Echoing the views of many proponents of appropriate technology and the soft energy path, Hayes contends that "dispersed solar sources are more compatible than centralized technologies with social equity, freedom and cultural pluralism."[2]

An eagerness to interpret technical artifacts in political language is by no means the exclusive property of critics of large-scale, high-technology systems. A long lineage of boosters has insisted that the biggest and best that science and industry made available were the best guarantees of democracy, freedom, and social justice. The factory system, automobile, telephone, radio, television, space program, and of course nuclear power have all at one time or another been described as democratizing, liberating forces. David Lilienthal's *TVA: Democracy on the March*, for example, found this promise in the phosphate fertilizers and electricity that technical progress was bringing to rural Americans during the 1940s.[3] Three decades later Daniel Boorstin's *The Republic of Technology* extolled television for "its power to disband armies, to cashier presidents, to create a whole new democratic world.[4] Scarcely a new invention comes along that someone doesn't proclaim it as the salvation of a free society.

It is no surprise to learn that technical systems of various kinds are deeply interwoven in the conditions of modern politics. The physical arrangements of industrial production, warfare, communications, and the like have fundamentally changed the exercise of power and the experience of citizenship. But to go beyond this obvious fact and to argue that certain technologies in *themselves* have political properties seems, at first glance, completely mistaken. We all know that people have politics; things do not. To discover either virtues or evils in aggregates of steel, plastic, transistors, integrated circuits, chemicals, and the like seems just plain wrong, a way of mystifying human artifice and of avoiding the true sources, the human sources of freedom and oppression, justice and injustice. Blaming the hardware appears even more foolish than blaming the victims when it comes to judging conditions of public life.

Hence, the stern advice commonly given those who flirt with the notion that technical artifacts have political qualities: What matters is not technology itself, but the social or economic system in which it is embedded. This maxim, which in a number of variations is the central premise of a theory that can be called the social determination of technology, has an obvious wisdom. It serves as a needed corrective to those who focus uncritically upon such things as "the computer and its social impacts" but who fail to look behind technical devices to see the social circumstances of their development, deployment, and use. This view provides an antidote to naive technological determinism–the idea that technology develops as the sole result of an internal dynamic and then, unmediated by any other influence, molds society to fit its patterns. Those who have not recognized the ways in which technologies are shaped by social and economic forces have not gotten very far.

But the corrective has its own shortcomings; taken literally, it suggests that technical *things* do not matter at all. Once one has done the detective work necessary to reveal the social origins– power holders behind a particular instance of technological change–one will have explained everything of importance. This conclusion offers comfort to social scientists. It validates what they had always suspected, namely, that there is nothing distinctive about the study of technology in the first place. Hence, they can return to their standard models of social power– those of interest-group politics, bureaucratic politics, Marxist models of class struggle, and the like–and have everything they need. The social determination of technology is, in this view, essentially no different from the social determination of, say, welfare policy or taxation.

There are, however, good reasons to believe that technology is politically significant in its own right, good reasons why the standard models of social science only go so far in accounting for what is most interesting and troublesome about the subject. Much of modern social and political thought contains recurring statements of what can be called a theory of technological politics, an odd mongrel of notions often crossbred with orthodox liberal, conservative, and socialist philosophies.[5] The theory of technological politics draws attention to the momentum of large-scale sociotechnical systems, to the response of modern societies to certain technological imperatives, and to the ways human ends are powerfully transformed as they are adapted to technical means. This perspective offers a novel framework of interpretation and explanation for some of the more puzzling patterns that have taken shape in and around the growth of modern material culture. Its starting point is a decision to take technical artifacts seriously. Rather than insist that we immediately reduce everything to the interplay of social forces, the theory of technological politics suggests that we pay attention to the characteristics of technical objects and the meaning of those characteristics. A necessary complement to, rather than a replacement for, theories of the social determination of technology, this approach identifies certain technologies as political phenomena in their own right. It points us back, to borrow Edmund Husserl's philosophical injunction, *to the things themselves.*

In what follows I will outline and illustrate two ways in which artifacts can contain political properties. First are instances in which the invention, design, or arrangement of a specific technical device or system becomes a way of settling an issue in the affairs of a particular community. Seen in the proper light, examples of this kind are fairly straightforward and easily under stood. Second are cases of what can be called "inherently political technologies," man-made systems that appear to require or to be strongly compatible with particular kinds of political relationships. Arguments about cases of this kind are much more troublesome and closer to the heart of the matter. By the term "politics" I mean arrangements of power and authority in human associations as well as the activities that take place within those arrangements. For my purposes here, the term "technology" is understood to mean all of modern practical artifice, but to avoid confusion I prefer to speak of "technologies" plural, smaller or larger pieces or systems of hardware of a specific kind.[6] My intention is not to settle any of the issues here once and for all, but to indicate their general dimensions and significance.

### *Technical Arrangements and Social Order*

ANYONE WHO has traveled the highways of America and has gotten used to the normal height of overpasses may well find something a little odd about some of the bridges over the park ways on Long Island, New York. Many of the overpasses are extraordinarily low, having as little as nine feet of clearance at the curb. Even those who happened to notice this structural peculiarity would not be inclined to attach any special meaning to it. In our accustomed way of looking at things such as roads and bridges, we see the details of form as innocuous and seldom give them a second thought.

It turns out, however, that some two hundred or so low- hanging overpasses on Long Island are there for a reason. They were deliberately designed and built that way by someone who wanted to achieve a particular social effect. Robert Moses, the master builder of roads, parks, bridges, and other public works of the 1920s to the 1970s in New York, built his overpasses ac cording to specifications that would discourage the presence of buses on his parkways. According to evidence provided by Moses' biographer, Robert A. Caro, the reasons reflect Moses social class bias and racial prejudice. Automobile-owning whites of "upper" and "comfortable middle" classes, as he called them, would be free to use the parkways for recreation and commuting. Poor people and blacks, who normally used public transit, were kept off the roads because the twelve-foot tall buses could not handle the overpasses. One consequence was to limit access of racial minorities and low-income groups to Jones Beach, Moses' widely acclaimed public park. Moses made doubly sure of this result by vetoing a proposed extension of the Long Island Railroad to Jones Beach.

Robert Moses' life is a fascinating story in recent U. S. political history. His dealings with mayors, governors, and presidents; his careful manipulation of legislatures, banks, labor unions, the press, and public opinion could be studied by political scientists for years. But the most important and enduring results of his work are his technologies, the vast engineering projects that give New York much of its present form. For generations after Moses' death and the alliances he forged have fallen apart, his public works, especially the highways and bridges he built to favor the use of the automobile over the development of mass transit, will continue to shape that city. Many of his monumental structures of concrete and steel embody a systematic social inequality, a way of engineering relationships among people that, after a time, became just another part of the landscape. As New York planner Lee Koppleman told Caro about the low bridges on Wantagh Parkway, "The old son of a gun had made sure that buses would *never* be able to use his goddamned parkways."[7]

Histories of architecture, city planning, and public works contain many examples of physical arrangements with explicit or implicit political purposes. One can point to Baron Haussmann's broad Parisian thoroughfares, engineered at Louis Napoleon's direction to prevent any recurrence of street fighting of the kind that took place during the revolution of 1848. Or one can visit any number of grotesque concrete buildings and huge plazas constructed on university campuses in the United States during the late 1960s and early 1970s to defuse student demonstrations. Studies of industrial machines and instruments also turn up interesting political stories, including some that violate our normal expectations about why technological innovations are made in the first place. If we suppose that new technologies are introduced to achieve increased efficiency, the history of technology shows that we will sometimes be disappointed. Technological change expresses a panoply of human motives, not the least of which is the desire of some to have dominion over others even though it may require an occasional sacrifice of cost savings and some violation of the normal standard of trying to get more from less.

One poignant illustration can be found in the history of nineteenth-century industrial mechanization. At Cyrus McCormick's reaper manufacturing plant in Chicago in the middle 1880s, pneumatic molding machines, a new and largely untested innovation, were added to the foundry at an estimated cost of $500,000. The standard economic interpretation would lead us to expect that this step was taken to modernize the plant and achieve the kind of efficiencies that mechanization brings. But historian Robert Ozanne has put the development in a broader context. At the time, Cyrus McCormick II was engaged in a battle with the National Union of Iron Molders. He saw the addition of the new machines as a way to 'weed out the bad element among the men," namely, the skilled workers who had organized the union local in Chicago.[8] The new machines, manned by unskilled laborers, actually produced inferior castings at a higher cost than the earlier process. After three years of use the machines were, in fact, abandoned, but by that time they had served their purpose–the destruction of the union. Thus, the story of these technical developments at the McCormick factory cannot be adequately understood outside the record of workers' attempts to organize, police repression of the labor movement in Chicago during that period, and the events surrounding the bombing at Haymarket Square. Technological history and U.S. political history were at that moment deeply intertwined.

In the examples of Moses' low bridges and McCormick's molding machines, one sees the importance of technical arrangements that precede the *use* of the things in question. It is obvious that technologies can be used in ways that enhance the power, authority, and privilege of some over others, for ex ample, the use of television to sell a candidate. In our accustomed way of thinking technologies are seen as neutral tools that can be used well or poorly, for good, evil, or something in between. But we usually do not stop to inquire whether a given device might have been designed and built in such a way that it produces a set of consequences logically and temporally *prior to any of its professed uses*. Robert Moses' bridges, after all, were used to carry automobiles from one point to another; McCormick's machines were used to make metal castings; both technologies, however, encompassed purposes far beyond their immediate use. If our moral and political language for evaluating technology includes only categories having to do with tools and uses, if it does not include attention to the meaning of the de signs and arrangements of our artifacts, then we will be blinded to much that is intellectually and practically crucial.

Because the point is most easily understood in the light of particular intentions embodied in physical form, I have so far offered illustrations that seem almost conspiratorial. But to recognize the political dimensions in the shapes of technology does not require that we look for conscious conspiracies or malicious intentions. The organized movement of handicapped people in the United States during the 1970s pointed out the countless ways in which machines, instruments, and structures of common use–buses, buildings, sidewalks, plumbing fixtures, and so forth–made it impossible for many handicapped persons to move freely about, a condition that systematically excluded them from public life. It is safe to say that designs unsuited for the handicapped arose more from long-standing neglect than from anyone's active intention. But once the issue was brought to public attention, it became evident that justice required a remedy. A whole range of artifacts have been redesigned and rebuilt to accommodate this minority.

Indeed, many of the most important examples of technologies that have political consequences are those that transcend the simple categories "intended" and "unintended" altogether. These are instances in which the very process of technical development is so thoroughly biased in a particular direction that it regularly produces results heralded as wonderful breakthroughs by some social interests and crushing setbacks by others. In such cases it is neither correct nor insightful to say, "Someone intended to do somebody else harm." Rather one must say that the technological deck has been stacked in advance to favor certain social interests and that some people were bound to receive a better hand than others.

The mechanical tomato harvester, a remarkable device perfected by researchers at the University of California from the late 1940s to the present offers an illustrative tale. The machine is able to harvest tomatoes in a single pass through a row, cutting the plants from the ground, shaking the fruit loose, and (in the newest models) sorting the tomatoes electronically into large plastic gondolas that hold up to twenty-five tons of produce headed for canning factories. To accommodate the rough motion of these harvesters in the field, agricultural researchers have bred new varieties of tomatoes that are hardier, sturdier, and less tasty than those previously grown. The harvesters replace the system of handpicking in which crews of farm workers would pass through the fields three or four times, putting ripe tomatoes in lug boxes and saving immature fruit for later harvest.[9] Studies in California indicate that the use of the machine reduces costs by approximately five to seven dollars per ton as compared to hand harvesting.[10] But the benefits are by no means equally divided in the agricultural economy. In fact, the machine in the garden has in this instance been the occasion for a thorough re shaping of social relationships involved in tomato production in rural California.

By virtue of their very size and cost of more than $50,000 each, the machines are compatible only with a highly concentrated form of tomato growing. With the introduction of this new method of harvesting, the number of tomato growers declined from approximately 4,000 in the early 1960s to about 600 in 1973, and yet there was a substantial increase in tons of tomatoes produced. By the late 1970s an estimated 32,000 jobs in the tomato industry had been eliminated as a direct consequence of mechanization.[11] Thus, a jump in productivity to the benefit of very large growers has occurred at the sacrifice of other rural agricultural communities.

The University of California's research on and development of agricultural machines such as the tomato harvester eventually became the subject of a lawsuit filed by attorneys for California Rural Legal Assistance, an organization representing a group of farm workers and other interested parties. The suit charged that university officials are spending tax monies on projects that benefit a handful of private interests to the detriment of farm workers, small farmers, consumers, and rural California generally and asks for a court injunction to stop the practice. The university denied these charges, arguing that to accept them "would require elimination of all research with any potential practical application."[12]

As far as I know, no one argued that the development of the tomato harvester was the result of a plot. Two students of the controversy, William Friedland and Amy Barton, specifically exonerate the original developers of the machine and the hard tomato from any desire to facilitate economic concentration in that industry.[13] What we see here instead is an ongoing social process in which scientific knowledge, technological invention, and corporate profit reinforce each other in deeply entrenched patterns, patterns that bear the unmistakable stamp of political and economic power. Over many decades agricultural research and development in U.S. land-grant colleges and universities has tended to favor the interests of large agribusiness concerns.[14] It is in the face of such subtly ingrained patterns that opponents of innovations such as the tomato harvester are made to seem "antitechnology" or "antiprogress." For the harvester is not merely the symbol of a social order that rewards some while punishing others; it is in a true sense an embodiment of that order.

Within a given category of technological change there are, roughly speaking, two kinds of choices that can affect the relative distribution of power, authority, and privilege in a community. Often the crucial decision is a simple "yes or no" choice—are we going to develop and adopt the thing or not? In recent years many local, national, and international disputes about technology have centered on "yes or no" judgments about such things as food additives, pesticides, the building of highways, nuclear reactors, dam projects, and proposed high-tech weapons. The fundamental choice about an antiballistic missile or supersonic transport is whether or not the thing is going to join society as a piece of its operating equipment. Reasons given for and against are frequently as important as those concerning the adoption of an important new law.

A second range of choices, equally critical in many instances, has to do with specific features in the design or arrangement of a technical system after the decision to go ahead with it has already been made. Even after a utility company wins permission to build a large electric power line, important controversies can remain with respect to the placement of its route and the design of its towers; even after an organization has decided to institute a system of computers, controversies can still arise with regard to the kinds of components, programs, modes of access, and other specific features the system will include. Once the mechanical tomato harvester had been developed in its basic form, a design alteration of critical social significance—the addition of electronic sorters, for example—changed the character of the machine's effects upon the balance of wealth and power in California agriculture. Some of the most interesting research on technology and politics at present focuses upon the attempt to demonstrate in a detailed, concrete fashion how seemingly innocuous design features in mass transit systems, water projects, industrial machinery, and other technologies actually mask social choices of profound significance. Historian David Noble has studied two kinds of automated machine tool systems that have different implications for the relative power of management and labor in the industries that might employ them. He has shown that although the basic electronic and mechanical components of the record/playback and numerical control systems are similar, the choice of one design over another has crucial consequences for social struggles on the shop floor. To see the matter solely in terms of cost cutting, efficiency, or the modernization of equipment is to miss a decisive element in the story.[15]

From such examples I would offer some general conclusions. These correspond to the interpretation of technologies as "forms of life" presented in the previous chapter, filling in the explicitly political dimensions of that point of view.

The things we call "technologies" are ways of building order in our world. Many technical devices and systems important in everyday life contain possibilities for many different ways of ordering human activity. Consciously or unconsciously, deliberately or inadvertently, societies choose structures for technologies that influence how people are going to work, communicate, travel, consume, and so forth over a very long time. In the processes by which structuring decisions are made, different people are situated differently and possess unequal degrees of power as well as unequal levels of awareness. By far the greatest latitude of choice exists the very first time a particular instrument, system, or technique is introduced. Because choices tend to become strongly fixed in material equipment, economic investment, and social habit, the original flexibility vanishes for all practical purposes once the initial commitments are made. In that sense technological innovations are similar to legislative acts or political foundings that establish a framework for public order that will endure over many generations. For that reason the same careful attention one would give to the rules, roles, and relationships of politics must also be given to such things as the building of highways, the creation of television networks, and the tailoring of seemingly insignificant features on new machines. The issues that divide or unite people in society are settled not only in the institutions and practices of politics proper, but also, and less obviously, in tangible arrangements of steel and concrete, wires and semiconductors, nuts and bolts.

### Inherently Political Technologies

NONE OF the arguments and examples considered thus far addresses a stronger, more troubling claim often made in writings about technology and society—the belief that some technologies are by their very nature political in a specific way. According to this view, the adoption of a given technical system unavoidably brings with it conditions for human relationships that have a distinctive political cast—for example, centralized or de-centralized, egalitarian or inegalitarian, repressive or liberating. This is ultimately what is at stake in assertions such as those of Lewis Mumford that two traditions of technology, one authoritarian, the other democratic, exist side-by-side in Western history. In all the cases cited above the technologies are relatively flexible in design and arrangement and variable in their effects. Although one can recognize a particular result produced in a particular setting, one can also easily imagine how a roughly similar device or system might have been built or situated with very much different political consequences. The idea we must now examine and evaluate is that certain kinds of technology do not allow such flexibility, and that to choose them is to choose unalterably a particular form of political life.

A remarkably forceful statement of one version of this argument appears in Friedrich Engels' little essay "On Authority" written in 1872. Answering anarchists who believed that authority is an evil that ought to be abolished altogether, Engels launches into a panegyric for authoritarianism, maintaining, among other things, that strong authority is a necessary condition in modern industry. To advance his case in the strongest possible way, he asks his readers to imagine that the revolution has already occurred. "Supposing a social revolution dethroned the capitalists, who now exercise their authority over the production and circulation of wealth. Supposing, to adopt entirely the point of view of the anti- authoritarians, that the land and the instruments of labour had become the collective property of the workers who use them. Will authority have disappeared or will it have only changed its form?"[16]

His answer draws upon lessons from three sociotechnical systems of his day, cotton-spinning mills, railways, and ships at sea. He observes that on its way to becoming finished thread, cotton moves through a number of different operations at different locations in the factory. The workers perform a wide variety of tasks, from running the steam engine to carrying the products from one room to another. Because these tasks must be coordinated and because the timing of the work is "fixed by the authority of the steam," laborers must learn to accept a rigid discipline. They must, according to Engels, work at regular hours and agree to subordinate their individual wills to the persons in charge of factory operations. If they fail to do so, they risk the horrifying possibility that production will come to a grinding halt. Engels pulls no punches. "The automatic machinery of a big factory," he writes, "is much more despotic than the small capitalists who employ workers ever have been."[17]

Similar lessons are adduced in Engels's analysis of the necessary operating conditions for railways and ships at sea. Both require the subordination of workers to an "imperious authority" that sees to it that things run according to plan. Engels finds that far from being an idiosyncrasy of capitalist social organization, relationships of authority and subordination arise "independently of all social organization, and are imposed upon us together with the material conditions under which we produce and make products circulate." Again, he intends this to be stern advice to the anarchists who, according to Engels, thought it possible simply to eradicate subordination and superordination at a single stroke. All such schemes are nonsense. The roots of unavoidable authoritarianism are, he argues, deeply implanted in the human involvement with science and technology. "If man, by dint of his knowledge and inventive genius, has subdued the forces of nature, the latter avenge themselves upon him by subjecting him, insofar as he employs them, to a veritable despotism independent of all social organization.[18]

Attempts to justify strong authority on the basis of supposedly necessary conditions of technical practice have an ancient history. A pivotal theme in the *Republic* is Plato's quest to borrow the authority of *technology* and employ it by analogy to buttress his argument in favor of authority in the state. Among the illustrations he chooses, like Engels, is that of a ship on the high seas. Because large sailing vessels by their very nature need to be steered with a firm hand, sailors must yield to their captain's commands; no reasonable person believes that ships can be run democratically. Plato goes on to suggest that governing a state is rather like being captain of a ship or like practicing medicine as a physician. Much the same conditions that require central rule and decisive action in organized technical activity also create this need in government.

In Engels's argument, and arguments like it, the justification for authority is no longer made by Plato's classic analogy, but rather directly with reference to technology itself. If the basic case is as compelling as Engels believed it to be, one would expect that as a society adopted increasingly complicated technical systems as its material basis, the prospects for authoritarian ways of life would be greatly enhanced. Central control by knowledgeable people acting at the top of a rigid social hierarchy would seem increasingly prudent. In this respect his stand in "On Authority" appears to be at variance with Karl Marx's position in Volume I of *Capital*. Marx tries to show that increasing mechanization will render obsolete the hierarchical division of labor and the relationships of subordination that, in his view, were necessary during the early stages of modern manufacturing. "Modern Industry," he writes, "sweeps away by technical means the manufacturing division of labor, under which each man is bound hand and foot for life to a single detail operation. At the same time, the capitalistic form of that industry reproduces this same division of labour in a still more monstrous shape; in the factory proper, by converting the workman into a living appendage of the machine."[19] In Marx's view the conditions that will eventually dissolve the capitalist division of labor and facilitate proletarian revolution are conditions latent in industrial technology itself The differences between Marx's position in *Capital* and Engels's in his essay raise an important question for socialism: What, after all, does modern technology make possible or necessary in political life? The theoretical tension we see here mirrors many troubles in the practice of freedom and authority that had muddied the tracks of socialist revolution.

Arguments to the effect that technologies are in some sense inherently political have been advanced in a wide variety of contexts, far too many to summarize here. My reading of such notions, however, reveals there are two basic ways of stating the case. One version claims that the adoption of a given technical system actually requires the creation and maintenance of a particular set of social conditions as the operating environment of that system.

Engels's position is of this kind. A similar view is offered by a contemporary writer who holds that "if you accept nuclear power plants, you also accept a techno-scientific industrial-military elite. Without these people in charge, you could not have nuclear power."[20] In this conception some kinds of technology require their social environments to be structured in a particular way in much the same sense that an automobile requires wheels in order to move. The thing could not exist as an effective operating entity unless certain social as well as material conditions were met. The meaning of "required" here is that of practical (rather than logical) necessity~ Thus, Plato thought it a practical necessity that a ship at sea have one captain and an unquestionably obedient crew.

A second, somewhat weaker, version of the argument holds that a given kind of technology is strongly compatible with, but does not strictly require, social and political relationships of a particular stripe. Many advocates of solar energy have argued that technologies of that variety are more compatible with a democratic, egalitarian society than energy systems based on coal, oil, and nuclear power; at the same time they do not maintain that anything about solar energy requires democracy. Their case is, briefly, that solar energy is decentralizing in both a technical and political sense: technically speaking, it is vastly more reasonable to build solar systems in a disaggregated, widely distributed manner than in large-scale centralized plants; politically speaking, solar energy accommodates the attempts of individuals and local communities to manage their affairs effectively be cause they are dealing with systems that are more accessible, comprehensible, and controllable than huge centralized sources. In this view solar energy is desirable not only for its economic and environmental benefits, but also for the salutary institutions it is likely to permit in other areas of public life.[21]

Within both versions of the argument there is a further distinction to be made between conditions that are internal to the workings of a given technical system and those that are external to it. Engels's thesis concerns internal social relations said to be required within cotton factories and railways, for example; what such relationships mean for the condition of society at large is, for him, a separate question. In contrast, the solar advocate's belief that solar technologies are compatible with democracy pertains to the way they complement aspects of society removed from the organization of those technologies as such.

There are, then, several different directions that arguments of this kind can follow. Are the social conditions predicated said to be required by, or strongly compatible with, the workings of a given technical system? Are those conditions internal to that system or external to it (or both)? Although writings that address such questions are often unclear about what is being asserted, arguments in this general category are an important part of modern political discourse. They enter into many attempts to explain how changes in social life take place in the wake of technological innovation. More important, they are often used to buttress attempts to justify or criticize proposed courses of action involving new technology. By offering distinctly political reasons for or against the adoption of a particular technology, arguments of this kind stand apart from more commonly employed, more easily quantifiable claims about economic costs and benefits, environmental impacts, and possible risks to public health and safety that technical systems may involve. The issue here does not concern how many jobs will be created, how much income generated, how many pollutants added, or how many cancers produced. Rather, the issue has to do with ways in which choices about technology have important consequences for the form and quality of human associations.

If we examine social patterns that characterize the environments of technical systems, we find certain devices and systems almost invariably linked to specific ways of organizing power and authority. The important question is: Does this state of affairs derive from an unavoidable social response to intractable properties in the things themselves, or is it instead a pattern imposed independently by a governing body, ruling class, or some other social or cultural institution to further its own purposes?

Taking the most obvious example, the atom bomb is an inherently political artifact. As long as it exists at all, its lethal properties demand that it be controlled by a centralized, rigidly hierarchical chain of command closed to all influences that might make its workings unpredictable. The internal social system of the bomb must be authoritarian; there is no other way. The state of affairs stands as a practical necessity independent of any larger political system in which the bomb is embedded, independent of the type of regime or character of its rulers. Indeed, democratic states must try to find ways to ensure that the social structures and mentality that characterize the management of nuclear weapons do not "spin off" or "spill over" into the polity as a whole.

The bomb is, of course, a special case. The reasons very rigid relationships of authority are necessary in its immediate presence should be clear to anyone. If, however, we look for other instances in which particular varieties of technology are widely perceived to need the maintenance of a special pattern of power and authority, modern technical history contains a wealth of examples. Alfred D. Chandler in *The Visible Hand*, a monumental study of modern business enterprise, presents impressive documentation to defend the hypothesis that the construction and day-to day operation of many systems of production, transportation, and communication in the nineteenth and twentieth centuries require the development of particular social form–a large-scale centralized, hierarchical organization administered by highly skilled managers. Typical of Chandler's reasoning is his analysis of the growth of the railroads.[22]

Technology made possible fast, all-weather transportation; but safe, regular, reliable movement of goods and passengers, as well as the continuing maintenance and repair of locomotives, rolling stock, and track, roadbed, stations, roundhouses, and other equipment, required the creation of a sizable administrative organization. It meant the employment of a set of managers to supervise these functional activities over an extensive geographical area; and the appointment of an administrative command of middle and top executives to monitor, evaluate, and coordinate the work of managers responsible for the day-to-day operations.

Throughout his book Chandler points to ways in which technologies used in the production and distribution of electricity, chemicals, and a wide range of industrial goods "demanded" or "required" this form of human association. "Hence, the operational requirements of railroads demanded the creation of the first administrative hierarchies in American business."[23]

Were there other conceivable ways of organizing these aggregates of people and apparatus? Chandler shows that a previously dominant social form, the small traditional family firm, simply could not handle the task in most cases. Although he does not specu-late further, it is clear that he believes there is, to be realistic, very little latitude in the forms of power and authority appropriate within modern sociotechnical systems. The properties of many modern technologies.[24] But the weight of argument and empirical evidence in *The Visible Hand* suggests that any significant departure from the basic pattern would be, at best, highly unlikely.

It may be that other conceivable arrangements of power and authority, for example, those of decentralized, democratic worker self-management, could prove capable of administering factories, refineries, communications systems, and railroads as well as or better than the organizations Chandler describes. Evidence from automobile assembly teams in Sweden and worker- managed plants in Yugoslavia and other countries is often presented to salvage these possibilities. Unable to settle controversies over this matter here, I merely point to what I consider to be their bone of contention. The available evidence tends to show that many large, sophisticated technological systems are in fact highly compatible with centralized, hierarchical managerial control. The interesting question, however, has to do with whether or not this pattern is in any sense a requirement of such systems, a question that is not solely empirical. The matter ultimately rests on our judgments about what steps, if any, are practically necessary in the workings of particular kinds of technology and what, if anything, such measures require of the structure of human associations. Was Plato right in saying that a ship at sea needs steering by a decisive hand and that this could only be accomplished by a single captain and an obedient crew? Is Chandler correct in saying that the properties of large-scale systems require centralized, hierarchical managerial control?

To answer such questions, we would have to examine in some detail the moral claims of practical necessity (including those advocated in the doctrines of economics) and weigh them against moral claims of other sorts, for example, the notion that it is good for sailors to participate in the command of a ship or that workers have a right to be involved in making and administering decisions in a factory. It is characteristic of societies based on large, complex technological systems, however, that moral reasons other than those of practical necessity appear increasingly obsolete, "idealistic," and irrelevant. Whatever claims one may wish to make on behalf of liberty, justice, or equality can be immediately neutralized when confronted with arguments to the effect, "Fine, but that's no way to run a railroad" (or steel mill, or airline, or communication system, and so on). Here we en counter an important quality in modern political discourse and in the way people commonly think about what measures are justified in response to the possibilities technologies make avail able. In many instances, to say that some technologies are inherently political is to say that certain widely accepted reasons of practical necessity–especially the need to maintain crucial technological systems as smoothly working entities– have tended to eclipse other sorts of moral and political reasoning.

One attempt to salvage the autonomy of politics from the bind of practical necessity involves the notion that conditions of human association found in the internal workings of technological systems can easily be kept separate from the polity as a whole. Americans have long rested content in the belief that arrangements of power and authority inside industrial corporations, public utili-ties, and the like have little bearing on public institutions, practices, and ideas at large. That "democracy stops at the factory gates" was taken as a fact of life that had nothing to do with the practice of political freedom. But can the internal politics of technology and the politics of the whole community be so easily separated? A recent study of business leaders in the United States, contempo-rary exemplars of Chandler's "visible hand of management," found them remark ably impatient with such democratic scruples as "one man one vote. If democracy doesn't work for the firm, the most critical institution in all of society, American executives ask, how well can it be expected to work for the government of a nation–particularly when that government attempts to interfere with the achievements of the firm? The authors of the report observe that patterns of authority that work effectively in the corporation be come for businessmen "the desirable model against which to compare political and economic relationships in the rest of society."[25] While such findings are far from conclusive, they do reflect a sentiment increasingly common in the land: what dilemmas such as the energy crisis require is not a redistribution of wealth or broader public participation but, rather, stronger, centralized public and private management.

An especially vivid case in which the operational requirements of a technical system might influence the quality of public life is the debates about the risks of nuclear power. As the supply of uranium for nuclear reactors runs out, a proposed alternative fuel is the plutonium generated as a byproduct in reactor cores. Well-known objections to plutonium recycling focus on its unaccepta-ble economic costs, its risks of environmental contamination, and its dangers in regard to the international proliferation of nuclear weapons. Beyond these concerns, however stands another less widely appreciated set of hazards–those that involve the sacrifice of civil liberties. The widespread use of plutonium as a fuel increases the chance that this toxic substance might be stolen by terror-ists, organized crime, or other per sons. This raises the prospect, and not a trivial one, that extraordinary measures would have to be taken to safeguard plutonium from theft and to recover it should the substance be stolen. Workers in the nuclear industry as well as ordinary citizens outside could well become subject to background security checks, covert surveillance, wiretapping, informers, and even emergency measures under martial law–all justified by the need to safeguard plutonium.

Russell W. Ayres's study of the legal ramifications of plutonium recycling concludes: "With the passage of time and the increase in the quantity of plutonium in existence will come pressure to eliminate the traditional checks the courts and legislatures place on the activities of the executive and to develop a powerful central authority better able to enforce strict safeguards." He avers that "once a quantity of plutonium had been stolen, the case for literally turning the country upside down to get it back would be overwhelming." Ayres anticipates and worries about the kinds of thinking that, I have argued, characterize inherently political technologies. It is still true that in a world in which human beings make and maintain artificial systems nothing is "required" in an absolute sense. Nevertheless, once a course of action is under way, once artifacts such as nuclear power plants have been built and put in operation, the kinds of reasoning that justify the adaptation of social life to technical requirements pop up as spontaneously as flowers in the spring. In Ayres's words, "Once recycling begins and the risks of plutonium theft become real rather than hypothetical, the case for governmental infringement of protected rights will seem compelling."[26] After a certain point, those who cannot accept the hard requirements and imperatives will be dismissed as dreamers and fools.

\* \* \*

The two varieties of interpretation I have outlined indicate how artifacts can have political qualities. In the first instance we noticed ways in which specific features in the design or arrangement of a device or system could provide a convenient means of establishing patterns of power and authority in a given setting. Technologies of this kind have a range of flexibility in the dimensions of their material form. It is precisely because they are flexible that their consequences for society must be understood with reference to the social actors able to influence which de signs and arrangements are chosen. In the second instance we examined ways in which the intractable properties of certain kinds of technology are strongly, perhaps unavoidably, linked to particular institutionalized patterns of power and authority. Here the initial choice about whether or not to adopt something is decisive in regard to its consequences. There are no alternative physical designs or arrangements that would make a significant difference; there are, furthermore, no genuine possibilities for creative intervention by different social systems–capitalist or socialist–that could change the intractability of the entity or significantly alter the quality of its political effects.

To know which variety of interpretation is applicable in a given case is often what is at stake in disputes, some of them passionate ones, about the meaning of technology for how we live. I have argued a "both/and" position here, for it seems to me that both kinds of understanding are applicable in different circumstances. Indeed, it can happen that within a particular complex of technology–a system of communication or transportation, for example–some aspects may be flexible in their possibilities for society, while other aspects may be (for better or worse) completely intractable. The two varieties of interpretation I have examined here can overlap and intersect at many points.

These are, of course, issues on which people can disagree. Thus, some proponents of energy from renewable resources now believe they have at last discovered a set of intrinsically democratic, egalitarian, communitarian technologies. In my best estimation, however, the social consequences of building renewable energy systems will surely depend on the specific configurations of both hardware and the social institutions created to bring that energy to us. It may be that we will find ways to turn this silk purse into a sow's ear. By comparison, advocates of the further development of nuclear power seem to believe that they are working on a rather flexible technology whose adverse social effects can be fixed by changing the design parameters of reactors and nuclear waste disposal systems. For reasons indicated above, I believe them to be dead wrong in that faith. Yes, we may be able to manage some of the "risks" to public health and safety that nuclear power brings. But as society adapts to the more dangerous and apparently indelible features of nuclear power, what will be the long-range toll in human freedom?

My belief that we ought to attend more closely to technical objects themselves is not to say that we can ignore the contexts in which those objects are situated. A ship at sea may well re quire, as Plato and Engels insisted, a single captain and obedient crew. But a ship out of service, parked at the dock, needs only a caretaker. To understand which technologies and which con texts are important to us, and why, is an enterprise that must involve both the study of specific technical systems and their history as well as a thorough grasp of the concepts and controversies of political theory. In our times people are often willing to make drastic changes in the way they live to accommodate technological innovation while at the same time resisting similar kinds of changes justified on political grounds. If for no other reason than that, it is important for us to achieve a clearer view of these matters than has been our habit so far.

# Notes.

1. Lewis Mumford, "Auhoritarian and Democratic Technics," *Technology and Culture* 5:1-8, 1964.
2. Denis Hayes, *Rays of Hope: The Transition to a Post-Petroleum World* (New York: W. W. Norton, 1977), 71, 159.
3. David Lillienthal, *T.V.A.: Democracy on the March* (New York: Harper and Brothers, 1944), 72-83.
4. Daniel J. Boorstin, *The Republic of Technology* (New York: Harper and Row, 1978), 7.
5. Langdon Winner, *Autonomous Technology: Technics-Out-of-Control as a Theme in Political Thought* (Cambridge: MIT Press, 1977).

6. The meaning of "technology" I employ in this essay does not encompass some of the broader definitions of that concept found in contemporary literature, for example, the notion of "technique" in the writings of Jacques Ellul. My purposes here are more limited. For a discussion of the difficulties that arise in attempts to define "technology," see *Autonomous Technology*, 8-12.

7. Robert A. Caro, *The Power Broker: Robert Moses and the Fall of New York* (New York: Random House, 1974), 318, 481, 514, 546, 951-958, 952.

8. Robert Ozanne, *A Century of Labor-Management Relations at McCormick and International Harvester* (Madison: University of Wisconsin Press, 1967), 20.

9. The early history of the tomato harvester is told in Wayne D. Rasmussen, "Advances in American Agriculture: The Mechanical Tomato Harvester as a Case Study," *Technology and Culture* 9:531-543, 1968.

10. Andrew Schmitz and David Seckler, "Mechanized Agriculture and Social Welfare: The Case of the Tomato Harvester," *American Journal of Agricultural Economics* 52:569-577, 1970.

11. William H. Friedland and Amy Barton, "Tomato Technology," *Society*13:6, September/October 1976. See also William H. Friedland, *Social Sleepwalkers: Scientific and Technological Research in California Agriculture*, University of California, Davis, Department of Applied Behavioral Sciences, Research Monograph No. 13, 1974.

12. *University of California Clip Sheet* 54:36, May 1, 1979.

13. "Tomato Technology."

14. A history and critical analysis of agricultural research in the land-grant colleges is given in James Hightower, *Hard Tomatoes, Hard Times* (Cambridge: Schenkman, 1978).

15. David F. Noble, *Forces of Production: A Social History of Machine Tool Automation* (New York: Alfred A. Knopf, 1984).

16. Friedrich Engels, "On Authority," in *The Marx-Engels Reader*, ed. 2, Robert Tucker (ed.) (New York: W. W. Norton, 1978), 731.

17. Ibid.

18. Ibid., 732, 731.

19. Karl Marx, *Capital*, vol. 1, ed. 3, translated by Samuel Moore and Edward Aveling (New York: Modern Library, 1906), 530.

20. Jerry Mander, *Four Arguments for the Elimination of Television* (New York: William Morrow, 1978), 44.

21. See, for example, Robert Argue, Barbara Emanuel, and Stephen Graham, *The Sun Builders: A People's Guide to Solar, Wind and Wood Energy in Canada* (Toronto: Renewable Energy in Canada, 1978). "We think decentralization is an implicit component of renewable energy; this implies the de centralization of energy systems, communities and of power. Renewable energy doesn't require mammoth generation sources of disruptive transmission corridors. Our cities and towns, which have been dependent on centralized energy supplies, may be able to achieve some degree of autonomy, thereby controlling and administering their own energy needs." (16)

22. Alfred D. Chandler, Jr., *The Visible Hand: The Managerial Revolution in American Business* (Cambridge: Belknap, 1977), 244.

23. Ibid.

24. Ibid., 500.

25. Leonard Silk and David Vogel, *Ethics and Profits: The Crisis of Confidence in American Business* (New York: Simon and Schuster, 1976), 191.

26. Russell W. Ayres, "Policing Plutonium: The Civil Liberties Fallout," *Harvard Civil Rights–Civil Liberties Law Review* 10 (1975): 443, 413-414, 374.

# Article 32 ↵

Alexander Z. Ibsen*

## The Politics of Airplane Production: The Emergence of Two Technological Frames in the Competition Between Boeing and Airbus

University of Arizona, Department of Sociology, P.O. Box 210027, Tucson, AZ 85721-0027, United States

## KEYWORDS

Airplanes Boeing Airbus
Two-party democracy Frames
Technological philosophy

## ABSTRACT

Economic models of technological innovation, as well as modern sociological approaches to the study of organizations, predict that two-actor markets will eventually evolve into one dominant technological logic. Why is it, then, that the only two global manufacturers of large commercial airplanes have developed diametrically opposed technological philosophies? Based on secondary historical sources, this article employs a theory of two- party democracies from political science and the theory of sociotechnical frames to explain why Boeing pilots are allowed ultimate command of their aircraft whereas Airbus confers this authority to the flight computer.

## 1. Introduction

For anyone who has ever flown on a large airplane owned by an airline based in an affluent country, the chances are almost exactly 50% that the plane will be made by Boeing Commercial Airplanes, and 50% that it will be made by Airbus S.A.S. At the same time, it is 100% certain that it will not be made by anyone else. Most passengers probably cannot tell the difference, nor will they care about the type of aircraft they boarded; indeed, they are more interested in flight comfort, safety, and reliability, and it makes little difference whether the plane was manufactured by Boeing or Airbus.

The truth is, however, that there are significant differences in the cockpits of airliners built by the two companies. The Boeing pilot is in full command of the airplane and its flight computer, whereas in an Airbus airplane the computer has ultimate control over the pilot. The differences are both visual and technical, and highlight two very different technological philosophies that have gradually emerged in modern commercial aviation.

This paper utilizes the political theory of two-party democracies as well as social constructivist theories of sociotechnical change to explain the emergence of these two radically different technological philosophies. The two systems will be broadly introduced before the theoretical perspectives adopted here are presented. Relying on insider testimonies reproduced in published works, the paper attempts to reverse-engineer the two companies' trajectories that have led to such divergent technologies in contemporary aviation. Although the different technological philosophies have been widely commented on separately, no attempt has been made to analyze the two strategies within one overarching framework. Consequently, one of the most important high-tech industries has escaped academic attention with regretful loss of important insights.

## 2. Two technological philosophies

With the launch of Airbus's A-320 family of single-aisle aircraft in 1988, and with Boeing's introduction of the B-777 wide-body plane six years later, both companies divested themselves of decades of mechanical flight control systems in favor of

* Tel.: þ1 520 621 3531; fax: þ1 520 621 9875.
E-mail address: ibsen@email.arizona.edu

0160-791X/$ — see front matter © 2009 Elsevier Ltd. All rights reserved. doi:10.1016/j.techsoc.2009.10.006

fully computerized fly-by-wire technology. All ensuing types of aircraft from both producers did, and will in the foreseeable future, rely on this type of flight control. Functionally speaking, there are few differences between Boeing and Airbus. They both introduce computer interpretation and transformation of information between the pilot's commands and the aircraft's physical reactions.

In digital fly-by-wire, the pilot's motions on handles and levers in the cockpit are transmitted to the primary flight control computers via control surfaces, and are further introduced to the flight actuators only after the computers have assessed the command as compatible with the plane's design limits as well as its current course in the air. A curious principle of aviation is that systems of aircraft design and flight control must choose a position on a stability/control continuum. Less stable aircraft are more agile and capable of variable performance in the air. On the other hand, demands on pilots increase as the system approaches more control and less stability. With fly-by-wire, a plane is allowed to give up considerable stability in favor of performance and control due to relaxed pilot-work intensity by computers.

A NASA historian comments: "Aeronautical engineers employed computers in flight control systems not because they represented a new technology and were 'progress for progress' sake', but because they were part of a solution to the flight control problem" [1, p. 128]. This particular technology was first introduced by NASA in the Apollo program in an exercise module used to prepare astronauts for lunar landings. Thereafter fly-by-wire was used almost exclusively by American commercial and military pilots, culminating in the introduction of the first digital (as opposed to analog) computer system for the F-8 project at the Dryden Flight Research Center in the early 1970s [1, pp. 57–69]. The militaristic growth and devel- opment of American fly-by-wire evolved from the availability of U.S. government research funds for such projects.

European air travel also had an early introduction to fly-by-wire technology in the Anglo-French Concorde, which was fitted with an analog version of the computer system. On both sides of the Atlantic, therefore, the technology was well-known and pursued by researchers. And while it had a civil origin in Europe, Boeing has from the beginning maintained close connections with military aeronautics [2]. Table 46 provides an overview of the current flight control systems of Boeing and Airbus. Details will not be worked through here, except for those pertaining to the two technological philosophies.

As Table 1 illustrates, during normal flight, the computers in both systems interject between pilot and plane actuators to make sure the aircraft remains airborne. This is secured by flight control calculation, which prevents it from stalling, loosing load factor, being short of speed, or banking too strongly. Details differ between the two versions, but the basics are the same. The true difference appears when we move from normal control law to secondary or alternate law. In the Boeing system, there are no longer any restrictions on the pilot's input whereas some still apply for the Airbus pilot. A Boeing pilot is free to choose this control law at any time during flight; it only automatically activates when multiple systems in an Airbus machine fail. The same is true for the direct control law: both aircraft will under this law completely eliminate the computerized command interjection, and pilots will navigate in the same way they would have steered a fully mechanical plane except, the Airbus pilot cannot initiate this control by him/herself whereas a Boeing pilot can. In the jargon of the airline industry, the Airbus version is said to employ 'hard' envelope protection, whereas the Boeing uses 'soft'.

In addition to computer differences, the cockpits of the two airliners also look distinctly different. By dispensing with certain mechanical elements, digital fly-by-wire aircraft have no need for the classical instruments and navigation equipment that was

**Table 1 Comparison of the two flight control systems.**

| AIRBUS | | | |
|---|---|---|---|
| **Normal Law** | **Alternate Law** | **Direct Law** | **Mechanical Back-Up** |
| **BOEING** | | | |
| **Normal Law** | | Secondary Law | Direct Law |
| | | No Protections | Conventional Airplane |
| **Pitch Attitude Protection** | | | |
| **High Angle of Attack Protection** | | | |
| **Thrust Asymmetry Compensation** | | | |
| **Speed Protection** | | | |
| **Bank Angle Protection** | | | |
| **Yaw Control** | | | |

Sources: A-320 flight manual. Flight controls. Denver, CO: Jeppesen; 1993. B-777 flight manual. Flight controls. Denver, CO: Jeppesen; 1996.

needed to maneuver older airplanes. This is obvious in Airbus cockpits in the A-320 family and later models, which are fitted with liquid crystal displays rather than analog control panels; also the aircraft is navigated by one-hand control sticks that look identical to the joysticks used in video games. In contrast, Boeing's 777 model has maintained the traditional steering yoke, which looks and even feels like the conventional stick on mechanical aircraft. This is because it includes sophisticated feedback machinery that makes it behave as if the pilot's input was directly transferred to the actuators. This function is called 'feel' in aviation. Therefore, the B-777 yoke is nothing more than a gigantic joystick that pretends to be a conventional steering yoke.

Hence, the two manufacturers offer different implementations of the same technology. Airbus makes pilots the handlers of flight computers. This is reflected in Northwest Captain Kenneth Waldrip's statement, made at the introduction of the A-320 to the American market: "It's a dream to flydbut you'd better make sure that the pilot flying it understands that computer" [3, p. 1534]. This does not mean that greater computer skill is required from Airbus pilots than from Boeing pilots; it simply means that Airbus pilots need to be aware that the flight control system will not permit them to exercise any command they want. By comparison, if there are warnings, or there is shaking in the yoke's 'feel' system, or other problems may arise, Boeing pilots can decide on and initiate any command freely. At the launch of the B-777, a brochure advertising the new aircraft stated Boeing's technological philosophy: "The pilot is the final authority for the operation of the airplane" [4]. The statement was, in all likelihood, meant to counter any anxiety on the part of potential purchasers about the new and highly computerized model.

Any system of automation, such as digital flight control, needs to balance numerous factors relating to both humans and machines. Fundamentally, the pre-set interpretation of human input by a machine must, in some way, be matched by a non- fixed interpretation of the machine's behavior by the human. There is an inherent asymmetry in this flow of information: whereas feedback must be enhanced to help the human, the automated technology does not need feedback [5]. In the air, feedback has to take into account not only the interplay between pilot and computer, but also the plane's actual physical behavior. It is this latter requirement-dand its solutiondthat has caused the two companies to chose different paths.

# 3. A global duopoly

After Lockheed Martin pulled out of the airplane production business in the early 1980s and McDonnell Douglas was acquired by Boeing a decade later, only Boeing and Airbus were left to manufacture the largest commercial airplanes, resulting in one of only a few global duopolies. The industry of airplane manufacturing is highly capital intensive due to the great demand for expensive technology and the first-class expertise of the manpower involved, which helps to explain why there are no new market entrants.

In markets where perfect substitutes are available, economists assume that rational companies avoid direct price wars and try to use non-price methods to differentiate their products instead [6]. Such a situation is likely to occur in duopolistic markets. When duopolistic production involves technology-intensive manufacturing, economic theory further predicts that the competitors will engage in technological 'leapfrogging' by alternately supplanting each others' inventions [7]. Hence, economic models of duopolies expect only temporary differences in technological philosophiesdessentially only for a brief period after a new innovation has taken place. This has not been true in modern aviation. Rather, aviation technology lasts for decades. For instance, except for some upgrading of software and flight display in the flight deck, the famous B-747 'jumbo jet' continues to rely on technology from the late 1960s. Therefore, manufacturers offer products that incorporate a decades-long spectrum of inventions. It has been documented that Airbus and Boeing respond to technological innovations from competitors with investment that yields price cuts, and vice versa, rather than following suit in technological adoptions [8]. In other words, the 'leapfrogging' phenomenon seen in other industries is not found in aviation.

Another theory comes from sociology. When organizations are subject to similar kinds of market pressure, New Insti- tutional theory assumes that the broader environment influences contestants equally and simultaneously, with the result that all market actors adopt similar organizational strategies [9]. The market for commercial jets is a good example: although passengers are the ones who purchase air travels, the consumption of aircraft is really done by the airlines. With a few exceptions, mainly in the low-cost carriers, airlines operate with fleets of planes of different sizes and performance abilities. Therefore, Boeing and Airbus compete for the same buyers who keep their purchases for many years. The fact that the technological strategies are so different runs against the predictions of New Institutional theory.

It is possible that political factors distort the picture so that the market alone cannot be held responsible. Indeed, given the political importance of employment creation, export revenue, and national prestige of both Boeing and Airbus, it is not surprising that both companies have caused numerous headlines. At times the market in which the two giants function seems more politically than economically driven. Every few years, one or both companies are the focus of trade disputes from either side of the Atlantic [10–13]. A final agreement between the Americans and the Europeans might never be reached due to the highly complex politics involved.

The political involvement in aircraft manufacturing is not surprising. Economically speaking, attempts by governments to smooth out the competitive disadvantages facing their home company is expected when trade is international [14]. In fact, by studying the few cases of successful aircraft manufacture, commentators have reached the conclusion that only companies that have enjoyed extensive state sponsorship and domestic help internationally have prevailed [15]. Political involvement has direct economic consequences to the producers. For example, price hikes that occurred as a result of political disputes have been documented in the air jet market [16].

However, there is nothing in the political environment that explains the adoption of opposite technological philosophies. Essentially, the question as to whether to keep the pilot in ultimate command or remand this privilege to the computer is a question of strategy that does not rest on experience or on political pressure, since both Boeing and Airbus have access to the same technology. What is different is how the two companies have chosen it to function.

The technological developments in the aircraft industry cannot, therefore, be accounted for by either economists' models, sociological explanations, or simply by pointing to political rivalry. Surely all these factors matter for certain parts of the industry, but with regard to the question of the choice of man or machine, none offers a satisfactory answer. We shall have to look for it elsewhere.

## 4. The politics of airplane production

The claim here is that the duopoly of aircraft production resembles the political struggle within a two-party political system. In a classic model from political science, Anthony Downs [17] reversed the conventional relationship between elections and party ideologies. Instead of assuming that parties win elections based on the appropriateness of their agenda, his theory gives elections preeminence, with the implication that all party action is aimed at maximizing votes [p. 35]. Political ideology serves two roles for democratic parties in this theory. First, it serves the heuristic purpose of making the party appear consistent across different political actions. In order to be identified as an ideology in the first place, the alleged purpose motivating party activity must be stable and internally consistent: "ideologies are never internally contradictory" [p. 113]. The other purpose is to eliminate uncertainty. By adhering to certain principles of action, voters have grounds to predict the likelihood of the outcome of their choice during elections. On the other hand, voters will be divided in the degree to which they are uncertain of the results from election. Those most certain will also constitute the most fervent political interest group. Parties, therefore, chose ideological affiliation in alignment with those groups that have the strongest belief in the outcome from successful elections. In effect, "uncertainty forces rational governments to regard some voters as more important than others" [p. 95].

There is an important parallel to duopolies in this model. According to Downs, both parties in two-party democracies try to appeal to the majority of votersdor the average voterdin order to capture the largest base of support [p. 68]. Both parties will therefore go to great lengths to try to resemble each other as much as possible in political appeal. To distinguish one party's candidate from the other, the party will develop a systematic ideology that is only modestly different from its competitor's. It follows from the majority principle in politics that both the government and the voters are interested in only "marginal alterations in the structure of government activity" [p. 53]. This distribution of the majority principle is, however, only fulfilled as long as there is a large measure of political consensus in the population of voters [p. 114].

The market for mid- and large-size airplanes meets these theoretical requirements well. There is great consensus among market actors as to what constitutes an attractive product, namely, a safe and economically efficient aircraft. The majority opinion is that safety must never be compromised; a dictum adhered to with equal strength at both Airbus and Boeing. Lastly, although there are only two suppliers, there are several interest groups that have a stake in the product design, just as there are many potential interest groups within a democratic system.

Fig. 1 attempts to corroborate the claim that the basic two-party strategies of democracies applies to the duopoly of airplane manufacture. When considering seat capacity, the figure shows that neither company has tried to specialize in only one segment of the market. Both companies have, throughout their commercial duel, responded to every launch by the other by offering compatible, albeit slightly different alternatives. By using the jargon of political science, the attempt by both companies to offer aircraft for the entire seat capacity spectrum is equivalent to the fight for the 'average voter'.

## 5. Technological frames

In his exposition on sociotechnical change, Wiebe Bijker [18] offers as a demand for a theory of technological development that it situates the object of study within a social context of both users and producers [p. 47]. All existing technology is an accomplishment within a web of social actors who accept the claims to problem solving, goals, and assumptions of the invention. This accomplishment is what Bijker calls a 'technological frame' [pp. 124–25]. Neither one person nor even one side of the market alone is fully able to design this technological frame. Rather, the accomplishment of a viable technological frame is settled in relationship between several social groups, leaving no one fully in charge of the outcome.

Relevant groups in modern airplane manufacturing are the two producers (Boeing and Airbus), airline carriers, engine manufacturers, national governments, pilots, and air transportation agencies. All of these contribute to any technological choices and to developments from both Boeing and Airbus.

## 5.1 Airbus: technological frame of dependence

The adoption of digital fly-by-wire with hard envelope protection was certainly not a fad limited to one particular Airbus model, the A-320 family. In fact, all later Airbus models did, and will continue to use the same technological philosophy. Airbus affirms its system's adherence to the strictest safety requirements; above all, however, the economic benefits emerging from the new plane's better in-air performance, easier maintenance, lower weight, and better fuel consumption seem to have played an even greater role [19]. The economic benefits accrue to those who pay for manpower, maintenance, fuel, and repairdthe airlines. This section will show how Airbus's flight control system is part of a technological frame that has been shaped to appeal to the airlines.

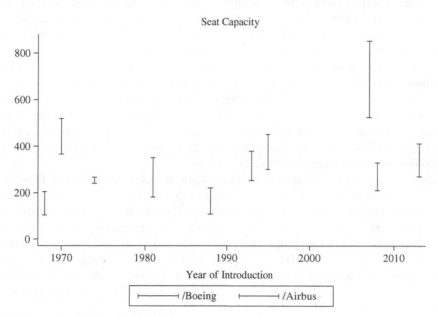

**Fig. 1.  Seat Capacity as an illustration of duopoly strategy.**

Note: The Boeing families are, chronologically, B-737; B-747; B-757/B-767; B-777; B-787. The Airbus order is A-300/A-310; A-320; A-220/A-340; A-380; A-350.
Sources: www.boeing.com/commerical; www.airbus.com/en/aircraftfamilies/productcompare/

When introduced to American carriers, the A-320 was harshly attacked by flight crews. Pilots' unions on both sides of the Atlantic were opposed to Airbus's system, mainly because it reduced the number of jobs, but also due to initial suspicions regarding safety with the hard envelope protection [12, p. 163]. In the words of a United pilot at the time: "This sort of sophistication [hard envelope protection] should be left to the single-seat fighter, where it appropriately belongs and where the pilot can bail out in a hurry when the inevitable occursda privilege neither I nor my passengers enjoy" [20].

Regardless which decade one looks at, pilots and their associations constitute a strong interest group in aviation. For instance, Robert Crandall, former CEO of American Airlines, told Jean Pierson, then managing director of Airbus, that because American Airlines' pilots were opposed to the new cockpit, the company could not buy the A-320, despite American's interest [21, p. 98]. A survey of 132 pilots of advanced aircraft found that pilots endorsed a human-centered philosophy and saw fully automated flight control systems as creating a heavier mental workload. In particular, pilots expressed a desire to maintain control of the most complex parts of their job, such as communicating, managing, and planning, especially in high workload situations [22]. The so-called 'human-centered avionics' approach to pilot-work has maintained that automation has the unintended tendency to tune out small errors and create opportunities for large ones; to diminish the workload in the relaxed parts of the flight and add to it in the busiest phases; and to amplify the importance of ongoing communication between crew members even as the immediate incentives to communicate are muted [4].

It was apparent that Airbus could not rely on support from the people who would actually operate the new technology in the air. However, after the Airline Deregulation Act was adopted in 1978, the aviation industry in the United States changed dramatically, and competition between carriers suddenly became an important factor. With a growing number of potential purchasers, rather than a few large ones, the desires and needs of individual companies had to be reckoned with in order to successfully introduce new aviation technology. Although Airbus is a European company, as Gerard Blanc (Airbus's executive vice president for operations at the time of the A-320 launch) testified: "All of our big turning points were in the U.S. market" [21, p. 100]. And, those turning points were discovered with the airlines.

It is due to the airlines' desire for competition and lowered prices that they have pitched the two giants against one another [21, p. 224]. In the American market, much of the acceptance of the A-320 was not a matter of the plane's techno- logical achievements but due to Boeing's reluctance to comply with American carriers' desire for a modernized version of the B-737. According to Airbus spokesman Robert Alizart, "Boeing should have killed this upstart. If Boeing had produced a clean sheet of paper the A-320 would never have become Airbus's bread and butter" [21, p. 100]. However, competition alone would probably have resulted in nothing more than disappointment for Airbus had the company not had something to offer besides low sales prices.

The answer lies in the technological frame Airbus negotiated. First of all, the A-320's fly-by-wire with hard envelope protection was completely new to the market. This feature itself appealed to airlines interested in the technological prestige of having the first mover advantage with a new machine. Most important, though, was the fact that Airbus introduced its new technology with the promise that future aircraft would utilize the same flight control system and cockpit configuration. This principle of commonality, well-known in the airplane industry, offers carriers the advantage of focusing on one type of tech- nology throughout all their equipment. It gives airlines the advantage of buying multiple parts from the same supplier, the opportunity to engage with only one form of pilot training, with all the benefits that come from specialized know-how. In the words of an industry commentator: "Cockpit commonality has been the cornerstone of cockpit design in Airbus aircraft" [23].

Airbus's success at the American market was a direct result of their conscious strategy to establish fleet commonality. In interviews with Northwest Airlines representatives, John Newhouse [21] found that American carriers who purchased the A-320 did so because Airbus explicitly announced that future modelsdbeginning with the A-330 and A-340dwould be built with the same cockpit configuration. "This commonality in the Airbus family is known to have tilted a number of sales campaigns toward Airbus" [p. 102]. In fact, the A-380 Superjumbo, launched almost 20 years after the A-320, flies with almost the exact same technology as that of its predecessor. Not only does this signal the prescience of the A-320 technology, but also Airbus's persistence in adhering to its philosophy of fleet commonality, and the wisdom of this early strategy.

In real terms, the benefit to airlines of fleet commonality is clearly revealed in a February 15, 2008 press release, issued by EADS (Airbus's parent company). It explains that the European Aviation Agency and the Federal Aviation Authority jointly approved reduced training requirements for flying the Superjumbo for pilots who were certified for all of Airbus's digital fly-by-wire models (A-320 family, A-330, and A-340). In other words, within less than two weeks, pilots who used to fly planes carrying no more than 130 passengers could be certified to airplanes carrying as many as 850. EADS states that this gives airlines significant cost savings since training times can be halved compared to standard rating courses. How is this possible? EADS explains: "Reduced transition training is only possible due to the unique flight operational commonality between Airbus fly-by-wire aircraft. Commonality is a fundamental design criterion for Airbus as demonstrated by the fact that [reduced transition training] is available now for all combinations of Airbus fly-by-wire aircraft in service" [24].

Airbus's fleet commonality design is a technological frame that has fostered loyalty from many airlines. It is a technological frame because the technical details of the flight control system do more than simply facilitate the introduction of new models to the market. Instead, the technological frame actively shapes future company strategy and success. Even the choice of developing new models has been partially made with a view to preserving the technological frame. For instance, Hanko von Lachner, Airbus's general secretary, said: "An argument in favor of the A-380 was Boeing's 777. It was a better airplane than our A-340. But we calculated that the A-380 would help to protect the A-340. An airline that bought the A-380 would be unlikely to buy the Boeing airplane" [21, p. 155].

Airbus's technological frame is therefore one of dependence. The company anticipated possible future technological trends, developed a flight control system it would stick to without yielding, and thereby made airlines reliant on their products if they wanted to make money on the equipment already in their fleet. True, the hostile pilots had to be converted, but once several large airlines were swayed, their flight crew became specialized in the same technological frame of dependence as their employer. Today, half of the pilots in several countries are only able to operate an Airbus plane. And as a result, it is harder to find incendiary or negative remarks about digital fly-by-wire with hard envelope protection. As expected from candidates in a two-party democracy, Airbus chose to affiliate with the one group in the duopoly that was likely to appreciate the company's technological ideology, namely, the airlines.

## 5.2 Boeing: technological frame of accommodation

The reason Boeing chose a different technological philosophy lies in the company's decision to affiliate its technological frame with pilots. When digital fly-by-wire technology seemed inevitable, Boeing chose to implement its own version, even though it needed a technological frame that was different from the one Airbus had introduced. It took Boeing eight years to produce its response: the B-777. Karl Sabbagh [25] followed the B-777 project from within the company, and he related, "John Cashman, Boeing's chief test pilot on the 77, was instrumental right from the beginning in making sure that the fly-by-wire system reflected the views of pilots rather than relying on engineers". This led to the decision to "let the pilot make the final decision rather than the fly-by-wire computers" [p. 149].

'Softer' envelope protection, which can be overridden, reflects pilots' general attitude to the safety of digital fly-by-wire. For instance, the Journal of the Airline Pilots Association published a piece written by a member pilot in 2000 which instructed plane crash investigators to "first assume that the FCS [flight control system]dand not the pilotdinduced it [the accident] until proven otherwise," when investigating accidents involving aircraft fitted with fly-by-wire [26].

Regarding the implementation of 'feel' feedback in instruments and retaining the traditional yoke, Sabbagh [25] reports that "Boeing pilots who worked on the system tried very had not to turn the 777 into a plane that is flown by reading things rather than feeling them" [p. 153]. Pilots' desires were also taken into account by Boeing in maintaining the traditional yoke. Sabbagh explains that the designers of the 777 fly-by-wire system wanted pilots to feel at home, and they built artificial feedback into the system that gave useful information to the pilot about how far s/he had pulled the lever. Apparently, there "was an almost religious fervor in the way the system's designers left a degree of freedom for the pilot in the system" [p. 153]. It is interesting to note that whereas today's pilots might favor a cockpit that resembles traditional aircraft, laboratory experiments suggest that individuals without any flight experience are more reliable when navigating with an untraditional sidestick [27].

Only two new models have been developed by Boeing that implement digital fly-by-wire flight controldthe B-777 and the new B-787 Dreamliner (scheduled for operation sometime in 2010). The latter will contain virtually the same digital fly-by- wire as its predecessor, and the cockpit configurations will be almost identical. This includes 'feel' feedback in some instruments, as well as a yoke instead of a sidestick [28,29]. Neil Adams, manager of business development at Rockwell Collins Systems Division (the company that furnishes Boeing's cockpits on the 777 and 787), explained: "Boeing has tried to make the cockpit of the B-787 identical to that of the B-777, so a pilot can go in [to the cockpit] blindfolded, touch it, and it feels exactly the same" [29, p. 51]. As a result, B-777 pilots can obtain certification for the B-787 in five days or less. At first glance, it looks as if Boeing's technological frame is identical to that of Airbus in that Boeing, too, aims for airlines' loyalty through fleet commonality. Closer inspection reveals this is not the case.

Of course, the American company has to appeal to airlines just as its European competitor. The important thing to bear in mind, though, is that Boeing's technological frame was developed before the final product was introduced to the market. By allowing pilots into the development of their system, airlines were later presented with a technological solution that was furnished in accordance with the opinions of the pilots. This process resulted in a technological frame that did not attempt to introduce something radically new, but instead something that was compatible with what already existed. This is noteworthy because Boeing explicitly tried to set limitations on the technology they mastered. Here too, the testimony of the test pilot in the 777 project is illuminating. John Cashman explained: "We really want to keep the airplane flying just like he's [the pilot] always flown it. We don't want him to have to learn new techniques. We're trying to keep the airplane so the pilot, when he climbs into it, doesn't have to learn anything new" [25, p. 159].

Boeing's technological frame therefore means establishing commonality between its new models and older onesdand even with smaller aircraft made by other non-Airbus companies. Outside of the military, digital fly-by-wire does not exist in any of the smaller regional jets (as of 2009), or in any of the older larger models. In developing Boeing's fly-by-wire system and its cockpit design, Adams from Rockwell Collins stated: "What we are trying to do is create the 'feel' of a mechanical cable system. It allows the pilots to feel like they are flying a 1950 aircraft in 2007" [29, p. 50]. The direct benefits of this technological philosophy do not really get to the airlines. Airline management neither enjoy the right to override flight control systems nor are they the ones to feel the feedback in cockpit instruments that resemble older mechanical aircraft.

Boeing's technological frame is therefore one of 'accommodation.' Pilots' needs and desires are diligently implemented in the flight deck by the company, and pilots are allowed to command the plane fully as they see fit. Airlines are not forced into technological dependence, as they are by Airbus, but receive new aircraft that behave as close as possible to smaller regional jets and older large aircraft. Leaving aside all marketing strategies and tactics adopted by the company, we notice that Boeing's technological frame has been adjusted to meet the desires of the flight crew. The ideological alliance with this latter group distinguishes Boeing's policy from that of Airbus, and explains the choice to abandon strong envelope protection and the retention of more traditional flight deck instruments with tactile feedback built in. When the systems were launched, Airbus was looking ahead at what would be the future technological norm, whereas Boeing looked back at what already existed.

# 6. Conclusion

This paper has argued that marketing strategies and technical development alone cannot account for the emergence of different technological adoptions for commercial airplanes. Instead, attention has to be given to the ideological alignments of those who manufacture the aircraft. Politics in two-party democracies (insofar as voters share a general agreement of desirable outcomes from elections) often involve efforts to become as similar to the opponent as possible, while still striving to maintain a unique identity. This identity is secured by ideological commitments with certain groups of voters. Based on testimonies by some authors who have been privy to the technical planning processes of both Boeing and Airbus, this paper has shown that in today's duopoly of airplane manufacture, both companies forged ideological alliances, but each with a different social group.

Boeing diligently maintained its commitment to the desires of pilots, whereas Airbus engaged in new alliances with the airlines. The idea of 'technological frames' was used to address the social context in which any technological application gets credibility and receives its final form. Boeing's frame was described as one of 'accommodation,' and Airbus's was characterized as a frame of 'dependence.'

After more than a decade of coexistence between these two philosophies of flight control, the initial debate as to the best way has calmed, which must surely be attributed to the fact that both systems have been proved to work safely. Also, the situation has yet to occur where it can undeniably be determined that either company's flight control system would have prevented an accident befalling a plane from the competitor. The technological frames have both managed to settle and exist side by side.

The question now is: is it possible that the debate will reappear? It seems likely that the next great restructuring of the airline business will again raise the issue of automation. Within the next decade, or so, air travel in the United States might be permitted to proceed at each pilot's discretion, which is called 'free flight' air traffic control. Today planes must follow certain fixed routes, more or less like cars on interstate highways. However, recent advances in global positioning satellites, new ground/air communication links, enhanced collision-avoidance systems onboard planes, and powerful automation could make it possible to let pilots fly the shortest route between two points. This, of course, has the potential of reducing fuel consumption and is therefore highly attractive to airline carriers.

As discussed, both of the manufacturing giants will have to participate in new politics if 'free flight' control is introduced. Air traffic controllers are likely to resist that idea, given the likelihood of some job losses. Pilots and airlines, on the other hand, might favor the arrangement, although probably for different reasons: pilots might tend to prefer arrangements that increase their decision power in the air, whereas airlines are most interested in ways to minimize expenses.

The decision for Boeing and Airbus is with whom they will collaborate for the next technological frame. Whatever the outcome of future decisions about 'free flight' and an onboard flight control system, the technological philosophy will undoubtedly again occupy center stage. In the words of one commentator: "Understanding what human/technology capabilities would exist in a free flight world is essential to evaluating its safety" [30, p. 845].

## Acknowledgements

The author is grateful to Doctor Theodore Beneigh at Embry-Riddle Aeronautical University for help to understand the technical aspects of modern flight control systems.

## References

1. Tomayk JE. Computers take flight: a history of NASA's pioneering digital fly-by-wire project. Washington, DC: National Aeronautics and Space Administration; 2000.
2. Lawrence PK, Thornton DW. Deep stall: the turbulent story of Boeing commercial airplanes. Aldershot, UK/Burlington, VT: Ashgate; 2005.
3. Mitchell W. Flying the electric skies. Science 1989;244:1532–4.
4. Sweet W. The glass cockpit: pilots who work in glass cockpits throw no stones, despite some deep ambivalences. Institute of Electrical and Electronics Engineers (IEEE) Spectrum 1995;32:30–8.
5. Norman DA. The 'problem' with automation: inappropriate feedback and interaction, not 'over automation'. Philosophical Transactions of the Royal Society of London. Series B, Biological Sciences 1990;327:585–93.
6. Beckman SR. Cournot and Bertrand games. Journal of Economic Education 2003;34:27–35.
7. Giovannetti E. Perpetual leapfrogging in Bertrand duopoly. International Economic Review 2001;42:671–96.
8. Tombak MM. Strategic asymmetry. Journal of Economic Behavior and Organization 2006;61:339–50.
9. DiMaggio PJ, Powell W. The iron cage revisited: institutional isomorphism and collective rationality in organizational fields. American Sociological Review 1983;48:147–60.
10. Carbaugh RJ, Olienyk J. Boeing–Airbus subsidy dispute: a sequel. Global Economy Journal 2004;4:1–9.
11. Carbaugh RJ, Olienyk J. Boeing–Airbus subsidy dispute: an economic and trade perspective. Global Economy Quarterly 2001;2:261–82.
12. Lynn M. Birds of prey: Boeing vs. Airbus, a battle for the skies. New York: Four Walls Windows; 1998.
13. Love W, Sandholtz W. David and Goliath: Airbus vs. Boeing in Asia. In: Aggarwal VK, editor. Winning in Asia, European style: market and nonmarket strategies for success. New York: Palgrave; 2001. p. 187–224.
14. Garcia Pires AJ. Losers, winners and prisoner's dilemma in international subsidy wars. CEPR Discussion Papers 2006;5979.
15. Hira A, de Oliveira LG. Take off and crash: lessons from the diverging fates of the Brazilian and Argentine aircraft industries. Competition and Change 2007;11:329–47.

16. Irwin DA, Pavcnik N. Airbus versus Boeing revisited: international competition in the aircraft market. Journal of International Economics 2004;64: 223–45.
17. Downs A. An economic theory of democracy. New York: Harper & Row; 1957.
18. Bijker WE. Of bicycles, bakelites, and bulbs: towards a theory of sociotechnical change. Cambridge, MA: MIT Press; 1997.
19. Briere D, Traverse P. Airbus A320/A330/A340 electrical flight controls: a family of fault-tolerant systems. Twenty-Third Annual International Symposium on Fault-Tolerant Computing. 1993: 616–623.
20. Fulford GA. Letter. Science 1989;245:582–3.
21. Newhouse J. Boeing versus Airbus: the inside story of the greatest international competition in business. New York: Vintage Books; 2008.
22. Tenney YJ, Rogers WH, Pew RW. Pilot opinions on cockpit automation issues. International Journal of Aviation Psychology 1998;8:103–20.
23. Ian P. Avionics for a colossus. Avionics Magazine 2000;24:20–2.
24. European Aeronautic Defense and Space Co. (EADS). Reduced pilot training now approved for the A-380. Press Release, 2008.
25. Sabbagh K. 21st century jet: the making and marketing of the Boeing 777. New York: Scribner; 1996.
26. Stowe S. Fly-by-wire: a primer for aviation accident investigators. Air Line Pilot 2000;69:18–21.
27. Beringer DB. Applying performance-controlled systems, fuzzy logic, and fly-by-wire controls to general aviation. DOT/FAA/AM-02/7, 2002: 1–8.
28. Ramsey JW. Boeing 787: integration's next step. Avionics Magazine 2005;29:20–9.
29. Ramsey JW. The Dreamliner, in control. Avionics Magazine 2007;31:46–55.
30. Barnett A. Free-flight and en route air safety: a first-order analysis. Operations Research 2000;48:833–45.

Alexander Z. Ibsen is currently a Ph.D. candidate in Sociology at the University of Arizona.

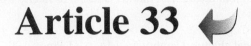

# Article 33

Hebe Vessuri *

# Science, Politics, and Democratic Participation in Policy-Making:
# A Latin American View

Dpto. Estudio de la Ciencia, Instituto Venezolano de Investigaciones Cient´ıfcas (IVIC), Apartado 21827, Caracas 1020-A, Venezuela

## ABSTRACT

How can science respond to the particular needs of Latin American societies? How can regional funding of regional science positively influence its growth? The answers to such questions rest on analyses of the configurations of state and politics, relations between instru- mental science and the democratic process, and the demographic features of science and tech- nology. The extent to which one can expect a better future through science in Latin America and the Caribbean depends as much on political problems and history as on scientific and technological development alone. True development will only come with significant political and economic change.

## 1. Introduction

How can science and technology respond to the specific needs of Latin American societies? What is the best way to fund and to influence the growth of science in the region? There is a growing body of empirical knowledge produced by sociol- ogists and historians of science and economists of innovation that is related to the incidental details of science, technology, and develop- ment in Latin America. But real answers to such questions require a more synthetic understanding of the many ingredients of development, and they have persistently eluded the region, as wit- nessed by the great defeats and uncertainties surrounding efforts so far. The present paper will not attempt this major synthetic task, but more modestly seek to identify some of the social trends that have accompanied the institutionalization of science in Latin America at a time when it was becoming a leading productive force in the world.

Two main theses underlie my argument:

- The limited and frustrated development of science and technology (S&T) capacities in Latin America and the Carib- bean (LAC) after the Second World War was part and parcel of a broad process of economic and political change set in motion to manage a post-colonial world, and must be viewed in that context. To a large extent, research grew in teaching institutions that were often distant from industry, and did not make major demands on local scientific institutions. Thus the region turned out some good scientists and engineers, although domestic research systems did not reach a critical size and national innovation systems lacked density. Particularly when it was funded with monies from development aid, research tended to focus on technical fixes rather than on helping the countries to increase their self-sufficiency.
- The new conditions of globalization (in addition to the particular contexts in which the countries in the region function after 50 years of "development"), point to the fact that LAC is entering a new territory, one not yet on the maps but whose culture (all optimistic rhetoric to the contrary) is characterized by growing exclusion and concentration. One novelty is that research and development (R&D) seems no longer to be considered by international aid agen- cies as a luxury of developing countries, but rather a fundamental component of economic success. Obviously, scientific activities per se cannot achieve anything unless there is a long-term commitment to development. To ensure a more active participation in the new international scenarios, the region must strengthen its S&T infrastruc- ture. But there is still more rhetoric than action in North/South research cooperation and few efficacious recipes available. Private capital has replaced development aid as the main external funding source, while lobbies for science in Latin America remain weak.

* Corresponding author. Fax: +58-212-504-1092.
E-mail address: hvessuri@hotmail.com (H. Vessuri).

0160-791X/03/$ - see front matter © 2003 Elsevier Science Ltd. All rights reserved. doi:10.1016/S0160-791X(03)00020-4

# 2. State and politics

There exist today strong pressures to adopt neoliberal policies to remove the state from theoretical debates about economic development. By contrast, there is a "bring the state back in" movement that sees successful industrial policymaking as heavily dependent on political elites being accessible to and working closely with entrepreneurs and corporations. Instead of the Weberian tradition that would insulate political bureaucratic elites from class interests and social groups, some blend of autonomy and integration is now admitted as crucial to formulating and pursuing policy goals in a coherent and systematic manner in order to yield desired results.

The state usually establishes the institutional context for economic activity, and economic outcomes are influenced by the constraints and incentives that political elites create for entrepreneurs and firms. Different state structures create different capacities for state interventions, which thus define the range of roles for state actions. Developmental outcomes depend on whether these roles fit the social context and how well they are executed. It has been persuasively argued [1] that states must enjoy embedded autonomy in order to provide appropriate incentives for entrepren- eurial firms to flourish and become strong enough to compete effectively in the global marketplace. But the institutional arrangement of the business community, i.e., firms and entrepreneurs, is just as important as the state structure in facilitating the policies so crucial in newly industrializing countries. Adjustments by both state and capital are needed to make good use of scientific and technological progress.

The persistence of the free market, the imperatives of profit, the demands of exten- sive capital, and property reproduction are the bulwarks of capitalism. As such, these reinforce ideas of continuity, consolidation, and adjustment within already-established powers. An alliance between power factors jointly determines the policies for ensuring, through the persistence of mechanisms such as those just mentioned, the flow of capital to foster innovations and the applications of scientific progress to meet global economic competition. Science policy is not powerful by itself. Often its main result is the operationalization and legitimization of decisions that have accumulated or were made by reasons foreign to science policy. But in the processes that shape and drive current science, there is power involved, frequently subordinated to economic and technological forces that try to impose their particular rationalities on science. Under conditions in which science policy has institutionalized the subordination of science to "interests," the classic relationship formulated by Francis Bacon according to which "science is power," has been turned on its head since power has established itself over knowledge. In fact, the weakness of the local lobbies for science in confrontation with the resources and power of foreign interests as represented by the "Washington consensus" has actually led to a worsening of conditions for R&D in Latin America [2].

The different parties involved resort to experts to dissolve disputes or decide on scientific-technical projects. One of the elements weakening scientific authority is that when a project stumbles, its promoters can almost always find some expert to assure the public that everything is in competent hands. To the extent that expertise may be contradicted by counter-expertise or that scientific councils require a proportional representation in the guise of a political parliament, one enters a dense and impenetrable forest of agreements and compromises that weaken both political and the scientific justifications.

Traditionally, the basic strategy of science policy referred to the general level of R&D resources. It assumes that there exists a subordination with regard to some unknown—and may be unknowable—social optimum. The fundamental purpose has been the aggregate maximization of the budget [3]. So far in Latin America, budget distribution held very little concern for those in charge of designing policies and planning S&T, except when forced by political and economic decisionmakers. Decisions relied more on historical quotas and stakeholder pressures than on calculations of marginal productivity for comparative uses of research money. At the same time, in the multiplicity of existing specialized scientific groups, there has not been a clear theoretical basis for establishing a scientific order or hierarchy of priorities among different scientific fields. In part, this is why bureaucracies are always asking for more resources. Their ability to do something new depends on receiving new funds, because in general they have been unable to redistribute historically allocated funds.

In the symbiosis between the state and business in the most advanced countries, the rhetorical privilege of knowledge, rationality, and full disclosure of information, is particularly significant, painting a picture in which there is little interference by the power configurations through which this knowledge becomes socially applied. The political dimension is juggled in what is depicted as the triumph of depoliticization. Science and politics are conceived as overcoming classical opposition via the scientification of society, that is, they appear to have finally resolved their historical antagonism through the subordination of politics to science. But, of course, politics is alive and well. And the successful resolution of the problems of development varies according to political possibilities, the capacity to adapt to the new global dynamics, and the assertion of political will.

The development of capitalism at the world level has exposed nations on the peripheries to forces that have brought increasing disorder to them. Politics in the latter is hostage to multiple restrictions imposed by a power system in societies that have to manage at the same time the macro-economic order, economic scarcity, and social inequality. Politics in LAC must overcome numerous obstacles. It cannot be ignored that one out of four Latin Americans still live on less than one dollar per day and inequity in income distribution is more marked in this region than in any other. The provider state is in perpetual crisis and in the underdeveloped version current in LAC it is unable to respond to multiple social needs. Administrative dis- organization and disorder as well as fiscal restrictions affect state performance. This does not mean that less government is needed but that the regulatory and welfare functions of the public sector ought to assume a different aspect, with greater ability to confront both the organizational and disorganizational capacities of both the public and the private domains.

Linked to this is the syndrome of short-term demands: immediate electoral dividends seem to be the rule in the current political game. Even when they have a genuine democratic concern, politicians are wholly absorbed trying to resolve the concrete and immediate problems of their constituencies. It is not easy for them to pay to look long range, which is nevertheless what is essential for industrial and S&T strategies and for the constitution of a broad educated social base, given the uncertainties of technology investment prospects, the displacement of the labor force by tech- nology, and the technological impetus underlying the creation of large corporate groups.

## 3. Instrumental science and the democratic process

The old model of the relationship between science and society was a contractual one, as if between two autonomous entities that agreed on certain principles of exchange in order to achieve independent but mutually beneficial aims. While not comprehending the precise content of science itself, society was ready to be blindly deferential to its internal workings, casting scientific responsibility in simple regu- lations of scientific boundaries. For a long time the "use-abuse" model implied that whatever knowledge or innovation emerged from the black box of science, it was socially neutral unless and until societal actors put it to beneficient or nefarious use. At most, public concern over scientific responsibility concentrated on the classic examples of atomic scientists and other war-related researchers. Otherwise the model accepted scientists as trusted individuals and self-regulation as adequate for protect- ing scientific integrity through systems of social and technical norms thought to reinforce individual integrity and openness, collegiality, and the appeal to evidence (e.g., Merton [4]).

But after several decades of increasing disparity between the rhetoric and the practice of science, a new model of science and scientific practice has emerged, one that promotes a different relationship between science and society. Science has become a leading productive force. However, this is not a science that simply pro- duces abstract truths about the natural world but rather *instrumental science*, resulting from a prolonged process of knowledge subordination to the imperatives of economic activity. Modern scientific ideas, which began developing from around 1600, took almost three centuries to find extensive economic application [5]. Industry did not begin to rely seriously on scientific explanation until around 1875.

Since then, science has acquired increasing strength in the United States and the rest of the industrialized world, and at present it depends to a large extent on the patronage of an organized type of power—the industrial corporation. The presence of (multiple and conflicting) interests in the research enterprise is confirmed by the existence of the new scientist-entrepreneur, the incubation of technology- or science- based firms in academic realms, the transformation of university institutions, and other incentives to harness a scientist's personal ambitions to profit, technical progress, and economic gain.

Knowledge resulting from instrumental science is fundamentally information that increases possibilities for the control of both nature and people, that multiples the power of controllers across a wide spectrum of activities ranging from business to defense. As control potential is greater than ever, the extent to which society can expect to control innovation has itself come to occupy a prominent place in science policy debates in the advanced countries [6,7].

At the same time, socioeconomic inequity reflects the inability of significant seg- ments of the population to appropriate the benefits of public investment in R&D. Alienation reflects the inability of individuals or groups to control the impacts of R&D on their lives. The democratic process, from local protests to grass-root interest groups and eventually to legislation, appears as the natural avenue for change. A unifying theme that emerges from the rapidly evolving social context is the need for democratic control over science and technology. Instrumental science requires democratic forms of participation and accountability to ensure integrity and responsibility.

Technologies with the ability to dramatically widen social access may nevertheless be used predominantly on behalf of particular social groups. For example, in Great Britain it has been shown that members of the new virtual middle classes are the predominant users of virtual community care and thus gain a systematic advantage [8]. Social exclusion is not limited to lack of on-line access. The case of the Venezue- lan higher education community also illustrates that it may arise because already- advantaged people are able to engage with the technology in ways that advantage them even further. Systems of wired welfare tend to advantage people who have the time, reflexivity, inclination, and resources necessary to act [9]. Democracy presupposes political actors who use all available information and knowledge more intensely and are capable of unleashing experimentation and learning processes in a variety of domains, from the school system to exports, from government institutions to universities, from hospitals to communication industries. What is ultimately needed is not just a reduction in some physical gap separating ordinary citizens from science, but their acquisition of the means to form an opinion about the practices and politics that affect their daily lives and then to take action on the basis of these opinions.

The relationship between science and public opinion is a complex precondition for the functioning of modern mass societies. But in the depoliticization of the bulk of the population and the crumbling of the public domain in the current order, what obtains is an alliance between technical expertise and a manipulatively influenced public, with the distorted resonance that scientific information provokes in the gigantic body of a deformed public opinion [10]. Although in LAC the mass media, particularly TV, has an immense influence, ironically enough public deliberation about fundamental options has become practically impossible. Instead of open democratic communication, there is bare-knuckle competition for control of the issues that will reach public agendas. The relative poverty of political information degrades ever further the democratic climate, fostering cynicism, isolation, and rejection within the public, while only a few groups intervene in deliberations and public decisionmaking. The middle-class consumer has grown enormously in most countries of the region, but it is the consumer who feels threatened by current difficulties and uncertainties and who continues without assuming the voice of the citizen [11].

How can the R&D community contribute to a more democratically responsive S& T policy in LAC? In the late 20th century, individual scientists created new organiza- tions, such as the Sociedade Brasileira para o Progresso da Ciencia, the Asociacio´n Venezolana para el Avance de la Ciencia (AsoVAC), and the Asociacio´n Colombiana para el Avance de la Ciencia (ACAC), to help them act as citizens, although they hardly shed the special mantle of their expertise. Governments likewise chartered new scientific advisory committees to communicate scientific propositions and inform political positions, and it became part and parcel of scientific responsibility to advise government from a presumably neutral standpoint. In LAC, special ethics and bioethics committees sprang up although most still lack strength and seem to be more ritualistic and imitative ornaments rather than genuine representatives of responsible public opinion.

The idea of a more democratic R&D policy understandably generates fear and resistance among some scientists worried about the history of failed and immoral attempts to exert political control of science. But it is undeniable that scientists as a social group have historically identified themselves more often than not with elitist views and postures. Thus when claims are made equating a more democratically responsive R&D system with an authoritarian regime, with populist dictatorship, or with blunt ignorant attacks on science, the concept of democracy is itself undermined. Scientists usually work under the assumption that either there is broad consensus in society for scientific inquiry of any kind, or that the extant mechanisms of funding, priority setting, and conducting research are sufficiently consensual. Rendering this assumption true means that assuring the presence of democratic forms in decision making about research must occur prior to discussions about limiting—or for that matter, before conducting research. Increased democratic input into R&D policy decisions can in fact empower science by creating stronger linkages between research goals and societal goals, linkages that then ensure strong public support well into the future.

But public opposition may also reflect a rational desire for more democratic control over technologies and institutions that profoundly influence daily life. The option, in fact, is not between good science in itself (returning to the spirit of the 19th century) and science for development. Neither should science be presented as affording ready-made solutions to problems that may have a variety of causes. Things are not so simple, particularly when they concern development. Unless the trend toward increased socioeconomic inequity is successfully redressed in LAC, it is likely that politicians will no longer be prepared to support S&T funding, since social welfare expenditure will yield a higher electoral payoff, let alone the fact that clearly large segments of the population have not benefited and will not benefit from the national investment in science and technology. Therefore, the standard argument that only scientists are qualified to determine appropriate priorities and directions for research is intrinsically self-serving and thus politically unconvincing—and not only in Latin America.

The distribution of wealth in Latin America has grown increasingly inequitable over the past two decades. Income disparity between the top and bottom 10% of households is higher than ever. Poverty and misery have reached unexpected levels in countries like Argentina, which has had a relatively significant R&D infrastructure.

If broader (instead of the current limited) democratic regimes were in power in the region, it could be the case that the vast majority of the poor might eventually dismiss as vacuous the promises that economic development programs, when successful in creating wealth, will eventually trickle down with effects on job creation, better education, housing, and health. A biomedical R&D effort that focuses on diseases of affluence or old age may be seen as failing to serve the public health needs of the poor. Such a conclusion could stimulate political action that would support different biomedical R&D priorities or a shifting of funds from R&D to other programs.

The participation of citizens in the assessment of new technologies or the inclusion of diverse interests in scientific advisory committees is not yet a common feature in LAC. But there are a number of social experiments that aim at what some scholars have labeled the "co-production" of science [12], generally meaning that what counts as science, and what makes science reliable, is its production by a collaboration of scientists and non-scientists who incorporate values and criteria from both communities.

Mere observation shows that many of the few who do science and technology in the region often multiply themselves to produce relevant research in the best sense of the term, and there is ample evidence that when scientists work cooperatively with knowledgeable activists from outside the research community, science as well as society can benefit. Increased sensitivity about social, cultural, and economic factors all reflect the input of groups motivated by societal rather than scientific interests.

Consider a couple of illustrations in a special issue on relevant science in Latin America published by the journal *Interciencia*. The first concerns Brazilian agronomists, botanists, eco-physiologists, other scientists and technologists as well as producers, who have managed to "build" soil fertility in the immense Brazilian *cerrados* to achieve an efficient and profitable agriculture. As a precondition for success, research relied on experimentation to create new production conditions and on farmers for implementation of the recommended agricultural practices [13]. Another example is the research carried out by a public institution in Costa Rica on specific poisons of Central American snakes. But it is also devoted to the local production of antidotes whose distribution is coordinated with the health ministries of the Central American countries to guarantee an adequate distribution of antidotes to all the region, undergraduate and graduate education, and a broad social intervention to establish training programs for prevention and handling of ophidian accidents [14].

## 4. Latin American S&T demography in the context of globalization

There are comparatively few scientists and engineers in LAC, some 130,000 full- time equivalent (FTE). The United States has eight times this number (962,000). Almost two out of five Latin American S&T researchers are in Brazil (50,000), which also has 90,000 graduate students—20,000 in doctoral programs. Argentina has 28,500 researchers, with a growing graduate enrollment but still with limitations on the number of available fellowships (some 3850 graduate scholarships granted in 1997). Mexico had close to 20,000 researchers in 1996 and 18,070 graduate scholarship-holders. Chile, Venezuela, and Colombia have less than 10,000 researchers each, and even fewer graduate students, although all three are working to increase these numbers. When the population active in the labor force is considered, LAC has on average 0.77 FTE researchers for every thousand economically active persons (EAP). Argentina has the highest indicator, with almost two researchers per thousand EAP, followed by Chile, Cuba, and Costa Rica, each of which surpasses one per thousand. This contrasts with the US, which has an index of 7.4, or even Portugal, with 2.4.

There is an insufficient local development in undergraduate and graduate S&T education, and an important number of university students who complete their studies in advanced countries do not return to their country of origin, joining the many highly qualified LAC professionals who have already emigrated. It is estimated that between 1961 and 1983, 700,000 profession- als and highly qualified persons emi- grated to the US, Canada, and United Kingdom—equivalent to almost four times the total number of scientists who carry out full-time research activities in the region, and the flow has increased since then.

The reasons for this continuous drain of the region's professionals toward the developed countries are fundamentally structural in nature. Estimating the minimal cost of a tertiary education in LAC to be US$25,000, the emigration of professionals during the last 35 years has cost LAC US$30 billion. Since the region annually invest US$3 billion in S&T activities, the resulting loss through expatriation of its professionals represents ten years of regional investment, and nine times more than the direct investment of the Inter-American Development Bank (IDB) in the region's S&T since 1961 [15].

During the 1990s, some Latin American countries started programs of higher- education reform aiming to adjust train- ing to the new market conditions. An instrumentalization of knowledge institutions can be observed in their production and reproduction of scientists, professionals, and technologists to satisfy market demands. In general, education is driven increasingly by the development of marketable skills in the professional competence market. As the numbers of researchers and engineers grew, it coincided with and fed the emergent internationally mobile labor market. The better higher-education institutions served as incubators of local and foreign innovative businesses, and local university graduates increasingly sought posts abroad. This contributed to increasing vulnerability of the local labor market.

The flight of competencies has become an urgent matter for designers of public policies who have responsibilities to meet current and future national needs by managing the productive retention of human resources. What has happened in LAC, Africa, and Southeast Asia shows that in order to produce more development, it is not enough to establish the structural bases of capitalism. The process is far more complex and involves exchange, financial, cultural, and other mechanisms linked to the production and utilization of knowledge.

The profound inequalities and asymmetries in LAC societies present serious ballast for any international collaboration that seeks a more-balanced and less-distorted world. The current gap in scientific knowledge and technological know-how between the advanced countries and LAC can only be overcome through concerted national and international effort. It has become so obvious that the new world order is more based on science, that backward countries naturally appear as a new frontier for the development of international S&T. However, international research collaboration, particularly that funded from development aid, tended in the past to focus on technical short-term fixes, and was insufficient if not counterproductive for helping the southern countries to increase their self-sufficiency through the construction of local research capacities.

Wealthy countries are thus altering their positions toward international projects to improve the scientific capabilities of devel- oping ones. New international collabor- ations are promoted by the World Bank, for example, which previously considered research a luxury for developing countries. Today the Bank backs the development of knowledge, including science. Direct support of research in developing countries is now seen as a priority, as a fundamental component of economic success, on the assumption that in order to be competitive developing countries need to build knowledge-based industries. Scientific lobbies from LAC for the "coordination of research efforts," the "construction of research capabilities in the South," and "equal partnership" are finally getting a hearing in North American and European institutions where the policies of development aid are designed.

Yet for the problems to be correctly grasped by both sides, it is necessary to negotiate the terms of collaboration. How LAC and other developing regions respond to the new strategy will be crucial to promoting an effective transformation. This is why it is important to debate the *what* and the *how* now. Among wealthy countries, it has been common to think simply in terms of S&T knowledge transfer, although there is growing reluctance by providers of sophisticated technologies to transfer them without restric- tions. Even when problems are adequately understood by one side at the negotiating table, it is still necessary to transmit the correct message to the other side.

It is also the case that lobbies for science remain weak in developing countries, where politicians are rarely prepared to attend meetings for negotiating on research matters. What is most missing is a more powerful and efficacious lobbying for LAC science and technology as a basic component of public policy in developing countries so that they are in a better condition of being equal partners with associates in other regions.

# 5. Conclusion

In a region such as Latin America, the resonance of that mythological vision of a harmonious and rich future thanks to science and technology declines today under the weight of the economic crisis. But the attraction of a technological society per- sists, despite or perhaps because real technological changes have been accompanied by so much deprivation, conflict, and maladjustment. The expectation is that techno- scientific society will miraculously solve intensely painful transformations produced by industrial capital- ism, making it unnecessary to worry about the present marked by the lack of equity and social justice.

In the last analysis, the question is whether one may expect a better tomorrow in LAC through science, whether political prob- lems and history suggest the adoption of a good dose of skepticism when facing our scientific-technical prospects. True reform will only come with significant political and economic changes. Original social practices and new theoretical categories are needed that allow the construction of visible and desirable futures, custom-made for social groups and their problems, needs, and expectations. In the future, there will certainly be an important place for science and technology, but their direction will be given as a result of achieving a more complete humane social project. In this attempt, LAC society will probably change beyond its current shape. Some of these changes are already clear, but making them possible in a world of necessity is our challenge.

# References

1  Evans P. Embedded autonomy: States and industrial transformation. Princeton, NJ: Princeton Univer- sity Press, 1995.
2  Katz J. Cambios en la estructura y comportamiento del aparato productivo latinoamericano en los an˜ os 1990: Despue´s del 'Consenso de Washington', ¿que´?" Conference prepared for the 25th Anniversary of Universidad Auto´noma Metropolitana of Me´xico, 1999.
3.  Averch HA. A strategic analysis of science and technology policy. Baltimore, MD: The John Hopkins University Press, 1985.
4.  Merton RK. Science and democratic social structure. In: Merton RK, editor. Social theory and social structure. New York: Free Press, 1949.
5.  Rosenberg N, Birdzell L. How the West grew rich: The economic transformation of the industrial world. New York: Basic Books, 1986.
6.  Remington JA. Beyond Big Science in America: The binding of inquiry. Social Studies of Science 1988;18(1).
7.  Epstein S. Impure science: Aids, activism, and the politics of knowledge. University of California Press, 1996.
8.  Virtual Society Programme. Virtual society? The social science of electronic technologies. Economic and Social Research Council, CRICT. Uxbridge, UK: Brunel University, 1999.
9.  Plaz Power I, Vessuri H. La telematizacio´n de la educacio´n superior en Venezuela, entre la equidad y la exclusio´n. Educacio´n Superior y Sociedad 2000;11(1 & 2):157–80 (in Spanish).
10.  Stompka P. Science and democracy. World Social Science Report. Paris: UNESCO, 1999.
11.  Brunner JJ. Ame´rica Latina y el Caribe frente al nuevo milenio. 1999. Coleccio´n Documentos. La visio´n de las nuevas gen- eraciones. <<http://www.vision99.com/brunner>> (in Spanish).
12.  Jasanoff S. Beyond epistemology: Relativism and engagement in the politics of science. Social Studies of Science 1996;26: 397–418.
13.  Paterniani E, Malavolta E. La conquista del 'cerrado' en el Brasil. Victoria de la investigacio´ n cient´ıfica. Interciencia 1999;24(3):173 (in Spanish).
14.  Gutierrez JM, Rojas G. Instituto Clodomiro Picado: Ciencia y tecnolog´ıa endo´genas en la solucio´ n de un problema de salud pu´blica en Centroame´rica. Interciencia 1999;24(3):182–6 (in Spanish).
15.  Lema F. ERL viaje de Ulises: itinerarios y retornas de la inteligencia emigrada. In: Lema F, editor. Pensar la ciencia: los desafíos éticos y políticos del conocimiento en la posmodernidad. Caracas: IESALC/UNESCO, 2000.

**Hebe Vessuri** is a senior researcher in the Department of Science Studies at the Instituto Venezolano de Investigaciones Científicas, Caracas, Venezuela. An Argentine-born Venezuelan anthropologist, she is inter- ested in problems of scientific and technological learning in developing countries and has written exten- sively on the sociology and social history of Latin American science in the twentieth century. Her books include *37 modos de hacer ciencia en América Latina* (with H. Gómez and H. Jaramillo, 1997), and she was a contributor to UNESCO's World Science Report 1998 (1998) and 2000 (2002). She has recently edited issue 168 of International Social Science Journal devoted to "Science and its Cultures" (2001;168:195–368) and a special issue of Science, Technology & Society on "Innovation Context and Strategy of Scientific Research in Latin America" (2002;7(2):201–378).

# Article 34

Thomas L. Friedman

# It's a Flat World, After All

In 1492 Christopher Columbus set sail for India, going west. He had the Niña, the Pinta and the Santa Maria. He never did find India, but he called the people he met "Indians" and came home and reported to his king and queen: "The world is round." I set off for India 512 years later. I knew just which direction I was going. I went east. I had Lufthansa business class, and I came home and reported only to my wife and only in a whisper: "The world is flat."

And therein lies a tale of technology and geoeconomics that is fundamentally reshaping our lives—much, much more quickly than many people realize. It all happened while we were sleeping, or rather while we were focused on 9/11, the dot-com bust and Enron—which even prompted some to wonder whether globalization was over. Actually, just the opposite was true, which is why it's time to wake up and prepare ourselves for this flat world, because others already are, and there is no time to waste.

I wish I could say I saw it all coming. Alas, I encountered the flattening of the world quite by accident. It was in late February [2004], and I was visiting the Indian high-tech capital, Bangalore, working on a documentary for the Discovery Times channel about outsourcing. In short order, I interviewed Indian entrepreneurs who wanted to prepare my taxes from Bangalore, read my X-rays from Bangalore, trace my lost luggage from Bangalore and write my new software from Bangalore. The longer I was there, the more upset I became—upset at the realization that while I had been off covering the 9/11 wars, globalization had entered a whole new phase, and I had missed it. I guess the eureka moment came on a visit to the campus of Infosys Technologies, one of the crown jewels of the Indian outsourcing and software industry. Nandan Nilekani, the Infosys C.E.O., was showing me his global video-conference room, pointing with pride to a wall-size flat-screen TV, which he said was the biggest in Asia. Infosys, he explained, could hold a virtual meeting of the key players from its entire global supply chain for any project at any time on that supersize screen. So its American designers could be on the screen speaking with their Indian software writers and their Asian manufacturers all at once. That's what globalization is all about today, Nilekani said. Above the screen there were eight clocks that pretty well summed up the Infosys workday: 24/7/365. The clocks were labeled U.S. West, U.S. East, G.M.T., India, Singapore, Hong Kong, Japan, Australia.

"Outsourcing is just one dimension of a much more fundamental thing happening today in the world," Nilekani explained. "What happened over the last years is that there was a massive investment in technology, especially in the bubble era, when hundreds of millions of dollars were invested in putting broad-band connectivity around the world, undersea cables, all those things." At the same time, he added, computers became cheaper and dispersed all over the world, and there was an explosion of e-mail software, search engines like Google and proprietary software that can chop up any piece of work and send one part to Boston, one part to Bangalore and one part to Beijing, making it easy for anyone to do remote development. When all of these things suddenly came together around 2000, Nilekani said, they "created a platform where intellectual work, intellectual capital, could be delivered from anywhere. It could be disaggregated, delivered, distributed, produced and put back together again—and this gave a whole new degree of freedom to the way we do work, especially work of an intellectual nature. And what you are seeing in Bangalore today is really the culmination of all these things coming together."

At one point, summing up the implications of all this, Nilekani uttered a phrase that rang in my ear. He said to me, "Tom, the playing field is being leveled." He meant that countries like India were now able to compete equally for global knowledge work as never before—and that America had better get ready for this. As I left the Infosys campus that evening and bounced along the potholed road back to Bangalore, I kept chewing on that phrase: "The playing field is being leveled."

"What Nandan is saying," I thought, "is that the playing field is being flattened. Flattened? Flattened? My God, he's telling me the world is flat!"

Here I was in Bangalore—more than 500 years after Columbus sailed over the horizon, looking for a shorter route to India using the rudimentary navigational technologies of his day, and returned safely to prove definitively that the world was round—and one of India's smartest engineers, trained at his country's top technical institute and backed by the most modern technologies of his day, was telling me that the world was flat, as flat as that screen on which he can host a meeting of his whole global supply chain. Even more interesting, he was citing this development as a new milestone in human progress and a great opportunity for India and the world—the fact that we had made our world flat!

This has been building for a long time. Globalization 1.0 (1492 to 1800) shrank the world from a size large to a size medium, and the dynamic force in that era was countries globalizing for resources and imperial conquest. Globalization 2.0

(1800 to 2000) shrank the world from a size medium to a size small, and it was spearheaded by companies globalizing for markets and labor. Globalization 3.0 (which started around 2000) is shrinking the world from a size small to a size tiny and flattening the playing field at the same time. And while the dynamic force in Globalization 1.0 was countries globalizing and the dynamic force in Globalization 2.0 was companies globalizing, the dynamic force in Globalization 3.0—the thing that gives it its unique character—is individuals and small groups globalizing. Individuals must, and can, now ask: where do I fit into the global competition and opportunities of the day, and how can I, on my own, collaborate with others globally? But Globalization 3.0 not only differs from the previous eras in how it is shrinking and flattening the world and in how it is empowering individuals. It is also different in that Globalization 1.0 and 2.0 were driven primarily by European and American companies and countries. But going forward, this will be less and less true. Globalization 3.0 is not only going to be driven more by individuals but also by a much more diverse—non-Western, nonwhite—group of individuals. In Globalization 3.0, you are going to see every color of the human rainbow take part.

"Today, the most profound thing to me is the fact that a 14-year-old in Romania or Bangalore or the Soviet Union or Vietnam has all the information, all the tools, all the software easily available to apply knowledge however they want," said Marc Andreessen, a co-founder of Netscape and creator of the first commercial Internet browser. "That is why I am sure the next Napster is going to come out of left field. As bioscience becomes more computational and less about wet labs and as all the genomic data becomes easily available on the Internet, at some point you will be able to design vaccines on your laptop."

Andreessen is touching on the most exciting part of Globalization 3.0 and the flattening of the world: the fact that we are now in the process of connecting all the knowledge pools in the world together. We've tasted some of the downsides of that in the way that Osama bin Laden has connected terrorist knowledge pools together through his Qaeda network, not to mention the work of teenage hackers spinning off more and more lethal computer viruses that affect us all. But the upside is that by connecting all these knowledge pools we are on the cusp of an incredible new era of innovation, an era that will be driven from left field and right field, from West and East and from North and South. Only 30 years ago, if you had a choice of being born a B student in Boston or a genius in Bangalore or Beijing, you probably would have chosen Boston, because a genius in Beijing or Bangalore could not really take advantage of his or her talent. They could not plug and play globally. Not anymore. Not when the world is flat, and anyone with smarts, access to Google and a cheap wireless laptop can join the innovation fray.

When the world is flat, you can innovate without having to emigrate. This is going to get interesting. We are about to see creative destruction on steroids.

How did the world get flattened, and how did it happen so fast?

It was a result of 10 events and forces that all came together during the 1990's and converged right around the year 2000. Let me go through them briefly. The first event was 11/9. That's right—not 9/11, but 11/9. Nov. 9, 1989, is the day the Berlin Wall came down, which was critically important because it allowed us to think of the world as a single space. "The Berlin Wall was not only a symbol of keeping people inside Germany; it was a way of preventing a kind of global view of our future," the Nobel Prize-winning economist Amartya Sen said. And the wall went down just as the windows went up—the breakthrough Microsoft Windows 3.0 operating system, which helped to flatten the playing field even more by creating a global computer interface, shipped six months after the wall fell.

The second key date was 8/9. Aug. 9, 1995, is the day Netscape went public, which did two important things. First, it brought the Internet alive by giving us the browser to display images and data stored on websites. Second, the Netscape stock offering triggered the dot-com boom, which triggered the dot-com bubble, which triggered the massive overinvestment of billions of dollars in fiber-optic telecommunications cable. That overinvestment, by companies like Global Crossing, resulted in the willy-nilly creation of a global undersea-underground fiber network, which in turn drove down the cost of transmitting voices, data and images to practically zero, which in turn accidentally made Boston, Bangalore and Beijing next-door neighbors overnight. In sum, what the Netscape revolution did was bring people-to-people connectivity to a whole new level. Suddenly more people could connect with more other people from more different places in more different ways than ever before.

No country accidentally benefited more from the Netscape moment than India. "India had no resources and no infrastructure," said Dinakar Singh, one of the most respected hedge-fund managers on Wall Street, whose parents earned doctoral degrees in biochemistry from the University of Delhi before emigrating to America. "It produced people with quality and by quantity. But many of them rotted on the docks of India like vegetables. Only a relative few could get on ships and get out. Not anymore, because we built this ocean crosser, called fiber-optic cable. For decades you had to leave India to be a professional. Now you can plug into the world from India. You don't have to go to Yale and go to work for Goldman Sachs." India could never have afforded to pay for the bandwidth to connect brainy India with high-tech America, so American shareholders paid for it. Yes, crazy overinvestment can be good. The overinvestment in railroads turned out to be a great boon for the American economy. "But the railroad overinvestment was confined to your own country and so, too, were the benefits," Singh said. In the case of the digital railroads, "it was the foreigners who benefited." India got a free ride.

The first time this became apparent was when thousands of Indian engineers were enlisted to fix the Y2K—the year 2000—computer bugs for companies from all over the world. (Y2K should be a national holiday in India. Call it "Indian Interdependence Day," says Michael Mandelbaum, a foreign-policy analyst at Johns Hopkins.) The fact that the Y2K work could be outsourced to Indians was made possible by the first two flatteners, along with a third, which I call "workflow." Workflow is shorthand for all the software applications, standards and electronic transmission pipes, like middleware, that connected all those computers and fiber-optic cable. To put it another way, if the Netscape moment connected people to people like never before, what the workflow revolution did was connect applications to applications so that people all over the world could work together in manipulating and shaping words, data and images on computers like never before.

Indeed, this breakthrough in people-to-people and application-to-application connectivity produced, in short order, six more flatteners—six new ways in which individuals and companies could collaborate on work and share knowledge. One was "outsourcing." When my software applications could connect seamlessly with all of your applications, it meant that all kinds of work—from accounting to software-writing—could be digitized, disaggregated and shifted to any place in the world where it could be done better and cheaper. The second was "offshoring." I send my whole factory from Canton, Ohio, to Canton, China. The third was "open-sourcing." I write the next operating system, Linux, using engineers collaborating together online and working for free. The fourth was "insourcing." I let a company like UPS come inside my company and take over my whole logistics operation—everything from filling my orders online to delivering my goods to repairing them for customers when they break. (People have no idea what UPS really does today. You'd be amazed!). The fifth was "supply-chaining." This is Wal-Mart's specialty. I create a global supply chain down to the last atom of efficiency so that if I sell an item in Arkansas, another is immediately made in China. (If Wal-Mart were a country, it would be China's eighth-largest trading partner.) The last new form of collaboration I call "informing"—this is Google, Yahoo and MSN Search, which now allow anyone to collaborate with, and mine, unlimited data all by themselves.

So the first three flatteners created the new platform for collaboration, and the next six are the new forms of collaboration that flattened the world even more. The 10th flattener I call "the steroids," and these are wireless access and voice over Internet protocol (VoIP). What the steroids do is turbocharge all these new forms of collaboration, so you can now do any one of them, from anywhere, with any device.

The world got flat when all 10 of these flatteners converged around the year 2000. This created a global, Web-enabled playing field that allows for multiple forms of collaboration on research and work in real time, without regard to geography, distance or, in the near future, even language. "It is the creation of this platform, with these unique attributes, that is the truly important sustainable breakthrough that made what you call the flattening of the world possible," said Craig Mundie, the chief technical officer of Microsoft.

No, not everyone has access yet to this platform, but it is open now to more people in more places on more days in more ways than anything like it in history. Wherever you look today—whether it is the world of journalism, with bloggers bringing down Dan Rather; the world of software, with the Linux code writers working in online forums for free to challenge Microsoft; or the world of business, where Indian and Chinese innovators are competing against and working with some of the most advanced Western multinationals—hierarchies are being flattened and value is being created less and less within vertical silos and more and more through horizontal collaboration within companies, between companies and among individuals.

Do you recall "the IT revolution" that the business press has been pushing for the last 20 years? Sorry to tell you this, but that was just the prologue. The last 20 years were about forging, sharpening and distributing all the new tools to collaborate and connect. Now the real information revolution is about to begin as all the complementarities among these collaborative tools start to converge. One of those who first called this moment by its real name was Carly Fiorina, the former Hewlett-Packard C.E.O., who in 2004 began to declare in her public speeches that the dot-com boom and bust were just "the end of the beginning." The last 25 years in technology, Fiorina said, have just been "the warm-up act." Now we are going into the main event, she said, "and by the main event, I mean an era in which technology will truly transform every aspect of business, of government, of society, of life."

As if this flattening wasn't enough, another convergence coincidentally occurred during the 1990's that was equally important. Some three billion people who were out of the game walked, and often ran, onto the playing field. I am talking about the people of China, India, Russia, Eastern Europe, Latin America and Central Asia. Their economies and political systems all opened up during the course of the 1990s so that their people were increasingly free to join the free market. And when did these three billion people converge with the new playing field and the new business processes? Right when it was being flattened, right when millions of them could compete and collaborate more equally, more horizontally and with cheaper and more readily available tools. Indeed, thanks to the flattening of the world, many of these new entrants didn't even have to leave home to participate. Thanks to the 10 flatteners, the playing field came to them!

It is this convergence—of new players, on a new playing field, developing new processes for horizontal collaboration—that I believe is the most important force shaping global economics and politics in the early 21st century. Sure, not all three billion can collaborate and compete. In fact, for most people the world is not yet flat at all. But even if we're talking about only 10 percent, that's

300 million people—about twice the size of the American work force. And be advised: the Indians and Chinese are not racing us to the bottom. They are racing us to the top. What China's leaders really want is that the next generation of underwear and airplane wings not just be "made in China" but also be "designed in China." And that is where things are heading. So in 30 years we will have gone from "sold in China" to "made in China" to "designed in China" to "dreamed up in China"—or from China as collaborator with the worldwide manufacturers on nothing to China as a low-cost, high-quality, hyperefficient collaborator with worldwide manufacturers on everything. Ditto India. Said Craig Barrett, the C.E.O. of Intel, "You don't bring three billion people into the world economy overnight without huge consequences, especially from three societies"—like India, China and Russia—"with rich educational heritages."

That is why there is nothing that guarantees that Americans or Western Europeans will continue leading the way. These new players are stepping onto the playing field legacy free, meaning that many of them were so far behind that they can leap right into the new technologies without having to worry about all the sunken costs of old systems. It means that they can move very fast to adopt new, state-of-the-art technologies, which is why there are already more cellphones in use in China today than there are people in America.

If you want to appreciate the sort of challenge we are facing, let me share with you two conversations. One was with some of the Microsoft officials who were involved in setting up Microsoft's research center in Beijing, Microsoft Research Asia, which opened in 1998—after Microsoft sent teams to Chinese universities to administer I.Q. tests in order to recruit the best brains from China's 1.3 billion people. Out of the 2,000 top Chinese engineering and science students tested, Microsoft hired 20. They have a saying at Microsoft about their Asia center, which captures the intensity of competition it takes to win a job there and explains why it is already the most productive research team at Microsoft: "Remember, in China, when you are one in a million, there are 1,300 other people just like you."

The other is a conversation I had with Rajesh Rao, a young Indian entrepreneur who started an electronic-game company from Bangalore, which today owns the rights to Charlie Chaplin's image for mobile computer games. "We can't relax," Rao said. "I think in the case of the United States that is what happened a bit. Please look at me: I am from India. We have been at a very different level before in terms of technology and business. But once we saw we had an infrastructure that made the world a small place, we promptly tried to make the best use of it. We saw there were so many things we could do. We went ahead, and today what we are seeing is a result of that. There is no time to rest. That is gone. There are dozens of people who are doing the same thing you are doing, and they are trying to do it better. It is like water in a tray: you shake it, and it will find the path of least resistance. That is what is going to happen to so many jobs—they will go to that corner of the world where there is the least resistance and the most opportunity. If there is a skilled person in Timbuktu, he will get work if he knows how to access the rest of the world, which is quite easy today. You can make a website and have an e-mail address and you are up and running. And if you are able to demonstrate your work, using the same infrastructure, and if people are comfortable giving work to you and if you are diligent and clean in your transactions, then you are in business."

Instead of complaining about outsourcing, Rao said, Americans and Western Europeans would "be better off thinking about how you can raise your bar and raise yourselves into doing something better. Americans have consistently led in innovation over the last century. Americans whining—we have never seen that before."

Rao is right. And it is time we got focused. As a person who grew up during the cold war, I'll always remember driving down the highway and listening to the radio, when suddenly the music would stop and a grim-voiced announcer would come on the air and say: "This is a test. This station is conducting a test of the Emergency Broadcast System." And then there would be a 20-second high-pitched siren sound. Fortunately, we never had to live through a moment in the cold war when the announcer came on and said, "This is a not a test."

That, however, is exactly what I want to say here: "This is not a test."

The long-term opportunities and challenges that the flattening of the world puts before the United States are profound. Therefore, our ability to get by doing things the way we've been doing them—which is to say not always enriching our secret sauce—will not suffice any more. "For a country as wealthy as we are, it is amazing how little we are doing to enhance our natural competitiveness," says Dinakar Singh, the Indian-American hedge-fund manager. "We are in a world that has a system that now allows convergence among many billions of people, and we had better step back and figure out what it means. It would be a nice coincidence if all the things that were true before were still true now, but there are quite a few things you actually need to do differently. You need to have a much more thoughtful national discussion."

If this moment has any parallel in recent American history, it is the height of the cold war, around 1957, when the Soviet Union leapt ahead of America in the space race by putting up the Sputnik satellite. The main challenge then came from those who wanted to put up walls; the main challenge to America today comes from the fact that all the walls are being taken down and many other people can now compete and collaborate with us much more directly. The main challenge in that world was from those practicing extreme Communism, namely Russia, China and North Korea. The main challenge to America today is from those practicing extreme capitalism, namely China, India and South Korea. The main objective in that era was building a strong state, and the main objective in this era is building strong individuals.

Meeting the challenges of flatism requires as comprehensive, energetic and focused a response as did meeting the challenge of Communism. It requires a president who can summon the nation to work harder, get smarter, attract more young women and men to science and engineering and build the broadband infrastructure, portable pensions and health care that will help every American become more employable in an age in which no one can guarantee you lifetime employment.

We have been slow to rise to the challenge of flatism, in contrast to Communism, maybe because flatism doesn't involve ICBM missiles aimed at our cities. Indeed, the hot line, which used to connect the Kremlin with the White House, has been replaced by the help line, which connects everyone in America to call centers in Bangalore. While the other end of the hot line might have had Leonid Brezhnev threatening nuclear war, the other end of the help line just has a soft voice eager to help you sort out your AOL bill or collaborate with you on a new piece of software. No, that voice has none of the menace of Nikita Khrushchev pounding a shoe on the table at the United Nations, and it has none of the sinister snarl of the bad guys in "From Russia with Love." No, that voice on the help line just has a friendly Indian lilt that masks any sense of threat or challenge. It simply says: "Hello, my name is Rajiv. Can I help you?"

No, Rajiv, actually you can't. When it comes to responding to the challenges of the flat world, there is no help line we can call. We have to dig into ourselves. We in America have all the basic economic and educational tools to do that. But we have not been improving those tools as much as we should. That is why we are in what Shirley Ann Jackson, the 2004 president of the American Association for the Advancement of Science and president of Rensselaer Polytechnic Institute, calls a "quiet crisis"—one that is slowly eating away at America's scientific and engineering base.

"If left unchecked," said Jackson, the first African-American woman to earn a Ph.D. in physics from M.I.T., "this could challenge our pre-eminence and capacity to innovate." And it is our ability to constantly innovate new products, services and companies that has been the source of America's horn of plenty and steadily widening middle class for the last two centuries. This quiet crisis is a product of three gaps now plaguing American society. The first is an "ambition gap." Compared with the young, energetic Indians and Chinese, too many Americans have gotten too lazy. As David Rothkopf, a former official in the Clinton Commerce Department, puts it, "The real entitlement we need to get rid of is our sense of entitlement." Second, we have a serious numbers gap building. We are not producing enough engineers and scientists. We used to make up for that by importing them from India and China, but in a flat world, where people can now stay home and compete with us, and in a post-9/11 world, where we are insanely keeping out many of the first-round intellectual draft choices in the world for exaggerated security reasons, we can no longer cover the gap. That's a key reason companies are looking abroad. The numbers are not here. And finally we are developing an education gap. Here is the dirty little secret that no C.E.O. wants to tell you: they are not just outsourcing to save on salary. They are doing it because they can often get better-skilled and more productive people than their American workers.

These are some of the reasons that Bill Gates, the Micro-soft chairman, warned the governors' conference in a Feb. 26 speech that American high-school education is "obsolete." As Gates put it: "When I compare our high schools to what I see when I'm traveling abroad, I am terrified for our work force of tomorrow. In math and science, our fourth graders are among the top students in the world. By eighth grade, they're in the middle of the pack. By 12th grade, U.S. students are scoring near the bottom of all industrialized nations. . . . The percentage of a population with a college degree is important, but so are sheer numbers. In 2001, India graduated almost a million more students from college than the United States did. China graduates twice as many students with bachelor's degrees as the U.S., and they have six times as many graduates majoring in engineering. In the international competition to have the biggest and best supply of knowledge workers, America is falling behind."

We need to get going immediately. It takes 15 years to train a good engineer, because, ladies and gentlemen, this really is rocket science. So parents, throw away the Game Boy, turn off the television and get your kids to work. There is no sugar-coating this: in a flat world, every individual is going to have to run a little faster if he or she wants to advance his or her standard of living. When I was growing up, my parents used to say to me, "Tom, finish your dinner—people in China are starving." But after sailing to the edges of the flat world for a year, I am now telling my own daughters, "Girls, finish your homework—people in China and India are starving for your jobs."

I repeat, this is not a test. This is the beginning of a crisis that won't remain quiet for long. And as the Stanford economist Paul Romer so rightly says, "A crisis is a terrible thing to waste."

# Critical Thinking

1. What does the author mean, "the world is flat"?
2. In a world of such environmental, biotic, and resource variability, how can it be "flat"? What are some of the "environmental" assumptions the author is making about the Earth? About its peoples?
3. This article was written in 2005. What were some of the "headline" environmental issues then? What are some of the issues now, in 2012, seven years later? How might our current environmental issues and future ones impact this "flat world" argument?

4. How does "flattening the world" contribute to our goal of "environmental sustainability" or "sustainable development"?
5. What do Articles 5 and 6 have to do with "global development"?
6. Identify in this article three key terms, concepts, or principles that are used in your textbook (environmental science, economics, sociology, history, geography, etc.) or employed in the discipline you are currently studying. (Note: The terms, concepts, or principles may be implicit, explicit, implied, or inferred.)

THOMAS L. FRIEDMAN is the author of "*The World Is Flat: A Brief History of the Twenty-First Century*," to be published this week by Farrar, Straus & Giroux and from which this article is adapted. His column appears on the Op-Ed page of *The Times*, and his television documentary "Does Europe Hate Us?" was shown on the Discovery Channel on April 7, 2005.

# Article 35

Pankaj Ghemawat

## Why the World Isn't Flat

Globalization has bound people, countries, and markets closer than ever, rendering national borders relics of a bygone era—or so we're told. But a close look at the data reveals a world that's just a fraction as integrated as the one we thought we knew. In fact, more than 90 percent of all phone calls, Web traffic, and investment is local. What's more, even this small level of globalization could still slip away.

Ideas will spread faster, leaping borders. Poor countries will have immediate access to information that was once restricted to the industrial world and traveled only slowly, if at all, beyond it. Entire electorates will learn things that once only a few bureaucrats knew. Small companies will offer services that previously only giants could provide. In all these ways, the communications revolution is profoundly democratic and liberating, leveling the imbalance between large and small, rich and poor. The global vision that Frances Cairncross predicted in her *Death of Distance* appears to be upon us. We seem to live in a world that is no longer a collection of isolated, "local" nations, effectively separated by high tariff walls, poor communications networks, and mutual suspicion. It's a world that, if you believe the most prominent proponents of globalization, is increasingly wired, informed, and, well, "flat."

It's an attractive idea. And if publishing trends are any indication, globalization is more than just a powerful economic and political transformation; it's a booming cottage industry. According to the U.S. Library of Congress's catalog, in the 1990s, about 500 books were published on globalization. Between 2000 and 2004, there were more than 4,000. In fact, between the mid-1990s and 2003, the rate of increase in globalization -related titles more than doubled every 18 months.

Amid all this clutter, several books on the subject have man-aged to attract significant attention. During a recent TV interview, the first question I was asked—quite earnestly—was why I still thought the world was round. The interviewer was referring of course to the thesis of *New York Times* columnist Thomas L. Fried-man's bestselling book *The World Is Flat*. Friedman asserts that 10 forces—most of which enable connectivity and collaboration at a distance—are "flattening" the Earth and leveling a playing field of global competitiveness, the likes of which the world has never before seen.

It sounds compelling enough. But Friedman's assertions are simply the latest in a series of exaggerated visions that also include the "end of history" and the "convergence of tastes." Some writers in this vein view globalization as a good thing—an escape from the ancient tribal rifts that have divided humans, or an opportunity to sell the same thing to everyone on Earth. Others lament its cancerous spread, a process at the end of which everyone will be eating the same fast food. Their arguments are mostly characterized by emotional rather than cerebral appeals, a reliance on prophecy, semiotic arousal (that is, treating every-thing as a sign), a focus on technology as the driver of change, an emphasis on education that creates "new" people, and perhaps above all, a clamor for attention. But they all have one thing in common: They're wrong.

In truth, the world is not nearly as connected as these writers would have us believe. Despite talk of a new, wired world where information, ideas, money, and people can move around the planet faster than ever before, just a fraction of what we consider globalization actually exists. The portrait that emerges from a hard look at the way companies, people, and states interact is a world that's only beginning to realize the potential of true global integration. And what these trend's backers won't tell you is that globalization's future is more fragile than you know.

## The 10 Percent Presumption

The few cities that dominate international financial activity—Frankfurt, Hong Kong, London, New York—are at the height of modern global integration; which is to say, they are all relatively well connected with one another. But when you examine the numbers, the picture is one of extreme connectivity at the local level, not a flat world. What do such statistics reveal? Most types of e conomic activity that could be conducted either within or across borders turn out to still be quite domestically concentrated.

One favorite mantra from globalization champions is how "investment knows no boundaries." But how much of all the capital being invested around the world is conducted by companies outside of their home countries? The fact is, the total amount of the world's capital formation that is generated from foreign direct investment (FDI) has been less than 10 percent for the last three years for which data are available (2003–05). In other words, more than 90 percent of the fixed investment around the world is still domestic. And though merger waves can push the ratio higher, it has never reached 20 percent. In a thoroughly globalized environment, one would expect this number to be much higher—about 90 percent, by my calculation. And FDI isn't an odd or unrepresentative example.

The levels of internationalization associated with cross-border migration, telephone calls, management research and education, private charitable giving, patenting, stock investment, and trade, as a fraction of gross domestic product (GDP), all stand much closer to 10 percent than 100 percent. The biggest exception in absolute terms—the trade-to-GDP—recedes most of the way back down toward 20 percent if you adjust for certain kinds of double-counting. So if someone asked me to guess the internationalization level of some activity about which I had no particular information, I would guess it to be much closer to 10 percent—than to 100 percent. I call this the "10 Percent Presumption."

More broadly, these and other data on cross-border integration suggest a semiglobalized world, in which neither the bridges nor the barriers between countries can be ignored. From this perspective, the most astonishing aspect of various writings on globalization is the extent of exaggeration involved. In short, the levels of internationalization in the world today are roughly an order of magnitude lower than those implied by globalization proponents.

## A Strong National Defense

If you buy into the more extreme views of the globalization triumphalists, you would expect to see a world where national borders are irrelevant, and where citizens increasingly view themselves as members of ever broader political entities. True, communications technologies have improved dramatically during the past 100 years. The cost of a three-minute telephone call from New York to London fell from $350 in 1930 to about 40 cents in 1999, and it is now approaching zero for voice-over-Internet telephony. And the Internet itself is just one of many newer forms of connectivity that have progressed several times faster than plain old telephone service. This pace of improvement has inspired excited proclamations about the pace of global integration. But it's a huge leap to go from predicting such changes to asserting that declining communication costs will obliterate the effects of distance. Although the barriers at borders have declined significantly, they haven't disappeared.

To see why, consider the Indian software industry—a favorite of Friedman and others. Friedman cites Nandan Nilekani, the CEO of the second-largest such firm, Infosys, as his muse for the notion of a flat world. But what Nilekani has pointed out privately is that while Indian software programmers can now serve the United States from India, access is assured, in part, by U.S. capital being invested—quite literally—in that outcome. In other words, the success of the Indian IT industry is not exempt from political and geographic constraints. The country of origin matters—even for capital, which is often considered stateless.

Or consider the largest Indian software firm, Tata Consultancy Services (TCS). Friedman has written at least two columns in *The New York Times* on TCS's Latin American operations: "[I]n today's world, having an Indian company led by a Hungarian-Uruguayan servicing American banks with Montevidean engineers managed by Indian technologists who have learned to eat Uruguayan veggie is just the new normal," Friedman writes. Perhaps. But the real question is why the company established those operations in the first place. Having worked as a strategy advisor to TCS since 2000, I can testify that reasons related to the tyranny of time zones, languages, and the need for proximity to clients' local operations loomed large in that decision. This is a far cry from globalization proponents' oft-cited world in which geography, language, and distance don't matter.

Trade flows certainly bear that theory out. Consider Canadian-U.S. trade, the largest bilateral relationship of its kind in the world. In 1988, before the North American Free Trade Agreement (NAFTA) took effect, merchandise trade levels between Canadian provinces—that is, within the country—were estimated to be 20 times as large as their trade with similarly sized and similarly distant U.S. states. In other words, there was a built-in "home bias." Although NAFTA helped reduce this ratio of domestic to international trade—the home bias—to 10 to 1 by the mid-1990s, it still exceeds 5 to 1 today. And these ratios are just for merchandise; for services, the ratio is still several times larger. Clearly, the borders in our seemingly "borderless world" still matter to most people.

Geographical boundaries are so pervasive, they even extend to cyberspace. If there were one realm in which borders should be rendered meaningless and the globalization proponents should be correct in their overly optimistic models, it should be the Internet. Yet Web traffic within countries and regions has increased far faster than traffic between them. Just as in the real world, Internet links decay with distance. People across the world may be getting more connected, but they aren't connecting with each other. The aver-age South Korean Web user may be spending several hours a day online—connected to the rest of the world in theory—but he is probably chatting with friends across town and e-mailing family across the country rather than meeting a fellow surfer in Los Angeles. We're more wired, but no more "global."

Just look at Google, which boasts of supporting more than 100 languages and, partly as a result, has recently been rated the most globalized website. But Google's operation in Russia (cofounder Sergey Brin's native country) reaches only 28 percent of the market there, versus 64 percent for the Russian market leader in search services, Yandex, and 53 percent for Rambler.

Indeed, these two local competitors account for 91 percent of the Russian market for online ads linked to Web searches. What has stymied Google's expansion into the Russian market? The biggest reason is the difficulty of designing a search engine to handle the linguistic complexities of the Russian language. In addition, these local competitors are more in tune with the Russian market, for example, developing payment methods through traditional banks to compensate for the dearth of credit cards. And, though Google has doubled its reach since 2003, it's had to set up a Moscow office in Russia and hire Russian software engineers, underlining the continued importance of physical location. Even now, borders between countries define—and constrain—our movements more than globalization breaks them down.

## Turning Back the Clock

If globalization is an inadequate term for the current state of integration, there's an obvious rejoinder: Even if the world isn't quite flat today, it will be tomorrow. To respond, we have to look at trends, rather than levels of integration at one point in time. The results are telling. Along a few dimensions, integration reached its all-time high many years ago. For example, rough calculations suggest that the number of long-term international migrants amounted to 3 percent of the world's population in 1900—the high-water mark of an earlier era of migration— versus 2.9 percent in 2005.

Along other dimensions, it's true that new records are being set. But this growth has happened only relatively recently, and only after long periods of stagnation and reversal. For example, FDI stocks divided by GDP peaked before World War I and didn't return to that level until the 1990s. Several economists have argued that the most remarkable development over the long term was the declining level of internationalization between the two World Wars. And despite the records being set, the current level of trade intensity falls far short of completeness, as the Canadian-U.S. trade data suggest. In fact, when trade economists look at these figures, they are amazed not at how much trade there is, but how little.

It's also useful to examine the considerable momentum that globalization proponents attribute to the constellation of policy changes that led many countries—particularly China, India, and the former Soviet Union—to engage more extensively with the international economy. One of the better-researched descriptions of these policy changes and their implications is provided by economists Jeffrey Sachs and Andrew Warner:

"The years between 1970 and 1995, and especially the last decade, have witnessed the most remarkable institutional harmonization and economic integration among nations in world history. While economic integration was increasing throughout the 1970s and 1980s, the extent of integration has come sharply into focus only since the collapse of communism in 1989. In 1995, one dominant global economic system is emerging."

Yes, such policy openings are important. But to paint them as a sea change is inaccurate at best. Remember the 10 Percent Presumption, and that integration is only beginning. The policies that we fickle humans enact are surprisingly reversible. Thus, Francis Fukuyama's *The End of History*, in which liberal democracy and technologically driven capitalism were supposed to have triumphed over other ideologies, seems quite quaint today. In the wake of Sept. 11, 2001, Samuel Huntington's *Clash of Civilizations* looks at least a bit more prescient. But even if you stay on the economic plane, as Sachs and Warner mostly do, you quickly see counterevidence to the supposed decisiveness of policy openings. The so-called Washington Consensus around market-friendly policies ran up against the 1997 Asian currency crisis and has since frayed substantially—for example, in the swing toward neopopulism across much of Latin America. In terms of economic outcomes, the number of countries—in Latin America, coastal Africa, and the former Soviet Union—that have dropped out of the "convergence club" (defined in terms of narrowing productivity and structural gaps vis-à-vis the advanced industrialized countries) is at least as impressive as the number of countries that have joined the club. At a multilateral level, the suspension of the Doha round of trade talks in the summer of 2006—prompting *The Economist* to run a cover titled "The Future of Globalization" and depicting a beached wreck—is no promising omen. In addition, the recent wave of cross-border mergers and acquisitions seems to be encountering more protectionism, in a broader range of countries, than did the previous wave in the late 1990s.

Of course, given that sentiments in these respects have shifted in the past 10 years or so, there is a fair chance that they may shift yet again in the next decade. The point is, it's not only possible to turn back the clock on globalization-friendly policies, it's relatively easy to imagine it happening. Specifically, we have to entertain the possibility that deep international economic integration may be inherently incompatible with national sovereignty—especially given the tendency of voters in many countries, including advanced ones, to support more protectionism, rather than less. As Jeff Immelt, CEO of GE, put it in late 2006, "If you put globalization to a popular vote in the U.S., it would lose." And even if cross-border integration continues on its upward path, the road from here to there is unlikely to be either smooth or straight. There will be shocks and cycles, in all likelihood, and maybe even another period of stagnation or reversal that will endure for decades. It wouldn't be unprecedented.

The champions of globalization are describing a world that doesn't exist. It's a fine strategy to sell books and even describe a potential environment that may someday exist. Because such episodes of mass delusion tend to be relatively short-lived even when they do achieve broad currency, one might simply be tempted to wait this one out as well. But the stakes are far too high for that. Governments that buy into the flat world are likely to pay too much attention to the "golden straitjacket" that Friedman emphasized in his earlier book, *The Lexus and the Olive* Tree, which is supposed to ensure that economics matters more and more and politics less and less. Buying into this version of an integrated world—or worse, using it as a basis for policymaking—is not only unproductive; It is dangerous.

## Critical Thinking

1. What is Pankaj Ghemawat's point of view?
2. What is the "10 percent presumption"?
3. How do Ghemawat's arguments against a "flat" world differ from Friedman's?
4. How does the point of view of this article fit into the discussion of alternative futures presented in Article 1?

PANKAJ GHEMAWAT is the Anselmo Rubiralta professor of global strategy at IESE Business School and the Jaime and Josefina Chua Tiampo professor of business administration at Harvard Business School. His new book is *Redefining Global Strategy* (Boston: Harvard Business School Press, September 2007).

# Article 36

## Should the Federal Government Require That All Internet Traffic Be Treated Equally?

**Selected, Edited, and with Issue Framing Material by:**
M. Ethan Katsh, *University of Massachusetts, Amherst*

**YES: Marvin Ammori,** from "The Case for Net Neutrality," *Foreign Affairs* (2014)

**NO: Deborah T. Tate,** from "Net Neutrality 10 Years Later: A Still Unconvinced Commissioner," *Federal Communications Law Journal* (2014)

### Learning Outcomes

*After reading this issue, you will be able to:*

- Articulate what it means to treat all Internet traffic "equally."
- Define "broadband providers," "edge providers," and "end users," and describe the relationship between them.
- Identify the consequences of legally classifying broadband providers as "common carriers" under the Telecommunications Act of 1996.
- State the policy arguments for and against government regulation of the Internet.

### ISSUE SUMMARY

**YES:** Attorney Marvin Ammori argues that the Federal Communications Commission (FCC) should regulate Internet service providers to assure that some websites are neither given preferential treatment nor charged arbitrary fees in order to reach end users.

**NO:** Former FCC Commissioner Deborah Tate argues that the benefits of an open Internet are best preserved and protected by free market forces, not government agencies like the FCC.

### Where Do You Stand?

The Internet has experienced astonishing growth and development over the past 20 years. In 1995, there were approximately 23,000 websites worldwide; today that number is nearly 900 million. The number of Internet users worldwide in 1995 was 40 million; today that number approaches 3 billion. Most users in 1995 accessed the Internet through dial-up connections on telephone lines, at speeds of about 30 kb/s; today broadband access is commonplace, at speeds typically 10,000 times faster than dial-up. Broadband providers such as Comcast and Verizon operate the transmission lines that connect individual subscribers (known as end users) to the Internet's broader backbone network.

While broadband providers connect end users to the network, so-called edge providers create the content, services, and applications that end users eventually access. Edge providers range from very large companies like Amazon and Google to small organizations and individual bloggers. Like the speed of the network itself, the sophistication of Internet content and applications has also grown enormously in the last several years. In 1995, websites and applications such as Google, Facebook, Twitter, Wikipedia, Skype, NetFlix, and Amazon did not exist. Mobile applications, social media, most e-commerce sites, multi-player gaming, and streaming audio and video were similarly unknown. Today, of course, these sites and applications are commonplace. They also take up significantly more resources and bandwidth than did Internet applications a decade ago.

The growth of such technologically demanding content has changed the relationship between edge providers and broadband providers. Some broadband providers have suggested that websites and applications that take up large amounts of bandwidth should pay more for broadband service. Because broadband providers connect edge providers to end users, this suggestion has led some to worry that broadband providers will block end users from accessing certain edge provider content, or otherwise degrade that content, unless the edge provider agrees to pay higher fees. Put more concretely, the concern is that a broadband provider may (for example) deliberately slow down or block end user access to YouTube videos unless YouTube agrees to pay the broadband provider much higher fees. The idea that broadband providers should be required to treat all edge providers and all Internet content equally, regardless of its substance or platform, has been termed "net neutrality" or "Internet openness."

The concept of net neutrality caught the attention of the Federal Communications Commission (FCC), a federal agency that is charged with overseeing and regulating a wide variety of communications (from television and radio to cell phones and remote controls). In the mid- 2000s, the FCC began initial efforts to regulate broadband providers in order to prevent widely different treatment of edge providers in the future.

The extent to which the FCC can impose regulations on broadband providers depends on how those providers are classified under federal law. The Telecommunications Act of 1996 provides two possibilities for classifying broadband providers: as telecommunications carriers or as information service providers. Telecommunications carriers provide basic communications services for a fee directly to the public (like telephone service or a dial-up Internet connection). Information service providers, by contrast, provide enhanced services like storing, processing, and retrieving information.

In the real world, this distinction is murky: broadband providers typically provide both basic broadband access and a platform of enhanced services. Legally, however, the distinction is important. Information service providers can only be lightly regulated by the FCC. Telecommunications carriers, on the other hand, may be regulated much more heavily. That is because they are treated as "common carriers" under another federal law— Title II of the Communications Act of 1934—meaning that they are obligated to provide information to the FCC upon request, are prohibited from discriminating in their services or practices, and must charge "just and reasonable" rates.

In 2005, the FCC classified broadband providers as information service providers, a classification that was upheld by the U.S. Supreme Court. Even though this classification meant that broadband providers could not be regulated as "common carriers," the FCC left open the possibility that it might still seek to regulate the broadband industry in some other way. Three years later, it did just that. In 2008, in response to subscriber complaints that broadband provider Comcast had interfered with their use of certain peer-to-peer networking applications, the FCC ordered Comcast to develop a new approach for managing bandwidth demand and to disclose the details of that approach to the FCC. Comcast challenged the order in U.S. District Court, on the grounds that the FCC lacked the authority to regulate Comcast's practices. In 2010, the court agreed, concluding that the FCC had failed to demonstrate that it possessed the authority to regulate broadband providers' management practices. The court's decision partially rested on the fact that the FCC classified broadband providers as information service providers, not telecommunications carriers.

After the ruling in *Comcast,* the FCC debated whether to formally reclassify broadband as a telecommunications service, which would have allowed it to regulate broadband providers as common carriers under Title II. Ultimately, however, the FCC decided not to reclassify broadband service. Instead, it issued an "Open Internet Order" in 2010 that imposed certain requirements on broadband providers not to block or discriminate against edge provider content. That order was challenged by broadband provider Verizon Communications as an impermissible regulation that exceeded the scope of the FCC's authority. In January 2014, the U.S. Court of Appeals for the District of Columbia Circuit agreed, vacating the relevant portions of the Open Internet Order and holding that broadband providers could not be regulated under the Telecommunications Act unless the FCC specifically classified them as common carriers.

In the wake of the *Verizon* case, the FCC began work on a middle-ground approach to broadband regulation. In May 2014, the FCC released an official proposal that would permit broadband providers to draw certain distinctions between websites requiring high and low broadband use, respectively. Not long afterward, however, the FCC abruptly changed course. In February 2015, FCC Chair Tom Wheeler unveiled a new proposal to reclassify broadband providers as telecommunications carriers. This move would allow the FCC to impose more stringent regulations on the way such providers treat web traffic that flows over their networks. The five-member commission approved the new proposal by a vote of three to two on February 26, 2015.

Mr. Wheeler's change of heart reflected net neutrality policies that have been aggressively pursued by the Obama administration. After a decade of so-called "light-touch" regulation of broadband providers, in November 2014 President Obama announced his position that the Internet should be regulated as a public utility, with the "strongest possible rules" to require broadband providers to treat all Internet traffic equally. Within days, Mr. Wheeler publicly announced his support for the same policy.

Although the FCC approved the classification of broadband providers as telecommunications carriers subject to greater regulation, the legal and policy debates over that classification and the FCC's regulatory powers are likely to carry on for years to come.

The following readings reflect the state of the debate just before the FCC adopted its new proposal. Attorney Marvin Ammori, a specialist in communications law, likens the Internet to a highway and net neutrality to the principle that traffic should not be divided into "fast" and "slow" lanes by broadband providers. He argues that government regulation of broadband providers is valid as a matter of legal principle and necessary as a matter of good public policy. In contrast, former FCC Commissioner Deborah Tate argues that regulation of broadband providers as common carriers is outside the FCC's legal bounds and is particularly unwise as a practical matter. She notes that the free market can better assure open access to all Internet users and further argues that the FCC's resources are better spent on protecting children and intellectual property holders from illegal online activities.

# The Case for Net Neutrality

. . . Net neutrality holds that Internet service providers (ISPs) shouldn't offer preferential treatment to some websites over others or charge some companies arbitrary fees to reach users. By this logic, AT&T, for example, shouldn't be allowed to grant iTunes Radio a special "fast lane" for its data while forcing Spotify to make do with choppier service.

In January 2014, a U.S. federal appeals court, in a case brought by Verizon, struck down the net neutrality rules adopted by the FCC in 2010, which came close to fulfilling Obama's pledge despite a few loopholes. Shortly after the court's decision, Netflix was reportedly forced to pay Comcast tens of millions of dollars per year to ensure that Netflix users who connect to the Internet through Comcast could stream movies reliably; Apple reportedly entered into its own negotiations with Comcast to secure its own special treatment. Sensing an opening, AT&T and Verizon filed legal documents urging the FCC to allow them to set up a new pricing scheme in which they could charge every website a different price for such special treatment.

. . . FCC Chair Tom Wheeler circulated a proposal to the FCC's four other commissioners, two Democrats and two Republicans, for rules that would allow broadband providers to charge content providers for faster, smoother service. The proposal would also authorize ISPs to make exclusive deals with particular providers, so that PayPal could be the official payment processor for Verizon, for example, or Amazon Prime could be the official video provider for Time Warner Cable.

Word of the proposal leaked to the press and sparked an immediate backlash. One hundred and fifty leading technology companies, including Amazon, Microsoft, and Kickstarter, sent a letter to the FCC calling the plan a "grave threat to the Internet." In their own letter to the FCC, over 100 of the nation's leading venture capital investors wrote that the proposal, if adopted as law, would "stifle innovation," since many start-ups and entrepreneurs wouldn't be able to afford to access a fast lane. Activist groups organized protests outside the FCC's headquarters in Washington and accused Wheeler, a former lobbyist for both the cable and the wireless industries, of favoring his old clients over the public interest. Nonetheless, . . . the FCC released its official proposal, concluding tentatively that it could authorize fast lanes and slow lanes on the Internet. . . .

. . . Preferably working with policymakers of all stripes supportive of open markets, the Obama administration should ensure that the FCC adopts rules that maintain the Internet as basic infrastructure that can be used by entrepreneurs, businesses, and average citizens alike—not a limited service controlled by a few large corporations. In the arcane world of federal administrative agencies, that guarantee comes down to whether the FCC adopts rules that rely on flimsy legal grounds, as it has in the past, or ones that rely on the solid foundation of its main regulatory authority over "common carriers," the legal term the U.S. government uses to describe firms that transport people, goods, or messages for a fee, such as trains and telephone companies. In 1910, Congress designated telephone wires as a common carrier service and decreed that the federal government should regulate electronic information traveling over wires in the same way that it regulated the movement of goods and passengers on railroads across state lines through the now defunct Interstate Commerce Commission, which meant that Congress could prevent companies from engaging in discrimination and charging unreasonable access fees. When the FCC was created in 1934 by the Communications Act, those common carrier rules were entrusted to it through a section of the law known as Title II. Today, the broadband wires and networks on which the Internet relies are the modern-day equivalent of these phone lines, and they should be regulated as such: like telephone companies before them, ISPs should be considered common carriers. This classification is crucial to protecting the Internet as public infrastructure that users can access equally, whether they run a multinational corporation or write a political blog.

However, in 2002, Michael Powell, then chair of the FCC, classified ISPs not as common carriers but as "an information service," which has handicapped the FCC's ability to enforce net neutrality and regulate ISPs ever since. If ISPs are not reclassified as common carriers, Internet infrastructure will suffer. By authorizing payments for fast lanes, the FCC will encourage ISPs to cater to those customers able and willing to pay a premium, at the expense of upgrading infrastructure for those in the slow lanes.

The stakes for the U.S. economy are high: failing to ban ISPs from discriminating against companies would make it harder for tech entrepreneurs to compete, because the costs of entry would rise and ISPs could seek to hobble service for competitors unwilling or unable to pay special access fees. Foreign countries would likely follow Washington's lead, enacting protectionist measures that would close off foreign markets to U.S. companies. But the harm would extend even further. Given how much the Internet has woven itself into every aspect of daily life, the laws governing it shape economic and political decisions around the world and affect every industry, almost every business, and billions of people. If the Obama administration fails to reverse course on net neutrality, the Internet could turn into a patchwork of fiefdoms, with untold ripple effects.

## Innovation Superhighway

Net neutrality is not some esoteric concern; it has been a major contributor to the success of the Internet economy. Unlike in the late 1990s, when users accessed relatively hived-off areas of cyberspace through slow dial-up connections, the Internet is now defined by integration. The credit for this improvement goes to high-speed connections, cellular networks, and short-distance wireless technologies such as WiFi and Bluetooth, which have allowed companies large and small—from Google to Etsy—to link up computers, smartphones, tablets, and wearable electronics. But all this integration has relied on a critical feature of the global Internet: no one needs permission from anyone to do anything.

Historically, ISPs have acted as gateways to all the wonderful (or not so wonderful) things connected to the Internet. But they have not acted as gatekeepers, determining which files and servers should load better or worse. From day one, the Internet was a public square, and the providers merely connected everyone, rather than regulating who spoke with whom. That allowed the Internet to evolve into a form of basic infrastructure, used by over a billion people today.

The Internet's openness has radically transformed all kinds of industries, from food delivery to finance, by lowering the barriers to entry. It has allowed a few bright engineers or students with an idea to launch a business that would be immediately available all over the world to over a billion potential customers. Start-ups don't need the leverage and bank accounts of Apple or Google to get reliable service to reach their users. In fact, historically, they have not paid any arbitrary fees to providers to reach users. Their costs often involve nothing more than hard work, inexpensive cloud computing tools, and off-the-shelf laptops and mobile devices, which are getting more powerful and cheaper by the day. As Marc Andreessen, a co-founder of Netscape and a venture capitalist, has pointed out, the cost of running a basic Internet application fell from $150,000 a month in 2000 to $1,500 a month in 2011. It continues to fall.

In some ways, the Internet is just the latest and perhaps most impressive of what economists call "general purpose technologies," from the steam engine to the electricity grid, all of which, since their inception, have had a massively disproportionate impact on innovation and economic growth. In a 2012 report, the Boston Consulting Group found that the Internet economy accounted for 4.1 percent (about $2.3 trillion) of GDP in the G-20 countries in 2010. If the Internet were a national economy, the report noted, it would be among the five largest in the world, ahead of Germany. And a 2013 Kauffman Foundation report showed that in the previous three decades, the high-tech sector was 23 percent more likely, and the information technology sector 48 percent more likely, to give birth to new businesses than the private sector overall.

That growth, impressive as it is, could be just the beginning, as everyday objects, such as household devices and cars, go online as part of "the Internet of Things." John Chambers, the CEO of Cisco Systems, has predicted that the Internet of Things could create a $19 trillion market in the near future. Mobile-based markets will only expand, too; the Boston Consulting Group projects that mobile devices will account for four out of five broadband connections by 2016.

## Not Neutrality

All this innovation has taken place without the permission of ISPs. But that could change as net neutrality comes under threat. ISPs have consistently maintained that net neutrality is a solution in search of a problem, but this often-repeated phrase is simply wrong. In the United States, both small and large providers have already violated the very principles that net neutrality is designed to protect. Ever since 2005, the FCC has pursued a policy that resembles net neutrality but that allows enough room for interpretation for firms to find ways to undermine it. From 2005 to 2008, the largest ISP in the United States, Comcast, used technologies that monitor all the data coming from users to secretly block so-called peer-to-peer technologies, such as BitTorrent and Gnutella. These tools are popular for streaming online TV (sometimes illegally), using cloud-based storage and sharing services such as those provided by Amazon, and communicating through online phone services such as Skype. In 2005, a small ISP in North Carolina called Madison River Communications blocked Vonage, a company that allows customers to make cheap domestic and international telephone calls over the Internet. From 2007 to 2009, AT&T's contract with Apple required the latter to block Skype and other competing phone services on the iPhone, so that customers could not use them when connected to a cellular network. From 2011 to 2013, AT&T, Sprint, and Verizon blocked all the functionality of Google Wallet, a mobile payment system, on Google Nexus smartphones, likely because all three providers are part of a competing joint venture called Isis.

In the EU, widespread violations of net neutrality affect at least one in five users, according to a 2012 report from the Body of European Regulators for Electronic Communications. Restrictions affect everything from online phone services and peer-to-peer technologies to gaming applications and e-mail. In 2011, the Netherlands' dominant mobile carrier, KPN, saw that its text-messaging revenue was plummeting and made moves to block applications such as WhatsApp and Skype, which allow users to send free texts. Across the Atlantic, in 2005, the Canadian telecommunications company Telus used its control of the wires to block the website of a union member taking part in a strike against the company.

Opponents of net neutrality insist that efforts to enforce it are unnecessary, because market competition will ensure that companies act in their customers' best interests. But true competition doesn't exist among ISPs. In the United States, local cable monopolies are often the only game in town when it comes to high-speed access and usually control over two-thirds of the market. In places where there are real options, users rarely switch services because of the penalties that providers charge them for terminating their contracts early.

Some skeptics of strong regulation have proposed rules requiring companies merely to disclose their technical discrimination policies, but those wouldn't solve the problem either. Even in the United Kingdom, which boasts both healthy competition among ISPs and robust disclosure laws, companies still frequently discriminate against various types of Internet traffic. Indeed, wherever you look, the absence of rules enforcing net neutrality virtually guarantees that someone will violate the principle. As it stands now, after the FCC's rules were struck down in January, U.S. law does little to protect net neutrality. As companies push the boundaries, violations will become more common—and not just in the United States.

If the FCC doesn't rein in U.S. ISPs, there is likely to be a domino effect abroad. Some foreign officials view the net neutrality movement as nothing more than an attempt to protect U.S. technology companies, since given their size, they are the main beneficiaries of net neutrality abroad. (Twitter, for example, does well in foreign markets only where the government doesn't block it and carriers don't charge extra for it.) Foreign ISPs have long hoped to exclude U.S. companies from their markets or at least charge them for access, and if U.S. providers are allowed to play similar games in the United States, it will give foreign governments the perfect excuse to give their ISPs what they want. Similarly, if the U.S. government continues to allow American ISPs to block or charge foreign technology companies, such as Spotify, which is based in Sweden, then sooner or later, other countries are likely to retaliate by giving their own providers a similar right. The result would be a global patchwork of fees and discriminatory rules.

Another danger is that if the Internet becomes less open in the United States, some forward-thinking foreign governments could enhance their net neutrality protections as a way of luring U.S. entrepreneurs and engineers to move abroad. Soon after the U.S. federal appeals court struck down the FCC's net neutrality rules in January, Neelie Kroes, a vice president of the EU Commission who is responsible for its digital agenda, asked on Twitter if she should "invite newly disadvantaged US startups to [the] EU, so they have a fair chance." By early April, the European Parliament had adopted tough net neutrality rules. Likewise, Chile, the first nation to adopt net neutrality rules, in 2010, has sought to attract global entrepreneurs through a government initiative called Start-Up Chile, which has invested millions of dollars in hundreds of foreign technology companies, most of which hail from the United States.

## Life in the Slow Land

Imagine if, years ago, MySpace had cut deals with cable and phone companies to block Facebook, if Lycos had colluded with AltaVista to crush Google, if Microsoft had contracted with service providers to protect Internet Explorer by blocking Mozilla Firefox. If ISPs are allowed to block, discriminate, and charge for different applications, such scenarios could become commonplace. The main reason they have not been is because the FCC, in 2005, stated that Internet access should be "operated in a neutral manner" and subsequently stepped in a few times to enforce that policy: against Madison River Communications regarding Vonage, against Comcast regarding peer-to-peer services, and against AT&T and Apple regarding Skype. The enforcement has not been completely consistent—in-store payments from Google Wallet are still being blocked on AT&T's, Verizon's, and T-Mobile's wireless networks—but it has still largely succeeded in imposing some discipline on the market.

Without that FCC regulation, the Internet would have come to look very different than it does today—a lot more like the cable industry, in fact. For decades, cable companies, such as Comcast and Time Warner Cable, and satellite TV providers, such as DirecTV, have acquired equity stakes in channels as part of their carriage deals. That arrangement has resulted in disputes over price tiers, with smaller channels claiming they get put into more expensive, limited service packages than a cable company's own channels. In a lengthy dispute with Comcast, for example, the independently owned Tennis Channel argued that it should be placed in the same basic service package as the Golf Channel and the NBC Sports Network, two sports channels that Comcast owns and provides to all its subscribers. In May 2013, a U.S. federal appeals court ruled in Comcast's favor; the Tennis Channel appealed to the Supreme Court, which in February declined to hear the case. Internet companies have never had to give up equity stakes as part of service deals to reach users or had to compete with firms that are owned by ISPs and thus given preferential treatment. And most of them would have run out of funding during the years of litigation if they had taken legal action like the Tennis Channel has.

A scenario in which websites have to acquiesce to ISPs in order to secure competitive access to the Internet would kill innovation. Small companies would no longer be able to reach every segment of the market at no extra cost. A new company's rivals, if they could afford it, would be able to pay for better service, thereby reducing consumers' choices. Many start-ups would be unable to pay expensive access fees and would simply not start up in the first place. Investors would end up putting larger sums in fewer companies, and with no clear limit on how much ISPs could charge, the potential rewards from successful investments might be smaller and would certainly be more uncertain than they are today.

It is unrealistic to expect competition among ISPs to prevent or limit such fees; it hasn't done so in the United Kingdom and other European markets. Nor can one argue that ISPs need the money. They already enjoy comically high profit margins on broadband delivery, and their operating costs continue to decrease. In weighing the potential damage to entrepreneurship against the financial gains of a few huge telecommunications companies, the U.S. government should back the entrepreneurs.

That's especially so since without net neutrality, telecommunications and cable companies could also stifle free expression by favoring the websites and applications of the largest media conglomerates over those of nonprofit news organizations, bloggers, and independent journalists and filmmakers. Permitting media giants to pay for a fast lane unavailable to all online outlets would raise the barriers to entry for all new publishing and sharing tools—eliminating innovations along the lines of Twitter, Tumblr, and WordPress. These tools, most of which started with extremely small investments, have helped citizens find new ways to petition and protest against their governments. New and better tools of this kind will continue to emerge only if the field is left open.

## Keeping the Internet Open

The Obama administration needs to get the rules governing the Internet right. Obama's initial, feeble attempts to do so came during his first term, when the FCC was chaired by Julius Genachowski, a law school classmate of Obama's who demonstrated a distinct lack of political insight and courage on the job. In 2010, the FCC adopted a set of net neutrality rules know as the Open Internet Order, which barred providers from blocking or giving preferential access to particular websites and applications and required more disclosure about their policies. Moreover, in the order, the FCC effectively prohibited ISPs from creating and charging for fast lanes, declaring them unreasonable. But under pressure from ISPs, Genachowski punched two gaping loopholes into these rules. He exempted mobile access from the order, even though more people now go online through their cell phones than through their home computers. He also made it possible for ISPs to violate net neutrality through connection deals that they make directly with websites—a loophole that Comcast has exploited in its shakedown of Netflix.

Ultimately, however, it was the FCC's 2002 definition of ISPs as "an information service," rather than a "common carrier," that overwhelmed the weak rules established in 2010. Last year, Verizon challenged the 2010 rules, arguing that they went beyond the FCC's jurisdiction given the commission's own classification of ISPs as an information service. Since they were not common carriers, they could not be regulated according to Title II of the Communications Act, which would allow the FCC to treat them like telephone companies and ban unreasonable Internet discrimination and access fees. In January 2014, a U.S. federal appeals court agreed with Verizon and struck down the 2010 FCC rules.

In legal terms, the FCC can easily address all these issues when it adopts a new order later this year. By reclassifying ISPs as common carriers, the FCC could regulate them as it does phone companies. It should not shy away from using the authority that Congress gave it; the Supreme Court, in 2005, made clear that the FCC has the power to change ISPs' classification. Getting the legal definition right is crucial, since the FCC's last two attempts to enforce net neutrality were struck down in court on jurisdictional grounds. In both cases, rather than relying on its main authority over common carriers under Title II, the FCC attempted to impose net neutrality requirements through weaker regulatory authorities, including Section 706 of the Telecommunications Act of 1996, which gives the FCC the authority to regulate broadband infrastructure deployment. Each time, the court's ruling was sharply dismissive of the FCC's legal reasoning, as nondiscrimination rules can be applied only to common carriers.

In addition to fixing the FCC's legal footing, the new order should close the two loopholes in the moribund 2010 rules. First, there should be no exceptions for restrictions on mobile access. That is particularly important since many start-ups now develop applications initially or even exclusively for mobile phones, such as Instagram and Uber. The FCC should also make clear that ISPs cannot charge websites for direct connections to their networks, as Comcast has done with Netflix.

. . . Although the Obama administration and the FCC are the main decision-makers, Republicans should recognize the need to support an open Internet. Over the years, some Republicans, including former FCC Chair Kevin Martin, who served under President George W. Bush; former House Representative Charles "Chip" Pickering; and former Senator Olympia Snowe, have supported net neutrality as the best way to promote entrepreneurship, freemarket competition, and free speech. Opposing an open Internet now would put the party on the wrong side of its values and on the wrong side of history.

A country's Internet infrastructure, just like its physical infrastructure, is essential to its economic competition and growth. According to the Organization for Economic Cooperation and Development, high-speed Internet is not only slower in New York City and San Francisco than it is in Seoul; it also costs five times as much. Suffering from an even more expensive, less robust, and more fragmented Internet infrastructure would put the entire U.S. economy in a global slow lane.

Washington faces a simple choice: allow the Internet to remain an a engine of innovation, a platform for speech in even the harshest tyrannies, and a unified connection for people across the globe—or cede control of the Internet to service providers motivated by their parochial interests. . . .

**MARVIN AMMORI** is an attorney and Internet freedom activist, and a Future Tense Fellow at the New America Foundation. He was formerly a law professor at the University of Nebraska—Lincoln College of Law, and remains affiliated with the Information Society Project at Yale Law School and the Center for Internet and Society at Stanford Law School.

# Net Neutrality 10 Years Later:
# A Still Unconvinced Commissioner

"Some men see things as they are and say, 'Why?'. . . I dream things that never were and say, 'Why not?'"

**Robert F. Kennedy, 1966**

## I. Introduction

From the moment I first heard the words "net neutrality," I marveled at the absolute brilliance of coining such a phrase—one that evokes such a democratic, neutral value proposition, yet threatens disastrous results for our economy. Interestingly, although net neutrality seemingly endorses the free and open nature of the Internet ecosystem, its impact would actually be burdensome and onerous. In fact, this so-called net neutrality goes directly against most American consumers' values, such as competition, freedom of choice, and less government regulation.

At the end of the FCC's first and only investigation on the subject, which involved the slowing of BitTorrent traffic by Comcast, I suggested that we change the dialogue to be much more concerned about whether the Internet is "safe and secure." Those fears have, sadly, come to fruition, as illustrated by recent data breaches afflicting the National Security Agency, the Internal Revenue Service, and the Target Corporation, among many others. Nevertheless, net neutrality seems to still hold the attention of policymakers in Washington, D.C.

The FCC in 2005 issued a seemingly benign "Internet policy statement" under former Chairman Kevin Martin. Then, in 2010, the FCC plowed forward with a newly expanded list of "net neutrality principles." Both forays into regulation of the Internet were held to exceed the legal authority of the FCC by the U.S. Court of Appeals for the D.C. Circuit.

Many scholars have discussed the regulatory and legal history of the latest ruling by the D.C. Circuit in *Verizon v. FCC*. As a former FCC Commissioner, I would be remiss to minimize the longstanding legal principle of *Chevron* deference that the judiciary affords federal expert agencies such as the FCC. At the same time, I believe it is equally important that the FCC—indeed, any agency or arm of our government—acts completely within its legal authority.

In *Verizon*, the FCC defended its net neutrality rules as a permissible exercise of the Commission's "ancillary jurisdiction," which supposedly emerged from a tapestry of other authorities within the broader Communications Act. The FCC also relied on its authority under section 706 of the Telecommunications Act, which tasks the FCC with encouraging the "deployment on a reasonable and timely basis of advanced telecommunications capability to all Americans" by using, among other tools, "regulating methods that remove barriers to infrastructure investment." Although the *Verizon* court recognized section 706 as a standalone fount of regulatory authority for the FCC, the court nonetheless vacated the net neutrality rules' core provisions on the grounds that they impermissibly imposed common carriage status on fixed broadband providers.

Despite its duo of losses, the FCC is now developing a *third* version of net neutrality rules. I cannot imagine it manages to find the authority to promulgate similar rules this time around. As a skeptic of net neutrality regulation, I believe this outcome will be for the best.

## II. Telecom Regulation and the Role of Government

Whenever the government acts, interestingly, it is often in *reaction* to a real or perceived problem that, if left unattended or unregulated, might cause harm. New regulations often emerge after a specific incident, perhaps involving toxic substances, dangerous medications, tainted food, or misleading product advertisements. Where perceived risk exists, government officials worry about political liability [if] they do nothing; to avert this prospect, they frequently resort to regulation.

The resulting government is far larger than that envisioned by the founding fathers, who established the United States as a constitutionally limited government. Today, the founders would probably struggle to recognize the nation's capital, which houses vast bureaucracies that span the city and sprawl into the surrounding states, and employs millions of federal workers and contractors. As the Chief Justice of the United States recently observed, the "administrative state wields vast power and touches almost every aspect of daily life." Indeed, the "overreach" of these federal agencies has never been more apparent, as demonstrated by the recent spate of congressional investigations of agencies acting outside their legal authority.

One such agency is the Federal Communications Commission ("FCC"), which Congress tasked with overseeing a sector that accounts for approximately one-sixth of nation's economy. Created, in part, as a response to the sinking of the *RMS Titanic,* to coordinate domestic and international radio communications, the FCC eventually took on a broad role in the telecommunications and media sectors. Approving new gadgets—now devices—and negotiating with global players in the satellite sector further broadened the FCC's purview. Yet, in my experience, most citizens have no idea how far the FCC's reach extends. Instead, many Americans think the Commission watches television all day in hopes of keeping "wardrobe malfunctions" and dirty words off the airwaves.

Whenever I speak to a civic club, I often explain the FCC's breadth by depicting a day in the life of an ordinary American. From the moment you turn on the news, open your garage door, use your remote control, switch radio stations, and listen to SiriusXM on your drive to work, you have probably spent more time with the FCC than your family. Much of the FCC's work aims to ensure all of these technologies operate so that consumers have the best possible experience, unimpeded by interference.

To be sure, preconceptions of the FCC's activities are not uncommon. Some people relate to the FCC as the federal overseer of our nation's emergency response systems, such as 911. Others are familiar with the FCC's placement of satellites for global telecommunications. Some even relate to the Commission's role in national security. And many parents whose children attend public schools have heard of the ERate program, which has connected almost every public school and library across this vast nation to the Internet.

I am quite honored to have had the opportunity to serve the American people at the FCC, especially to the extent that our work saved lives and enhanced economic investment in the next dazzling innovation. However, in a few instances during my tenure, the FCC ventured outside of its legal bounds. The issue of net neutrality was—and is—one such instance.

## III. A Commissioner's Experience with Net Neutrality

As one of the two original Commissioners to take issue with the entire premise of net neutrality, I could never quite fathom that we were spending countless man-hours at the FCC on it, holding public "hearings" around the country and attempting to create regulations out of whole cloth—all basically because of one lone complaint regarding an ISP that had slowed down some consumers' Internet speeds.

Similarly, in the second complaint—which involved the degradation, rather than the blocking, of Internet traffic—broadband provider Comcast voluntarily resolved the issue and promised the FCC it would not happen again. As my former colleague and FCC Commissioner Robert McDowell argued in his dissent from the *Open Internet Order*, "in the almost nine years since those fears were first sewn, net regulation lobbyists can point to fewer than a handful of cases of alleged misconduct, out of an infinite number of Internet communications. *All* of those cases were resolved in favor of consumers under *current* law."

Indeed, while the FCC has found that ninety-four percent of households have access to fixed broadband Internet, meeting the Commission's speed benchmark, the aforementioned formal complaints were the only two filed with the FCC alleging discrimination by a broadband provider. Juxtaposed against those two complaints are the 1.5 million indecency complaints—many of which are still pending—and many other consumer complaints clearly within the legal authority of the Commission, all of which remain unaddressed.

Informally designated "the Children's Commissioner" during my time at the FCC, I was and continue to be outspoken on issues regarding illegal online activities, such as child pornography and online predatory behavior targeting minors. In addition, as a Music City native, I often speak about the harms caused by online infringement of intellectual property rights. These problems hurt individuals, especially children, and the music industry. However, despite my ardent desire to crack down on these illegal, unethical, and economically harmful online activities, I could not embrace FCC net neutrality regulation, as it clearly exceeded the Commission's legal authority.

My first question to attorneys and government relations officials who frequented my office on the topic was usually "what is your definition of net neutrality?" I rarely received the same response. Indeed, net neutrality has been said to be "the most discussed, least understood concept in the world of internet policy." Under the FCC's conception of net neutrality, it requires broadband providers to allow their subscribers to (1) "access the lawful Internet content of their choice," (2) "run applications and use services of their choice, subject to the needs of law enforcement," and (3) "connect their choice of legal devices that do not harm the network."

My second question was "what is the basis of the FCC's legal authority to establish net neutrality regulations?" This question is important for advocates, attorneys, and policymakers, for the government should never reach the definitional question if it has no clear legal authority over the issue at the outset. And, indeed, that is what the D.C. Circuit recently opined—*for the second time*. Simply put, the court held, the FCC lacks the authority to impose common carriage regulation on broadband providers that are classified as information services under Title I of the Communications Act.

## IV. Net Neutrality is Not a Silver Bullet

In my work with women's and minority organizations, I am often asked how a particular proposal, law, or regulation may impact those groups specifically. I applaud the FCC for many of its public hearings and ongoing initiatives, especially as they relate to the low percentage of media ownership by women and minorities. The FCC has a long-established and very active Diversity Committee, which advises the Commission on a variety of issues across all sectors and routinely holds public hearings to examine the impact of or need for a particular rule or regulation which may enhance diversity.

When I am asked about net neutrality, my response is always the same: an Internet with light regulation and less oversight or intrusion by the government is better for *all* of us—including new application builders on the edge of the ecosystem, women running small businesses from home, and our youngest citizens taking Advanced Placement courses or learning a foreign language that was never before possible in their rural hometown. Allowing infrastructure providers and ISPs to invest in and expand high speed Internet throughout our country helps us all. The Internet's low entry costs and lack of barriers to create, upload, start up, and sell goods and services are especially beneficial to women and minorities with less access to capital than established firms. The underlying reason for the lack of women and minority ownership of radio and television entities is directly related to the high cost of entry and the difficulty of access to large capital or debt. However, since the advent of the Internet, those barriers have decreased greatly; both women and minorities are now unleashing their creativity, developing innovative services, and even producing independent films and videos at record numbers.

Net neutrality proponents need only look to the FCC's media ownership rules to see how a similar scheme might affect women and minorities. The Minority Media and Telecommunications Council ("MMTC"), which has long been an outspoken advocate for minority and women's ownership in the media space, undertook a study regarding the potential impact of similar Internet regulation on their constituencies. The report, entitled *Refocusing Broadband Policy: The New Opportunity Agenda for People of Color*, was co-authored by David Honig, president of MMTC, and Dr. Nicol Turner-Lee, vice president and chief research and policy officer at MMTC. The report explored current trends in minority broadband adoption and assessed the impact of Internet regulation, finding that it is actually diverting attention from important strategies aimed at closing the digital divide.

In a historical review of broadband policies initiated under the leadership of former FCC Chairman William Kennard, Honig and Lee suggest that "innovation has thrived within a minimalist regulatory framework facilitating technological advances and opportunities for consumers and entrepreneurs of color." Recognizing, however, that adoption gaps between African Americans, Hispanics, and Whites still persist, the authors cautioned against "stringent regulation until more of these communities are enabled by the platforms, products, and services that broadband provides." Honig further emphasized that "more regulation is not always the silver bullet for advancing digital inclusion."

One need only look at the dismal results from past over regulation in the media ownership space to pause before allowing the same to happen to women and minorities embarking on Internet-based businesses.

## V. The Democratization of Commerce

Beyond the opportunities in the media marketplace, women and minorities have also thrived in the e-commerce marketplace. Like mass media, entering this market is affordable and does not require a physical presence—bricks and mortar have been replaced by colorful graphics and product photos. Indeed, retail e-commerce weathered the recent and extended recession quite well, albeit with slower growth than prior to the financial crisis, falling from a high of forty-two percent year over year growth to about eighteen percent growth during the recession. Globally, e-commerce topped $1 trillion in 2012. All of this is good news for U.S. producers and consumers.

But none of this would have been possible if broadband subscribers were unable to search for and purchase products easily online. Nor would this explosion have occurred if there were providers who were blocking traffic, slowing it down, or otherwise making entrepreneurial entry difficult or expensive. Obviously these potential "what ifs" that net neutrality proponents continue to suggest have not and are not occurring, given that ecommerce is estimated to have a 10 percent global penetration by 2016 and Facebook would be the third largest nation in the world based on population.

Regulators should be leveling the playing field and opening the gates to competition at every level. In the former world of the old-fashioned telephone service, when there was one local provider in each market, telephone companies—like other utilities—were highly regulated at both the state and federal levels. This regulation encompassed everything from price to the privacy of customer information to 911 emergency services to the "Chinese wall" required between each phone company and the yellow pages. After the break-up of AT&T into Regional Bell Operating Companies, or "baby bells," the ensuing competition led to a world of choices for voice service on any type of handheld device—which could even be purchased at the local supermarket.

Even when the phone companies were highly regulated, they competed through marketing and advertising products and pricing. "Special access" provided a dedicated, secure line for crucial communications to corporations with hundreds of geographically dispersed retail outlets and hospitals and doctors to share patient information. Thus, even in a highly regulated market, phone companies could negotiate prices for special access and creatively market tools to entice and keep customers. Yet, eighteen years after the passage of the deregulatory 1996 Telecommunications Act, net neutrality proponents advocate turning the clock backwards and re-regulating marketing and pricing of Internet services. They propose a "free and open" Internet that denies broadband providers the freedom to negotiate with content companies to finance the networks of tomorrow.

It is widely accepted that broadband penetration and access for all of our citizens is absolutely critical. Nowadays, applying for a job, applying to college, and even making a health care appointment are often done online. Over seventy-five percent of teachers use the Internet for homework. Parents can check on their child's school attendance, test scores, events, and other pertinent educational data—often in real time. Many citizens also seek health care information and even sign up for health insurance online.

All of this requires Internet access—and, in many cases, faster broadband speeds than many Americans currently have. As many groups sought to help with broadband adoption, they found that "cost" was often a reason for lack of uptake even when the service was available to their home. Again, we see that lower cost alternatives—such as a "two-sided market" wherein one or more content companies help broadband providers shoulder the burden of the "last mile"—would be helpful in reaching those last Americans who remain offline.

## VI. Net Neutrality's Tenth Anniversary

The FCC has signaled it will continue to pursue net neutrality regulations—albeit not in court, for now. I am certain that the FCC's decision not to challenge the D.C. Circuit's decision involved the risk of hearing for the *third* time—and from the U.S. Supreme Court—that its net neutrality rules are illegal. Specifically, as FCC Chairman Tom Wheeler stated:

> The D.C. Circuit ruled that the FCC has the legal authority to issue enforceable rules of the road to preserve Internet freedom and openness . . . I intend to accept that invitation by proposing rules that will meet the court's test for preventing improper blocking of and discrimination among Internet traffic, ensuring genuine transparency in how Internet service providers manage traffic, and enhancing competition.

On February 19, 2014, Chairman Wheeler launched a public inquiry aimed at establishing an "updated" set of rules for an "open Internet." This marks the tenth anniversary of the FCC's original inquiry as to whether and how to regulate the Internet. At the same time, the White House issued a blog post mentioning President Barack Obama's support for net neutrality since his days in the U.S. Senate. It noted specifically that his campaign was "empowered by an open Internet" that allowed millions to interact in an "unprecedented fashion." We indeed have seen a new interest and rise in the civic engagement of our citizens, whether it involves a specific election or an issue or a cause. The Internet has connected people who care about a subject matter no matter where they are physically located. This connectivity is providing opportunities for us to discuss important issues of the day by returning to the "town square" online or becoming "the town crier" like Paul Revere. And who could forget the text messages and photos we all witnessed during the Arab Spring and other democratic movements worldwide. As the White House recognized, "[i]ndeed, an open Internet is an engine for freedom around the world." Later, the White House's blog post references the Internet as a hotbed for low cost entry and innovation, "building companies, creating jobs, improving vital services and fostering even more innovation along the way." Crucially, however, all these incredible successes for individuals, companies, civic engagement, and the spread of our democratic ideals, occurred under the *present regime*—one in which there is less government regulation, not more.

## VII. Conclusion

The world's insatiable appetite for more content, faster speeds, and wearable devices is almost unfathomable, especially given that much of this extraordinary innovation occurred in just the past few years. It is predicted that the growth will require more and more bandwidth—and, with it, better technologies to accommodate that growth. Advanced network management to enable the best possible consumer experience will rule the marketplace and consumers will continue to adopt and change with each new service, device, or application. Computer-to-computer communication will impact our homes, our vehicles, our health, and our everyday lives.

But this all depends on the ability of companies, investors, management teams, and brilliant young engineers to move nimbly and quickly to take advantage of each new trend by consumers. Nearly two *trillion* dollars sit on the sidelines, held by multinational companies that are waiting to see whether the United States government regulates the Internet, among other things. Meanwhile, regulatory uncertainty persists, even as other nations evolve—perhaps into global high-tech leaders.

As a nation, we face many challenges: ensuring that all children have access to the Internet at speeds and with devices in order to reach their full potential; conducting an unprecedented spectrum auction to ensure the viability and strength of wireless networks; and implementing technology and strategies to make the Internet as safe and secure as possible for every user and to thwart cybersecurity attacks that occur daily throughout the ecosystem. We want to ensure democracy thrives here and around the world and that the Internet remains an open medium for civic engagement everywhere.

However, none of these goals involve or rely upon new net neutrality rules being adopted and enforced by the FCC. Parents, teachers, consumers, entrepreneurs, and investors will choose the winners and losers through online chat, voting with their wallets, and adopting new technologies that have yet to be invented. The best way the FCC can influence the debate is by ending it. If and when a real problem emerges, shine a light on it and look out for the consumer backlash against any instigator or wrongdoer. Odds are the wrongdoers will not need an FCC monetary penalty, as they will be out of business altogether.

All this incredible success was enabled through the *current* framework of a light-touch regulatory process. Any further net neutrality regulation is not only unnecessary, but might also actually derail the Internet's next great expansion. We must refrain from regulation taking aim at shadows in order to continue the very real progress and promise of unleashing the very best America has to offer to our consumers, our creators, our children and indeed, the world.

**DEBORAH T. TATE** is special envoy to the International Telecommunication Union. She was appointed as a commissioner of the Federal Communications Commission by President George W. Bush in 2005 and served in that capacity until early 2009. She has also served as legal counsel and policy advisor to two Tennessee governors.

# SECTION 7

# Security and Surveillance

Advancements with online technology have led to increased threats to personal security, therefore resulting in an increase in the development and use of various surveillance tools. We are now experiencing a tension between a person's right to privacy and the security of confidential information such as social security numbers and credit card information; our increasing reliance on the Internet for convenience increases the likelihood of our personal information being revealed. We have hackers who believe that the Internet should be free of laws, regulations, and government intrusion; that there is an inherent right of freedom on the Internet. Yet, others feel the Internet should be regulated to protect individuals from cybercriminals. So, we are left asking the following questions: Do we take security over privacy? What are the tradeoffs? What are the true motivations behind increased security? How do we maintain values we deem important as a society, while protecting individual rights? The readings presented in this section draw attention to the complicated answers to these questions.

## Learning Objectives

1. Identify various surveillance technologies to defend against security risks.
2. Examine the use of security and surveillance technologies in terms of benefits and drawbacks.
3. Formulate opinions on internet regulation and other surveillance and security measures.

# Article 37

Torin Monahan

## Questioning Surveillance and Security

Unfortunately, security and liberty form a zero-sum equation. The inevitable trade-off: To increase security is to decrease liberty and vice versa.

Walter Cronkite, journalist

Now we all know that in times of war and certainly in this post-9/11 world, one of the most difficult questions we face is how to balance security and liberty.

Charles E. Schumer, U.S. senator

Since the 9/11 terrorist attacks, the government is charged with protecting the rights of the individual as well as ensuring our collective safety. The antiterrorist policies the government institutes will, by necessity, be more invasive.

Lynn M. Kuzma, political scientist

Why are questions about surveillance and security always framed in terms of trade-offs? Regardless of the forum, from popular media broadcasts to political speeches to academic publications, trade-offs are taken as the starting point for any discussion. Some of the most common expressions of trade-offs are security versus liberty, security versus privacy, security versus freedom, and security versus cost. But, seemingly, once the issues are presented in these terms, the only thing left to decide is whether the public is willing to make the necessary sacrifices to bring about greater national security. Absent are discussions about the politics behind surveillance and security systems, what one means by "security," what (or who) gets left out of the conversation, and the veracity of such assumptions about trade-offs to begin with. Occasionally, more astute critics will ask about the efficacy of surveillance systems in bringing about greater national security. The question is usually along the lines of "Do they work?"—meaning, are surveillance systems efficacious at preventing crime or terrorism? Although important, this type of question is really just an extension of the logic of trade-offs proffered in the opening quotes, because the implication is that if systems are not sufficiently effective, then they are not worth the sacrifice or investment.

This book argues that these are the wrong questions because they obscure the real changes underway and issues at play with the incorporation of surveillance technologies into public life. The questions, in other words, function as a rhetorical smoke screen, hiding deeper motivations and logics behind surveillance and security. Some of the obvious issues not discussed when talking about trade-offs are how surveillance contributes to spatial segregation and social inequality, how private high-tech industries are benefiting from the public revenue generated for these systems, and what the ramifications are of quantifying "security" (e.g., by the number of video cameras) for political purposes.

This chapter—along with the book as a whole—aims to dispel some of the smoke concealing deeper issues about surveillance and security. It starts, for the sake of fairness, by taking the wrong questions seriously, with a specific focus on the question of how efficacious surveillance systems are at bringing about greater security. Next, it proposes and discusses some of the questions that I see as being the right ones: why do we believe in trade-offs, what social relations are produced by surveillance systems, and how can surveillance be used to increase security without sacrificing civil liberties, if at all? In raising alternative questions of this sort, my goal is not to provide definitive answers but instead to open up the field of inquiry and to move beyond the fog surrounding current debates over these critically important topics.

## Taking the Wrong Questions Seriously

On February 12, 1993, two ten-year-old schoolboys kidnapped and murdered two-year-old Jamie Bulger in Merseyside, United Kingdom. Closed-circuit television (CCTV) footage showed Bulger being led by the hand out of a shopping center unbeknownst to his distracted mother. The boys proceeded to take him on a two-and-a-half mile walk, periodically beating him and taunting him along the way. When confronted by several concerned bystanders, the boys claimed that Jamie was their younger brother and that they were looking out for him, and no one intervened. When they reached a secluded railway line, the boys threw paint in Jamie's face and then beat him with stones, bricks, and an iron bar. Finally, he was laid across the railroad tracks with stones stacked on his head and was later run over by a train (Wikipedia 2004). The assailants could not be identified in the grainy video footage from the shopping center, but friends later turned them in. Nevertheless, the media played the tape countless times to a shocked public, and this had the effect of galvanizing tremendous support for public video surveillance in the United Kingdom (Rosen 2001).

Now, more than ten years after the Jamie Bulger killing, Great Britain boasts the most extensive system of public surveillance in the world, with more than four million cameras throughout the United Kingdom (Rice-Oxley 2004) and more than half a million in London alone (Norris 2004).[1] With the equivalent of one camera for every fourteen people, it is estimated that the average person in a large city like London is filmed three hundred times a day (Coaffee 2004). Yet in spite of this proliferation of video surveillance, surprisingly little evaluative research has been conducted on the effectiveness of surveillance in preventing crime, and the independent research that has been done is largely inconclusive.

Two of the most cited studies about surveillance efficacy were carried out in Airdrie and Glasgow, Scotland, in the mid-1990s. The Airdrie research compared total recorded crimes from two years before and two years after 1992—the year when twelve open street CCTV cameras were installed. The research found a 21 percent drop in recorded crimes in the area, so surveillance was determined to be a "success" (Short and Ditton 1995). Nonetheless, the report raises some doubts because it did not explicitly make mention of social factors such as population changes and unemployment rates in the area, which criminologists consider to be crucially important variables in explaining crime rates (Reiman 2000; LaFree 1998; Collins and Weatherburn 1995). The issue of geographical displacement of crime from one area to another is also problematic in this study, even though the authors claim otherwise:

[Adjacent] areas recorded slight increases in total crimes and offenses in the 2 years following the installation of CCTV. This increase is almost entirely accounted for by the growth in crimes relating to the possession or supply of drugs and to offences committed whilst on bail. Displacement would be suggested if these crimes declined in the CCTV area. However this was not the case. (Short and Ditton 1995: 3)

The interpretation here is that even though crimes did increase in surrounding areas, these were "natural" occurrences and therefore should not be attributed to displacement. In other words, drug offenses or offenses perpetrated while on bail do not count as crimes unless they are occurring (or declining) in CCTV areas. Because these crimes do not seem to fit the researchers' model of displacement, they are discounted.[2] Still, this can be considered a qualified success for surveillance.

The Glasgow research compared recorded crime offenses from two years before and one year after the installation of thirty-two open street CCTV cameras in 1994. In addition to looking at crime occurrences, this study also measured public perceptions of the system and observed camera monitoring by security personnel in a control room. The findings with regard to efficacy were a wash. As the report states, "The researchers suggest that the cameras were relatively successful, with some reductions in certain crime categories. Overall, however, the reductions in crime are no more significant than those in the control areas outwith [beyond] the camera locations" (Ditton et al. 1999: 1). Thus, the report continues, "CCTV cameras could not be said to have had a significant impact overall in reducing recorded crimes and offences" (Ditton et al. 1999: 2). The explanation provided for this lack of success is that people were generally unaware of the cameras, and without awareness there is no deterrence.

More recent research does nothing to clear up this muddy water about video surveillance efficacy. The *Christian Science Monitor* reports that after ten years of CCTV projects in the United Kingdom at a publicly funded cost of £250 million ($460 million)[3] that

research has yet to support the case for CCTV. A government review 18 months ago [in 2002] found that security cameras were effective in tackling vehicle crime but had limited effect on other crimes. Improved streetlighting recorded better results. (Rice-Oxley 2004: 1–2)

In a government review, which was mandated by the Home Office (the U.K. department in charge of public security) to see what general conclusions could be drawn from existing research, only twenty-four studies were found to be methodologically sound, and the overall outcome was that "CCTV appears to have no effect on violent crimes, a significant effect on vehicle crimes and it is most effective when used in car parks" (Armitage 2002: 5).

On the whole, what these studies from the United Kingdom indicate is that as gruesome as the Jamie Bulger murder was, it would not have been prevented with a more comprehensive system of video surveillance. Indeed, most crimes—violent or otherwise—are not prevented by surveillance. One bright spot within the evaluation literature on video surveillance is that it does appear to enable apprehending and convicting criminals after the fact (Gill 2004). But if the criterion for a worthwhile trade-off (of civil liberties, of privacy, of cost, etc.) is *prevention* of crime, then one must respond negatively to the question "Is it worth it?"

Oddly enough, given the astronomical crime rates in the United States, relatively speaking, one is hard pressed to find *any* independent evaluations of video surveillance in that country. There are several reasons for this. First, unlike many CCTV schemes in the United Kingdom, video surveillance in the United States is largely implemented in an ad hoc way by private companies rather than through public funds or with public oversight. This makes it difficult to even locate where the operational cameras are, let alone evaluate their effectiveness in some controlled way.[4] Second, the most obvious governmental agency for evaluating surveillance—the federal Office of Technology Assessment—was dissolved in 1995 because, as some say, they too produced reports that suggested politically unattractive regulation of private industries (Coates 1995).[5]

Third, in the United States, publicly funded video surveillance is most often used for generating revenue from traffic violations, such as running red lights, or it is trained on the urban poor on streets, on public transit, or in schools (Nieto, Johnston-Dodds, and Simmons 2002; Monahan, Chapter 7, this volume). Because of the stigma attached to poor minorities in the United States and the public's perception of surveillance systems as crime deterrents, it is highly unlikely that the general public would demand evaluation and oversight of surveillance, especially when those "public" systems are seldom focused on the more affluent.[6] Finally, for reasons that are explored in the next section, evaluations of technological systems, generally speaking, are simply not funded. Thus, of the more than 200 U.S. police agencies that employ CCTV systems, 96 percent conduct *no evaluation* of their effectiveness (Nieto, Johnston-Dodds, and Simmons 2002: 13).

One of the most well-known studies of video surveillance efficacy in the United States was conducted in low-income public housing in the late 1970s (Musheno, Levine, and Palumbo 1978). The researchers found that the use of video surveillance in New York City's public housing did not reduce crime or fear of it, even though CCTV's implementation came at great public cost of an estimated $10,000 per apartment (in three public buildings). The reasons for this "failure," the authors explain, stemmed from a conceptual deficiency as much as from technical limitations. The design strategy in public housing was predicated on the concept of "defensible space" (O. Newman 1972), implying that the agents of crime existed outside of the immediate community and that close collaboration between community members and police officers would keep deviants out. In fact, crime emerged from within the community, poor relations between residents and police prevented community members from contacting the police, vandals routinely disabled the surveillance equipment, and residents chose not to watch the video feeds, which were routed through their television sets.

There is more recent evidence to suggest that criminals are appropriating video surveillance systems that were originally intended to thwart them.[7] In the Frederick Douglas Towers, a public housing complex for seniors in Buffalo, New York, drug dealers established a crack cocaine operation using existing CCTV systems to monitor customers and keep a lookout for police. According to one law enforcement official, "The dealers were using all the security features of the senior apartments at Douglas to their advantage ... to screen who was coming up to the apartment and buzzing people inside the building" (Herbeck 2004). In another case in Virginia, four teenagers were "arrested on charges of operating a large-scale, well-organized crime ring that used surveillance, two-way radios, lookouts and disguises to stage at least 17 commercial burglaries over a 14-month period" (Branigin 2003). As an added twist to this story, the teenagers established their base of operations within a private, fortified, gated community with its own police force (Aquia Harbour 2004). When surveillance technologies originally intended to prevent crime are employed to facilitate crime or protect criminals, it lends a whole different meaning to the question of "Do they work?"

On the subject of traffic violations, cities with red-light surveillance programs do report a significant reduction in red-light runners at those intersections. A Washington, D.C., program reported a 63 percent decrease in red-light runners; Oxnard, California, reported a 42 percent decrease; and Fairfax, Virginia, reported a 40 percent decrease (Nieto, Johnston-Dodds, and Simmons 2002: 20). So, at least for this type of traffic crime, there has been demonstrated effectiveness. This conclusion is somewhat complicated, however, by the potential for increased rear-end collisions when people brake abruptly to avoid fines (Nieto, Johnston-Dodds, and Simmons 2002: 21).[8]

The history of eschewing publicly funded surveillance and security systems in the United States is shifting rapidly in the wake of the 9/11 attacks. Instead of being conceived of as deterrents to ordinary crimes, these systems are now being embraced by policy makers as counterterrorism and intelligence-gathering tools (Lyon 2003b). Perhaps the hottest area of development, along these lines, is in biometrics, meaning the range of technologies designed to measure and classify unique human attributes. Biometrics can include fingerprinting systems, face-recognition technologies, hand-geometry scanning, iris and/or retinal scans, odor identification, thermal face print scans, voice recognition, and so on (Woodward, Orlans, and Higgins 2002). These technologies are varied and complex and present many sociotechnical obstacles for "successful" use (contingent on the social context, the goals of the system designers and users, the interoperability of systems, etc.). The professional biometrics community, for instance, actively debates the appropriateness of some systems versus others (e.g., whether identifiers should be stored in a general database or within portable documents), and they frequently criticize each other for trying to push proprietary biometric "solutions" from which individual companies stand to benefit enormously should their technologies become industry standards.[9] In this respect, knowledge of these technologies is carefully regulated by a professional group, much like with the construction of "facts" in other scientific fields (Latour 1987; D. Hess 1997; M. Fortun and Bernstein 1998). The primary policy goal in the United States is to integrate unique biometric markers into identification documents, such as passports or national ID cards, and then harmonize these identity tokens with massive databases designed to screen for potential terrorists or to monitor the movements and activities of people more broadly. It is worthwhile noting that U.S. security agencies and industries were already moving toward the widespread application of biometric and other surveillance systems prior to 9/11. The attacks, however, provided the impetus for rapidly deploying the systems with as little public scrutiny or debate as possible (Lyon 2003e; Winner 2004).

But do biometrics work for the purpose of locating and stopping terrorists? According to the U.S. General Accounting Office,[10] although "the desired benefit is the prevention of the entry of travelers who are inadmissible to the United States" (Kingsbury 2003: 6), or "keeping the bad guys out" in President George W. Bush's parlance, the challenges to the success of biometric systems are manifold. Obstacles include labor increases, travel delays, tourism reduction, inadequate training, grandfathering arrangements, reciprocal requirements from other countries, exemptions, false IDs, "significant" costs, and circumvention of border systems by more than 350,000 illegal entries a year (U.S. Citizenship and Immigration Services 2002). In addition, more technical obstacles include managing a massive database of up to 240 million records and maintaining accurate "watch lists" for suspected terrorists.

A recent report by Privacy International is forceful in its denunciation of biometrics and national identity cards. The report argues that because no evidence exists that these systems can or do prevent terrorism, any link between these systems and antiterrorism is merely rhetorical:

> Of the 25 countries that have been most adversely affected by terrorism since 1986, eighty per cent have national identity cards, one third of which incorporate biometrics. This research was unable to uncover any instance where the presence of an identity card system in those countries was seen as a significant deterrent to terrorist activity. Almost two thirds of known terrorists operate under their true identity ... It is possible that the existence of a high integrity identity card would provide a measure of improved legitimacy for these people. (Privacy International 2004a: 2)

Thus, not only might biometric systems fail to perform their intended functions, they might have the opposite effect of deflecting inquiry away from terrorists who possess *valid* high-tech biometric IDs. This point should give policy makers pause, because all of the 9/11 attackers entered the United States legally with the requisite visas (Seghetti 2002). Finally, even with completely operational biometric and national ID systems in place, there are numerous ways to circumvent them, for instance, by pretending to be an "outlier" (or a person unable to provide accurate biometric data), acquiring a false identity, escaping watch lists (by providing false information or by virtue of being a "new recruit"), or spoofing identity (for instance, by using custom-made contact lenses to fool iris scanners) (Privacy International 2004a: 7–8). Regardless of the cost or complexity of implementing and harmonizing biometric systems across countries, it is clear that they can never be foolproof, and it is questionable whether they would even diminish threats (see Van der Ploeg [Chapter 11, this volume] for a detailed inquiry into the social effects of some of these systems along borders).

This section has sought to take seriously some of the questions about surveillance and security, as they are typically mobilized. Although the technologies discussed are clearly varied, complex, and contextually dependent, the purpose has been to probe the common underlying assumption of effectiveness that undergirds their deployment. *Efficacy operates, in a sense, as a prerequisite for any determination of whether trade-offs are worth it.* Concerning crime, evaluative studies of video surveillance indicate some success with car burglaries or traffic-related crimes but little or no success with the prevention of other crimes. The general inadequacy of surveillance for stopping violent crime has been acknowledged for some time and is usually attributed to the spontaneous nature of these crimes, which are often called "crimes of passion." One unanticipated consequence of CCTV, then, is that it may provide people with a false sense of security whereby they expose themselves to increased risks. With regard to terrorism, new biometric systems appear even more ill conceived: the technical and social difficulties are seemingly insurmountable, borders are porous (if incredibly dangerous for illegal immigrants), and costs are significant. Most important, when terrorists can and have entered countries like the United States and United Kingdom legally (or when they are already legal citizens or residents), then complex systems of documentation may do little to prevent legal entry in the future.

If we are to take the question "Do they work?" on its own terms, we are led to other questions: Why are there so few evaluative studies? And why are more independent evaluative studies not funded? One possible answer is that most people do not really want to know if surveillance and security systems work; people are afraid to hear that they might not work or that they are as (or more) vulnerable with them as without them. Although this may be true, it is perhaps too individualistic a response, which neglects the political and institutional forces at work. Another answer, engaged within the following chapters, is that *surveillance and security are important components of emerging neoliberal sensibilities and structures.* Contracts for surveillance systems are enormously lucrative for private industries, the likes of which influence local and national security policies. There are also overtly political reasons for the lack of evaluation studies. For example, in January 2004, the U.S. Department of Homeland Security disbanded an independent task force charged with evaluating security systems at U.S. points of entry. This move baffled some lawmakers, because the task force had "a lengthy research agenda, dedicated staff and budget to carry its work through 2004" (Strohm 2004). It seems that the fatal move of this group was to recommend an independent evaluation of the "U.S. Visitor and Immigrant Status Indicator Technology [US-VISIT] program, a biometric entry–exit system for the nation's borders" (Strohm 2004). By dissolving the task force, the Department of Homeland Security was able to postpone any conversation of US-VISIT's inadequacies and thereby avoid the need to justify the agency's (and the administration's) commitment to a flawed system.

Another related explanation for (inter)national commitment to systems with no demonstrable efficacy at preventing crime or terrorism could be strong cultural desires for retaliatory criminal justice, for catching and punishing criminals after the fact. Even if violent crimes like the murder of Jamie Bulger cannot be prevented, surveillance technologies nourish retributive impulses in societies by supporting judicial mechanisms of payback. Thus, punitive tendencies gain strength when the public, the media, politicians, and academics continue to ask questions that presume the effectiveness of technologies for meeting intended purposes but ignore unintended social changes. Surveillance and security systems may, of course, serve a largely symbolic function. If publics perceive enhanced safety, then this may ensure social order and renew faith in policy makers. Unfortunately, such widespread awareness of and subjection to invasive surveillance may actually increase public fears and aggravate existing social and economic vulnerabilities, as the chapters in this book show.

The belief in trade-offs is contingent on efficacy, so questions about efficacy can potentially undermine the dominant political discourse about what we are willing to give up to achieve security. This, in turn, would require a more nuanced political debate about security. Efficacy questions can also challenge widespread faith in technological progress by implying that real answers to threats of crime or terrorism will involve complex social arrangements that defy quick technological fixes. However, as the next section takes up, even if the answer was "Yes, they do work for their intended purposes," questions about efficacy and trade-offs are dangerously reductive to begin with.[11]

## Asking the Right Questions

The main problems with questions about trade-offs or efficacy are that root causes for crime or terrorism are not engaged and that deeper social changes brought about by surveillance and security systems are left uninterrogated. One need not embrace techno-logical determinism—or the simplistic belief that technology drives social change of its own accord without any human agency or intervention—to recognize the profound effects that security regimes have on social life. Surveillance and security systems are simultaneously social and technical, and in some ways this is not a new phenomenon: even before the automation of surveillance, modern bureaucracies and architectures functioned as pervasive technical systems of social control (Weber 2000; Foucault 1977). Technologies are neither separate from society nor are they neutral tools that can be applied discretely to social problems (e.g., crime or terrorism). Instead, technologies are thoroughly social inventions to begin with and are part of the social problems they are intended to correct (Winner 1977). As sociotechnical systems, then, surveillance and security are intimately intertwined with institu-tions, ideologies, and a long history of social inequality (Lyon 2001; Gandy 1993). From this standpoint, one can begin to ask the kinds of questions worth asking and answering—questions about power.

### Why Do We Believe in Trade-offs?

A simple answer to the question of why we believe in trade-offs is that, generally speaking, most people—academics included—think badly about technology. Popular opinion perceives technologies as somehow separate from society; they are neutral, efficient, accurate, and discrete tools used to achieve rational and intentional ends. When technologies fail, people blame "human error" or insufficiently evolved social institutions. And when technologies create more problems, sometimes disastrous ones, they are labeled as "side effects" or "unintended consequences" rather than addressed as problems inherent in the design of technologies themselves (Winner 1986).

Take the following argument as an example of how narrow conceptions of surveillance technologies promulgate the logic of trade-offs. In *The Costs of Privacy*, Steven Nock (1993) claims that surveillance arises out of necessity in modern societies, as a way to simulate traditional monitoring by people and to regulate social norms in a society now based on anonymity. Nock writes,

> As traditional methods of family supervision decline, institutional methods of surveillance arise that serve the same social control functions … New methods of information-gathering and dissemination by employers, creditors, and gov-ernments that strike many as worrisome, are not necessarily violations of privacy … Almost all [of these developments] depend on *voluntary self-disclosure* (the completion of credit, insurance or drivers license, or employment forms, for example) … It is certainly legitimate to be concerned about the elaboration of computerized methods of monitoring and tracking people. The use of those techniques, however, is governed by widespread standards of propriety and personal autonomy. (Nock 1993: 4, 13–14; italics added)

In Nock's formulation, surveillance technologies simply automate social control functions that existed previously, without any other meaningful changes in social relations. Moreover, as rational actors, each of us has evaluated the options and voluntarily chosen to participate in new surveillance regimes, seemingly without any coercion or without any sanctions if we had (somehow) chosen to opt out instead.

This view of surveillance technologies lends itself to a discussion of trade-offs because it implies that individuals have total control and intentionality with technology use. It perceives all people as equal rational actors, without any power asymmetries, and intimates that social relations or spaces cannot be altered unintentionally. Technological fixes, from this perspective, are natural social progressions, but—at the same time—technologies somehow operate outside of society, as tools that can be applied to social problems (Weinberg 2003). All that is left to do is for societies to collectively weigh the options and choose intelligently.

What is left out of this view of surveillance? Mainly, all the ways that technological systems produce social relations or have the capacity for such production.[12] The pure view of technology articulated by Nock ignores—is bound to ignore—ways that tech-nologies operate not only as tools but as creators of social worlds.[13] For instance, much like architecture, surveillance "programs" spaces for particular, acceptable activities so that non-sanctioned uses of space are discouraged by the environment. So, schools are for learning, malls are for shopping, streets are for driving, and so on. Provided that one adhere to the official program of a space, he or she will encounter little resistance, but should one try to appropriate a space for other uses, such as socializing, sleeping, or protesting, surveillance systems will be employed to discipline those activities. Thus, surveillance on college campuses is intended to protect property and provide public safety, but security personnel freely admit that they also monitor and record public protests and rallies, just to keep people in line (Brat 2004).

Surveillance technologies clearly alter social behavior and are intended to do so, usually as planned deterrents to deviant behavior *but not always with the outcomes intended*. They act as forms of social engineering that legislate norms for acceptable and unacceptable behaviors and actions, and they accomplish this task by individualizing people. As Jason Patton (2000) explains, when people cannot adjust their behavior to the reactions they perceive in others (i.e., physically removed observers), the social context becomes an ambiguous one where everyone is presumed to be individually deviant until proved otherwise. The result is a "panoptic" effect on social behavior (Foucault 1977), meaning that people tend to police themselves and refrain from any actions that might verify their presumed status as deviants in the eyes of unseen others. Rather than surveillance indicating a rationalized and distributed imposition on individual privacy,[14] however, surveillance is often applied selectively and with varying intensities according to one's social address (Phillips and Curry 2003); as such, surveillance can—and does—structure unequal power relations in societies (Cameron 2004; Van der Ploeg 2005; Kupchik and Monahan forthcoming).

Hille Koskela (2000), writing about video surveillance in Finland, adds to these observations a strong feminist critique. She finds that public surveillance does not deter violent crime against women, but the use of cameras does tend to objectify women, sterilize actions, and thereby masculinize space. The emphasis on visual surveillance is completely gendered, with women more often than not subjected to the disembodied gaze of men who operate the cameras that are concentrated in public spheres frequented by women (e.g., shopping malls, public transportation). Furthermore, even while under the presumably paternalistic eye of security cameras, any nonvisual harassment of women remains undocumented and uncorrected—from the official viewpoint, then, verbal abuse or threats never happen. The masculinization of space, which makes women the objects of surveillance, may be completely unintentional but is nevertheless a real production of social relations brought about by surveillance.

We can believe in trade-offs so long as we pretend that the only affective powers technologies have on social spaces, relations, or meanings are rationally chosen and intended. Thus, surveillance advocates can say, "A camera is just like having another officer on the beat" (Conde 2004: 1) or "There is no theoretical difference between surveillance through a camera lens and a naked eye" (Conde 2004: 2). And these conclusions are believable to the extent that any unintended social effects of the kinds described previously are discounted as side effects and to the extent that data are analyzed from afar without delving into the messy materialities of how surveillance systems work. Whereas side effects are seen as *unintended* consequences of surveillance systems, trade-offs are presented as *anticipated* undesirable outcomes, such as the loss of privacy or civil liberties. Contrary to this position, ethnographic studies of the coordination of CCTV security forces and the police in the United Kingdom reveal labor intensification rather than reduction for police personnel who must now respond to additional disturbances witnessed by camera operators (Goold 2004). Another compelling study finds antagonism caused by competing forms of expertise, such that CCTV operators tell the police to mind their own business, try to take credit for arrests, and sometimes come to blows—quite literally—fighting over jurisdiction (McCahill and Norris 2003). These observations reveal one dimension of how surveillance systems are thoroughly social and could never be just like having more police on the street.

Thinking badly about technology is only one answer for why people believe in trade-offs between what are seen as two goods, such as security and liberty. A perhaps more deep-rooted reason has to do with Western systems of logic predicated on dualities: good–bad, black–white, friend–enemy, and so on. This ingrained way of looking at the world explains the rhetorical power of statements such as President Bush's "Either you're for us, or you're against us" (G.W. Bush 2001), and it also explains the social value attributed to clarity and rationality. It is unfortunate that dualistic thinking also instills a profound intolerance for ambiguity and for the necessary messiness that characterizes social worlds (Derrida 1988). Social perceptions of technology are certainly not immune to dualistic logics, which are usually articulated as being "for" technological progress or being "anti-technology," with no middle ground in between. But there are many ways to measure progress (e.g., social, economic, environmental, emotional) and many possibilities for the design and incorporation of surveillance technologies into social spaces and public institutions.

### What Social Relations Do Surveillance and Security Systems Produce?

The question of what social relations are produced through the incorporation of surveillance into daily life directs inquiry toward a rich set of data, far less constrained than questions about trade-offs or efficacy. A different way of phrasing the question might be, "What effects do surveillance and security systems have on power, inequality, or democracy?" This question is intended to be not an argument for causality or determinism but, instead, following Foucault's lead, a recognition of the capacity of power to manifest in quotidian institutional operations that simultaneously generate and sustain social relations apart from any property of control that might be possessed by individuals (Foucault 1977, 1980). Clearly, surveillance is part of larger trends toward sociospatial segregation in modern societies (Caldeira 2000; Low 2003), but the social relations produced by these technologies may be difficult to spot when looking at high-tech systems (such as biometrics or video surveillance) alone. Instead, *by attending to the embedding of surveillance technologies into existing institutional systems and social practices, power relations are much easier to detect.*

Consider the following superb example of asking some of the right questions about everyday surveillance. Virginia Eubanks (2004; Chapter 6, this volume) writes about a small urban city in upstate New York where welfare and food stamp recipients have had their lives dramatically altered by the introduction of "electronic benefit transfer" (EBT) systems. Mandated of all states by the Welfare Reform Act of 1996, these systems signify an effort to crack down on food stamp fraud and, ostensibly, to reduce the stigma attached to using food stamps in public places. The EBT tracking, as a form of electronic surveillance, is intended to increase efficiency and reduce fraud, but at what social and financial cost?

Whereas current holders of EBT cards, who are more often than not women, were previously able to walk to local grocery stores to purchase food as they and their families needed it, they now must endure the added expense and inconvenience of hiring a cab or taking a bus some three miles to the nearest large-chain supermarket that accepts the magnetic-strip EBT cards. The local markets cannot afford, or choose not to implement, the systems necessary to accept the welfare cards as a method of payment. Even if the cardholders did elect to walk the additional distance, the main street that one must use to get to the large supermarket doubles as a state highway, at times without sidewalks, making the trip virtually impossible by foot, especially in winter months. This situation is certainly an impediment to "normal" living or economic assimilation, and the burdens of this card system are unduly shouldered by the poor.

EBT systems can be seen as important precursors to biometric national IDs, where the technologies are tested on the most vulnerable members of society first (Gilliom 2001). These systems can integrate biometric identifiers, as has been proposed by the General Accounting Office (1995), and they have the potential to track the movements and spending habits of individuals. Meanwhile, as public agencies and private companies slowly work out flaws in the system, they are draining much needed resources from the poor. For instance, the cards also double as mechanisms for receiving welfare benefits other than food stamps, and people are charged fees for requesting "cash back" at stores or withdrawing cash from ATMs. A *New York Times* article reports that a mother allotted $448 a month for her family to live on pays up to $2.35 for each transaction and that in 1999 the total number of fees charged to the poor per month was around $275,000 (Barstow 1999). A 2001 audit of the New York EBT system placed the surcharges at up to $700,151 per month (Feig 2001: 13). Moreover, few ATM machines accept the cards, cards often do not work across state lines, and—unlike ATM cards—no protections are offered if the cards are stolen and used by others.[15]

The EBT system serves as a case study of the complex deployment of surveillance technologies in everyday life. The question remains, What social relations are produced by it? Reinforced sociospatial segregation of and increased burden on the poor are two clear outcomes. This is seen with the ghettoizing of the poor in upstate New York: they must now endure added inconvenience and cost to purchase food from grocery stores in more affluent areas and then return to their economically segregated downtown apartments. This example also reveals one more dimension to the radically asymmetrical monitoring and tracking of the poor in the United States, whether in public schools, public transportation, public housing, or places of commerce. Finally, *this example draws attention to the vast profits that private companies stand to accrue at public expense.* As an example, with the privatization of the food stamp program, Citicorp Services, Inc., has been awarded lucrative contracts with 34 states, as well as with Guam and the Virgin Islands (Stegman, Lobenhofer, and Quinterno 2003: 14). And although the outsourcing of public services by states makes it difficult to determine total public costs, Citicorp's contract with California alone is for $250 million over seven years (Bartholow and Garcia 2002), with the potential for up to $450 million (*San Francisco Bay Guardian* 2001).

Pursuing the question of "What social relations are produced?" into the arena of privatized surveillance and security systems reveals a pattern of increased dependency and disempowerment of the poor, coupled with the state's relinquishment of its responsibility to meet the basic needs of citizens. A New York audit of Citicorp and Continental Card Services concluded that

> neither contractor produced all of the contract deliverables or regularly met performance standards. As a result, the EBT system is not meeting client expectations, is not providing the level of service to its users that was anticipated, and may be resulting in clients needlessly incurring surcharge fees to access their benefits. (Feig 2001: 4)

Although purportedly saving money for the public, privatization leaves little recourse to the poor when the system imposes serious difficulties or fails. Furthermore, once states have awarded contracts, costly and protracted legal action is their only alternative if they wish to correct problems. This example illustrates the destructiveness of neoliberal ideologies as they are hardwired into institutions and technological systems. The dual outcome of such arrangements is increased profitability for private companies and increased surveillance and marginalization of the poor (Duggan 2003; Comaroff and Comaroff 2000; Giroux 2004).

This is but one example, taken in detail to show how different surveillance and security regimes could be analyzed from a perspective of social change rather than from one of trade-offs or efficacy. Inquiry into border control and biometrics would likely yield similar findings. For example, the U.S. Department of Homeland Security has awarded a 10-year contract of up to $10 billion to the private company Accenture for biometric systems at U.S. ports of entry (Lichtblau and Markoff 2004). Meanwhile, the increased militarization of the border in California and Texas has produced a funnel effect with immigrants crossing in the most dangerous parts of the desert in Arizona and dying at record rates (Cornelius 2001). The social relations produced are those of empowerment for private industries, disempowerment, dependency, and danger for poor or marginalized groups, and inflexibility for the nation-state to provide both police security and human security for the people within—and outside—its borders. Indeed, security in terms of providing for the well-being of people (i.e., "human security" or "population security") has recently been fused with and largely eclipsed by national security apparatuses and logics (Collier, Lakoff, and Rabinow 2004). Thus, "natural" disasters like those caused by Hurricane Katrina serve both as symbols of this lack of institutional "preparedness" and, strangely enough, as rationales for further neoliberal undermining of social and environmental support mechanisms (Lakoff, Chapter 16, this volume).

### How Can Surveillance Be Used to Increase Security without Sacrificing Civil Liberties?

If the important questions about surveillance and security revolve around the production of social relations, as I have claimed, and if trade-offs are attractive, in part, because technologies are seen as somehow divorced from society, then the challenge lies in how to govern surveillance technologies well—with an awareness of their social embeddedness and an eye toward their social ramifications. It may be that most public surveillance systems are misguided and inappropriate to begin with. Clearly, mechanisms for evaluating and contesting such systems need to be developed. Nonetheless, civil libertarians, academics, and progressively minded citizens have been able to make precious few inroads in this direction given the current political climate of "the war on terror." Democratizing surveillance practices—in addition to strategic opposition—may be a second, complementary strategy for intelligent technology design and use.

The question of how to govern surveillance technologies well does not imply seeking a *balance* between security and liberty, because this scale metaphor connotes the same either–or logic of trade-offs: an increase on one side necessarily diminishes the other. Rather, it means asking questions about how surveillance can be used to increase security without sacrificing liberties, if at all, and perhaps even to augment liberties. Jeffrey Rosen (2004) writes, as a telling example of a technical solution to this problem, about two different kinds of body screening technologies for passengers at airports. The first displays naked bodies in anatomically correct detail, including any hidden objects that people may be carrying; the second "extracts the images of concealed objects and projects them onto a sexless mannequin" (Rosen 2004: 4). Both systems, which Rosen refers to as "the naked machine" and "the blob machine," respectively, provide the same degree of security, but the blob machine is less invasive by design. This example demonstrates that there are social and technical choices to be made when it comes to surveillance and security, should we take the time to inquire.

The comparison between the "naked" and the "blob" machines is intended to illustrate both the contingency of technological systems and the need for alternatives. It may be the case that neither machine is desirable or sufficiently democratic, for even the blob machine objectifies, scrutinizes, and individualizes people while shifting power to those doing the monitoring. If democratic or liberty-safeguarding designs are not readily available, then perhaps societies should insist on them before proceeding further. Most of the time, there will not be easy answers to the question of how to ensure national security without sacrificing liberties, but until this is seen as a question worth asking, it is likely that surveillance and security systems will continue to disproportionately impose upon and discriminate against women and poor, ethnic minorities.

A starting point would be to make surveillance systems more transparent and democratic. For most people, especially in the United States, surveillance is inherently ambiguous. It is unclear where the cameras (or other information-gathering devices) are, who owns the equipment, who is watching, what the policies are for collecting and disposing of data, to what use data will be put, and what rights people have. In the United Kingdom, under the Data Protection Act of 2000, there are strict rules governing data collection and retention,[16] including the disclosure of surveillance monitoring through signage (e.g., signs telling people when they are under surveillance), but even so, it is estimated that 73 percent of CCTV cameras in London alone are in noncompliance with these rules (McCahill and Norris 2002: 21).[17] The United States is far behind in even establishing basic disclosure policies and does not appear to be interested in catching up. Transparency would mean dissolving some of the many layers of ambiguity around surveillance and recognizing that just because data can be collected and saved indefinitely does not mean that they should be or that collecting and saving data is productive for maintaining and protecting civil society. Indeed, social forgetfulness is a core value in American society, tied to its frontier history (seen in idioms such as "a clean slate," "a fresh start," "forgive and forget"), so data collection, retention, and disposal policies should be critical elements in the governance of surveillance systems (Blanchette and Johnson 2002).

It stands to reason that the best way to increase transparency is to increase public participation in the governance of surveillance. From a policy perspective, this could be done by conducting surveys or interviews about the social effects of surveillance systems (not just about public approval) and using that data to inform public policy. It could be done by requiring a public vote on all surveillance systems and policies, just like for other infrastructure-related projects, but with choices that extend beyond "yes" or "no" to provide a range of options concerning the policies for such systems. Informational pamphlets on ballot initiatives could be distributed wherein one could find evaluations of existing systems elsewhere, discussions of the pros and cons, and so forth. Or, in a much stronger vein, incentives could be provided to enroll citizens of all walks of life into the policy-making process, including participation on subcommittees, citizen review panels, and oversight committees (Sclove 1995).

Some might argue that democratic transparency and participation may work well for local contexts and for relatively mundane purposes but not for national security, where secrecy is somehow mandated. I disagree with this objection. Greater transparency is needed on the level of national security so that individuals know their rights, security agents are held accountable, and contracts with private security industries are kept in check. Given recent revelations that President Bush authorized the U.S. National Security Agency to spy on citizens illegally, the pressing need for transparency and accountability to preserve civil liberties could not be more apparent. Moreover, the call for secrecy with national security neglects (rather than cultivates) public expertise—effectively forcing the public into passive identity roles instead of those of active, democratic agents. Although the U.S. Department of Homeland Security's efforts to enroll citizens into surveillance operations are obviously misguided and problematic, especially for their authoritarian approach to "participation" (see Marx, Chapter 3, this volume), members of the public are often acutely aware of security vulnerabilities but simply do not communicate them for fear of becoming targets of increased suspicion or legal retaliation (see Winner, Chapter 17, this volume). Public involvement may, in fact, help to limit violations of civil liberties, detect fraud, correct security vulnerabilities, and decrease the need for extensive surveillance systems.

Public involvement in data monitoring presents another venue for increasing transparency through participation. In combination with neighborhood-watch initiatives, the public could assist with monitoring cameras, as has been tried with reported success in public housing communities in Boston (Nieto 1997), or could get involved with "copwatch" organizations, which, if sensitive to community needs, could help protect vulnerable members of society (see Huey, Walby, and Doyle, Chapter 9, this volume). Unlike the case described earlier, where community members did not watch surveillance feeds on their television sets (Musheno, Levine, and Palumbo 1978), far better results could likely be produced by designating responsibility to specific community members (or to volunteers) in on-site control rooms or on the streets. The difference revolves around the "valence" (C.G. Bush 1997) of sociotechnical systems: watching television is a passive and removed social experience, but being directly responsible for community safety is a uniquely active experience. At the very least, security personnel doing the monitoring can remain proximate to communities, visible to and approachable by people within communities rather than located in remote "surveillance farms" far away both physically and socially from the people they observe. Naturally, an informed public debate about the merits of public surveillance should precede any community-watching scenario. Part of this should include asking questions of how to provide adequate oversight of surveillance practices, identifying—in advance—specific criteria for "successful" surveillance interventions, and specifying when and under what conditions the systems will be disabled. Absent such discussions, this recommendation could easily fold into a "snitch" or "tattling" culture, where community members spy on each other and contribute to a society of widespread suspicion, discrimination, and social control (see Marx, Chapter 3, this volume).

Unfortunately, efforts at achieving transparency and democracy are not only absent from the current surveillance landscape but being pushed further beyond the horizon, making them harder to imagine, let alone attain, with every passing moment. As the example of the EBT system for welfare recipients demonstrates, the privatization of surveillance, security, and public services delegates technical decisions to companies with profit imperatives rather than social equality agendas. The same could be said of private security forces in malls, gated communities, business improvement districts, war zones, and disaster areas. And the same could be said of vast urban surveillance systems outsourced to private companies by cities or implemented by the private sector without any public oversight or jurisdiction. Finally, the policy aftershocks of 9/11—namely, the USA PATRIOT and Homeland Security Acts—have made public surveillance at once more secretive and pervasive, so the public sector does not exactly provide a model worth emulating in this regard.

Increasing transparency and democratic participation in the governance of surveillance systems are not guaranteed mechanisms for achieving national security or human security or for preserving civil liberties, of course, but they are surely steps in the right direction. The approach advocated here, then, takes the social embeddedness and anticipated ramifications of technologies as a departure point and is therefore predisposed to notice social inequalities earlier in the process and better equipped to mitigate them (Woodhouse and Nieusma 2001; Guston and Sarewitz 2002). The key is seeing surveillance systems as political entities with the capacity to produce social relations—whether intended or not—and then asking how they can be employed to achieve democratic outcomes. From this perspective, "good" surveillance systems would be those that corrected power asymmetries and increased human security in societies. One example might be the website Scorecard.org, which collects and disseminates information about toxic releases in local neighborhoods, assigns blame for environmental contamination (when possible), and provides action items for people to get involved in monitoring industries and cleaning up their communities (K. Fortun 2004). Surveillance systems are more likely to meet the goal of power correction if they are designed for "structural flexibility" (Monahan 2005a), meaning that they are democratic, participatory, localized, and open to alteration.

## Conclusion

This chapter has set out to destabilize the framing of surveillance and security in terms of trade-offs. Although conversations about trade-offs—between security and liberty, for example—may serve a strategic purpose of drawing attention to matters of importance and values worth preserving, these debates artificially constrain inquiry by offering little room to talk about deeper social changes underway with the incorporation of surveillance technologies into everyday life. These changes include the ongoing privatization of public spaces and services; increased social and spatial segregation along class, race, and gender lines; and disproportionate burdens and risks placed on marginalized groups in society. Moreover, questions about trade-offs or balances or efficacy are all predicated on an uninterrogated assumption that taking national security seriously must perforce threaten liberty or other social goods. It is worth probing the veracity of such assumptions and the reasons why they are so attractive.

I began by taking questions about trade-offs on their own terms, specifically evaluating the efficacy of surveillance systems in preventing crime or terrorism. It turns out that there are very few independent evaluative studies and that they are inconclusive at best. There is evidence to suggest that surveillance systems may deter vehicular and traffic crimes but that they do not deter violent crimes at all. In the domain of national security, there is no evidence to suggest efficacy, in spite of the great financial costs, institutional labor, and public inconvenience. In fact, surveillance and biometric systems may provide a false sense of security, thereby increasing vulnerability across the board. The absence of studies and debates about efficacy could mean that most people—or at least most policy makers and industry contractors—do not really want to know if surveillance and security systems work.

Even if surveillance and security systems were highly effective, I assert that questions about trade-offs are still misguided. Better questions worth asking include the following: Why do we believe in trade-offs? What social relations are produced by surveillance systems? How can surveillance be used to increase security without sacrificing civil liberties? Tentative answers might be that relations of inequality are produced, that technologies are not seen as the social and political agents that they are, and that transparent policies and democratic governance of surveillance would help amend the situation. My purpose has been not to present these alternative questions as the only ones worth asking or to answer them definitively but instead to open up the conversation, moving beyond trade-offs to a fuller consideration of the role of surveillance in society. The chapters that follow extend the conversation in this way by analyzing the politics of surveillance and security in everyday life.

## Acknowledgments

Special thanks to Gary T. Marx and Michael Musheno for their generous comments on this chapter and on the volume as a whole.

## Notes

1. This is not meant to imply direct causality between the Bulger killing and the rise of CCTV systems in the United Kingdom, because certainly other factors such as fear of terrorists contribute to this trend. That said, immediately following the Bulger murder, "John Major's Conservative government decided to devote more than three-quarters of its crime-prevention budget to encourage local authorities to install CCTV" (Rosen 2001).
2. Other scholars have criticized the Airdrie study for similar reasons: that crime did rise in peripheral areas and even increased in the district by 20 percent (S. Graham 1998; Dawson 1994; Davies 1995).
3. Other reports calculating public and private expenditures on CCTV put the figure at anywhere from £225 million to £450 million being spent per year in the United Kingdom (Nieto, Johnston-Dodds, and Simmons 2002: 9).
4. In fact, a few activist countersurveillance groups have emerged to respond to this lack of knowledge and oversight with cameras monitoring public spaces (Monahan forthcoming; Institute for Applied Autonomy 2004; New York Surveillance Camera Players 2002).
5. It is more likely that the Office of Technology Assessment (OTA) produced balanced reports about the complexity of technologies and that policy makers were frustrated that these reports could not translate into simple or clear-cut policy recommendations (Bimber 1996; Sarewitz 1996).
6. Of course the affluent are filmed regularly in places of commerce, like shopping malls or banks, but these are almost exclusively privately owned surveillance systems deployed on private property, not public systems monitoring public space. A similar observation could be made of the monitoring of the affluent in private gated communities.
7. I would categorize these appropriations of surveillance systems as instances of *countersurveillance:* intentional, tactical uses or disruptions of surveillance technologies to correct institutional power asymmetries (Monahan forthcoming). Like other appropriations of technology (Eglash et al. 2004), countersurveillance reveals the underdetermination of technology and destabilizes deterministic views of technological progress. Gary T. Marx (2003b) calls such acts of resistance to dominant uses of surveillance "a tack in the shoe," exploiting ironic vulnerabilities in larger projects of total public surveillance.
8. Potential conflicts of interest also exist when cities and private companies profit handsomely from the operation of these red-light systems. As a California report relates, "In San Diego, a judge dismissed nearly 300 tickets in a class-action lawsuit, ruling that the evidence was unreliable because the system is privately run and the company is paid through a percentage of the fines" (Nieto, Johnston-Dodds, and Simmons 2002: 21).
9. For an example of one such professional community, see http://biometrics.propagation. net/forums/.
10. In 2004, the U.S. General Accounting Office was officially renamed the "Government Accountability Office." The legislation that enacted this change was the "GAO Human Capital Reform Act," which was signed into law by President Bush on July 7, 2004. Among other things, this legislation "will allow the agency [the Government Accountability Office] to break its link to the federal employee pay system and adopt compensation practices that are more closely tied to job performance and

other factors" (Barr 2004). This means increased instability for government workers and signals the gradual elimination of unionized labor in the federal government. Of course, the symbolism of the name change is crucial: it signals the embracing of neoliberal ideologies, new managerial practices, and disciplinary organizational structures. Elsewhere, I have called these trends *fragmented centralization*, indicating the simultaneous centralization of decision-making authority and decentralization of accountability for (and instability brought about by) those decisions (Monahan 2005a, 2005b).

11. Some technology critics may instead seek to question the purposes served by surveillance—or the stated intended goals of these technologies in specific contexts. This line of inquiry would be a fine starting point if surveillance policies were transparent and rationales were clear. For almost all deployments of surveillance on the public (whether by state agents or by industry agents), this is not the case. There is no enlightened, objective perspective one could achieve to parse policy goals, technologies, and social contexts. Questions of power are more complicated than that, and policy motives are often obscure, influenced by multiple ideological and professional interests.

12. A recognition of the contingent design of all technologies is also often absent from these formulations. This perspective is known as the "social construction of technology" (e.g., Bijker, Hughes, and Pinch 1987; Bijker and Law 1992) and is one way to track the complex design processes that lead to the systems that we often take for granted. Rather than being outside of society and impinging on it in some deterministic way, technologies and social practices exist in dynamic and mutually shaping relationships.

13. Staples (2000) offers a compelling case for the many ways that new forms of electronic, "postmodern" surveillance are radically different from previous, "modern" ones. Mainly, contemporary surveillance is systematic and impersonal, targets bodies more than people, is locally integrated into everyday practices, and scrutinizes and profiles everyone as potentially "deviant," in advance of any evidence or informed suspicion to that effect. Haggerty and Ericson (2000) similarly theorize the distributed, decentralized power and politics of contemporary surveillance regimes. The potential of electronic surveillance for monitoring everyone equally, however, should not imply the removal of asymmetrical power relations, discrimination, or profiling; if anything, these particularistic inequalities are perpetuated, extended, and simultaneously masked by the rhetoric of universalistic (read "objective") surveillance and security (Curry 2004).

14. Privacy is, of course, an ambiguous and hyperindividualized concept that does not account very well for encroachments on social spaces and practices absent targeted individual scrutiny, usually in "private" domains. One way to overcome the limitations of privacy as a conceptual category is to expand it beyond legal definitions to include multiple forms of information generation, access, and expression in modern societies (DeCew 1997; Phillips forthcoming). Another approach is to focus on trust relations, which hold communities and cultures together—manifested either in contestations of social power or in voluntary disclosures for the sake of intimacy or social cohesion (Bourdieu 1977; de Certeau 1984; de Certeau, Giard, and Mayol 1998).

15. In another example, in August 2001, a computer glitch incorrectly registered close to six thousand EBT transactions, double-charging many people (Shesgreen and Hollinshed 2001).

16. The data protection guidelines issued by the Organization for Economic Cooperation and Development provide a related template for regulating surveillance technologies; however, such guidelines were crafted with the primary aim of facilitating trade, not protecting privacy, so their use may be limited for thinking about the power relations engendered by new technologies (Clarke 1989).

17. Goold (2004) also cautions that police officers may require additional oversight to ensure that they do not interfere with control room operators or tamper with surveillance data—two practices that were identified in a study he carried out in the United Kingdom.

# Article 38

Kevin L. Parker

## The Utility of Cyberpower

Prepared by: Robert Weiner, *University of Massachusetts, Boston*

### Learning Outcomes

*After reading this article, you will be able to:*
• Understand what is meant by cyberspace.
• Understand what is the relationship between realism and the defense of U.S. national interest in cyberspace.

After more than 50 years, the Korean War has not officially ended, but artillery barrages seldom fly across the demilitarized zone.[1] U.S. forces continue to fight in Afghanistan after more than 10 years, with no formal declaration of war.[2] Another conflict rages today with neither bullets nor declarations. In this conflict, U.S. adversaries conduct probes, attacks, and assaults on a daily basis.[3] The offensives are not visible or audible, but they are no less real than artillery shells or improvised explosive devices. This conflict occurs daily through cyberspace.

To fulfill the U.S. military's purpose of defending the nation and advancing national interests, today's complex security environment requires increased engagement in cyberspace.[4] Accordingly, the Department of Defense (DOD) now considers cyberspace an operational domain.[5] Similar to other domains, cyberspace has its own set of distinctive characteristics. These attributes present unique advantages and corresponding limitations. As the character of war changes, comprehending the utility of cyberpower requires assessing its advantages and limitations in potential strategic contexts.

## Defining Cyberspace and Cyberpower

A range of definitions for cyberspace and cyberpower exist, but even the importance of establishing definitions is debated. Daniel Kuehl compiled 14 distinct definitions of cyberspace from various sources, only to conclude he should offer his own.[6] Do exact definitions matter? In bureaucratic organizations, definitions do matter because they facilitate clear division of roles and missions across departments and military services. Within DOD, some duplication of effort may be desirable but comes at a high cost; therefore, definitions are necessary to facilitate the rigorous analyses essential for establishing organizational boundaries and budgets.[7] In executing assigned roles, definitions matter greatly for cross-organizational communication and coordination.

No matter how important, precise definitions to satisfy all viewpoints and contexts are elusive. Consider defining the sea as all the world's oceans. This definition lacks sufficient clarity to demarcate bays or riverine waterways. Seemingly inconsequential, the ambiguity is of great consequence for organizations jurisdictionally bound at a river's edge. Unlike the sea's constant presence for millennia, the Internet is a relatively new phenomenon that continues to expand and evolve rapidly. Pursuing single definitions of cyberspace and cyberpower to put all questions to rest may be futile. David Lonsdale argued that from a strategic perspective, definitions matter little. In his view, "what really matters is to perceive the infosphere as a place that exists, understand the nature of it and regard it as something that can be manipulated and used for strategic advantage."[8] The definitions below are consistent with Lonsdale's viewpoint and suffice for the purposes of this discussion, but they are unlikely to satisfy practitioners who wish to apply them beyond a strategic perspective.

> Cyberspace: the domain that exists for inputting, storing, transmitting, and extracting information utilizing the electromagnetic spectrum. It includes all hardware, software, and transmission media used, from an initiator's input (e.g., fingers making keystrokes, speaking into microphones, or feeding documents into scanners) to presentation of the information for user cognition (e.g., images on displays, sound emitted from speakers, or document reproduction) or other action (e.g., guiding an unmanned vehicle or closing valves). Cyberpower: The potential to use cyberspace to achieve desired outcomes.[9]

## Advantages of Wielding Cyberpower

With these definitions being sufficient for this discussion, consider the advantages of operations through cyberspace.

Cyberspace provides worldwide reach. The number of people, places, and systems interconnecting through cyberspace is growing rapidly.[10] Those connections enhance the military's ability to reach people, places, and systems around the world. Operating in cyberspace provides access to areas denied in other domains. Early airpower advocates claimed airplanes offered an alternative to boots on the ground that could fly past enemy defenses to attack power centers directly.[11] Sophisticated air defenses developed quickly, increasing the risk to aerial attacks and decreasing their advantage. Despite current cyberdefenses that exist, cyberspace now offers the advantage of access to contested areas without putting operators in harm's way. One example of directly reaching enemy decision makers through cyberspace comes from an event in 2003, before the U.S. invasion of Iraq. U.S. Central Command reportedly emailed Iraqi military officers a message on their secret network advising them to abandon their posts.[12] No other domain had so much reach with so little risk.

Cyberspace enables quick action and concentration. Not only does cyberspace allow worldwide reach, but its speed is unmatched. With aerial refueling, air forces can reach virtually any point on the earth; however, getting there can take hours. Forward basing may reduce response times to minutes, but information through fiber optic cables moves literally at the speed of light. Initiators of cyberattacks can achieve concentration by enlisting the help of other computers. By discretely distributing a virus trained to respond on command, thousands of co-opted botnet computers can instantly initiate a distributed denial-of-service attack. Actors can entice additional users to join their cause voluntarily, as did Russian "patriotic hackers" who joined attacks on Estonia in 2007.[13] With these techniques, large interconnected populations could mobilize on an unprecedented scale in mass, time, and concentration.[14]

Cyberspace allows anonymity. The Internet's designers placed a high priority on decentralization and built the structure based on the mutual trust of its few users.[15] In the decades since, the number of Internet users and uses has grown exponentially beyond its original conception.[16] The resulting system makes it very difficult to follow an evidentiary trail back to any user.[17] Anonymity allows freedom of action with limited attribution.

Cyberspace favors offense. In Clausewitz' day, defense was stronger, but cyberspace, due to the advantages listed above, currently favors the attack.[18]

Historically, advantages from technological leaps erode over time.[19] However, the current circumstance pits defenders against quick, concentrated attacks, aided by structural security vulnerabilities inherent in the architecture of cyberspace.

Cyberspace expands the spectrum of nonlethal weapons. Joseph Nye described a trend, especially among democracies, of antimilitarism, which makes using force "a politically risky choice."[20] The desire to limit collateral damage often has taken center stage in NATO operations in Afghanistan, but this desire is not limited to counterinsurgencies.[21] Precision-guided munitions and small-diameter bombs are products of efforts to enhance attack capabilities with less risk of collateral damage. Cyberattacks offer nonlethal means of direct action against an adversary.[22] The advantages of cyberpower may be seductive to policymakers, but understanding its limitations should temper such enthusiasm. The most obvious limitation is that your adversary may use all the same advantages against you. Another obvious limitation is its minimal influence on non-networked adversaries. Conversely, the more any organization relies on cyberspace, the more vulnerable it is to cyberattack. Three additional limitations require further attention.

Cyberspace attacks rely heavily on second order effects. In Thomas Schelling's terms, there are no brute force options through cyberspace, so cyberoperations rely on coercion.[23] Continental armies can occupy land and take objectives by brute force, but success in operations through cyberspace often hinges on how adversaries react to provided, altered, or withheld information. Cyberattacks creating kinetic effects, such as destructive commands to industrial control systems, are possible. However, the unusual incidents of malicious code causing a Russian pipeline to explode and the Stuxnet worm shutting down Iranian nuclear facility processes were not ends.[24] In the latter case, only Iranian leaders' decisions could realize abandonment of nuclear technology pursuits. Similar to strategic bombing's inability to collapse morale in World War II, cyberattacks often rely on unpredictable second order effects.[25] If Rear Adm. Wylie is correct in that war is a matter of control, and "its ultimate tool . . . is the man on the scene with a gun," then operations through cyberspace can only deliver a lesser form of control.[26] Evgeny Morozov quipped, "Tweets, of course, don't topple governments; people do."[27]

Cyberattacks risk unintended consequences. Just as striking a military installation's power system may have cascading ramifications on a wider population, limiting effects through interconnected cyberspace is difficult. Marksmanship instructors teach shooters to consider their maximum range and what lies beyond their targets. Without maps for all systems, identifying maximum ranges and what lies beyond a target through cyberspace is impossible.

Defending against cyberattacks is possible. The current offensive advantage does not make all defense pointless. Even if intrusions from sophisticated, persistent attacks are inevitable, certain defensive measures (e.g., physical security controls, limiting user access, filtering and antivirus software, and firewalls) do offer some protection. Redundancy and replication are resilience strategies that can deter some would-be attackers by making attacks futile.[28] Retaliatory responses via cyberspace or other means can also enhance deterrence.[29] Defense is currently disadvantaged, but offense gets no free pass in cyberspace.

# Expectations and Recommendations

The advantages and limitations of using cyberpower inform expectations for the future and several recommendations for the military.

Do not expect clear, comprehensive policy soon.[30] Articulating a comprehensive U.S. strategy for employing nuclear weapons lagged 15 years behind their first use, and the timeline for clear, comprehensive cyberspace policy may take longer.[31] Multiple interests collide in cyberspace, forcing policy makers to address concepts that traditionally have been difficult for Americans to resolve. Cyberspace, like foreign policy, exposes the tension between defaulting to realism in an ungoverned, anarchic system, and aspiring to the liberal ideal of security through mutual recognition of natural rights. Cyberspace policy requires adjudicating between numerous priorities based on esteemed values such as intellectual property rights, the role of government in business, bringing criminals to justice, freedom of speech, national security interests, and personal privacy. None of these issues is new. Cyberspace just weaves them together and presents them from unfamiliar angles. For example, free speech rights may not extend to falsely shouting fire in crowded theaters, but through cyberspace all words are broadcast to a global crowded theater.[32]

Beyond the domestic front, the Internet access creates at least one significant foreign policy dilemma. While it can help mobilize and empower dissidents under oppressive governments, it also can provide additional population control tools to authoritarian leaders.[33] The untangling of these sets of overlapping issues in new contexts is not likely to happen quickly. It may take several iterations, and it may only occur in crises. Meanwhile, the military must continue developing capabilities for operating through cyberspace within current policies.

## Defend in Depth—Inner Layers

Achieving resilience requires evaluating dependencies and vulnerabilities at all levels. Starting inside the firewall and working outward, defense begins at the lowest unit level. Organizations and functions should be resilient enough to sustain attacks and continue operating. In a period of declining budgets, decision makers will pursue efficiencies through leveraging technology.[34] Therefore, prudence requires reinvesting some of the savings to evaluate and offset vulnerabilities created by new technological dependencies.[35] Future war games should not just evaluate what new technologies can provide, but also they should consider how all capabilities would be affected if denied access to cyberspace.

Beyond basic user responsibilities, forces providing defense against cyberattacks require organizations and command structures particular to their function. Martin van Creveld outlined historical evolutions of command and technological developments. Consistent with his analysis, military cyberdefense leaders should resist the technology-enabled urge to centralize and master all available information at the highest level. Instead, their organizations should act semi-independently, set low decision thresholds, establish meaningful regular information reporting, and use formal and informal communications.[36] These methods can enhance "continuous trial-and-error learning essential to collectively make sense of disabling surprises" and shorten response times.[37] Network structures may be more appropriate for this type of task than traditional hierarchical military structures.[38] Whatever the structure, military leaders must be willing to subordinate tradition and task-organize their defenses for effectiveness against cyberattacks.[39] After all, weapons "do not triumph in battle; rather, success is the product of man-machine weapon systems, their supporting services of all kinds, and the organization, doctrine, and training that launch them into battle."[40]

## Defend in Depth—Outer Layers

Defending against cyberattacks takes more than firewalls. Expanding defense in depth requires creatively leveraging influence. DOD has no ownership or jurisdiction over the civilian sectors operating the Internet infrastructure and developing computer hardware and software. However, DOD systems are vulnerable to cyberattack through each of these avenues beyond their control.[41] Richard Clarke recommended federal regulation starting with the Internet backbone as the best way to overcome systemic vulnerabilities.[42] Backlash over potential legislation regulating Internet activity illustrates the problematic nature of regulation.[43] So, how can DOD effect change seemingly beyond its control? Label it "soft power" or "friendly conquest of cyberspace," but the answer lies in leveraging assets.[44]

One of DOD's biggest assets to leverage is its buying power. In 2011, DOD spent over $375 billion on contracts.[45] The military should, of course, use its buying power to insist on strict security standards when purchasing hardware and software. However, it also can use its acquisition process to reduce vulnerabilities through its use of defense contractors. Similar to detailed classification requirements, contracts should specify network security protocols for all contract firms as well as their suppliers, regardless of the services provided. Maintaining stricter security protocols than industry standards would become a condition of lucrative contracts. Through its contracts, allies, and position as the nation's largest employer, DOD can affect preferences to improve outer layer defenses.[46]

## Develop an Offensive Defense

Even in defensive war, Clausewitz recognized the necessity of offense to return enemy blows and achieve victory.[47] Robust offensive capabilities can enhance deterrence by affecting an adversary's decision calculus.[48] DOD must prepare for contingencies calling for offensive support to other domains or independent action through cyberspace.

The military should develop offensive capabilities for potential scenarios but should purposefully define its preparations as defense. Communicating a defensive posture is important to avoid hastening a security-dilemma-inspired cyberarms race that may have already started.[49] Over 20 nations reportedly have some cyberwar capability.[50] Even if it is too late to slow others' offensive development, controlling the narrative remains important.[51] Just as the name Department of Defense sends a different message than its former name—War Department—developing defensive capabilities to shut down rogue cyberattackers sounds significantly better than developing offensive capabilities that "knock [the enemy] out in the first round."[52]

Do not expect rapid changes in international order or the nature of war. Without question, the world is changing, but world order does not change overnight. Nye detailed changes due to globalization and the spread of information technologies, including diffusion of U.S. power to rising nations and nonstate actors. However, he claimed it was not a "narrative of decline" and wrote, "The United States is unlikely to decay like ancient Rome or even to be surpassed by another state."[53] Adapting to current trends is necessary, but changes in the strategic climate are not as dramatic as some proclaim.

Similarly, some aspects of war change with the times while its nature remains constant. Clausewitz advised planning should account for the contemporary character of war.[54] Advances in cyberspace are changing war's character but not totally eclipsing traditional means. Sir John Slessor noted, "If there is one attitude more dangerous than to assume that a future war will be just like the last one, it is to imagine that it will be so utterly different that we can afford to ignore all the lessons of the last one."[55] Further, Lonsdale advised exploiting advances in cyberspace but not to "expect these changes to alter the nature of war."[56] Wars will continue to be governed by politics, affected by chance, and waged by people even if through cyberspace.[57]

## Do not Overpromise

Advocates of wielding cyberpower must bridle their enthusiasm enough to see that its utility only exists within a strategic context. Colin Gray claimed airpower enthusiasts "all but invited government and the public to ask the wrong questions and hold air force performance to irrelevant standards of superheroic effectiveness."[58] By touting decisive, independent, strategic capabilities, airpower advocates often failed to meet such hyped expectations in actual conflicts. Strategic contexts may have occurred where airpower alone could achieve strategic effects, but more often, airpower was one of many tools employed.

Cyberpower is no different. Gray claimed, "When a new form of war is analyzed and debated, it can be difficult to persuade prophets that prospective efficacy need not be conclusive."[59] Cyberpower advocates must recognize not only its advantages, but also its limitations applied in a strategic context.

## Conclusion

If cyberpower is the potential to use cyberspace to achieve desired outcomes, then the strategic context is key to understanding its utility. As the character of war changes and cyberpower joins the fight alongside other domains, military leaders must make sober judgments about what it can contribute to achieving desired outcomes. Decision makers must weigh the opportunities and advantages cyberspace presents against the vulnerabilities and limitations of operations in that domain. Sir Arthur Tedder discounted debate over one military arm or another winning wars single-handedly. He insisted, "All three arms of defense are inevitably involved, though the correct balance between them may and will vary."[60] Today's wars may involve more arms, but Tedder's concept of applying a mix of tools based on their advantages and limitations in the strategic context still stands as good advice.

## Notes

1. See Chico Harlan, "Korean DMZ troops exchange gunfire," *Washington Post*, 30 October 2010, <http://www.washingtonpost.com/wp-dyn/content/article/2010/10/29/AR2010102906427.html>. Bullets occasionally fly across the demilitarized zone, but occurrences are rare.
2. See Authorization for Use of Military Force, Public Law 107–40, 107th Cong., 18 September 2001, <http://www.gpo.gov/fdsys/pkg/PLAW-107publ40/html/PLAW-107publ40.htm >. The use of military force in Afghanistan was authorized by the U.S. Congress in 2001 through Public Law 107–40, which does not include a declaration of war.
3. "DOD systems are probed by unauthorized users approximately 250,000 times an hour, over 6 million times a day." Gen. Keith Alexander, director, National Security Agency and Commander, U.S. Cyber Command (remarks, Center for Strategic and International Studies Cybersecurity Policy Debate Series: US Cybersecurity Policy and the Role of US Cybercom, Washington, DC, 3 June 2010, 5), <http://www.nsa.gov/public_info/_files/speeches_testimonies/100603_alexander_transcript.pdf>.

4. "The purpose of this document is to provide the ways and means by which our military will advance our enduring national interests . . . and to accomplish the defense objectives in the 2010 Quadrennial Defense Review." Joint Chiefs of Staff, *The National Military Strategy of the United States of America, 2011: Redefining America's Military Leadership* (Washington, DC: United States Government Printing Office [GPO], 8 February 2011), i.

5. DOD, *DOD Strategy for Operating in Cyberspace* (Washington, DC: GPO, July 2011), 5.

6. Daniel T. Kuehl, "From Cyberspace to Cyberpower: Defining the Problem," in *Cyberpower and National Security,* eds. Franklin D. Kramer, Stuart H. Starr, and Larry K. Wentz (Dulles, VA: Potomac Books, 2009): 26–28.

7. *Staff Report to the Senate Committee on Armed Services, Defense Organization: The Need for Change,* 99th Cong., 1st sess., 1985, Committee Print, 442–44.

8. David J. Lonsdale, *The Nature of War in the Information Age: Clausewitzian Future* (London: Frank Cass, 2004), 182.

9. See Joseph S. Nye, Jr., *The Future of Power* (New York: PublicAffairs, 2011), 123. This definition is influenced by the work of Nye.

10. "From 2000 to 2010, global Internet usage increased from 360 million to over 2 billion people," DOD Strategy for Operating in Cyberspace, 1.

11. Giulio Douhet, *The Command of the Air* (Tuscaloosa, AL: University of Alabama Press, 2009), 9.

12. Richard A. Clarke and Robert K. Knake, *Cyber War: The Next Threat to National Security and What to Do about It* (New York: HarperCollins Publisher, 2010), 9–10.

13. Nye, 126.

14. Audrey Kurth Cronin, "Cyber-Mobilization: The New Levée en Masse," *Parameters* (Summer 2006): 77–87.

15. Clarke and Knake, 81–84.

16. See Clarke and Knake, 84–85. Trends in the number of Internet-connected devices threaten to use up all 4.29 billion available addresses based on the original 32-bit numbering system.

17. Clay Wilson, "Cyber Crime," in *Cyberpower and National Security,* eds. Franklin D. Kramer, Stuart H. Starr, Larry Wentz (Washington, DC: NDU Press, 2009), 428.

18. Carl von Clausewitz, *On War,* ed. and trans. Michael Howard and Peter Paret (Princeton, NJ: Princeton University Press, 1976), 357; John B. Sheldon, "Deciphering Cyberpower: Strategic Purpose in Peace and War," *Strategic Studies Quarterly* (Summer 2011): 98.

19. Martin van Creveld, *Command in War* (Cambridge, MA: Harvard University Press, 1985), 231.

20. Nye, 30.

21. Dexter Filkins, "US Tightens Airstrike Policy in Afghanistan," *New York Times,* 21 June 2009, <http://www.nytimes.com/2009/06/22/world/asia/22airstrikes.html>.

22. "We will improve our cyberspace capabilities so they can often achieve significant and proportionate effects with less cost and lower collateral impact." Chairman of the Joint Chiefs of Staff *The National Military Strategy of the United States of America 2011: Redefining America's Military Leadership* (Washington, DC: GPO, 2011), 19.

23. Thomas C. Schelling, *Arms and Influence* (New Haven, CT: Yale University, 2008), 2–4.

24. For Russian pipeline, see Clarke and Knake, 93; for Stuxnet, see Nye, 127.

25. Lonsdale, 143–45.

26. Rear Adm. J.C. Wylie, *Military Strategy: A General Theory of Power Control* (Annapolis, MD: Naval Institute Press, 1989), 74.

27. Evgeny Morozov, *The Net Delusion: The Dark Side of Internet Freedom* (New York: PublicAffairs, 2011), 19.

28. Nye, 147.

29. Richard L. Kugler, "Deterrence of Cyber Attacks," *Cyberpower and National Security,* eds. Franklin D. Kramer, Stuart H. Starr, and Larry K. Wentz (Washington, DC: NDU Press, 2009), 320.

30. See United States Office of the President, *International Strategy for Cyberspace: Prosperity, Security, and Openness in a Networked World,* May 2011.

31. See Clarke and Knake, 155. International strategy for cyberspace addresses diplomacy, defense, and development in cyberspace but fails to outline relative priorities for conflicting policy interests. 31.

32. First Amendment free speech rights and their limits have been a contentious issue for decades. "Shouting fire in a crowded theater" comes from a 1919 U.S. Supreme Court case, *Schenck v. United States.* Justice Oliver Wendell Holmes' established context as relevant for limiting free speech. An "imminent lawless action" test superseded his "clear and present danger" test in 1969, <http://www.pbs.org/wnet/supremecourt/capitalism/landmark_schenck.html>.

33. Morozov, 28.

34. "Today's information technology capabilities have made this vision [of precision logistics] possible, and tomorrow's demand for efficiency has made the need urgent." Gen. Norton Schwartz, chief of staff, U.S. Air Force, "Toward More Efficient Military Logistics," address on 29 March 2011, to the 27th Annual Logistics Conference and Exhibition, Miami, FL, <http://www.af.mil/shared/media/document/AFD-110330-053.pdf>.

35. Chris C. Demchak, *Wars of Disruption and Resilience: Cybered Conflict, Power, and National Security* (Athens, GA: University of Georgia Press, 2011), 44.
36. Van Creveld, 269–70.
37. Demchak, 73.
38. Antoine Bousquet, *The Scientific Way of Warfare: Order and Chaos on the Battlefields of Modernity* (New York: Columbia University Press, 2009), 228–29.
39. See R.A. Ratcliff, *Delusions of Intelligence: Enigma, Ultra, and the End of Secure Ciphers* (Cambridge, UK: Cambridge University Press, 2006), 229–30. Allied World War II Enigma code-breaking offers a successful example of creatively task organizing without rigid hierarchy.
40. Colin S. Gray, *Explorations in Strategy* (Westport, CT: Praeger, 1996), 133.
41. *DOD Strategy for Operating in Cyberspace*, 8.
42. Clarke and Knake, 160.
43. Geoffrey A. Fowler, "Wikipedia, Google Go Black to Protest SOPA," *Wall Street Journal*, 18 January 2012, <http://online.wsj.com/article/SB10001424052970204555904577167873208040252.html?mod=WSJ_Tech_LEADTop>; Associated Press, "White House objects to legislation that would undermine 'dynamic' Internet," Washington Post, 14 January 2012, <http://www.washingtonpost.com/politics/courts-law/white-house-objects-to-legislation-that-would-undermine-dynamic-internet/2012/01/14/gIQAJsFcyP_story.html>.
44. "Soft power," see Nye, 81–82; "friendly conquest," see Martin C. Libicki, *Conquest in Cyberspace: National Security and Information Warfare* (Cambridge, UK: Cambridge University Press, 2007), 166.
45. U.S. Government, USASpending.gov official Web site, "Prime Award Spending Data," <http://www.usaspending.gov/explore?carryfilters=on> (18 January 2012). "2011" refers to the fiscal year.
46. DOD Web site, "About the Department of Defense," <http://www.defense.gov/about> (18 January 2012). DOD employs 1.4 million active, 1.1 million National Guard/Reserve, 718,000 civilian personnel.
47. Clausewitz, 357.
48. Kugler, "Deterrence of Cyber Attacks," 335.
49. "Many observers postulate that multiple actors are developing expert [cyber] attack capabilities." Ibid., 337.
50. Clarke and Knake, 144.
51. "Narratives are particularly important in framing issues in persuasive ways." Nye, 93–94.
52. Quote from Gen. Robert Elder as commander of Air Force Cyber Command. See Clarke and Knake, 158; Defense Tech, "Chinese Cyberwar Alert!" 15 June 2007, <http://defensetech.org/2007/06/15/chinese-cyberwar-alert>.
53. Nye, 234.
54. Clausewitz, 220.
55. John Cotesworth Slessor, *Air Power and Armies* (Tuscaloosa, AL: University of Alabama Press, 2009), iv.
56. Lonsdale, 232.
57. Clausewitz, 89.
58. Gray, 58.
59. Colin S. Gray, *Modern Strategy* (Oxford, UK: Oxford University Press, 1999), 270.
60. Arthur W. Tedder, *Air Power in War* (Tuscaloosa: University of Alabama Press, 2010), 88.

## Critical Thinking

1. What is the greatest threat to U.S. cybersecurity?
2. Why is it so difficult to defend U.S. cyberspace?
3. What recommendations would you make to defend U.S. cyberspace?

## Create Central

www.mhhe.com/createcentral

# Internet References

**Department of Defense Strategy for Operating in Cyberspace**
    http://www.defense.gov/news/d20110714.cyber.pdf
**Economist debates cyberwar**
    http://www.economist.com/debate/overview/256
**National Security Agency**
    https://www.nsa.gov

**KEVIN L. PARKER,** U.S. Air Force, is the commander of the 100th Civil Engineer Squadron at RAF Mildenhall, United Kingdom. He holds a BS in civil engineering from Texas A&M University, an MA in human resource development from Webster University, and an MS in military operational art and science and an MPhil in military strategy from Air University. He has deployed to Saudi Arabia, Kyrgyzstan, and twice to Iraq.

Lt. Col. Kevin Parker, "The Utility of Cyberpower," *Military Review,* May/June 2014, pp 26–33. HQ. Department of the Army, US Army Combined Arms Center.

# Article 39 ↵

## Can Technology Protect Americans from International Cybercriminals?

Selected, Edited, and with Issue Framing Material by:

Thomas A. Easton, *Thomas College*

**YES: Randy Vanderhoof,** from "Testimony Before the House Committee on Science, Space, and Technology, Subcommittees on Oversight and Research and Technology, Hearing on 'Can Technology Protect Americans from International Cybercriminals?'" U.S. House of Representatives (2014)

**NO: Charles H. Romine**, from "Testimony Before the House Committee on Science, Space, and Technology, subcommittees on Oversight and Research and Technology, Hearing on 'Can Technology Protect Americans from International Cybercriminals?'" U.S. House of Representatives (2014)

## Learning Outcomes

*After reading this issue, you will be able to:*
• Describe the potential consequences of theft of credit card data.
• Explain what measures might be taken to prevent hacker attacks on the computer systems of major retailers.
• Discuss why, even with the best technology, cybercrime is unlikely to be stopped entirely.

## ISSUE SUMMARY

**YES**: Randy Vanderhoof argues that as the United States' payment system shifts from credit cards with magnetic stripes (whose data, stored on merchant computer systems, are a prime target for hackers) to smart cards with embedded microchips (which do not make data available to hackers), the rate of credit card fraud will decline rapidly, as it already has in other countries.

**NO**: Charles H. Romine, Director of the National Institute of Standards and Technology's (NIST) Information Technology Laboratory, argues that technology is not enough to solve the cybercrime problem. The NIST works on smart card systems, but also develops guidelines, standards, and best practices essential to making the technology work. Fighting cybercriminals requires not just technology, but also policy, legal, and economic efforts.

## Where Do You Stand?

Physicist Gregory Benford says he wrote the very first computer virus, way back in the late 1960s. It was not designed to do harm, just to test the idea of a program that could spread from computer to computer, but it was a virus. As computers became more sophisticated, so did viruses and other "malware." By the 1990s, there was much alarm about hackers (see Bruce Sterling, *The Hacker Crackdown: Law and Disorder on the Electronic Frontier,* Bantam, 1992; http://www.gutenberg.org/ebooks/101). With the advent of the Internet a little later, malware starred in credit card fraud, identity theft, and more. As the problem got worse, it gave rise to antivirus software and the computer security industry. Today cybercrime costs the United states a bit less than one percent of its Gross Domestic Product (GDP)(see "Net Losses: Estimating the Global Cost of Cybercrime: Economic Impact of Cybercrime II," Center for Strategic and International Studies, June 2014; http://www.mcafee.com/us/resources/reports/rp-economic-impact-cybercrime2.pdf).

Come the twenty-first century, and while computer security and fraud remain of concern, people have begun to worry about cyberwar. In June 2010, the Stuxnet worm attacked Iranian nuclear facilities. It used stolen digital certificates to take control over software and interfere with the normal function of nuclear power plants, electrical distribution systems, and oil pipelines. Early reports said the Stuxnet worm was so complex that it must have taken large teams of programmers, millions of dollars in funding, and many months of work to produce it. Iran insisted it had to be an Israeli-American cyber-attack, and on

June 1, 2012, David E. Sanger reported in "Obama Order Sped up Wave of Cyberattacks against Iran," *New York Times,* that interviews with European, U.S., and Israeli officials have revealed that in 2006, President George W. Bush initiated the development of the Stuxnet worm under the codename Olympic Games. Samuel Greengard, "The New Face of War," *Communications of the ACM* (December 2010), considers this a sign of the way wars will be fought in the future. "The risk of cyber-warfare is growing, and many . . . warn that political leaders aren't entirely tuned into the severity of the threat." It must be taken seriously, for it is only a matter of time before cyberwar is real. Richard A. Clarke and Richard K. Knake, *Cyber War: The Next Threat to National Security and What to Do about It* (HarperCollins, 2010), stress that because society is now totally dependent on telecommunications networks, it is also vulnerable to widespread, long-lasting damage. James P. Farwell and Rafal Rohozinski, "Stuxnet and the Future of Cyber War," *Survival* (February/March 2011), note that cyberwar "offers great potential for striking at enemies with less risk than using traditional means." They also note that many cyberwar techniques are rooted in cybercrime (viruses, worms, bot-nets, identity theft, hacking, fraud, and more).

The methods of defending against cyberwar and cyberterrorism are also rooted in the fight against cybercrime. Few people today do not have antivirus and/or anti-malware software on their computers. The U.S. government has long sought extensions to digital telephony and the Internet of traditional wiretapping laws that permitted law-enforcement agencies to listen in on the conversations of criminal suspects (see Declan McCullagh, "FBI: We Need Wiretap-Ready Web Sites—Now," *CNET News,* May 4, 2012; http://news.cnet.com/8301-1009_3-57428067-83 /fbi-we-need-wiretap-ready-web-sites-now/). After September 11, 2001, the War on Terrorism began and every tool that promised to help identify terrorists before or catch them after they committed their dreadful acts was seen as desirable. However, when the Department of Defense's Defense Advanced Research Projects Agency (DARPA) proposed a massive computer system capable of sifting through purchases, tax data, court records, Google searches, emails, and other information from government and commercial databases to seek suspicious patterns of behavior, many people objected that this amounted to a massive assault on privacy and was surely in violation of the Fourth Amendment to the U.S. Constitution (which established the right of private citizens to be secure against unreasonable searches and seizures; "unreasonable" has come to mean "without a search warrant" for physical searches of homes and offices and "without a court order" for interceptions of mail and wiretappings of phone conversations). This Total or Terrorism Information Awareness (TIA) program soon died although many of its components continued under other names; see Shane Harris, "TIA Lives On," *National Journal* (February 25, 2006). See also Hina Shamsi and Alex Abdo, "Privacy and Surveillance Post-9/11," *Human Rights* (Winter 2011).

Is cybercrime more like cyberwar? Matthew Goldstein, Nicole Perlroth, and David E. Sanger, report in "Hackers' Attack Cracked 10 Financial Firms in Major Assault," *New York Times* (October 4, 2014), that the hackers responsible for breaching JPMorgan Chase and nine other major financial firms, affecting more than 80 million homes and businesses, "are thought to be operating from Russia and appear to have at least loose connections with officials of the Russian government." There is now serious concern that a hacker attack could cause a major financial crisis. And with the involvement of foreign governments, it could easily be an act of war. John Stone is sure that "Cyber War Will Take Place!" *Journal of Strategic Studies* (February 2013); if commercial attacks are acts of war, the war may already be under way. At the end of 2014, Sony Pictures was hacked, embarrassing documents were released, and threats were issued to keep the movie "The Interview" (about the assassination of North Korea's leader) from being released; the U.S. government accused North Korea of the hacking and called it an act of cyberwar; see for example "Sony Hack: North Korea Threatens US as Row Deepens" (http://www.bbc.com/news/world-asia-30573040).

General Keith Alexander, head of the Defense Department's U.S. Cyber Command (http://www.defense.gov/home/features/2010/0410_cybersec/), is preparing as if cyberwar is a real threat. Peter Sommer and Ian Brown, "Reducing Systemic Cybersecurity Risk" OECD (Organization for Economic Co-operation and Development)/IFP (International Futures Programme) Project on "Future Global Shocks," 2011), conclude "that very few single cyber-related events have the capacity to cause a global shock. Governments nevertheless need to make detailed preparations to withstand and recover from a wide range of unwanted cyber events, both accidental and deliberate. There are significant and growing risks of localized misery and loss as a result of compromise of computer and telecommunications services." Simson L. Garfinkel, "The Cybersecurity Risk," *Communications of the ACM* (June 2012), argues that the reason why we have not already built more secure computer systems is that "it is more cost-effective to create systems without redundancy or resiliency." Gary McGraw, "Cyber War Is Inevitable (Unless We Build Security In)," *Journal of Strategic Studies* (February 2013), argues that this needs to change.

What is the best way to defend against cybercriminals and their more extreme cousins, the cyberwarriors? R. Scott Kemp, "Cyberweapons: Bold Steps in a Digital Darkness?" *Bulletin of the Atomic Scientists* ( June 7, 2012) (http://www.thebulletin.org/web-edition/op-eds/cyberweapons-bold-steps-digital-darkness), argues that "We are at a key turning point . . . in which a nation must decide what role cyberweapons will play in its national defense. . . . for the United States and other highly developed nations whose societies are critically and deeply reliant on computers, the safe approach is to direct cyber research at purely defensive applications." According to Richard Stone, "A Call to Cyber Arms," *Science* (March 1, 2013), the U.S. and other governments are putting a great deal of effort not only into devising ways to defend against cyber-espionage and cyber-attacks against industrial, defense, and commercial infrastructure, but also into ways to go on the offensive.

Most discussions of the topic focus on the role of technology in defending against cyber-attacks, and indeed on March 4, 2014, the United States House of Representatives' Committee on *Science*, Subcommittees on Oversight and Research and Technology held a hearing on "Can Technology Protect Americans from International Cybercriminals?" The YES selection is drawn from the testimony before this hearing of Randy Vanderhoof, executive director of the Smart Card Alliance. He argues that as the United States' payment system shifts from credit cards with magnetic stripes (whose data, stored on merchant computer systems, are a prime target for hackers) to smart cards with embedded microchips (which do not make data available to hackers), the rate of credit card fraud will decline rapidly, as it already has in other countries. His focus is very much on commerce, and given the JPMorgan Chase attack, perhaps that is appropriate. The NO selection is drawn from the testimony of Charles H. Romine, director of the Information Technology Laboratory of the National Institute of Standards and Technology. He argues that technology alone is not enough to solve the cybercrime problem. The NIST works on smart card systems, but also develops guidelines, standards, and best practices essential to making the technology work. Fighting cybercriminals requires not just technology, but also policy, legal, and economic efforts.

YES

Randy Vanderhoof

# Testimony Before the House Committee on Science, Space, and Technology, Subcommittees on Oversight and Research and Technology, Hearing on "Can Technology Protect Americans from International Cybercriminals?"

On behalf of the Smart Card Alliance and its members, I thank you for the opportunity to testify today. We applaud the Subcommittees' leadership and foresight in examining important issues in the payments industry, especially on increasing instances of international cybercriminals committing payment data breaches and the role of EMV (Europay, Mastercard, and Visa) chip payment technology to help secure the U.S. payments infrastructure.

The Smart Card Alliance is a non-profit organization established in 2001 that provides education about smart card chip technology and applications and operates a collaborative, open forum among leaders in various industries including payments, mobile, transportation, government, healthcare, and access security. The Alliance's members from the payment ecosystem include payment brands, card issuers, payment processors, merchants and technology providers.

Shortly after the four major payments brands, American Express, Discover, MasterCard and Visa, announced incentives to introduce secure EMV chip cards for the U.S. market and aligned timelines for fraud liability shift dates in 2015 and 2017, the Smart Card Alliance organized a new payments-only industry association, the EMV Migration Forum. The Forum was formed specifically to address issues that require broad cooperation and coordination across many constituents in the payments space to ensure the successful adoption of EMV-enabled cards, devices, and terminals across the U.S. market, and to ensure that migration in the U.S. market is efficient, timely and effective. The Forum has more than 150 member companies, including global payments brands, financial institutions, merchants, processors, acquirers, regional debit networks, industry associations and industry suppliers.

The Smart Card Alliance and the EMV Migration Forum have been the leading advocates for accelerating the adoption of secure payments technology to address the growing fraud problem in the United States and to ensure citizens traveling outside of the U.S. will have a safe and convenient payments experience.

The focus of my testimony will be on the state of payment card technology and the payments acceptance ecosystem, including differences between the magnetic stripe cards used in the U.S. and EMV chip cards used in more than 80 countries, the status of U.S. migration to EMV chip cards, and the benefits for the U.S. moving to EMV chip cards to increase security, reduce counterfeit card fraud, and reduce the likelihood of future data breaches by devaluing the payments data that is present in the retail and financial systems.

## Increasing Instances of Cybercrime in the U.S. Highlight Need for EMV Chip Cards

Cybercrime targeting government and commercial enterprises is a growing problem in the U.S. In 2013, data breaches became more damaging, with one in three people who received a data breach notification letter becoming an identity fraud victim, up from one in four in 2012.

While cybercrime is a known threat across many industries, criminals are increasingly targeting retail store chains with sophisticated attacks in order to extract credit card data from millions of transactions. Attacks against retailers are particularly damaging because of their effects on large numbers of consumers, banks and merchants at the same time. The results of a single attack, which we saw most recently with retailer Target, can be millions of dollars' worth of credit card fraud and the need to close and reissue tens of millions of payment card accounts to prevent further fraud. There are also other unquantified costs of payment data breaches, including the time and money to investigate and clean up after the breach, lost business and damaged reputations for the merchants and banks involved.

U.S. House of Representatives, 2014.

The opportunity for huge financial gains with little chance of criminal prosecution from these stolen card accounts also provides the incentive for hackers to penetrate deeper into compromised networks to extract additional personal information beyond payments data, including email addresses and phone numbers, putting consumers' privacy at further risk.

Increasing instances of attacks against retailers are due in part to the fact that U.S. magnetic stripe payment card information is highly valuable data for hackers, who can sell it on the black market to criminals for large profits. For example, the black market price for several million card accounts stolen from the Target breach was between $26.60 and $44.80 each prior to Dec. 19, 2013.

Criminals are willing to pay such high prices for U.S. magnetic stripe card data because of the ease with which that data can be used to create counterfeit payment cards for fraud. It's very simple to write stolen magnetic stripe payment card information to a different magnetic stripe payment card. This is why the U.S. is the only region where counterfeit card fraud continues to grow. The U.S. accounted for 47.3% of global fraud losses in 2012, despite only accounting for 23.5% of the total transactions, and U.S. issuer losses due to counterfeiting account for 26.5% of global fraud losses.

The financial industry has very strict data security standards, called the Payment Card Industry Data Security Standard (PCI DSS), in place to protect payments data and other sensitive personal information captured and stored by retail systems and processors. These standards and best practices are effective deterrents against a lot of criminal activity, but not enough for increasingly sophisticated criminals and attacks. Additional security measures are needed and are already used globally including EMV chip cards, advanced encryption technologies and tokenization.

EMV chip cards in particular can reduce the threat of financial cybercrime by removing the economic incentive for criminals. Replacing magnetic stripe payment data with secure EMV chip payment data devalues U.S. payment data in the eyes of criminals because, if stolen, EMV chip payment data cannot be used to create counterfeit payment cards.

The positive news is that the U.S. payments system is undertaking a migration to EMV chip card technology, and this will present significant barriers for criminals engaging in payment card counterfeiting. Although the U.S. payments system is complex, the industry has recognized the need to move as quickly as possible to EMV chip card payments. I am encouraged by the movement and progress from all industry stakeholders towards implementation of the technology.

Next, I will explain EMV chip card technology and why it is secure, how it can help to address mounting U.S. payment data security problems, and what the current status of U.S. EMV migration is.

## Introduction to EMV Chip Payment Technology

EMV chip payment cards are based on widely used and highly secure smart card technology, also referred to as "smart chip" technology. Smart cards—which can look like a card but can also take on different forms—have embedded integrated circuit chips, powerful minicomputers that can be programmed for different applications. Through the chip, the smart card can store and access data and applications securely, and exchange data securely with readers and other systems. Smart cards are ideal for many applications, especially payments, because they provide high levels of security and privacy protection, are easily carried, and do not require their own power source to operate effectively.

Smart cards are currently used to secure many applications worldwide, including:

- Identity applications including employee ID badges for physical access to buildings and secure computer and network access; citizen ID documents; electronic passports; driver's licenses; and online authentication devices. Today, smart card technology is used by all U.S. federal employees and contractors with Personal Identity Verification (PIV) credentials to secure access to government systems and buildings; in U.S. citizens' passports to secure identity information; and in federal programs like the TSA First Responder Authentication Credential (FRAC), the TSA Transportation Worker Identification Credential (TWIC) and the Department of Defense Common Access Card (CAC)
- Healthcare applications including citizen health ID cards; health provider ID cards; portable medical records cards. Smart card technology is now being recommended in legislation to create a pilot for a proposed Medicare Common Access Card (H.R. 3024)
- Mobile applications including billions of mobile phone subscriber identity modules (SIMs) in use today, plus in NFC-enabled phones to secure mobile wallets
- And lastly, with global payment standard EMV chip cards, now used in more than 80 countries worldwide with 1.6 billion payments cards issued to date, and the focus of this testimony

## EMV: A Global Perspective

It was growing counterfeit card fraud that originally led the global payments industry to move to smart chip technology for bank cards and to develop the global EMV standard for bank cards based on chip card technology. The EMV specification, first available in 1996 and managed by EMVCo, defines the global interoperable standard for smart chip-based bank cards.

Financial institutions in Europe, Latin America, Asia/Pacific and Canada are issuing EMV chip cards for credit and debit payment or migrating to EMV issuance. According to EMVCo, approximately 1.6 billion EMV cards have been issued globally and 24 million point of sale (POS) terminals accept EMV cards as of Q4 2012. This represents 44.7% of the total payment cards in circulation and 76.4% of the POS terminals installed globally.

There have been a number of historical factors behind the adoption of EMV chip technology in these other countries. The most important factors have been high fraud rates and the cost and reliability of the communications infrastructure. In markets in Western Europe, Australia, Latin America, and Canada the rate of credit card fraud had been much worse than what the U.S. market has historically experienced. These higher fraud rates, plus the lack of low cost, reliable communications at the retail level, led countries to adopt EMV chip technology to enable greater security at the card and offline payments processing at the terminal level. Each of these markets are smaller than the U.S. market, with fewer financial institutions and merchants to convert to chip technology, so the business case to make the investment in EMV has been very strong. Countries that have implemented EMV chip technology have seen their counterfeit fraud decline by as much as 67%.

The U.S. is one of the last countries to move to EMV chip technology, but has now started its migration. Between July 2011 and June 2012, American Express, Discover, MasterCard and Visa announced plans for moving the U.S. to an EMV-based payments infrastructure. The plans included a series of incentives and policy changes aligning around a target date of October 2015 for card issuers and merchants to complete their implementation of EMV chip cards, terminals and processing systems. ATM operators and retail petroleum outlets were given until 2016 and 2017, respectively, to complete their EMV migrations.

It is important to note that the target dates are not mandates, as U.S. payment brands do not have the ability to set requirements. What they can, and did, was mandate payments processors who connect through their global networks to support EMV chip data in transactions by April 1, 2013. This is the only mandate for U.S. EMV chip implementation.

The payment brands have offered card-issuing financial institutions and merchants an incentive to move to EMV chip technology in the form of a counterfeit fraud liability shift. After the target EMV chip migration dates, the payment brands will shift the responsibility for any fraud resulting from a payment transaction to the party using the least secure technology. This may be either the issuer of the card or the merchant accepting the payment card.

As an example, if a merchant can accept EMV chip cards and the cardholder presents a magnetic stripe card and there is fraud, the issuer would bear the liability for fraud. Conversely, if a cardholder presents an EMV chip card for payment and the merchant only accepts magnetic stripe cards, the merchant would be liable for any fraud. If both parties have deployed EMV and fraud results from that transaction, the current rules for fraud liability are applied.

This fraud liability shift ensures that those who have made the investment in EMV chip technology will not bear responsibility or cost from fraud from another stakeholder who has not made their system more secure. The goal of the liability shift is to encourage both issuers and merchants to move to EMV technology at the same time so that fraud is removed from the system, not shifted from one party to another.

## Status of U.S. EMV Migration

The U.S. payments industry is approximately two years into the planned four-year migration to adopt EMV chip technology. Industry stakeholders have been meeting regularly at Smart Card Alliance conferences and EMV Migration Forum meetings and within other industry organizations to address issues that require coordination and cooperation among multiple payments industry participants to ensure a timely and cost effective industry-wide migration to chip technology in the U.S.

The migration to chip cards in the U.S. is complex, expensive and difficult to coordinate. The U.S. market is the largest individual market to convert to chip cards. With over 12,000 financial institutions that issue cards, an estimated 1.2 billion cards in the market, over 10 million POS devices in retail stores, and another 100,000 ATMs installed, the United States payments market is larger than all of Europe's payments markets combined. To date, an estimated 10 to 15 million chip cards have been issued to U.S. consumers, mostly to those who travel frequently outside of the U.S. and who benefit from having the same chip cards that are used in those countries' retail outlets and ATMs. This progress represents less than 2% of the total number of cards in the market. Retailers have replaced approximately 1 million of the more than 10 million POS terminals in stores, but nearly all of these are still operating only as magnetic stripe accepting devices until the software is tested and certified by the acquirers and the stores are ready to begin accepting chip cards.

Implementing EMV chip technology for U.S. debit is also very complex. Complexities result from having 19 debit networks for PIN debit card transactions and the need for compliance with the 2011 Federal Reserve Rulemaking, "Regulation II, Debit Card Interchange Fees and Routing," interpretation of the Durbin Amendment under the Dodd Frank Act. The rulemaking requires that there be at least two unrelated debit card networks supported on each card issued and that merchants have the option to decide which network to route those transactions to each time a debit card is used.

Accommodating these debit routing rules through agreements among all of the debit networks and the global brands, as well as determining the impact of recent court decisions challenging the Federal Reserve rules, have created uncertainty among issuers and merchants about how to implement EMV chip technology for debit transactions. Today the industry is working on ways to comply with the current rules and still be able to accommodate potential changes that may result from further decisions by the courts, and progress has been made.

## How EMV Chip Cards Prevent Counterfeit Card Fraud

Chip technology in conjunction with the global EMV payments application standard has proven to be the most effective tool to prevent counterfeit card fraud and maintain the requirements for global interoperability of payment cards for issuers, merchants and consumers. The counterfeit fraud protection comes from two aspects of this technology:

1. The secure storage of the cardholder data inside the chip rather than on a magnetic stripe
2. The dynamic payment transaction data generated by the chip when it is presented to the payment reader for processing the card in a physical retail setting.

The chip itself is a powerful microcomputer with active defenses that prevent tampering with the application and the information it stores inside its memory. Even if chip data were to be copied, it could not be used to create a usable copy onto another chip card because each chip is programmed with a secret key known only to the issuer. The less secure magnetic stripe has no defenses to prevent a criminal from reading the stripe and reprogramming that same card data onto another magnetic stripe, creating an undetectable copy of the original card.

Chip-enabled terminals in retail stores are programmed to pass dynamic security information to the chip before the chip will pass the uniquely generated cryptographic electronic signature to the terminal to complete a payment transaction. This feature is the first line of defense against the use of counterfeit cards that is possible today with magnetic stripe cards.

The chip generates a one time, unique security code, called a cryptogram, for each chip payment transaction that is passed through the chip terminal and through the retailer's POS system and payments processing network. The security cryptogram is verified by the issuer processor to determine that the card used to start the transaction is authentic and that the transaction data was unique to that card. Therefore, a counterfeit copy of that card or a second transaction with the same unique card data would be detected by the issuer and the message normally sent back to the retailer to complete the transaction would deny the transaction.

In addition, EMV chip transactions do not include other data needed for magnetic stripe transactions. This means that any stolen data cannot be used to create a fraudulent transaction in an EMV chip or magnetic stripe environment.

The dynamic data generated by EMV chip cards and the omission of data used in magnetic stripe transactions greatly devalue any payment data that is present in the retailer's or third party processor systems since the chip data cannot be made into counterfeit cards to commit fraud. For example, if EMV chip data had been present in the retailers' systems that were recently victimized by a POS malware attack that extracted card transaction data, the impact of the data breach would have been significantly lessened for the merchant, the card issuers and the consumers through greatly reduced risk of counterfeiting and the resulting card fraud.

The EMV standard also supports additional security mechanisms including the manner with which consumers verify their identities, called Cardholder Verification Methods (CVMs). The EMV standard supports signature, PIN and/or no CVM. Chip-based payment cards that use signature as a CVM have all of the security benefits that the chip and the EMV transaction data provide for protection from counterfeiting and resulting fraud. Chip-based payment cards that use PINs as a CVM provide an added layer of security that prevents the physical card from being used if it is lost or stolen. In the U.S., card issuers will decide which CVMs they want to support based on customer profiles and card management considerations. Merchants can decide which CVMs available on each card they will accept in their retail outlets. As a result, it is likely we will see EMV chip cards issued with a mix of signature, PIN and no CVMs in the U.S.

The issuance of chip cards in the U.S. does not mean the elimination of the magnetic stripe altogether. Financial institutions will continue to issue chip cards with a magnetic stripe on the back for the foreseeable future in order to enable consumers to continue to use these cards at merchant locations that haven't yet upgraded to chip, or in some countries who have not yet adopted the EMV chip standard.

These magnetic stripes that will remain on the backs of bank-issued EMV chip cards do not pose a fraud threat to card issuers or consumers when chip-enabled merchant terminals are widely deployed. When issued on a chip card, a magnetic stripe has different information stored, so when swiped at an EMV chip-accepting terminal, it signals to the terminal that the card was issued with a chip. The terminal will then force the card to be used as a more secure chip card rather than as a less secure magnetic stripe card at that device.

Another scenario is where that chip card's magnetic stripe is copied and a card is created with that card's data written to another magnetic stripe on an unauthorized second card. When that counterfeit card is swiped at a merchant terminal that can process a chip transaction, the terminal would also direct the customer to use the chip. Because the chip doesn't exist on this counterfeit card, the transaction will be declined. If the counterfeit card is used at a terminal that does not support a chip, the card would be accepted unless the issuer flags the transaction based on certain usage analytics or if the cardholder reported the card lost or stolen.

After the fraud liability shift date, if the copied card made with the magnetic stripe data of a chip card is used at a terminal that does not support a chip, and the card is accepted even though it is a copy, the merchant would be responsible for that fraud because it did not have the more secure EMV chip handling capability that would have detected the card was a counterfeit. This is the reason for the liability shift discussed earlier; it's important for both the issuance and acceptance infrastructures to move to chip at the same time to provide the most protection from counterfeit card fraud.

In a third scenario where chip payment card data is intercepted and used to make an online purchase, there are additional security measures that online merchants use, including the three or four digit card security code printed on the card (and which is not available from either the magnetic stripe or the chip), the cardholder's billing address information, or both. Online purchases where the EMV chip is not used in the payment transaction, called Card-Not-Present (CNP) transactions, are not protected by the issuance of EMV chip cards. However, there are other ways to manage CNP fraud risk that are being used today and new technologies that are being developed to address this problem.

To summarize, the security features that EMV chip cards provide to the market in conjunction with the chip reading terminals and advanced payments processing upgrades to support dynamic data are a powerful set of tools to take counterfeit fraud out of the payments system. These security features reduce the likelihood of, or the resulting damage from, any future data breaches against retailers, processors and financial institutions.

# Conclusion

In summary, the U.S. reliance on magnetic stripe payment cards has made the country a target for fraud. Evidence to support this are: the increasing attacks on U.S. retailers, of which the FBI found at least 22 instances in the past year, and the fact that the U.S. is the only region where counterfeit card fraud rises consistently. Hackers are motivated by the big profits that they can make from selling U.S. magnetic stripe payment data on the black market to criminals to make and use counterfeit magnetic stripe cards.

Joining more than 80 countries and implementing EMV chip technology will greatly devalue U.S. payment card data in the eyes of criminals because it cannot be used to create counterfeit chip or magnetic stripe cards. Other countries that implemented EMV chip payments saw fraud decrease by as much as 67%.

While the move to EMV chip payments in the U.S. is a complex and expensive undertaking, it is a critical one that will benefit our entire payments system. I am encouraged by the payments industry's recognition that we need to move EMV chip technology. I am even more encouraged by the fact that many of the largest financial institutions are now issuing EMV chip cards and big retail chains are moving quickly to put in place the chip-enabled terminals and working with their acquirer processors to enable those devices to begin accepting chip transactions by the October 2015 targeted completion dates.

RANDY VANDERHOOF is the executive director of the Smart Card Alliance, a nonprofit organization that promotes smart card chip technology to address the growing fraud problem.

Charles H. Romine

# Testimony Before the House Committee on Science, Space, and Technology, Subcommittees on Oversight and Research and Technology, Hearing on "Can Technology Protect Americans from International Cybercriminals?"

## Background

Cybertheft can occur at a scale unlike physical crimes. It can have multiple victims and a much larger impact than would be possible in conventional criminal activity. As we know, one breach can affect thousands—if not millions—of citizens. Cybertheft also can be perpetrated at the speed of electronic transactions. This makes interception difficult and places a strong reliance on preventive security controls. They also can occur without the physical presence of the criminal. This is possible because we work and live in an increasingly interconnected digital world. This introduces jurisdiction, legal and policy complexities as well as difficulty in attribution to the criminals themselves.

In response to the title of the hearing: "Can Technology Protect Americans from International Cybercriminals?"—my response would be: technology alone cannot solve these problems. However, we do believe that effective use of technology can make it more difficult for criminals to perpetrate these crimes, can make it easier for organizations to recover from serious incidents, and can, in some cases, prevent such incidents from occurring.

For example, technology can make it difficult to clone payment cards with stolen credentials or use the information to make online purchases. Smart cards using chip-and-pin technologies can make theft of the information stored on the card more difficult; however, often the attacks and exploits are not on the cards themselves, but are instead against the supporting payment infrastructure. We believe it takes a holistic approach that includes technology, training and awareness, policy, legal, economic and international efforts, to bring cybertheft, one of many different cyberthreats we face, under control.

With that background, today I would like to discuss some of the Department of Commerce National Institute of Standards and Technology's (NIST) activities that accelerate the development and deployment of security technologies and assist the US Government and other stakeholders and partners in protecting their information and communications infrastructure against cyberthreats, including cybertheft.

## The Role of NIST in Cybersecurity

NIST's overall mission is to promote U.S. innovation and industrial competitiveness by advancing measurement science, standards, and technology in ways that enhance economic security and improve our quality of life. Our work in addressing technical challenges related to national priorities has ranged from projects related to the Smart Grid and electronic health records to atomic clocks, advanced nanomaterials, and computer chips.

In the area of cybersecurity, we have worked with federal agencies, industry, and academia since 1972, starting with the development of the Data Encryption Standard, when the potential commercial benefit of this technology became clear. Our role, to research, develop and deploy information security standards and technology to protect information systems against threats to the confidentiality, integrity and availability of information and services, was strengthened through the Computer Security Act of 1987 and reaffirmed through the Federal Information Security Management Act of 2002 (FISMA).

NIST accomplishes its mission in cybersecurity through collaborative partnerships with our customers and stakeholders in industry, government, academia, standards bodies, consortia and international partners.

Our broader work in the areas of information security, trusted networks, and software quality is applicable to a wide variety of users, from small and medium enterprises to large private and public organizations, including federal government agencies and companies involved with critical infrastructure.

U.S. House of Representatives, 2014.

We employ collaborative partnerships with our customers and stakeholders to take advantage of their technical and operational insights and to leverage the resources of a global community. These collaborative efforts, and our private sector collaborations in particular, are constantly being expanded by new initiatives, including in recent years through the National Initiative for Cybersecurity Education (NICE), the National Strategy for Trusted Identities in Cyberspace (NSTIC), the National Cybersecurity Center of Excellence (NCCoE), and in implementation of Executive Order 13636, "Improving Critical Infrastructure Cybersecurity."

## NIST Cybersecurity Research, Standards and Guidelines

The E-Government Act recognized the importance of information security to the economic and national security interests of the United States. The Federal Information Security Management Act of 2002 (FISMA), Title III of the E-Government Act, included duties and responsibilities for NIST to develop standards and guidelines for Federal information systems.

The NIST Special Publications and Interagency Reports provide those management, operational, and technical security guidelines for Federal agencies and cover a broad range of topics such as Basic Input/Output System (BIOS) management and measurement, key management and derivation, media sanitization, electronic authentication, security automation, Bluetooth and wireless protocols, incident handling and intrusion detection, malware, cloud computing, public key infrastructure, risk assessments, supply chain risk management, authentication, access control, security automation and continuous monitoring.

Beyond these documents—which are peer-reviewed throughout industry, government, and academia—NIST conducts workshops, awareness briefings, and outreach to ensure comprehension of standards and guidelines, to share ongoing and planned activities, and to aid in scoping guidelines in a collaborative, open, and transparent manner.

In addition, NIST maintains the National Vulnerability Database (NVD), a repository of standards-based vulnerability management reference data. The NVD makes available information on vulnerabilities, impact measurements, detection techniques, and remediation assistance. It provides reference data that enable government, industry and international security automation capabilities. The NVD also plays a role in the efforts of the Payment Card Industry (PCI) to identify and mitigate vulnerabilities. The PCI uses the NVD vulnerability metrics to discern the IT vulnerability in point-of-sale devices and determine what risks are unacceptable for that industry.

NIST researchers develop and standardize cryptographic mechanisms that are used throughout the world to protect information at rest and in transit. These mechanisms provide security services, such as confidentiality, integrity, authentication, non-repudiation and digital signatures, to protect sensitive information. The NIST algorithms and associated cryptographic guidelines are developed in a transparent and inclusive process, leveraging cryptographic expertise around the world. The results are in standard, interoperable cryptographic mechanisms that can be used by all industries.

NIST has a complementary program, in coordination with the Government of Canada, to certify independent commercial calibration laboratories to test commercially available IT cryptographic modules, to ensure that they have implemented the NIST cryptographic standards and guidelines correctly. These testing laboratories exist around the globe and test hundreds of individual cryptographic modules yearly.

## NIST Engagement with Industry

It is important to note that the impact of NIST's activities under FISMA extend beyond providing the means to protect Federal IT systems. They provide the cybersecurity foundations for the public trust that is essential to our realization of the national and global productivity and innovation potential of electronic business and its attendant economic benefits. Many organizations voluntarily follow NIST standards and guidelines, reflecting their wide acceptance throughout the world.

Beyond NIST's responsibilities under FISMA, under the provisions of the National Technology Transfer and Advancement Act (PL 104-113) and related OMB Circular A-119, NIST is tasked with the key role of encouraging and coordinating federal agency use of voluntary consensus standards and participation in the development of relevant standards, as well as promoting coordination between the public and private sectors in the development of standards and in conformity assessment activities. NIST works with other agencies, such as the Department of State, to coordinate standards issues and priorities with the private sector through consensus standards organizations such as the American National Standards Institute (ANSI), the International Organization for Standardization (ISO), the Institute of Electrical and Electronic Engineers (IEEE), the Internet Engineering Task Force (IETF), and the International Telecommunications Union (ITU).

Partnership with industry to develop, maintain, and implement voluntary consensus standards related to cybersecurity best ensures the interoperability, security and resiliency of the global infrastructure needed to make us all more secure. It also allows this infrastructure to evolve in a way that embraces both security and innovation—allowing a market to flourish to create new types of secure products for the benefit of all Americans.

NIST works extensively in smart card standards, guidelines and best practices. NIST developed the standard for the US Government Personal Identity Verification (PIV) Card, and actively works with the ANSI and the ISO on global cybersecurity standards for use in smart cards, smart card cryptography and the standards for the international integrated circuit card. [ANSI 504; ISO 7816 and ISO 24727]

NIST also conducts cybersecurity research and development in forward looking technology areas, such as security for federal mobile environments and techniques for measuring and managing security. These efforts focus on improving the trustworthiness of IT components such as claimed identities, data, hardware, and software for networks and devices. Additional research areas include developing approaches to balancing safety, security, reliability in the nation's supply chain; enabling mobile device and application security; securing the nation's cyber-physical systems; enabling continuous security monitoring; providing advanced security measurements and testing; investigating security analytics and big data; developing standards, modeling, and measurements to achieve end-to-end security over heterogeneous, multi-domain networks; and investigating technologies for detection of anomalous behavior and quarantines.

In addition, further development of cybersecurity standards will be needed to improve the security and resiliency of critical U.S. information and communication infrastructure. The availability of cybersecurity standards and associated conformity assessment schemes is essential in these efforts, which NIST supports to help enhance the deployment of sound security solutions and builds trust among those creating and those using the solutions throughout the country.

## Cybersecurity Framework

As you know, NIST has spent the last year working to convene the US Critical Infrastructure sectors to build a Cybersecurity Framework as part of Executive Order 13636. The Cybersecurity Framework, released last month, was created through collaboration between industry and government, and consists of standards, guidelines, and practices to promote the protection of critical infrastructure. The prioritized, flexible, repeatable, and cost-effective approach of the Framework helps owners and operators of critical infrastructure to manage cybersecurity-related risk. The Framework is already being implemented by industry, adopted by infrastructure sectors and is reducing cyber risks to our critical infrastructure, including the finance industry.

## National Strategy for Trusted Identities in Cyberspace

NIST also houses the National Program Office established to lead implementation of the National Strategy for Trusted Identities in Cyberspace (NSTIC). NSTIC is an initiative that aims to address one of the most commonly exploited vectors of attack in cyberspace: the inadequacy of passwords for authentication.

The 2013 Data Breach Investigations Report (conducted by Verizon in concert with the U.S. Department of Homeland Security) noted that in 2012, 76% of network intrusions exploited weak or stolen credentials. In line with the results of this report, Target has revealed that the compromised credential of one of its business partners was the vector used to access its network.

NSTIC aims to address this issue by collaborating with the private sector to catalyze a marketplace of better identity and authentication solutions—an "Identity Ecosystem" that raises the level of trust associated with the identities of individuals, organizations, networks, services, and devices online. NIST has funded a dozen pilots and supported work in the privately led Identity Ecosystem Steering Group (IDESG) to craft standards to improve authentication online.

## National Cybersecurity Center of Excellence

In 2012, the National Cybersecurity Center of Excellence (NCCoE) was formed as a partnership between NIST, the State of Maryland, and Montgomery County to accelerate the adoption of security technologies that are based on standards and best practices. The center is a vehicle for NIST to work directly with businesses across various industry sectors on applied solutions to cybersecurity challenges. Today the NCCoE has programs working with the healthcare, financial services, and energy sectors in addition to addressing challenges that cut across sectors including: mobile device security, software asset management, cloud security, and identity management.

NIST and the NCCOE work extensively in standards and guidelines, as well as research and development in hardware roots of trust. Stronger security assurances can be possible by grounding security mechanisms in roots of trust. Roots of trust are highly reliable hardware, firmware, and software components that perform specific, critical security functions. Because roots of trust are inherently trusted, they must be secure by design. As such, many roots of trust are implemented in hardware so that malware cannot tamper with the functions they provide. Roots of trust provide a firm foundation from which to build security and trust.

In 2013, NIST and the NCCOE worked with government and industry partners on guidelines for hardware-rooted security features in mobile devices. These guidelines focus on device integrity, isolation, and protected storage features that are supported by roots of trust, and we continue our work to protect fundamental system firmware, commonly known as the BIOS. NIST continues working with key members of the computer industry on the use of roots of trust to improve the security of BIOS, computers and systems overall.

## Additional Research Areas

NIST performs research and development in related technologies, such as the usability of systems including electronic health records, voting machines, biometrics and software interfaces. NIST is performing basic research on the mathematical foundations needed to determine the security of information systems. In the areas of digital forensics, NIST is enabling improvements in forensic analysis through the National Software Reference Library and computer forensics tool testing. Software assurance metrics, tools, and evaluations developed at NIST are being implemented by industry to help strengthen software against hackers. NIST responds to government and market requirements for biometric standards by collaborating with other federal agencies, academia, and industry partners to develop and implement biometrics evaluations, enable usability, and develop standards (fingerprint, face, iris, voice/speaker, and multimodal biometrics). NIST plays a central role in defining and advancing standards, and collaborating with customers and stakeholders to identify and reach consensus on cloud computing standards.

## Conclusion

We at NIST recognize that we have an essential role to play in helping industry, consumers and government entities to counter cyber theft and cyberthreats. We look forward to continuing our work, along with our federal government partners, our private sector collaborators, and our international colleagues to establish and continually improve the comprehensive set of technical solutions, standards, guidelines, and best practices necessary to realize this vision. . . .

CHARLES H. ROMINE is director of the Information Technology Laboratory of the National Institute of Standards and Technology.

# SECTION 8

## War and Terrorism

Issues concerning war and terrorism have become more complicated as technology has advanced. Consider the evolution of war from utilizing man to man combat, to airplane fly over bombings, to missile launches to nuclear weapons to computer combat. The threat against national security may not be limited to an individual with a gun or a bomb, but now also needs to include someone sitting in front of a computer. World dominance may not be just a matter of strategic weaponry, but also of technological mastery. In light of the new technological age and the ways people can use computers in warfare, is there ever truly a peace time, or are we involved in one continuous digital battle? With the anonymity of online appearances, it can be difficult to determine sources of terrorism. A new battleground has emerged, and the readings in this section highlight the direction of technological warfare.

### Learning Objectives

1. Identify the impact technology has on war and terrorism.
2. Describe the ways technology has changed the characteristics of war primarily in the ways battles are fought.
3. Consider the evolution of war and what technological advancements mean for its future.

# Article 40 ↵

John Arquilla, David Ronfeldt, and Michele Zanini

## Networks, Netwar, and Information-Age Terrorism

The rise of network forms of organization is a key consequence of the ongoing information revolution. Business organizations are being newly energized by networking, and many professional militaries are experimenting with flatter forms of organization. In this [selection], we explore the impact of networks on terrorist capabilities, and consider how this development may be associated with a move away from emphasis on traditional, episodic efforts at coercion to a new view of terror as a form of protracted warfare. Seen in this light, the recent bombings of U.S. embassies in East Africa, along with the retaliatory American missile strikes, may prove to be the opening shots of a war between a leading state and a terror network. We consider both the likely context and the conduct of such a war, and offer some insights that might inform policies aimed at defending against and countering terrorism.

### A New Terrorism (With Old Roots)

The age-old phenomenon of terrorism continues to appeal to its perpetrators for three principal reasons. First, it appeals as a weapon of the weak—a shadowy way to wage war by attacking asymmetrically to harm and try to defeat an ostensibly superior force. This has had particular appeal to ethnonationalists, racist militias, religious fundamentalists, and other minorities who cannot match the military formations and firepower of their "oppressors"— the case, for example, with some radical Middle Eastern Islamist groups vis-à-vis Israel, and, until recently, the Provisional Irish Republican Army (PIRA) vis-à-vis Great Britain.

Second, terrorism has appealed as a way to assert identity and command attention—rather like proclaiming, "I bomb, therefore I am." Terrorism enables a perpetrator to publicize his identity, project it explosively, and touch the nerves of powerful distant leaders. This kind of attraction to violence transcends its instrumental utility. Mainstream revolutionary writings may view violence as a means of struggle, but terrorists often regard violence as an end in itself that generates identity or damages the enemy's identity.

Third, terrorism has sometimes appealed as a way to achieve a new future order by willfully wrecking the present. This is manifest in the religious fervor of some radical Islamists, but examples also lie among millenarian and apocalyptic groups, like Aum Shinrikyo in Japan, who aim to wreak havoc and rend a system asunder so that something new may emerge from the cracks. The substance of the future vision may be only vaguely defined, but its moral worth is clear and appealing to the terrorist.

In the first and second of these motivations or rationales, terrorism may involve retaliation and retribution for past wrongs, whereas the third is also about revelation and rebirth, the coming of a new age. The first is largely strategic; it has a practical tone, and the objectives may be limited and specific. In contrast, the third may engage a transcendental, unconstrained view of how to change the world through terrorism.

Such contrasts do not mean the three are necessarily at odds; blends often occur. Presumptions of weakness (the first rationale) and of willfulness (in the second and third) can lead to peculiar synergies. For example, Aum's members may have known it was weak in a conventional sense, but they believed that they had special knowledge, a unique leader, invincible willpower, and secret ways to strike out.

These classic motivations or rationales will endure in the information age. However, terrorism is not a fixed phenomenon; its perpetrators adapt it to suit their times and situations. What changes is the conduct of terrorism—the operational characteristics built around the motivations and rationales.

This [selection] addresses, often in a deliberately speculative manner, changes in organization, doctrine, strategy, and technology that, taken together, speak to the emergence of a "new terrorism" attuned to the information age. Our principal hypotheses are as follows:

- **Organization.** Terrorists will continue moving from hierarchical toward information-age network designs. Within groups, "great man" leaderships will give way to flatter decentralized designs. More effort will go into building arrays of transnationally internetted groups than into building stand-alone groups.
- **Doctrine and strategy.** Terrorists will likely gain new capabilities for lethal acts. Some terrorist groups are likely to move to a "war paradigm" that focuses on attacking U.S. military forces and assets. But where terrorists suppose that

"information operations" may be as useful as traditional commando-style operations for achieving their goals, systemic *disruption* may become as much an objective as target *destruction*. Difficulties in coping with the new terrorism will mount if terrorists move beyond isolated acts toward a new approach to doctrine and strategy that emphasizes campaigns based on swarming.

- **Technology.** Terrorists are likely to increasingly use advanced information technologies for offensive and defensive purposes, as well as to support their organizational structures. Despite widespread speculation about terrorists using cyberspace warfare techniques to take "the Net" down, they may often have stronger reasons for wanting to keep it up (e.g., to spread their message and communicate with one another).

In short, terrorism is evolving in a direction we call *netwar*. Thus, after briefly reviewing terrorist trends, we outline the concept of netwar and its relevance for understanding information-age terrorism. In particular, we elaborate on the above points about organization, doctrine, and strategy, and briefly discuss how recent developments in the nature and behavior of Middle Eastern terrorist groups can be interpreted as early signs of a move toward netwar-type terrorism.

Given the prospect of a netwar-oriented shift in which some terrorists pursue a war paradigm, we then focus on the implications such a development may have for the U.S. military. We use these insights to consider defensive antiterrorist measures, as well as proactive counterterrorist strategies. We propose that a key to coping with information-age terrorism will be the creation of interorganizational networks within the U.S. military and government, partly on the grounds that it takes networks to fight networks.

## Recent Views About Terrorism

Terrorism remains a distinct phenomenon while reflecting broader trends in irregular warfare. The latter has been on the rise around the world since before the end of the Cold War. Ethnic and religious conflicts, recently in evidence in areas of Africa, the Balkans, and the Caucasus, for awhile in Central America, and seemingly forever in the Middle East, attest to the brutality that increasingly attends this kind of warfare. These are not conflicts between regular, professional armed forces dedicated to warrior creeds and Geneva Conventions. Instead, even where regular forces play roles, these conflicts often revolve around the strategies and tactics of thuggish paramilitary gangs and local warlords. Some leaders may have some professional training; but the foot soldiers are often people who, for one reason or another, get caught in a fray and learn on the job. Adolescents and children with high-powered weaponry are taking part in growing numbers. In many of these conflicts, savage acts are increasingly committed without anyone taking credit—it may not even be clear which side is responsible. The press releases of the protagonists sound high-minded and self-legitimizing, but the reality at the local level is often about clan rivalries and criminal ventures (e.g., looting, smuggling, or protection rackets).[1]

Thus, irregular warfare has become endemic and vicious around the world. A decade or so ago, terrorism was a rather distinct entry on the spectrum of conflict, with its own unique attributes. Today, it seems increasingly connected with these broader trends in irregular warfare, especially as waged by nonstate actors. As Martin Van Creveld warns:

> In today's world, the main threat to many states, including specifically the U.S., no longer comes from other states. Instead, it comes from small groups and other organizations which are not states. Either we make the necessary changes and face them today, or what is commonly known as the modern world will lose all sense of security and will dwell in perpetual fear.[2]

Meanwhile, for the past several years, terrorism experts have broadly concurred that this phenomenon will persist, if not get worse. General agreement that terrorism may worsen parses into different scenarios. For example, Walter Laqueur warns that religious motivations could lead to "superviolence," with millenarian visions of a coming apocalypse driving "postmodern" terrorism. Fred Iklé worries that increased violence may be used by terrorists to usher in a new totalitarian age based on Leninist ideals. Bruce Hoffman raises the prospect that religiously-motivated terrorists may escalate their violence in order to wreak sufficient havoc to undermine the world political system and replace it with a chaos that is particularly detrimental to the United States—a basically nihilist strategy.[3]

The preponderance of U.S. conventional power may continue to motivate some state and nonstate adversaries to opt for terror as an asymmetric response. Technological advances and underground trafficking may make weapons of mass destruction (WMD—nuclear, chemical, biological weapons) ever easier for terrorists to acquire.[4] Terrorists' shifts toward looser, less hierarchical organizational structures, and their growing use of advanced communications technologies for command, control, and coordination, may further empower small terrorist groups and individuals who want to mount operations from a distance.

There is also agreement about an emergence of two tiers of terror: one characterized by hard-core professionals, the other by amateur cut-outs.[5] The deniability gained by terrorists operating through willing amateurs, coupled with the increasing accessibility of ever more destructive weaponry, has also led many experts to concur that terrorists will be attracted to engaging in more lethal destruction, with increased targeting of information and communications infrastructures.[6]

Some specialists also suggest that "information" will become a key target—both the conduits of information infrastructures and the content of information, particularly the media.[7] While these target-sets may involve little lethal activity, they offer additional theaters of operations for terrorists. Laqueur in particular foresees that, "If the new terrorism directs its energies toward information warfare, its destructive power will be exponentially greater than any it wielded in the past—greater even than it would be with biological and chemical weapons."[8] New planning and scenario-building is needed to help think through how to defend against this form of terrorism.[9]

Such dire predictions have galvanized a variety of responses, which range from urging the creation of international control regimes over the tools of terror (such as WMD materials and advanced encryption capabilities), to the use of coercive diplomacy against state sponsors of terror. Increasingly, the liberal use of military force against terrorists has also been recommended. Caleb Carr in particular espoused this theme, sparking a heated debate.[10] Today, many leading works on combating terrorism blend notions of control mechanisms, international regimes, and the use of force.[11]

Against this background, experts have begun to recognize the growing role of networks—of networked organizational designs and related doctrines, strategies, and technologies—among the practitioners of terrorism. The growth of these networks is related to the spread of advanced information technologies that allow dispersed groups, and individuals, to conspire and coordinate across considerable distances. Recent U.S. efforts to investigate and attack the bin Laden network (named for the central influence of Osama bin Laden) attest to this. The rise of networks is likely to reshape terrorism in the information age, and lead to the adoption of netwar—a kind of information-age conflict that will be waged principally by nonstate actors. Our contribution . . . is to present the concept of netwar and show how terrorism is being affected by it.

# The Advent of Netwar—Analytical Background[12]

The information revolution is altering the nature of conflict across the spectrum. Of the many reasons for this, we call attention to two in particular. First, the information revolution is favoring and strengthening network forms of organization, often giving them an advantage over hierarchical forms. The rise of networks means that power is migrating to nonstate actors, who are able to organize into sprawling multi-organizational networks (especially all-channel networks, in which every node is connected to every other node) more readily than can traditional, hierarchical, state actors. Nonstate-actor networks are thought to be more flexible and responsive than hierarchies in reacting to outside developments, and to be better than hierarchies at using information to improve decisionmaking.[13]

Second, as the information revolution deepens, conflicts will increasingly depend on information and communications matters. More than ever before, conflicts will revolve around "knowledge" and the use of "soft power."[14] Adversaries will emphasize "information operations" and "perception management"—that is, media-oriented measures that aim to attract rather than coerce, and that affect how secure a society, a military, or other actor feels about its knowledge of itself and of its adversaries. Psychological disruption may become as important a goal as physical destruction.

Thus, major transformations are coming in the nature of adversaries, in the type of threats they may pose, and in how conflicts can be waged. Information-age threats are likely to be more diffuse, dispersed, multidimensional, and ambiguous than more traditional threats. Metaphorically, future conflicts may resemble the Oriental game of *Go* more than the Western game of chess. The conflict spectrum will be molded from end to end by these dynamics:

- *Cyberwar*—a concept that refers to information-oriented military warfare—is becoming an important entry at the military end of the spectrum, where the language has normally been about high-intensity conflicts (HICs).
- *Netwar* figures increasingly at the societal end of the spectrum, where the language has normally been about low-intensity conflict (LIC), operations other than war (OOTW), and nonmilitary modes of conflict and crime.[15]

Whereas cyberwar usually pits formal military forces against each other, netwar is more likely to involve nonstate, paramilitary, and irregular forces—as in the case of terrorism. Both concepts are consistent with the views of analysts such as Van Creveld, who believe that a "transformation of war" is under way.[16] Neither concept is just about technology; both refer to comprehensive approaches to conflict—comprehensive in that they mix organizational, doctrinal, strategic, tactical, and technological innovations, for offense and defense.

## Definition of Netwar

To be more precise, netwar refers to an emerging mode of conflict and crime at societal levels, involving measures short of traditional war, in which the protagonists use network forms of organization and related doctrines, strategies, and technologies attuned to the information age. These protagonists are likely to consist of dispersed small groups who communicate, coordinate, and conduct their campaigns in an internetted manner, without a precise central command. Thus, information-age netwar differs from modes of conflict and crime in which the protagonists prefer formal, stand-alone, hierarchical organizations, doctrines, and strategies, as in past efforts, for example, to build centralized movements along Marxist lines.

The term is meant to call attention to the prospect that network-based conflict and crime will become major phenomena in the decades ahead. Various actors across the spectrum of conflict and crime are already evolving in this direction. To give a string of examples, netwar is about the Middle East's Hamas more than the Palestine Liberation Organization (PLO), Mexico's Zapatistas more than Cuba's Fidelistas, and the American Christian Patriot movement more than the Ku Klux Klan. It is also about the Asian Triads more than the Sicilian Mafia, and Chicago's Gangsta Disciples more than the Al Capone Gang.

This spectrum includes familiar adversaries who are modifying their structures and strategies to take advantage of networked designs, such as transnational terrorist groups, black-market proliferators of WMD, transnational crime syndicates, fundamentalist and ethno-nationalist movements, intellectual property and high-sea pirates, and smugglers of black-market goods or migrants. Some urban gangs, back-country militias, and militant single-issue groups in the United States are also developing netwar-like attributes. In addition, there is a new generation of radicals and activists who are just beginning to create information-age ideologies, in which identities and loyalties may shift from the nation-state to the transnational level of global civil society. New kinds of actors, such as anarchistic and nihilistic leagues of computer-hacking "cyboteurs," may also partake of netwar.

Many—if not most—netwar actors will be nonstate. Some may be agents of a state, but others may try to turn states into *their* agents. Moreover, a netwar actor may be both subnational and transnational in scope. Odd hybrids and symbioses are likely. Furthermore, some actors (e.g., violent terrorist and criminal organizations) may threaten U.S. and other nations' interests, but other netwar actors (e.g., peaceful social activists) may not. Some may aim at destruction, others at disruption. Again, many variations are possible.

The full spectrum of netwar proponents may thus seem broad and odd at first glance. But there is an underlying pattern that cuts across all variations: the use of network forms of organization, doctrine, strategy, and technology attuned to the information age.

## More About Organizational Design

The notion of an organizational structure qualitatively different from traditional hierarchical designs is not recent; for example, in the early 1960s Burns and Stalker referred to the organic form as "a network structure of control, authority, and communication," with "lateral rather than vertical direction of communication." In organic structure,[17]

> omniscience [is] no longer imputed to the head of the concern; knowledge about the technical or commercial nature of the here and now task may be located anywhere in the network; [with] this location becoming the ad hoc centre of control authority and communication.

In the business world, virtual or networked organizations are being heralded as effective alternatives to bureaucracies—as in the case of Eastman Chemical Company and the Shell-Sarnia Plant—because of their inherent flexibility, adaptiveness, and ability to capitalize on the talents of all members of the organization.[18]

What has long been emerging in the business world is now becoming apparent in the organizational structures of netwar actors. In an archetypal netwar, the protagonists are likely to amount to a set of diverse, dispersed "nodes" who share a set of ideas and interests and who are arrayed to act in a fully internetted "all-channel" manner. Networks come in basically three types (or topologies) (see Figure 1):[19]

- The *chain* network, as in a smuggling chain where people, goods, or information move along a line of separated contacts, and where end-to-end communication must travel through the intermediate nodes.
- The *star*, hub, or wheel network, as in a franchise or a cartel structure where a set of actors is tied to a central node or actor, and must go through that node to communicate and coordinate.
- The *all-channel network*, as in a collaborative network of militant small groups where every group is connected to every other.

Each node in the diagrams of Figure 1 may be to an individual, a group, an institution, part of a group or institution, or even a state. The nodes may be large or small, tightly or loosely coupled, and inclusive or exclusive in membership. They may be segmentary or specialized—that is, they may look alike and engage in similar activities, or they may undertake a division of labor based on specialization. The boundaries of the network may be well defined, or blurred and porous in relation to the outside environment. All such variations are possible.

Each type may be suited to different conditions and purposes, and all three may be found among netwar-related adversaries—e.g., the chain in smuggling operations, the star at the core of terrorist and criminal syndicates, and the all-channel type among militant groups that are highly internetted and decentralized. There may also be hybrids. For example, a netwar actor may have an all-channel council at its core, but use stars and chains for tactical operations. There may also be hybrids of network and hierarchical forms of organization, and hierarchies may exist inside particular nodes in a network. Some actors may have a hierarchical organization overall, but use networks for tactical operations; other actors may have an all-channel network design, but use hierarchical teams for tactical operations. Again, many configurations are possible, and it may be difficult for an analyst to discern exactly what type of networking characterizes a particular actor.

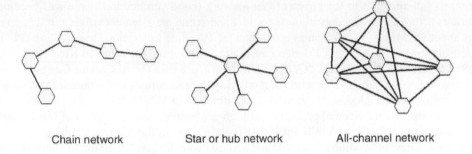

Chain network      Star or hub network      All-channel network

**Figure 1**

Of the three network types, the all-channel has been the most difficult to organize and sustain historically, partly because it may require dense communications. However, it gives the network form the most potential for collaborative undertakings, and it is the type that is gaining strength from the information revolution. Pictorially, an all-channel netwar actor resembles a geodesic "Bucky ball" (named for Buckminster Fuller); it does not resemble a pyramid. The design is flat. Ideally, there is no single, central leadership, command, or headquarters—no precise heart or head that can be targeted. The network as a whole (but not necessarily each node) has little to no hierarchy, and there may be multiple leaders. Decision-making and operations are decentralized, allowing for local initiative and autonomy. Thus the design may sometimes appear acephalous (headless), and at other times polycephalous (Hydra-headed).[20]

The capacity of this design for effective performance over time may depend on the presence of shared principles, interests, and goals—at best, an overarching doctrine or ideology—that spans all nodes and to which the members wholeheartedly subscribe. Such a set of principles, shaped through mutual consultation and consensus-building, can enable them to be "all of one mind," even though they are dispersed and devoted to different tasks. It can provide a central ideational, strategic, and operational coherence that allows for tactical decentralization. It can set boundaries and provide guidelines for decisions and actions so that the members do not have to resort to a hierarchy—"they know what they have to do."[21]

The network design may depend on having an infrastructure for the dense communication of functional information. All nodes are not necessarily in constant communication, which may not make sense for a secretive, conspiratorial actor. But when communication is needed, the network's members must be able to disseminate information promptly and as broadly as desired within the network and to outside audiences.

In many respects, then, the archetypal netwar design corresponds to what earlier analysts called a "segmented, polycentric, ideologically integrated network" (SPIN):[22]

> By segmentary I mean that it is cellular, composed of many different groups. . . . By polycentric I mean that it has many different leaders or centers of direction. . . . By networked I mean that the segments and the leaders are integrated into reticulated systems or networks through various structural, personal, and ideological ties. Networks are usually unbounded and expanding. . . . This acronym [SPIN] helps us picture this organization as a fluid, dynamic, expanding one, spinning out into mainstream society.

## Caveats About the Role of Technology

To realize its potential, a fully interconnected network requires a capacity for constant, dense information and communications flows, more so than do other forms of organization (e.g., hierarchies). This capacity is afforded by the latest information and communications technologies—cellular telephones, fax machines, electronic mail (e-mail), World Wide Web (WWW) sites, and computer conferencing. Moreover, netwar agents are poised to benefit from future increases in the speed of communication, dramatic reductions in the costs of communication, increases in bandwidth, vastly expanded connectivity, and integration of communication with computing technologies.[23] Such technologies are highly advantageous for a netwar actor whose constituents are geographically dispersed.

However, caveats are in order. First, the new technologies, however enabling for organizational networking, may not be the only crucial technologies for a netwar actor. Old means of communications such as human couriers, and mixes of old and new systems, may suffice. Second, netwar is not simply a function of the Internet; it does not take place only in cyberspace or the infosphere. Some key battles may occur there, but a war's overall conduct and outcome will normally depend mostly on what happens in the real world. Even in information-age conflicts, what happens in the real world is generally more important than what happens in the virtual worlds of cyberspace or the infosphere.[24] Netwar is not Internet war.

## Swarming, and the Blurring of Offense and Defense

This distinctive, often ad-hoc design has unusual strengths, for both offense and defense. On the offense, networks are known for being adaptable, flexible, and versatile vis-à-vis opportunities and challenges. This may be particularly the case where a set of actors can engage in *swarming*. Little analytic attention has been given to swarming, yet it may be a key mode of conflict in the information age. The cutting edge for this possibility is found among netwar protagonists.[25]

Swarming occurs when the dispersed nodes of a network of small (and perhaps some large) forces converge on a target from multiple directions. The overall aim is the *sustainable pulsing* of force or fire. Once in motion, swarm networks must be able to coalesce rapidly and stealthily on a target, then dissever and redisperse, immediately ready to recombine for a new pulse. In other words, information-age attacks may come in "swarms" rather than the more traditional "waves."

In terms of defensive potential, well-constructed networks tend to be redundant and diverse, making them robust and resilient in the face of adversity. Where they have a capacity for interoperability and shun centralized command and control, network designs can be difficult to crack and defeat as a whole. In particular, they may defy counterleadership targeting—attackers can find and confront only portions of the network. Moreover, the deniability built into a network may allow it to simply absorb a number of attacks on distributed nodes, leading the attacker to believe the network has been harmed when, in fact, it remains viable, and is seeking new opportunities for tactical surprise.

The difficulties of dealing with netwar actors deepen when the lines between offense and defense are blurred, or blended. When *blurring* is the case, it may be difficult to distinguish between attacking and defending actions, particularly when an actor goes on the offense in the name of self-defense. The *blending* of offense and defense will often mix the strategic and tactical levels of operations. For example, guerrillas on the defensive strategically may go on the offense tactically; the war of the *mujahideen* in Afghanistan provides a modern example.

The blurring of offense and defense reflects another feature of netwar: it tends to defy and cut across standard boundaries, jurisdictions, and distinctions between state and society, public and private, war and peace, war and crime, civilian and military, police and military, and legal and illegal. A government has difficulty assigning responsibility to a single agency—military, police, or intelligence—to respond.

Thus, the spread of netwar adds to the challenges facing the nation-state in the information age. Nation-state ideals of sovereignty and authority are traditionally linked to a bureaucratic rationality in which issues and problems can be neatly divided, and specific offices can be charged with taking care of specific problems. In netwar, things are rarely so clear. A protagonist is likely to operate in the cracks and gray areas of society, striking where lines of authority crisscross and the operational paradigms of politicians, officials, soldiers, police officers, and related actors get fuzzy and clash.

## Networks Versus Hierarchies: Challenges for Counternetwar

Against this background, we are led to a set of three policy-oriented propositions about the information revolution and its implications for netwar and counternetwar.[26]

### Hierarchies have a difficult time fighting networks

There are examples across the conflict spectrum. Some of the best are found in the failings of governments to defeat transnational criminal cartels engaged in drug smuggling, as in Colombia. The persistence of religious revivalist movements, as in Algeria, in the face of unremitting state opposition, shows the robustness of the network form. The Zapatista movement in Mexico, with its legions of supporters and sympathizers among local and transnational nongovernmental organizations (NGOs), shows that social netwar can put a democratizing autocracy on the defensive and pressure it to continue adopting reforms.

### It takes networks to fight networks

Governments that would defend against netwar may have to adopt organizational designs and strategies like those of their adversaries. This does not mean mirroring the adversary, but rather learning to draw on the same design principles of network forms in the information age. These principles depend to some extent upon technological innovation, but mainly on a willingness to innovate organizationally and doctrinally, and by building new mechanisms for interagency and multijurisdictional cooperation.

### Whoever masters the network form first and best will gain major advantages

In these early decades of the information age, adversaries who have adopted networking (be they criminals, terrorists, or peaceful social activists) are enjoying an increase in their power relative to state agencies.

Counternetwar may thus require effective interagency approaches, which by their nature involve networked structures. The challenge will be to blend hierarchies and networks skillfully, while retaining enough core authority to encourage and enforce adherence to networked processes. By creating effective hybrids, governments may better confront the new threats and challenges emerging in the information age, whether generated by terrorists, militias, criminals, or other actors.[27] The U.S. Counterterrorist Center, based at the Central Intelligence Agency (CIA), is a good example of a promising effort to establish a functional interagency network,[28] although its success may depend increasingly on the strength of links with the military services and other institutions that fall outside the realm of the intelligence community.

# Middle Eastern Terrorism and Netwar

Terrorism seems to be evolving in the direction of violent netwar. Islamic fundamentalist organizations like Hamas and the bin Laden network consist of groups organized in loosely interconnected, semi-independent cells that have no single commanding hierarchy.[29] Hamas exemplifies the shift away from a hierarchically oriented movement based on a "great leader" (like the PLO and Yasser Arafat).[30]

The netwar concept is consistent with patterns and trends in the Middle East, where the newer and more active terrorist groups appear to be adopting decentralized, flexible network structures. The rise of networked arrangements in terrorist organizations is part of a wider move away from formally organized, state-sponsored groups to privately financed, loose networks of individuals and subgroups that may have strategic guidance but enjoy tactical independence. Related to these shifts is the fact that terrorist groups are taking advantage of information technology to coordinate the activities of dispersed members. Such technology may be employed by terrorists not only to wage information warfare [IW], but also to support their own networked organizations.[31]

While a comprehensive empirical analysis of the relationship between (a) the structure of terrorist organizations and (b) group activity or strength is beyond the scope of this paper,[32] a cursory examination of such a relationship among Middle Eastern groups offers some evidence to support the claim that terrorists are preparing to wage netwar. The Middle East was selected for analysis mainly because terrorist groups based in this region have been active in targeting U.S. government facilities and interests, as in the bombings of the Khobar Towers, and . . . , the American embassies in Kenya and Tanzania.

## Middle Eastern Terrorist Groups: Structure and Actions

Terrorist groups in the Middle East have diverse origins, ideologies, and organizational structures, but can be roughly categorized into traditional and new-generation groups. Traditional groups date back to the late 1960s and early 1970s, and the majority of these were (and some still are) formally or informally linked to the PLO. Typically, they are also relatively bureaucratic and maintain a nationalist or Marxist agenda. In contrast, most new-generation groups arose in the 1980s and 1990s, have more fluid organizational forms, and rely on Islam as a basis for their radical ideology.

The traditional, more-bureaucratic groups have survived to this day partly through support from states such as Syria, Libya, and Iran. The groups retain an ability to train and prepare for terrorist missions; however, their involvement in actual operations has been limited in recent years, partly because of successful counterterrorism campaigns by Israeli and Western agencies. In contrast, the newer and less hierarchical groups, such as Hamas, the Palestinian Islamic Jihad (PIJ), Hizbullah, Algeria's Armed Islamic Group (GIA), the Egyptian Islamic Group (IG), and Osama bin Laden's Arab Afghans, have become the most active organizations in and around the Middle East.

### The traditional groups

Traditional terrorist groups in the Middle East include the Abu Nidal Organization (ANO), the Popular Front for the Liberation of Palestine (PFLP), and three PFLP-related splinters—the PFLP-General Command (PFLP-GC), the Palestine Liberation Front (PLF), and the Democratic Front for the Liberation of Palestine (DFLP).

The ANO was an integral part of the PLO until it became independent in 1974. It has a bureaucratic structure composed of various functional committees.[33] The activism it displayed in the 1970s and 1980s has lessened considerably, owing to a lessening of support from state sponsors and to effective counterterrorist campaigns by Israeli and Western intelligence services. 34 The very existence of the organization has recently been put into question, given uncertainty as to the whereabouts and fate of Abu Nidal, the leader of the group.[35]

The PFLP was founded in 1967 by George Habash as a PLO-affiliated organization. It has traditionally embraced a Marxist ideology, and remains an important PLO faction. However, in recent years it has suffered considerable losses from Israeli counter-terrorist strikes.[36] The PFLP-General Command split from the PFLP in 1968, and in turn experienced a schism in the mid-1970s. This splinter group, which called itself the PLF, is composed of three subgroups, and has not been involved in high-profile acts since the 1985 hijacking of the Italian cruise ship *Achille Lauro*.[37] The PFLP was subjected to another split in 1969, which resulted in the Democratic Front for the Liberation of Palestine. The DFLP resembles a small army more than a terrorist group—its operatives are organized in battalions, backed by intelligence and special forces.[38] DFLP strikes have become less frequent since the 1970s, and since the late 1980s it has limited its attacks to Israeli targets near borders.[39]

What seems evident here is that this old generation of traditional, hierarchical, bureaucratic groups is on the wane. The reasons are varied, but the point remains—their way of waging terrorism is not likely to make a comeback, and is being superseded by a new way that is more attuned to the organizational, doctrinal, and technological imperatives of the information age.

## The most active groups and their organization

The new generation of Middle Eastern groups has been active both in and outside the region in recent years. In Israel and the occupied territories, Hamas, and to a lesser extent the Palestinian Islamic Jihad, have shown their strength over the last four years with a series of suicide bombings that have killed more than one hundred people and injured several more.[40] Exploiting a strong presence in Lebanon, the Shi'ite Hizbullah organization has also staged a number of attacks against Israeli Defense Forces troops and Israeli cities in Galilee.[41]

The al-Gama'a al-Islamiya, or Islamic Group (IG), is the most active Islamic extremist group in Egypt. In November 1997 IG carried out an attack on Hatshepsut's Temple in Luxor, killing 58 tourists and 4 Egyptians. The Group has also claimed responsibility for the bombing of the Egyptian embassy in Islamabad, Pakistan, which left 16 dead and 60 injured.[42] In Algeria, the Armed Islamic Group (GIA) has been behind the most violent, lethal attacks in Algeria's protracted civil war. Approximately 70,000 Algerians have lost their lives since the domestic terrorist campaign began in 1992.[43]

Recently, the loosely organized group of Arab Afghans—radical Islamic fighters from several North African and Middle Eastern countries who forged ties while resisting the Soviet occupation of Afghanistan[44]—has come to the fore as an active terrorist outfit. One of the leaders and founders of the Arab Afghan movement, Osama bin Laden, a Saudi entrepreneur who bases his activities in Afghanistan,[45] is suspected of sending operatives to Yemen to bomb a hotel used by U.S. soldiers on their way to Somalia in 1992, plotting to assassinate President Clinton in the Philippines in 1994 and Egyptian President Hosni Mubarak in 1995, and of having a role in the Riyadh and Khobar blasts in Saudi Arabia that resulted in the deaths of 24 Americans in 1995 and 1996.[46] U.S. officials have pointed to bin Laden as the mastermind behind the U.S. embassy bombings in Kenya and Tanzania, which claimed the lives of more than 260 people, including 12 Americans.[47]

To varying degrees, these groups share the principles of the net-worked organization—relatively flat hierarchies, decentralization and delegation of decisionmaking authority, and loose lateral ties among dispersed groups and individuals.[48] For instance, Hamas is loosely structured, with some elements working openly through mosques and social service institutions to recruit members, raise funds, organize activities, and distribute propaganda. Palestinian security sources indicate that there are ten or more Hamas splinter groups and factions with no centralized operational leadership.[49] The Palestine Islamic Jihad is a series of loosely affiliated factions, rather than a cohesive group.[50] The pro-Iranian Hizbullah acts as an umbrella organization of radical Shiite groups, and in many respects is a hybrid of hierarchical and network arrangements; although the formal structure is highly bureaucratic, interactions among members are volatile and do not follow rigid lines of control.[51] According to the U.S. Department of State, Egypt's Islamic Group is a decentralized organization that operates without a single operational leader,[52] while the GIA is notorious for the lack of centralized authority.[53]

Unlike traditional terrorist organizations, Arab Afghans are part of a complex network of relatively autonomous groups that are financed from private sources forming "a kind of international terrorists' Internet."[54] The most notorious element of the network is Osama bin Laden, who uses his wealth and organizational skills to support and direct a multinational alliance of Islamic extremists. At the heart of this alliance is his own inner core group, known as Al-Qaeda ("The Base"), which sometimes conducts missions on its own, but more often in conjunction with other groups or elements in the alliance. The goal of the alliance is opposition on a global scale to perceived threats to Islam, as indicated by bin Laden's 1996 declaration of a holy war against the United States and the West. In the document, bin Laden specifies that such a holy war will be fought by irregular, light, highly mobile forces using guerrilla tactics.[55]

Even though bin Laden finances Arab Afghan activities and directs some operations, he apparently does not play a direct command and control role over all operatives. Rather, he is a key figure in the coordination and support of several dispersed activities.[56] For instance, bin Laden founded the "World Islamic Front for Jihad Against Jews and Crusaders."[57] And yet most of the groups that participate in this front (including Egypt's Islamic Group) remain independent, although the organizational barriers between them are fluid.[58]

From a netwar perspective, an interesting feature of bin Laden's Arab Afghan movement is its ability to relocate operations swiftly from one geographic area to another in response to changing circumstances and needs. Arab Afghans have participated in operations conducted by Algeria's GIA and Egypt's IG. Reports in 1997 also indicated that Arab Afghans transferred training operations to Somalia, where they joined the Islamic Liberation Party (ILP).[59] The same reports suggest that the Arab Afghan movement has considered sending fighters to Sinkiang Uighur province in western China, to wage a holy war against the Chinese regime.[60] This group's ability to move and act quickly (and, to some extent, to swarm) once opportunities emerge hampers counterterrorist efforts to predict its actions and monitor its activities. The fact that Arab Afghan operatives were able to strike the U.S. embassies in Kenya and Tanzania substantiates the claim that members of this network have the mobility and speed to operate over considerable distances.

Although the organizational arrangements in these groups do not match all the basic features of the network ideal,[61] they stand in contrast to more traditional groups. Another feature that distinguishes the newer generation of terrorist groups is their adoption of information technology.

## Middle Eastern Terrorist Groups and the Use of Information Technology

Information technology (IT) is an enabling factor for networked groups; terrorists aiming to wage netwar may adopt it not only as a weapon, but also to help coordinate and support their activities. Before exploring how Middle Eastern terrorist groups have embraced the new technology, we posit three hypotheses that relate the rise of IT to organization for netwar:

- The greater the degree of organizational networking in a terrorist group, the higher the likelihood that IT is used to support the network's decisionmaking.
- Recent advances in IT facilitate networked terrorist organizations because information flows are becoming quicker, cheaper, more secure, and more versatile.
- As terrorist groups learn to use IT for decisionmaking and other organizational purposes, they will be likely to use the same technology as an offensive weapon to destroy or disrupt.

Middle Eastern terrorist groups provide examples of information technology being used for a wide variety of purposes. As discussed below, there is some evidence to support the claim that the most active groups—and therefore the most decentralized groups—have embraced information technology to coordinate activities and disseminate propaganda and ideology.[62] At the same time, the technical assets and know-how gained by terrorist groups as they seek to form into multi-organizational networks can be used for offensive purposes—an Internet connection can be used for both coordination and disruption. The anecdotes provided here are consistent with the rise in the Middle East of what has been termed *techno-terrorism,* or the use by terrorists of satellite communications, e-mail, and the World Wide Web.[63]

Arab Afghans appear to have widely adopted information technology. According to reporters who visited bin Laden's headquarters in a remote mountainous area of Afghanistan, the terrorist financier has computers, communications equipment, and a large number of disks for data storage.[64] Egyptian "Afghan" computer experts are said to have helped devise a communication network that relies on the World Wide Web, e-mail, and electronic bulletin boards so that the extremists can exchange information without running a major risk of being intercepted by counterterrorism officials.[65]

Hamas is another major group that uses the Internet to share operational information. Hamas activists in the United States use chat rooms to plan operations and activities.[66] Operatives use e-mail to coordinate activities across Gaza, the West Bank, and Lebanon. Hamas has realized that information can be passed securely over the Internet because it is next to impossible for counterterrorism intelligence to monitor accurately the flow and content of Internet traffic. Israeli security officials have difficulty in tracing Hamas messages and decoding their content.[67]

During a recent counterterrorist operation, several GIA bases in Italy were uncovered, and each was found to include computers and diskettes with instructions for the construction of bombs.[68] It has been reported that the GIA uses floppy disks and computers to store and process instructions and other information for its members, who are dispersed in Algeria and Europe.[69] Furthermore, the Internet is used as a propaganda tool by Hizbullah, which manages three World Wide Web sites—one for the central press office (at www .hizbollah.org ), another to describe its attacks on Israeli targets (at www.moqawama.org), and the last for news and information (at www.almanar.com.lb).[70]

The presence of Middle Eastern terrorist organizations on the Internet is suspected in the case of the Islamic Gateway, a World Wide Web site that contains information on a number of Islamic activist organizations based in the United Kingdom. British Islamic activists use the World Wide Web to broadcast their news and attract funding; they are also turning to the Internet as an organizational and communication tool.[71] While the vast majority of Islamic activist groups represented in the Islamic Gateway are legitimate, one group—the Global Jihad Fund—makes no secret of its militant goals.[72] The appeal of the Islamic Gateway for militant groups may be enhanced by a representative's claim, in an Internet Newsnet article in August 1996, that the Gateway's Internet Service Provider (ISP) can give "CIA-proof" protection against electronic surveillance.[73]

## Summary Comment

This review of patterns and trends in the Middle East substantiates our speculations that the new terrorism is evolving in the direction of netwar, along the following lines:[74]

- An increasing number of terrorist groups are adopting networked forms of organization and relying on information technology to support such structures.
- Newer groups (those established in the 1980s and 1990s) are more networked than traditional groups.
- A positive correlation is emerging between the degree of activity of a group and the degree to which it adopts a networked structure.[75]

- Information technology is as likely to be used for organizational support as for offensive warfare.
- The likelihood that young recruits will be familiar with information technology implies that terrorist groups will be increasingly networked and more computer-friendly in the future than they are today.

# Terrorist Doctrines—The Rise of a "War Paradigm"

The evolution of terrorism in the direction of netwar will create new difficulties for counter-terrorism. The types of challenges, and their severity, will depend on the kinds of doctrines that terrorists develop and employ. Some doctrinal effects will occur at the operational level, as in the relative emphasis placed on disruptive information operations as distinct from destructive combat operations. However, at a deeper level, the direction in which terrorist netwar evolves will depend upon the choices terrorists make as to the overall doctrinal paradigms that shape their goals and strategies.

At least three terrorist paradigms are worth considering: terror as coercive diplomacy, terror as war, and terror as the harbinger of a "new world." These three engage, in varying ways, distinct rationales for terrorism—as a weapon of the weak, as a way to assert identity, and as a way to break through to a new world—discussed earlier in this [selection]. While there has been much debate about the overall success or failure of terrorism,[76] the paradigm under which a terrorist operates may have a great deal to do with the likelihood of success. Coercion, for example, implies distinctive threats or uses of force, whereas norms of "war" often imply maximizing destruction.

## The Coercive-Diplomacy Paradigm

The first paradigm is that of coercive diplomacy. From its earliest days, terrorism has often sought to persuade others, by means of symbolic violence, either to do something, stop doing something, or undo what has been done. These are the basic forms of coercive diplomacy,[77] and they appear in terrorism as far back as the Jewish Sicarii Zealots who sought independence from Rome in the first century AD, up through the Palestinians' often violent acts in pursuit of their independence today.

The fact that terrorist coercion includes violent acts does not make it a form of war—the violence is exemplary, designed to encourage what Alexander George calls "forceful persuasion," or "coercive diplomacy as an alternative to war."[78] In this light, terrorism may be viewed as designed to achieve specific goals, and the level of violence is limited, or proportional, to the ends being pursued. Under this paradigm, terrorism was once thought to lack a "demand" for WMD, as such tools would provide means vastly disproportionate to the ends of terror. This view was first elucidated over twenty years ago by Brian Jenkins— though there was some dissent expressed by scholars such as Thomas Schelling—and continued to hold sway until a few years ago.[79]

## The War Paradigm

Caleb Carr, surveying the history of the failures of coercive terrorism and the recent trends toward increasing destructiveness and deniability, has elucidated what we call a "war paradigm."[80] This paradigm, which builds on ideas first considered by Jenkins,[81] holds that terrorist acts arise when weaker parties cannot challenge an adversary directly and thus turn to asymmetric methods. A war paradigm implies taking a strategic, campaign-oriented view of violence that makes no specific call for concessions from, or other demands upon, the opponent. Instead, the strategic aim is to inflict damage, in the context of what the terrorists view as an ongoing war. In theory, this paradigm, unlike the coercive diplomacy one, does not seek a proportional relationship between the level of force employed and the aims sought. When the goal is to inflict damage generally, and the terrorist group has no desire or need to claim credit, there is an attenuation of the need for proportionality—the worse the damage, the better. Thus, the use of WMD can be far more easily contemplated than in a frame of reference governed by notions of coercive diplomacy.

A terrorist war paradigm may be undertaken by terrorists acting on their own behalf or in service to a nation-state. In the future, as the information age brings the further empowerment of nonstate and transnational actors, "stateless" versions of the terrorist war paradigm may spread. At the same time, however, states will remain important players in the war paradigm; they may cultivate their own terrorist-style commandos, or seek cut-outs and proxies from among nonstate terrorist groups.

Ambiguity regarding a sponsor's identity may prove a key element of the war paradigm. While the use of proxies provides an insulating layer between a state sponsor and its target, these proxies, if captured, may prove more susceptible to interrogation and investigative techniques designed to winkle out the identity of the sponsor. On the other hand, while home-grown commando-style terrorists may be less forthcoming with information if caught, their own identities, which may be hard to conceal, may provide undeniable evidence of state sponsorship. These risks for states who think about engaging in or supporting terrorism may provide yet more reason for the war paradigm to increasingly become the province of nonstate terrorists—or those with only the most tenuous linkages to particular states.

Exemplars of the war paradigm today are the wealthy Saudi jihadist, Osama bin Laden, and the Arab Afghans that he associates with. As previously mentioned, bin Laden has explicitly called for war-like terrorism against the United States, and especially against U.S. military forces stationed in Saudi Arabia. President Clinton's statement that American retaliation for the U.S. embassy bombings in East Africa represented the first shots in a protracted war on terrorism suggests that the notion of adopting a war paradigm to counter terror has gained currency.

## The New-World Paradigm

A third terrorist paradigm aims at achieving the birth of what might be called a "new world." It may be driven by religious mania, a desire for totalitarian control, or an impulse toward ultimate chaos.[82] Aum Shinrikyo would be a recent example. The paradigm harks back to the dynamics of millennialist movements that arose in past epochs of social upheaval, when *prophetae* attracted adherents from the margins of other social movements and led small groups to pursue salvation by seeking a final, violent cataclysm.[83]

This paradigm is likely to seek the vast disruption of political, social, and economic order. Accomplishing this goal may involve lethal destruction, even a heightened willingness to use WMD. Religious terrorists may desire destruction for its own sake, or for some form of "cleansing." But the ultimate aim is not so much the destruction of society as a rebirth after a period of chaotic disruption.

## The Paradigms and Netwar

All three paradigms offer room for netwar. Moreover, all three paradigms allow the rise of "cybotage"—acts of disruption and destruction against information infrastructures by terrorists who learn the skills of cyberterror, as well as by disaffected individuals with technical skills who are drawn into the terrorist milieu. However, we note that terrorist netwar may also be a battle of ideas—and to wage this form of conflict some terrorists may want the Net *up*, not down.

Many experts argue that terrorism is moving toward ever more lethal, destructive acts. Our netwar perspective accepts this, but also holds that some terrorist netwars will stress disruption over destruction. Networked terrorists will no doubt continue to destroy things and kill people, but their principal strategy may move toward the nonlethal end of the spectrum, where command and control nodes and vulnerable information infrastructures provide rich sets of targets.

Indeed, terrorism has long been about "information"—from the fact that trainees for suicide bombings are kept from listening to international media, through the ways that terrorists seek to create disasters that will consume the front pages, to the related debates about countermeasures that would limit freedom of the press, increase public surveillance and intelligence gathering, and heighten security over information and communications systems. Terrorist tactics focus attention on the importance of information and communications for the functioning of democratic institutions; debates about how terrorist threats undermine democratic practices may revolve around freedom of information issues.

While netwar may be waged by terrorist groups operating with any of the three paradigms, the rise of networked groups whose objective is to wage war may be the one most relevant to and dangerous from the standpoint of the military. Indeed, if terrorists perceive themselves as warriors, they may be inclined to target enemy military assets or interests. . . .

## [Conclusion] Targeting Terrorists in the Information Age

The transition from hierarchical to networked terrorist groups is likely to be uneven and gradual. The netwar perspective suggests that, for the foreseeable future, various networked forms will emerge, coexisting with and influencing traditional organizations. Such organizational diversity implies the need for a counterterrorism strategy that recognizes the differences among organizational designs and seeks to target the weaknesses associated with each.

Counterleadership strategies or retaliation directed at state sponsors may be effective for groups led by a charismatic leader who enjoys the backing of sympathetic governments, but are likely to fail if used against an organization with multiple, dispersed leaders and private sources of funding. Networked organizations rely on information flows to function, and disruption of the flows cripples their ability to coordinate actions. It is no coincidence, for instance, that while the separation between Hamas political and military branches is well documented, this terrorist group jealously guards information on the connections and degree of coordination between the two.[84]

At the same time, the two-way nature of connectivity for information networks such as the Internet implies that the dangers posed by information warfare are often symmetric—the degree to which a terrorist organization uses information infrastructure for offensive purposes may determine its exposure to similar attacks by countering forces. While it is true that terrorist organizations will often enjoy the benefit of surprise, the IW tactics available to them can also be adopted by counterterrorists.

The key task for counterterrorism, then, is the identification of organizational and technological terrorist networks. Once such structures are identified, it may be possible to insert and disseminate false information, overload systems, misdirect message traffic, preclude access, and engage in other destructive and disruptive activities to hamper and prevent terrorist operations.

# Notes

1. For an illuminating take on irregular warfare that emphasizes the challenges to the Red Cross, see Michael Ignatieff, "Unarmed Warriors," *The New Yorker*, March 24, 1997, pp. 56–71.

2. Martin Van Creveld, "In Wake of Terrorism, Modern Armies Prove to Be Dinosaurs of Defense," *New Perspectives Quarterly*, Vol. 13, No. 4, Fall 1996, p. 58.

3. See Walter Laqueur, "Postmodern Terrorism," *Foreign Affairs*, Vol. 75, No. 5, September/October 1996, pp. 24–36; Fred Iklé, "The Problem of the Next Lenin," *The National Interest*, Vol. 47, Spring 1997, pp. 9–19; Bruce Hoffman, *Responding to Terrorism Across the Technological Spectrum*, RAND, P-7874, 1994; Bruce Hoffman, Inside Terrorism, Columbia University Press, New York, 1998; Robert Kaplan, "The Coming Anarchy," *Atlantic Monthly*, February 1994, pp. 44–76.

4. See J. Kenneth Campbell, "Weapon of Mass Destruction Terrorism," Master's thesis, Naval Postgraduate School, Monterey, California, 1996.

5. Bruce Hoffman and Caleb Carr, "Terrorism: Who Is Fighting Whom?" *World Policy Journal*, Vol. 14, No. 1, Spring 1997, pp. 97–104.

6. For instance, Martin Shubik, "Terrorism, Technology, and the Socioeconomics of Death," *Comparative Strategy*, Vol. 16, No. 4, October–December 1997, pp. 399–414; as well as Hoffman, 1998.

7. See Matthew Littleton, "Information Age Terrorism," MA thesis, U.S. Naval Postgraduate School, 1995, and Brigitte Nacos, *Terrorism and the Media*, Columbia University Press, New York, 1994.

8. Laqueur, 1996, p. 35.

9. For more on this issue, see Roger Molander, Andrew Riddile, and Peter Wilson, *Strategic Information Warfare: A New Face of War*, RAND, MR-661-OSD, 1996; Roger Molander, Peter Wilson, David Mussington, and Richard Mesic, *Strategic Information Warfare Rising*, RAND, 1998.

10. Caleb Carr, "Terrorism as Warfare," *World Policy Journal*, Vol. 13, No. 4, Winter 1996–1997, pp. 1–12. This theme was advocated early by Gayle Rivers, *The War Against the Terrorists: How to Fight and Win, Stein and Day*, New York, 1986. For more on the debate, see Hoffman and Carr, 1997.

11. See, for instance, Benjamin Netanyahu, *Winning the War Against Terrorism*, Simon and Schuster, New York, 1996, and John Kerry (Senator), *The New War*, Simon & Schuster, New York, 1997.

12. This analytical background is drawn from John Arquilla and David Ronfeldt, *The Advent of Netwar*, RAND, MR-678-OSD, 1996, and David Ronfeldt, John Arquilla, Graham Fuller, and Melissa Fuller, *The Zapatista "Social Netwar" in Mexico*, RAND, MR-994-A, forthcoming. Also see John Arquilla and David Ronfeldt (eds.), *In Athena's Camp: Preparing for Conflict in the Information Age*, RAND, MR-880-OSD/RC, 1997.

13. For background on this issue, see Charles Heckscher, "Defining the Post-Bureaucratic Type," in Charles Heckscher and Anne Donnelon (eds.), *The Post-Bureaucratic Organization*, Sage, Thousand Oaks, California, 1995, pp. 50–52.

14. The concept of soft power was introduced by Joseph S. Nye in *Bound to Lead: The Changing Nature of American Power*, Basic Books, New York, 1990, and further elaborated in Joseph S. Nye and William A. Owens, "America's Information Edge," *Foreign Affairs*, Vol. 75, No. 2, March/April 1996.

15. For more on information-age conflict, netwar, and cyberwar, see John Arquilla and David Ronfeldt, "Cyberwar is Coming!" *Comparative Strategy*, Vol. 12, No. 2, Summer 1993, pp. 141–165, and Arquilla and Ronfeldt, 1996 and 1997.

16. Martin Van Creveld, *The Transformation of War*, Free Press, New York, 1991.

17. T. Burns and G. M. Stalker, *The Management of Innovation*, Tavistock, London, 1961, p. 121.

18. See, for instance, Jessica Lipnack and Jeffrey Stamps, *The Age of the Network*, Wiley & Sons, New York, 1994, pp. 51–78, and Heckscher, "Defining the Post-Bureaucratic Type," p. 45.

19. Adapted from William M. Evan, "An Organization-Set Model of Interorganizational Relations," in Matthew Tuite, Roger Chisholm, and Michael Radnor (eds.), *Interorganizational Decisionmaking*, Aldine Publishing Company, Chicago, 1972.

20. The structure may also be cellular, although the presence of cells does not necessarily mean a network exists. A hierarchy can also be cellular, as is the case with some subversive organizations. A key difference between cells and nodes is that the former are designed to minimize information flows for security reasons (usually only the head of the cell reports to the leadership), while nodes in principle can easily establish connections with other parts of the network (so that communications and coordination can occur horizontally).

21. The quotation is from a doctrinal statement by Louis Beam about "leaderless resistance," which has strongly influenced right-wing white-power groups in the United States. *See The Seditionist*, Issue 12, February 1992.

22. See Luther P. Gerlach, "Protest Movements and the Construction of Risk," in B. B. Johnson and V. T. Covello (eds.), *The Social and Cultural Construction of Risk*, D. Reidel Publishing Co., Boston, Massachusetts, 1987, p. 115, based on Luther P. Gerlach and Virginia Hine, *People, Power, Change: Movements of Social Transformation*, The Bobbs-Merrill Co., New York, 1970. This SPIN concept, a precursor of the netwar concept, was proposed by Luther Gerlach and Virginia Hine in the 1960s to depict U.S. social movements. It anticipates many points about network forms of organization that are now coming into focus in the analysis not only of social movements but also some terrorist, criminal, ethno-nationalist, and fundamentalist organizations.

23. See Wolf V. Heydenbrand, "New Organizational Forms," *Work and Occupations*, No. 3, Vol. 16, August 1989, pp. 323–357.

24. See Paul Kneisel, "Netwar: The Battle Over Rec.Music.White-Power," *ANTIFA INFOBULLETIN*, Research Supplement, June 12, 1996, unpaginated ASCII text available on the Internet. Kneisel analyzes the largest vote ever taken about the creation of a new Usenet newsgroup—a vote to prevent the creation of a group that was ostensibly about white-power music. He concludes that "The *war* against contemporary fascism will be won in the 'real world' off the net; but *battles* against fascist netwar are fought and won on the Internet." His title is testimony to the spreading usage of the term netwar.

25. Swarm networks are discussed by Kevin Kelly, *Out of Control: The Rise of Neo-Biological Civilization*, A William Patrick Book, Addison-Wesley Publishing Company, New York, 1994. Also see Arquilla and Ronfeldt, 1997.

26. Also see Alexander Berger, "Organizational Innovation and Redesign in the Information Age: The Drug War, Netwar, and Other Low-End Conflict," Master's Thesis, Naval Postgraduate School, Monterey, California, 1998, for additional thinking and analysis about such propositions.

27. For elaboration, see Arquilla and Ronfeldt, 1997, Chapter 19.

28. Vernon Loeb, "Where the CIA Wages Its New World War," *Washington Post*, September 9, 1998. For a broader discussion of interagency cooperation in countering terrorism, see Ashton Carter, John Deutch, and Philip Zelikow, "Catastrophic Terrorism," *Foreign Affairs*, Vol. 77, No. 6, November/December 1998, pp. 80–94.

29. Analogously, right-wing militias and extremist groups in the United States also rely on a doctrine of "leaderless resistance" propounded by Aryan nationalist Louis Beam. See Beam, 1992; and Kenneth Stern, *A Force Upon the Plain: The American Militia Movement and the Politics of Hate*, Simon and Schuster, New York, 1996. Meanwhile, as part of a broader trend toward netwar, transnational criminal organizations (TCOs) have been shifting away from centralized "Dons" to more networked structures. See Phil Williams, "Transnational Criminal Organizations and International Security," *Survival*, Vol. 36, No. 1, Spring 1994, pp. 96–113; and Phil Williams, "The Nature of Drug-Trafficking Networks," *Current History*, April 1998, pp. 154–159. As noted earlier, social activist movements long ago began to evolve "segmented, polycephalous, integrated networks." For a discussion of a social netwar in which human-rights and other peaceful activist groups supported an insurgent group in Mexico, see David Ronfeldt and Armando Martinez, "A Comment on the Zapatista 'Netwar'," in John Arquilla and David Ronfeldt, 1997, pp. 369–391.

30. It is important to differentiate our notions of information-age networking from earlier ideas about terror as consisting of a network in which all nodes revolved around a Soviet core (Claire Sterling, *The Terror Network*, Holt, Rinehart & Winston, New York, 1981). This view has generally been regarded as unsupported by available evidence (see Cindy C. Combs, *Terrorism in the Twenty-First Century*, Prentice-Hall, New York, 1997, pp. 99–119). However, there were a few early studies that did give credit to the possibility of the rise of terror networks that were bound more by loose ties to general strategic goals than by Soviet control (see especially Thomas L. Friedman, "Loose-Linked Network of Terror: Separate Acts, Ideological Bonds," *Terrorism*, Vol. 8, No. 1, Winter 1985, pp. 36–49).

31. For good general background, see Michael Whine, "Islamist Organisations on the Internet," draft circulated on the Internet, April 1998 (*www.ict.org.il/articles*).

32. We assume that group activity is a proxy for group strength. Group activity can be measured more easily than group strength, and is expected to be significantly correlated with strength. The relationship may not be perfect, but it is deemed to be sufficiently strong for our purposes.

33. Office of the Coordinator for Counterterrorism, *Patterns of Global Terrorism*, 1996, U.S. Department of State, Publication 10433, April 1997.

34. Loeb, 1998; and John Murray and Richard H. Ward (eds.), *Extremist Groups*, Office of International Criminal Justice, University of Illinois, Chicago, 1996.

35. Youssef M. Ibrahim, "Egyptians Hold Terrorist Chief, Official Asserts," *New York Times*, August 26, 1998.

36. Murray and Ward, 1996.

37. *Patterns of Global Terrorism*, 1996, and Murray and Ward, 1996.

38. Murray and Ward, 1996.

39. *Patterns of Global Terrorism*, 1995, 1996, 1997.

40. For instance, in 1997 Hamas operatives set off three suicide bombs in crowded public places in Tel Aviv and Jerusalem. On March 21, a Hamas satchel bomb exploded at a Tel Aviv café, killing three persons and injuring 48; on July 30, two Hamas suicide bombers blew themselves up in a Jerusalem market, killing 16 persons and wounding 178; on September 4, three suicide bombers attacked a Jerusalem pedestrian mall, killing at least five persons (in addition to the suicide bombers), and injuring at least 181. The Palestinian Islamic Jihad has claimed responsibility (along with Hamas) for a bomb that killed 20 and injured 75 others in March 1996, and in 1995 it carried out five bombings that killed 29 persons and wounded 107. See *Patterns of Global Terrorism*, 1995, 1996, 1997.

41. See "Hizbullah," Israeli Foreign Ministry, April 11, 1996. Available on the Internet at *http://www.israel-mfa.gov.il*.

42. See *Patterns of Global Terrorism*, 1995, 1996, 1997.

43. *Patterns of Global Terrorism*, 1997.

44. "Arab Afghans Said to Launch Worldwide Terrorist War," *Paris al-Watan al-'Arabi*, FBIS-TOT-96-010-L, December 1, 1995, pp. 22–24.
45. William Gertz, "Saudi Financier Tied to Attacks," *Washington Times*, October 23, 1996.
46. Tim Weiner, "U.S. Sees bin Laden as Ringleader of Terrorist Network," *New York Times*, August 21, 1998; M. J. Zuckerman, "Bin Laden Indicted for Bid to Kill Clinton," *USA Today*, August 26, 1998.
47. Pamela Constable, "Bin Laden 'Is Our Guest, So We Must Protect Him'," *Washington Post*, August 21, 1998.
48. We distinguish between deliberate and factional decentralization. Factional decentralization—prevalent in older groups—occurs when subgroups separate themselves from the central leadership because of differences in tactics or approach. Deliberate or operational decentralization is what distinguishes netwar agents from others, since delegation of authority in this case occurs because of the distinct advantages this organizational arrangement brings, and not because of lack of consensus. We expect both influences on decentralization to continue, but newer groups will tend to decentralize authority even in the absence of political disagreements.
49. "Gaza Strip, West Bank: Dahlan on Relations with Israel, Terrorism," *Tel Aviv Yedi'ot Aharonot*, FBIS-TOT-97-022-L, February 28, 1997, p. 18.
50. The leader of the PIJ's most powerful faction, Fathi Shaqaqi, was assassinated in October 1995 in Malta, allegedly by the Israeli Mossad. Shaqaqi's killing followed the assassination of Hani Abed, another PIJ leader killed in 1994 in Gaza. Reports that the group has been considerably weakened as a result of Israeli counterleadership operations are balanced by the strength demonstrated by the PIJ in its recent terrorist activity. See "Islamic Group Vows Revenge for Slaying of Its Leader," *New York Times*, October 30, 1995, p. 9.
51. Magnus Ranstorp, "Hizbullah's Command Leadership: Its Structure, Decision-Making and Relationship with Iranian Clergy and Institutions," *Terrorism and Political Violence*, Vol. 6, No. 3, Autumn 1994, p. 304.
52. *Patterns of Global Terrorism*, 1996.
53. "Algeria: Infighting Among Proliferating 'Wings' of Armed Groups," *London al-Sharq al-Aswat*, FBIS-TOT-97-021-L, February 24, 1997, p. 4.
54. David B. Ottaway, "US Considers Slugging It Out With International Terrorism," *Washington Post*, October 17, 1996, p. 25.
55. "Saudi Arabia: Bin-Laden Calls for 'Guerrilla Warfare' Against US Forces," *Beirut Al-Diyar*, FBIS-NES-96-180, September 12, 1996.
56. It is important to avoid equating the bin Laden network solely with bin Laden. He represents a key node in the Arab Afghan terror network, but there should be no illusions about the likely effect on the network of actions taken to neutralize him. The network conducts many operations without his involvement, leadership, or financing—and will continue to be able to do so should he be killed or captured.
57. "Militants Say There Will Be More Attacks Against U.S.," *European Stars and Stripes*, August 20, 1998.
58. For instance, there have been reports of a recent inflow of Arab Afghans into Egypt's Islamic Group to reinforce the latter's operations. See Murray and Ward, 1996, and "The CIA on Bin Laden," *Foreign Report*, No. 2510, August 27, 1998, pp. 2–3.
59. This move was also influenced by the Taliban's decision to curb Arab Afghan activities in the territory under its control as a result of U.S. pressure. See "Arab Afghans Reportedly Transfer Operations to Somalia," *Cairo al-Arabi*, FBIS-TOT-97-073, March 10, 1997, p. 1.
60. "Afghanistan, China: Report on Bin-Laden Possibly Moving to China," *Paris al-Watan al-'Arabi*, FBIS-NES-97-102, May 23, 1997, pp. 19–20.
61. While it is possible to discern a general trend toward an organizational structure that displays several features of a network, we expect to observe substantial differences (and many hierarchy/network hybrids) in how organizations make their specific design choices. Different network designs depend on contingent factors, such as personalities, organizational history, operational requirements, and other influences such as state sponsorship and ideology.
62. Assessing the strength of the relationship between organizational structure and use of information technology is difficult to establish. Alternative explanations may exist as to why newer groups would embrace information technology, such as age of the group (one could speculate that newer terrorist groups have on average younger members, who are more familiar with computers), or the amount of funding (a richer group could afford more electronic gadgetry). While it is empirically impossible to refute these points, much in organization theory supports our hypothesis that there is a direct relationship between a higher need for information technology and the use of network structures.
63. "Saudi Arabia: French Analysis of Islamic Threat," *Paris al-Watan al-'Arabi*, FBIS-NES-97-082, April 11, 1997, pp. 4–8.
64. "Afghanistan, Saudi Arabia: Editor's Journey to Meet Bin-Laden Described," *London al-Quds al-'Arabi*, FBIS-TOT-97-003-L, November 27, 1996, p. 4.
65. "Arab Afghans Said to Launch Worldwide Terrorist War," 1995.
66. "Israel: U.S. Hamas Activists Use Internet to Send Attack Threats," *Tel Aviv IDF Radio*, FBIS-TOT-97-001-L, 0500 GMT October 13, 1996.
67. "Israel: Hamas Using Internet to Relay Operational Messages," *Tel Aviv Ha'aretz*, FBIS-TOT-98-034, February 3, 1998, p. 1.

68. "Italy: Security Alters Following Algerian Extremists' Arrests," *Milan Il Giornale*, FBIS-TOT-97-002-L, November 12, 1996, p. 10.

69. "Italy, Vatican City: Daily Claims GIA 'Strategist' Based in Milan," *Milan Corriere della Sera*, FBIS-TOT-97-004-L, December 5, 1996, p. 9.

70. "Hizbullah TV Summary 18 February 1998," *Al-Manar Television World Wide Webcast*, FBIS-NES-98-050, February 19, 1998. Also see "Developments in Mideast Media: January–May 1998," Foreign Broadcast Information Service (FBIS), May 11, 1998.

71. "Islamists on Internet," FBIS Foreign Media Note-065EP96, September 9, 1996.

72. "Islamic Activism Online," FBIS Foreign Media Note-02JAN97, January 3, 1997.

73. The Muslim Parliament has recently added an Internet Relay Chat (IRC) link and a "Muslims only" List-Serve (automatic e-mail delivery service). See "Islamic Activism Online," FBIS Foreign Media Note-02JAN97, January 3, 1997.

74. Similar propositions may apply to varieties of netwar other than the new terrorism.

75. We make a qualification here. There appears to be a significant positive association between the degree to which a group is active and the degree to which a group is decentralized and networked. But we cannot be confident about the causality of this relationship or its direction (i.e., whether activity and strength affect networking, or vice-versa). A host of confounding factors may affect both the way groups decide to organize and their relative success at operations. For instance, the age of a group may be an important predictor of a group's success—newer groups are likely to be more popular; popular groups are more likely to enlist new operatives; and groups that have a large number of operatives are likely to be more active, regardless of organizational structure. Another important caveat is related to the fact that it is difficult to rank groups precisely in terms of the degree to which they are networked, because no terrorist organization is thought to represent either a hierarchical or network ideal-type. While the conceptual division between newer-generation and traditional groups is appropriate for our scope here, an analytical "degree of networking" scale would have to be devised for more empirical research.

76. See, for instance, William Gutteridge (ed.), *Contemporary Terrorism*, Facts on File, Oxford, England, 1986; Hoffman and Carr, 1997; and Combs, 1997.

77. See Alexander George and William Simons, *The Limits of Coercive Diplomacy*, Westview Press, Boulder, 1994.

78. Alexander George, *Forceful Persuasion: Coercive Diplomacy as an Alternative to War*, United States Institute of Peace Press, Washington, DC, 1991.

79. Brian Jenkins, *The Potential for Nuclear Terrorism*, RAND, P-5876, 1977; Thomas Schelling, "Thinking about Nuclear Terrorism," *International Security*, Vol. 6, No. 4, Spring 1982, pp. 68–75; and Patrick Garrity and Steven Maaranen, *Nuclear Weapons in a Changing World*, Plenum Press, New York, 1992.

80. Carr, 1996.

81. Brian Jenkins, *International Terrorism: A New Kind of Warfare*, RAND, P-5261, 1974.

82. For a discussion of these motives, see Laqueur, 1996; Iklé, 1997; and Hoffman, 1998, respectively.

83. See, for instance, Michael Barkun, *Disaster and the Millennium*, Yale University Press, New Haven, 1974; and Norman Cohn, *The Pursuit of the Millennium: Revolutionary Messianism in Medieval and Reformation Europe and Its Bearing on Modern Totalitarian Movements*, Harper Torch Books, New York, 1961.

84. Bluma Zuckerbrot-Finkelstein, "A Guide to Hamas," *Internet Jewish Post*, available at *http://www.jewishpost.com/jewishpost/jp0203/jpn0303.htm*.

**John Arquilla** is a senior consultant to the International Security Group at RAND Corporation and an associate professor of defense analysis at the Naval Postgraduate School in Monterey, California.

**David Ronfeldt** is a senior social scientist at RAND whose research focuses on issues such information revolution, netwar, and the rise of transnational networks of nongovernmental organizations.

**Michele Zanini** is a research at RAND. These experts are all contributors to the book Countering the *New Terrorism* (1999).

# Article 41

Gabriel Weimann

## WWW.Terror.Net

### How Modern Terrorism Uses the Internet

## Summary

- The great virtues of the Internet—ease of access, lack of regulation, vast potential audiences, and fast flow of information, among others—have been turned to the advantage of groups committed to terrorizing societies to achieve their goals.
- Today, all active terrorist groups have established their presence on the Internet. Our scan of the Internet in 2003–4 revealed hundreds of websites serving terrorists and their supporters.
- Terrorism on the Internet is a very dynamic phenomenon: websites suddenly emerge, frequently modify their formats, and then swiftly disappear—or, in many cases, seem to disappear by changing their online address but retaining much the same content.
- Terrorist websites target three different audiences: current and potential supporters; international public opinion; and enemy publics.
- The mass media, policymakers, and even security agencies have tended to focus on the exaggerated threat of cyberterrorism and paid insufficient attention to the more routine uses made of the Internet. Those uses are numerous and, from the terrorists' perspective, invaluable.
- There are eight different ways in which contemporary terrorists use the Internet, ranging from psychological warfare and propaganda to highly instrumental uses such as fundraising, recruitment, data mining, and coordination of actions.
- While we must better defend our societies against cyberterrorism and Internet-savvy terrorists, we should also consider the costs of applying counterterrorism measures to the Internet. Such measures can hand authoritarian governments and agencies with little public accountability tools with which to violate privacy, curtail the free flow of information, and restrict freedom of expression, thus adding a heavy price in terms of diminished civil liberties to the high toll exacted by terrorism itself.

## Introduction

The story of the presence of terrorist groups in cyberspace has barely begun to be told. In 1998, around half of the thirty organizations designated as "Foreign Terrorist Organizations" under the U.S. Antiterrorism and Effective Death Penalty Act of 1996 maintained websites; by 2000, virtually all terrorist groups had established their presence on the Internet. Our scan of the Internet in 2003–4 revealed hundreds of websites serving terrorists and their supporters. And yet, despite this growing terrorist presence, when policymakers, journalists, and academics have discussed the combination of terrorism and the Internet, they have focused on the overrated threat posed by cyberterrorism or cyberwarfare (i.e., attacks on computer networks, including those on the Internet) and largely ignored the numerous uses that terrorists make of the Internet every day.

In this report we turn the spotlight on these latter activities, identifying, analyzing, and illustrating ways in which terrorist organizations are exploiting the unique attributes of the Internet. The material presented here is drawn from an ongoing study (now in its sixth year) of the phenomenon, during which we have witnessed a growing and increasingly sophisticated terrorist presence on the World Wide Web. Terrorism on the Internet, as we have discovered, is a very dynamic phenomenon: websites suddenly emerge, frequently modify their formats, and then swiftly disappear—or, in many cases, seem to disappear by changing their online address but retaining much the same content. To locate the terrorists' sites, we have conducted numerous systematic scans of the Internet, feeding an enormous variety of names and terms into search engines, entering chat rooms and forums of supporters and sympathizers, and surveying the links on other organizations' websites to create and update our own lists of sites. This is often a herculean effort, especially because in some cases (e.g., al Qaeda's websites) locations and contents change almost daily.

The report begins by sketching the origins of the Internet, the characteristics of the new medium that make it so attractive to political extremists, the range of terrorist organizations active in cyberspace, and their target audiences. The heart of the report is an analysis of eight different uses that terrorists make of the Internet. These range from conducting psychological warfare to gathering information, from training to fundraising, from propagandizing to recruiting, and from networking to planning and coordinating terrorist acts. In each instance, we offer concrete examples drawn from our own research, from cases reported in the media, and from contacts with Western intelligence organizations. Although the bulk of the report amounts to a strong argument for the political, intelligence, and academic communities to pay much more attention to the dangers posed by terrorists' use of the Internet, the report concludes with a plea to those same communities not to overreact. The Internet may be attractive to political extremists, but it also symbolizes and supports the freedom of thought and expression that helps distinguish democracies from their enemies. Effective counterterrorist campaigns do not require, and may be undermined by, draconian measures to restrict Internet access.

## Modern Terrorism and the Internet

Paradoxically, the very decentralized network of communication that the U.S. security services created out of fear of the Soviet Union now serves the interests of the greatest foe of the West's security services since the end of the Cold War: international terror. The roots of the modern Internet are to be found in the early 1970s, during the days of the Cold War, when the U.S. Department of Defense was concerned about reducing the vulnerability of its communication networks to nuclear attack. The Defense Department decided to decentralize the whole system by creating an interconnected web of computer networks. After twenty years of development and use by academic researchers, the Internet quickly expanded and changed its character when it was opened up to commercial users in the late 1980s. By the mid-1990s, the Internet connected more than 18,000 private, public, and national networks, with the number increasing daily. Hooked into those networks were about 3.2 million host computers and perhaps as many as 60 million users spread across all seven continents. The estimated number of users in the early years of the twenty-first century is over a billion.

As it burgeoned, the Internet was hailed as an integrator of cultures and a medium for businesses, consumers, and governments to communicate with one another. It appeared to offer unparalleled opportunities for the creation of a forum in which the "global village" could meet and exchange ideas, stimulating and sustaining democracy throughout the world. However, with the enormous growth in the size and use of the network, utopian visions of the promise of the Internet were challenged by the proliferation of pornographic and violent content on the web and by the use of the Internet by extremist organizations of various kinds. Groups with very different political goals but united in their readiness to employ terrorist tactics started using the network to distribute their propaganda, to communicate with their supporters, to foster public awareness of and sympathy for their causes, and even to execute operations.

By its very nature, the Internet is in many ways an ideal arena for activity by terrorist organizations. Most notably, it offers

- easy access;
- little or no regulation, censorship, or other forms of government control;
- potentially huge audiences spread throughout the world;
- anonymity of communication;
- fast flow of information;
- inexpensive development and maintenance of a web presence;
- a multimedia environment (the ability to combine text, graphics, audio, and video and to allow users to download films, songs, books, posters, and so forth); and
- the ability to shape coverage in the traditional mass media, which increasingly use the Internet as a source for stories.

## An Overview of Terrorist Websites

These advantages have not gone unnoticed by terrorist organizations, no matter what their political orientation. Islamists and Marxists, nationalists and separatists, racists and anarchists: all find the Internet alluring. Today, almost all active terrorist organizations (which number more than forty) maintain websites, and many maintain more than one website and use several different languages.

As the following illustrative list shows, these organizations and groups come from all corners of the globe. (This geographical categorization, it should be noted, reveals the geographical diversity but obscures the fact that many groups are truly transnational, and even transregional, in character.)

- *From the Middle East, Hamas* (the Islamic Resistance Movement), the Lebanese Hezbollah (Party of God), the al Aqsa Martyrs Brigades, Fatah Tanzim, the Popular Front for the Liberation of Palestine (PFLP), the Palestinian Islamic Jihad, the Kahane Lives movement, the People's Mujahedin of Iran (PMOI—Mujahedin-e Khalq), the Kurdish Workers' Party (PKK), and the Turkish-based Popular Democratic Liberation Front Party (DHKP/C) and Great East Islamic Raiders Front (IBDA-C).
- *From Europe*, the Basque ETA movement, Armata Corsa (the Corsican Army), and the Irish Republican Army (IRA).
- *From Latin America*, Peru's Tupak-Amaru (MRTA) and Shining Path (Sendero Luminoso), the Colombian National Liberation Army (ELN-Colombia), and the Armed Revolutionary Forces of Colombia (FARC).

- *From Asia*, al Qaeda, the Japanese Supreme Truth (Aum Shinrikyo), Ansar al Islam (Supporters of Islam) in Iraq, the Japanese Red Army (JRA), Hizb-ul Mujehideen in Kashmir, the Liberation Tigers of Tamil Eelam (LTTE), the Islamic Movement of Uzbekistan (IMU), the Moro Islamic Liberation Front (MILF) in the Philippines, the Pakistan-based Lashkare-Taiba, and the rebel movement in Chechnya.

## Content

What is the content of terrorist sites? Typically, a site will provide a history of the organization and its activities, a detailed review of its social and political background, accounts of its notable exploits, biographies of its leaders, founders, and heroes, information on its political and ideological aims, fierce criticism of its enemies, and up-to-date news. Nationalist and separatist organizations generally display maps of the areas in dispute: the Hamas site shows a map of Palestine, the FARC site shows a map of Colombia, the LTTE site presents a map of Sri Lanka, and so forth. Despite the ever-present vocabulary of "the armed struggle" and "resistance," what most sides do not feature is a detailed description of their violent activities. Even if they expound at length on the moral and legal basis of the legitimacy of the use of violence, most sites refrain from referring to the terrorists' violent actions or their fatal consequences—this reticence is presumably inspired by propagandist and image-building considerations. Two exceptions to this rule are Hezbollah and Hamas, whose sites feature updated statistical reports of their actions ("daily operations") and tallies of both "dead martyrs" and "Israeli enemies" and "collaborators" killed.

## Audiences

Whom do the Internet terrorists target at their sites? An analysis of the content of the websites suggests three different audiences.

- *Current and potential supporters.* Terrorist websites make heavy use of slogans and offer items for sale, including T-shirts, badges, flags, and videotapes and audiocassettes, all evidently aimed at sympathizers. Often, an organization will target its local supporters with a site in the local language and will provide detailed information about the activities and internal politics of the organization, its allies, and its competitors.

- *International public opinion.* The international public, who are not directly involved in the conflict but who may have some interest in the issues involved, are courted with sites in languages other than the local tongue. Most sites offer versions in several languages. ETA's site, for instance, offers information in Castilian, German, French, and Italian; the MRTA site offers Japanese and Italian in addition to its English and Spanish versions; and the IMU site uses Arabic, English, and Russian. For the benefit of their international audiences, the sites present basic information about the organization and extensive historical background material (material with which the organization's supporters are presumably already familiar).

  Judging from the content of many of the sites, it appears that foreign journalists are also targeted. Press releases are often placed on the websites in an effort to get the organization's point of view into the traditional media. The detailed background information is also very useful for international reporters. One of Hezbollah's sites specifically addresses journalists, inviting them to interact with the organization's press office via e-mail.

- *Enemy publics.* Efforts to reach enemy publics (i.e., citizens of the states against which the terrorists are fighting) are not as clearly apparent from the content of many sites. However, some sites do seem to make an effort to demoralize the enemy by threatening attacks and by fostering feelings of guilt about the enemy's conduct and motives. In the process, they also seek to stimulate public debate in their enemies' states, to change public opinion, and to weaken public support for the governing regime.

# How Terrorists Use the Internet

We have identified eight different, albeit sometimes overlapping, ways in which contemporary terrorists use the Internet. Some of these parallel the uses to which everyone puts the Internet—information gathering, for instance. Some resemble the uses made of the medium by traditional political organizations—for example, raising funds and disseminating propaganda. Others, however, are much more unusual and distinctive—for instance, hiding instructions, manuals, and directions in coded messages or encrypted files.

## Psychological Warfare

Terrorism has often been conceptualized as a form of psychological warfare, and certainly terrorists have sought to wage such a campaign through the Internet. There are several ways for terrorists to do so. For instance, they can use the Internet to spread disinformation, to deliver threats intended to distill fear and helplessness, and to disseminate horrific images of recent actions, such as the brutal murder of the American journalist Daniel Pearl by his captors, a videotape of which was replayed on several terrorist websites. Terrorists can also launch psychological attacks through cyberterrorism, or, more accurately, through creating the fear of cyberterrorism. "Cyberfear" is generated when concern about what a computer attack *could* do (for example, bringing down airliners by disabling air traffic control systems, or disrupting national economies by wrecking the computerized systems that regulate stock markets) is amplified until the public believes that an attack *will* happen. The Internet—an uncensored medium that carries stories, pictures, threats, or messages regardless of their validity or potential impact—is peculiarly well suited to allowing even a small group to amplify its message and exaggerate its importance and the threat it poses.

Al Qaeda combines multimedia propaganda and advanced communication technologies to create a very sophisticated form of psychological warfare. Osama bin Laden and his followers concentrate their propaganda efforts on the Internet, where visitors to al Qaeda's numerous websites and to the sites of sympathetic, aboveground organizations can access prerecorded videotapes and audiotapes, CD-ROMs, DVDs, photographs, and announcements. Despite the massive onslaught it has sustained in recent years— the arrests and deaths of many of its members, the dismantling of its operational bases and training camps in Afghanistan, and the smashing of its bases in the Far East—al Qaeda has been able to conduct an impressive scare campaign. Since September 11, 2001, the organization has festooned its websites with a string of announcements of an impending "Large attack" on U.S. targets. These warnings have received considerable media coverage, which has helped to generate a widespread sense of dread and insecurity among audiences throughout the world and especially within the United States.

Interestingly, al Qaeda has consistently claimed on its websites that the destruction of the World Trade Center has inflicted psychological damage, as well as concrete damage, on the U.S. economy. The attacks on the Twin Towers are depicted as an assault on the trademark of the U.S. economy, and evidence of their effectiveness is seen in the weakening of the dollar, the decline of the U.S. stock market after 9/11, and a supposed loss of confidence in the U.S. economy both within the United States and elsewhere. Parallels are drawn with the decline and ultimate demise of the Soviet Union. One of bin Laden's recent publications, posted on the web, declared that "America is in retreat by the Grace of Almighty and economic attrition is continuing up to today. But it needs further blows. The young men need to seek out the nodes of the American economy and strike the enemy's nodes."

## Publicity and Propaganda

The Internet has significantly expanded the opportunities for terrorists to secure publicity. Until the advent of the Internet, terrorists' hopes of winning publicity for their causes and activities depended on attracting the attention of television, radio, or the print media. These traditional media have "selection thresholds" (multistage processes of editorial selection) that terrorists often cannot reach. No such thresholds, of course, exist on the terrorists' own websites. The fact that many terrorists now have direct control over the content of their message offers further opportunities to shape how they are perceived by different target audiences and to manipulate their own image and the image of their enemies.

As noted earlier, most terrorist sites do not celebrate their violent activities. Instead, regardless of the terrorists' agendas, motives, and location, most sites emphasize two issues: the restrictions placed on freedom of expression and the plight of comrades who are now political prisoners. These issues resonate powerfully with their own supporters and are also calculated to elicit sympathy from Western audiences that cherish freedom of expression and frown on measures to silence political opposition. Enemy publics, too, may be targets for these complaints insofar as the terrorists, by emphasizing the antidemocratic nature of the steps taken against them, try to create feelings of unease and shame among their foes. The terrorists' protest at being muzzled, it may be noted, is particularly well suited to the Internet, which for many users is *the* symbol of free, unfettered, and uncensored communication.

Terrorist sites commonly employ three rhetorical structures, all used to justify their reliance on violence. The first one is the claim that the terrorists have no choice other than to turn to violence. Violence is presented as a necessity foisted upon the weak as the only means with which to respond to an oppressive enemy. While the sites avoid mentioning how the terrorists victimize others, the forceful actions of the governments and regimes that combat the terrorists are heavily emphasized and characterized with terms such as "slaughter," "murder," and "genocide." The terrorist organization is depicted as constantly persecuted, its leaders subject to assassination attempts and its supporters massacred, its freedom of expression curtailed, and its adherents arrested. This tactic, which portrays the organization as small, weak, and hunted down by a strong power or a strong state, turns the terrorists into the underdog.

A second rhetorical structure related to the legitimacy of the use of violence is the demonizing and delegitimization of the enemy. The members of the movement or organization are presented as freedom fighters, forced against their will to use violence because a ruthless enemy is crushing the rights and dignity of their people or group. The enemy of the movement or the organization is the real terrorist, many sites insist: "Our violence is tiny in comparison to his aggression" is a common argument. Terrorist rhetoric tries to shift the responsibility for violence from the terrorist to the adversary, which is accused of displaying its brutality, inhumanity, and immorality.

A third rhetorical device is to make extensive use of the language of nonviolence in an attempt to counter the terrorists' violent image. Although these are violent organizations, many of their sites claim that they seek peaceful solutions, that their ultimate aim is a diplomatic settlement achieved through negotiation and international pressure on a repressive government.

## Data Mining

The Internet may be viewed as a vast digital library. The World Wide Web alone offers about a billion pages of information, much of it free—and much of it of interest to terrorist organizations. Terrorists, for instance, can learn from the Internet a wide variety of details about targets such as transportation facilities, nuclear power plants, public buildings, airports, and ports, and even about counterterrorism measures. Dan Verton, in his book *Black Ice: The Invisible Threat of Cyberterrorism* (2003), explains that "al-Qaeda cells now operate with the assistance of large databases containing details of potential targets in the U.S. They use the Internet to collect intelligence on those targets, especially critical economic nodes, and modern software enables them to study structural weaknesses in facilities as well as predict the cascading failure effect of attacking certain systems." According to Secretary of Defense Donald Rumsfeld, speaking on January 15, 2003, an al Qaeda training manual recovered in Afghanistan tells its readers, "Using public sources openly and without resorting to illegal means, it is possible to gather at least 80 percent of all information required about the enemy."

The website operated by the Muslim Hackers Club (a group that U.S. security agencies believe aims to develop software tools with which to launch cyberattacks) has featured links to U.S. sites that purport to disclose sensitive information such as code names and radio frequencies used by the U.S. Secret Service. The same website offers tutorials in creating and spreading viruses, devising hacking stratagems, sabotaging networks, and developing codes; it also provides links to other militant Islamic and terrorist web addresses. Specific targets that al Qaeda-related websites have discussed include the Centers for Disease Control and Prevention in Atlanta; FedWire, the money-movement clearing system maintained by the Federal Reserve Board; and facilities controlling the flow of information over the Internet. Like many other Internet users, terrorists have access not only to maps and diagrams of potential targets but also to imaging data on those same facilities and networks that may reveal counterterrorist activities at a target site. One captured al Qaeda computer contained engineering and structural features of a dam, which had been downloaded from the Internet and which would enable al Qaeda engineers and planners to simulate catastrophic failures. In other captured computers, U.S. investigators found evidence that al Qaeda operators spent time on sites that offer software and programming instructions for the digital switches that run power, water, transportation, and communications grids.

Numerous tools are available to facilitate such data collection, including search engines, e-mail distribution lists, and chat rooms and discussion groups. Many websites offer their own search tools for extracting information from databases on their sites. Word searches of online newspapers and journals can likewise generate information of use to terrorists; some of this information may also be available in the traditional media, but online searching capabilities allow terrorists to capture it anonymously and with very little effort or expense.

## Fundraising

Like many other political organizations, terrorist groups use the Internet to raise funds. Al Qaeda, for instance, has always depended heavily on donations, and its global fundraising network is built upon a foundation of charities, nongovernmental organizations, and other financial institutions that use websites and Internet-based chat rooms and forums. The Sunni extremist group Hizb al-Tahrir uses an integrated web of Internet sites, stretching from Europe to Africa, which asks supporters to assist the effort by giving money and encouraging others to donate to the cause of jihad. Banking information, including the numbers of accounts into which donations can be deposited, is provided on a site based in Germany. The fighters in the Russian breakaway republic of Chechnya have likewise used the Internet to publicize the numbers of bank accounts to which sympathizers can contribute. (One of these Chechen bank accounts is located in Sacramento, California.) The IRA's website contains a page on which visitors can make credit card donations.

Internet user demographics (culled, for instance, from personal information entered in online questionnaires and order forms) allow terrorists to identify users with sympathy for a particular cause or issue. These individuals are then asked to make donations, typically through e-mails sent by a front group (i.e., an organization broadly supportive of the terrorists' aims but operating publicly and legally and usually having no direct ties to the terrorist organization). For instance, money benefiting Hamas has been collected via the website of a Texas-based charity, the Holy Land Foundation for Relief and Development (HLF). The U.S. government seized the assets of HLF in December 2001 because of its ties to Hamas. The U.S. government has also frozen the assets of three seemingly legitimate charities that use the Internet to raise money—the Benevolence International Foundation, the Global Relief Foundation, and the Al-Haramain Foundation—because of evidence that those charities have funneled money to al Qaeda.

In another example, in January 2004, a federal grand jury in Idaho charged a Saudi graduate student with conspiring to help terrorist organizations wage jihad by using the Internet to raise funds, field recruits, and locate prospective U.S. targets—military and civilian—in the Middle East. Sami Omar Hussayen, a doctoral candidate in computer science in a University of Idaho program sponsored—ironically—by the National Security Agency, was accused of creating websites and an e-mail group that disseminated messages from him and two radical clerics in Saudi Arabia that supported jihad.

## Recruitment and Mobilization

The Internet can be used not only to solicit donations from sympathizers but also to recruit and mobilize supporters to play a more active role in support of terrorist activities or causes. In addition to seeking converts by using the full panoply of website technologies (audio, digital video, etc.) to enhance the presentation of their message, terrorist organizations capture information about the users who browse their websites. Users who seem most interested in the organization's cause or well suited to carrying out its work are then contacted. Recruiters may also use more interactive Internet technology to roam online chat rooms and cybercafes, looking for receptive members of the public, particularly young people. Electronic bulletin boards and user nets (issue-specific chat rooms and bulletins) can also serve as vehicles for reaching out to potential recruits.

Some would-be recruits, it may be noted, use the Internet to advertise themselves to terrorist organizations. In 1995, as reported by Verton in *Black Ice*, Ziyad Khalil enrolled as a computer science major at Columbia College in Missouri. He also became a Muslim activist on the campus, developing links to several radical groups and operating a website that supported Hamas. Thanks in large part to his Internet activities, he came to the attention of bin Laden and his lieutenants. Khalil became al Qaeda's procurement officer in the United States, arranging purchases of satellite telephones, computers, and other electronic surveillance technologies and helping bin Laden communicate with his followers and officers.

More typically, however, terrorist organizations go looking for recruits rather than waiting for them to present themselves. The SITE Institute, a Washington, D.C.-based terrorism research group that monitors al Qaeda's Internet communications, has provided chilling details of a high-tech recruitment drive launched in 2003 to recruit fighters to travel to Iraq and attack U.S. and coalition forces there. Potential recruits are bombarded with religious decrees and anti-American propaganda, provided with training manuals on how to be a terrorist, and—as they are led through a maze of secret chat rooms—given specific instructions on how to make the journey to Iraq. In one particularly graphic exchange in a secret al Qaeda chat room in early September 2003 an unknown Islamic fanatic, with the user name "Redemption Is Close," writes, "Brothers, how do I go to Iraq for Jihad? Are there any army camps and is there someone who commands there?" Four days later he gets a reply from "Merciless Terrorist." "Dear Brother, the road is wide open for you—there are many groups, go look for someone you trust, join him, he will be the protector of the Iraqi regions and with the help of Allah you will become one of the Mujahidin." "Redemption Is Close" then presses for more specific information on how he can wage jihad in Iraq. "Merciless Terrorist" sends him a propaganda video and instructs him to download software called Pal Talk, which enables users to speak to each other on the Internet without fear of being monitored.

Many terrorist websites stop short of enlisting recruits for violent action but they do encourage supporters to show their commitment to the cause in other tangible ways. "How can I help the struggle: A few suggestions," runs a heading on the Kahane Lives website; "Action alert: What you can do" is a feature on the Shining Path's website. The power of the Internet to mobilize activists is illustrated by the response to the arrest of Abdullah Ocalan, leader of the Kurdish terrorist group the PKK. When Turkish forces arrested Ocalan, tens of thousands of Kurds around the world responded with demonstrations within a matter of hours—thanks to sympathetic websites urging supporters to protest.

## Networking

Many terrorist groups, among them Hamas and al Qaeda, have undergone a transformation from strictly hierarchical organizations with designated leaders to affiliations of semi-independent cells that have no single commanding hierarchy. Through the use of the Internet, these loosely interconnected groups are able to maintain contact with one another—and with members of other terrorist groups. In the future, terrorists are increasingly likely to be organized in a more decentralized manner, with arrays of transnational groups linked by the Internet and communicating and coordinating horizontally rather than vertically.

Several reasons explain why modern communication technologies, especially computer-mediated communications, are so useful for terrorists in establishing and maintaining networks. First, new technologies have greatly reduced transmission time, enabling dispersed organizational actors to communicate swiftly and to coordinate effectively. Second, new technologies have significantly reduced the cost of communication. Third, by integrating computing with communications, they have substantially increased the variety and complexity of the information that can be shared.

The Internet connects not only members of the same terrorist organizations but also members of different groups. For instance, dozens of sites exist that express support for terrorism conducted in the name of jihad. These sites and related forums permit terrorists in places such as Chechnya, Palestine, Indonesia, Afghanistan, Turkey, Iraq, Malaysia, the Philippines, and Lebanon to exchange not only ideas and suggestions but also practical information about how to build bombs, establish terror cells, and carry out attacks.

## Sharing Information

The World Wide Web is home to dozens of sites that provide information on how to build chemical and explosive weapons. Many of these sites post *The Terrorist's Handbook* and *The Anarchist Cookbook*, two well-known manuals that offer detailed instructions on how to construct a wide range of bombs. Another manual, *The Mujahadeen Poisons Handbook*, written by Abdel-Aziz in 1996 and "published" on the official Hamas website, details in twenty-three pages how to prepare various homemade poisons, poisonous gases, and other deadly materials for use in terrorist attacks. A much larger manual, nicknamed "The Encyclopedia of Jihad" and prepared by al Qaeda, runs to thousands of pages; distributed through the Internet, it offers detailed instructions on how to establish an underground organization and execute attacks. One al Qaeda laptop found in Afghanistan had been used to make multiple visits to a French site run by the Société Anonyme (a self-described "fluc-tuating group of artists and theoreticians who work specifically on the relations between critical thinking and artistic practices"), which offers a two-volume *Sabotage Handbook* with sections on topics such as planning an assassination and antisurveillance methods.

This kind of information is sought out not just by sophisticated terrorist organizations but also by disaffected individuals prepared to use terrorist tactics to advance their idiosyncratic agendas. In 1999, for instance, a young man by the name of David Copeland planted nail bombs in three different areas of London: multiracial Brixton, the largely Bangladeshi community of Brick Lane, and the gay quarter in Soho. Over the course of three weeks, he killed 3 people and injured 139. At his trial, he revealed that he had learned his deadly techniques from the Internet, downloading *The Terrorist's Handbook and How to Make Bombs: Book Two*. Both titles are still easily accessible. A search for the keywords "terrorist" and "handbook" on the Google search engine found nearly four thousand matches that included references to guidebooks and manuals. One site gives instructions on how to acquire ammonium nitrate, Copeland's "first choice" of explosive material.

In Finland in 2002, a brilliant chemistry student who called himself "RC" discussed bomb-making techniques with other enthusiasts on a Finish Internet website devoted to bombs and explosives. Sometimes he posted queries on topics such as manufacturing nerve gas at home. Often he traded information with the site's moderator, whose messages carried a picture of his own face superimposed on Osama bin Laden's body, complete with turban and beard. Then RC set off a bomb that killed seven people, including himself, in a crowded shopping mall. The website frequented by RC, known as the Home Chemistry Forum, was shut down by its sponsor, a computer magazine. But a backup copy was immediately posted again on a read-only basis.

## Planning and Coordination

Terrorists use the Internet not only to learn how to build bombs but also to plan and coordinate specific attacks. Al Qaeda operatives relied heavily on the Internet in planning and coordinating the September 11 attacks. Thousands of encrypted messages that had been posted in a password-protected area of a website were found by federal officials on the computer of arrested al Qaeda terrorist Abu Zubaydah, who reportedly masterminded the September 11 attacks. The first messages found on Zubaydah's computer were dated May 2001 and the last were sent on September 9, 2001. The frequency of the messages was highest in August 2001. To preserve their anonymity, the al Qaeda terrorists used the Internet in public places and sent messages via public e-mail. Some of the September 11 hijackers communicated using free web-based e-mail accounts.

Hamas activists in the Middle East, for example, use chat rooms to plan operations and operatives exchange e-mail to coordinate actions across Gaza, the West Bank, Lebanon, and Israel. Instructions in the form of maps, photographs, directions, and technical details of how to use explosives are often disguised by means of steganography, which involves hiding messages inside graphic files. Sometimes, however, instructions are delivered concealed in only the simplest of codes. Mohammed Atta's final message to the other eighteen terrorists who carried out the attacks of 9/11 is reported to have read: "The semester begins in three more weeks. We've obtained 19 confirmations for studies in the faculty of law, the faculty of urban planning, the faculty of fine arts, and the faculty of engineering." (The reference to the various faculties was apparently the code for the buildings targeted in the attacks.)

Since 9/11, U.S. security agencies have monitored a number of websites that they believe are linked to al Qaeda and appear to contain elements of cyberplanning (e.g., directions for operatives, information for supporters and activists, calls for action, threats, and links to other websites):

- alneda.com, which, until it was closed down in 2002, is said by U.S. officials to have contained encrypted information to direct al Qaeda members to more secure sites, featured international news about al Qaeda, and published a variety of articles, books, and fatwas (the latter typically declaring war on the United States, Christianity, or Judaism);
- assam.com, which served as a mouthpiece for jihad in Afghanistan, Chechnya, and Palestine;
- almuhrajiroun.com, which in the late 1990s and early 2000s urged sympathizers to assassinate Pakistani president Pervez Musharraf;
- qassam.net, a site that U.S. officials claim is linked not only to al Qaeda but also to Hamas;
- jihadunspun.net, which offered a thirty-six-minute video of Osama bin Laden lecturing, preaching, and making threats;
- 7hj.7hj.com, which aimed to teach visitors how to hack into Internet networks and how to infect government and corporate websites with "worms" and viruses;
- aloswa.org, which featured quotations from bin Laden and religious legal rulings justifying the attacks of 9/11 and other assaults on the West;
- drasat.com, run (some experts suspect) by a fictional institution called the Islamic Studies and Research Center and reported to be the most credible of dozens of Islamist sites posting al Qaeda news; and
- jehad.net, alsaha.com, and islammemo.com, which are alleged to have posted al Qaeda statements as well as calls for action and directions for operatives.

# Conclusion

In a briefing given in late September 2001, Ronald Dick, assistant director of the FBI and head of the United States National Infrastructure Protection Center (NIPC), told reporters that the hijackers of 9/11 had used the Internet, and "used it well." Since 9/11, terrorists have only sharpened their Internet skills and increased their web presence. Today, terrorists of very different ideological persuasions—Islamist, Marxist, nationalist, separatist, racist—have learned many of the same lessons about how to make the most of the Internet. The great virtues of the Internet—ease of access, lack of regulation, vast potential audiences, fast flow of information, and so forth—have been turned to the advantage of groups committed to terrorizing societies to achieve their goals.

How should those societies respond? This is not the place to attempt anything like a definitive answer, but two things seem clear. First, we must become better informed about the uses to which terrorists put the Internet and better able to monitor their activities. As noted at the outset of this report, journalists, scholars, policymakers, and even security agencies have tended to focus on the exaggerated threat of cyberterrorism and paid insufficient attention to the more routine uses made of the Internet. Those uses are numerous and, from the terrorists' perspective, invaluable. Hence, it is imperative that security agencies continue to improve their ability to study and monitor terrorist activities on the Internet and explore measures to limit the usability of this medium by modern terrorists.

Second, while we must thus better defend our societies against terrorism, we must not in the process erode the very qualities and values that make our societies worth defending. The Internet is in many ways an almost perfect embodiment of the democratic ideals of free speech and open communication; it is a marketplace of ideas unlike any that has existed before. Unfortunately, as this report has shown, the freedom offered by the Internet is vulnerable to abuse from groups that, paradoxically, are themselves often hostile to uncensored thought and expression. But if, fearful of further terrorist attacks, we circumscribe our own freedom to use the Internet, then we hand the terrorists a victory and deal democracy a blow. We must not forget that the fear that terrorism inflicts has in the past been manipulated by politicians to pass legislation that undermines individual rights and liberties. The use of advanced techniques to monitor, search, track, and analyze communications carries inherent dangers. Although such technologies might prove very helpful in the fight against cyberterrorism and Internet-savvy terrorists, they would also hand participating governments, especially authoritarian governments and agencies with little public accountability, tools with which to violate civil liberties domestically and abroad. It does take much imagination to recognize that the long-term implications could be profound and damaging for democracies and their values, adding a heavy price in terms of diminished civil liberties to the high toll exacted by terrorism itself.

# Of Related Interest

A number of other publications from the United States Institute of Peace address issues related to terrorism and to the Internet and other forms of information technology. Note: Most of our reports can be downloaded from our website at www.usip.org/reports.

## Recent Special Reports on Terrorism

- *Terrorism in the Horn of Africa* (Special Report 113, January 2004)
- *Global Terrorism after the Iraq War* (Special Report 111, October 2003)
- *The Diplomacy of Counterterrorism: Lessons Learned, Ignored, and Disputed* (Special Report 80, January 2002)
- For terrorism and counterterrorism links, visit www.usip.org/library/topics/terrorism.html.

## Recent Reports from the Virtual Diplomacy Initiative

- *Creating a Common Communications Culture: Interoperability in Crisis Management* (January 2004)
- *Net Diplomacy I (Beyond Foreign Ministries), II (Beyond Old Borders), and III (2015 and Beyond)* (August 2002)
- *Information Technology and Peace Support Operations* (July 2002)
- For more resources, visit www.usip.org/virtualdiplomacy/index.html.

**Gabriel Weimann** is professor of communication at Haifa University, where he has taught since 1984. Dr. Weimann is a prolific analyst of terrorism and the mass media, and his publications include five books and more than 100 book chapters and articles. From 2003 to 2004, Dr. Weimann was a senior fellow at the United States Institute of Peace.

# Article 42

John T. Rourke

# Does Using Drones to Attack Terrorists Globally Violate International Law?

**Selected, Edited, and with Issue Framing Material by:**
**John T. Rourke,** *University of Connecticut, Storrs*

**YES: Mary Ellen O'Connell**, from "Lawful Use of Combat Drones," Testimony During Hearings on "Rise of the Drones II: Examining the Legality of Unmanned Targeting," before the Subcommittee on National Security and Foreign Affairs, Committee on Oversight and Government Reform, U.S. House of Representatives (2010)

**NO: Michael W. Lewis**, from "Examining the Legality of Unmanned Targeting," Testimony During Hearings on "Rise of the Drones II: Examining the Legality of Unmanned Targeting," before the Subcommittee on National Security and Foreign Affairs, Committee on Oversight and Government Reform, U.S. House of Representatives (2010)

---

## Learning Outcomes

**After reading this issue, you will be able to:**

- Understand what unmanned aerial vehicles (UVAs, drones) are and what their capabilities are.
- Discuss why UVAs are controversial weapons under international law.
- Comment on whether the upsurge of global terrorism has created a new realm of war that requires rethinking international way in many such areas as drones discussed here and the detention and treatment of terrorists, as discussed elsewhere in this volume.

---

### ISSUE SUMMARY

**YES:** Mary Ellen O'Connell, a research professor at the Kroc Institute, University of Notre Dame, and the Robert and Marion Short Professor of Law at the School of Law, University of Notre Dame, tells a congressional committee that the United States is failing more often than not to follow the most important single rule governing drones: restricting their use to the battlefield.

**NO:** Michael W. Lewis, a professor of law at Ohio Northern University's Pettit College of Law, disagrees, contending that there is nothing inherently illegal about using drones to target specific terrorists or groups of terrorists on or away from the battlefield.

**D**uring March and April 2010, the Subcommittee on National Security and Foreign Affairs of the Committee on Oversight and Government Reform in the U.S. House of Representatives held a series of hearings to look into the military use of unmanned aerial vehicles (UAVs, drones). These remotely piloted aircraft are capable of launching missiles and otherwise attacking targets, of using cameras and other sensors to gather intelligence, of facilitating communications, and of performing other tasks. The characteristics of the numerous types of UAVs in the U.S. military inventory vary considerably by mission, but one of the best known is the Predator. It is propeller driven, has a top speed of 135 mph, has a 450-mile range, is 27 feet long, has a 48-foot wingspan, can stay aloft for 20 hours, and is armed with two air-to-surface Hellfire missiles, each tipped with a warhead carrying 20 pounds of high explosives. Relative to piloted warplanes, UAVs are inexpensive, costing about one-tenth as much each. There are also great differences in the time and money spent creating pilots.

During the first session of the hearings on March 23, 2010, the subcommittee's chair, Representative John F. Tierney (D-MA), opened the inquiry by outlining its purpose. As Tierney put it with regard to the subject of this debate:

> . . . Over the last decade, the number of unmanned systems and their applications has grown rapidly. So too has the number of operational, political, and legal questions associated with this technology. The growing demand for and reliance on unmanned systems has serious implications. . . . As the United States is engaged in two wars abroad, unmanned systems, particularly unmanned aerial vehicles, have become a centerpiece of that war effort. In recent years, the Department of Defense's UAV inventory has rapidly grown in size, from 167 in 2002 to over 7000 today. Last year, for the first time, the U.S. Air Force trained more unmanned pilots than traditional fighter pilots.
>
> Some express no doubt that unmanned systems have been a boost to U.S. war efforts in the Middle East and South Asia. CIA Director Leon Panetta said last May that "drone strikes are the only game in town in terms of confronting or trying to disrupt the al Qaeda leadership." Media reports over the last year that the top two leaders of the Pakistani Taliban were killed by drone strikes also support this argument.
>
> But some critics argue that drone strikes are unethical at best and counter-productive at worst. They point to the reportedly high rate of civilian casualties . . . and argue that the strikes do more to stoke anti-Americanism than they do to weaken our enemies. . . . This is particularly relevant in the era of counter-insurgency doctrine, a central tenet of which is, "first, do no harm."
>
> It also may be the case that we are fighting wars with modern technology under an antiquated set of laws. For example, if the United States uses unmanned weapons systems, does that require an official declaration of war or an authorization for the use of force? . . .
>
> These trends are already forcing us to ask new questions about domestic airspace regulation: who is allowed to own unmanned systems, and where they are allowed to operate them?
>
> These are some of the questions that we will begin to answer in this hearing. Surely we will not conclude this conversation in one afternoon. . . .

In the following readings, two experts on international law relating to war take up the use of UAVs to attack targets away from an immediate war zone or "battlefield." Ellen O'Connell argues that such attacks violate international law. Michael Lewis disagrees.

# YES

**Mary Ellen O'Connell**

# Lawful Use of Combat Drones

Combat drones are battlefield weapons. They fire missiles or drop bombs capable of inflicting very serious damage. Drones are not lawful for use outside combat zones. Outside such zones, police are the proper law enforcement agents and police are generally required to warn before using lethal force. Restricting drones to the battlefield is the most important single rule governing their use. Yet, the United States is failing to follow it more often than not. At the very time we are trying to win hearts and minds to respect the rule of law, we are ourselves failing to respect a very basic rule: remote weapons systems belong on the battlefield.

## I. A Lawful Battlefield Weapon

The United States first used weaponized drones during the combat in Afghanistan that began on October 7, 2001. We requested permission from Uzbekistan, which was then hosting the U.S. air base where drones were kept. We also used combat drones in the battles with Iraq's armed forces in the effort to topple Saddam Hussein's government that began in March 2003. We are still using drones lawfully in the ongoing combat in Afghanistan. Drones spare the lives of pilots, since the unmanned aerial vehicle is flown from a site far from the attack zone. If a drone is shot down, there is no loss of human life. Moreover, on the battlefield drones can be more protective of civilian lives than high aerial bombing or long-range artillery. Their cameras can pick up details about the presence of civilians. Drones can fly low and target more precisely using this information. [The U.S. commander in Afghanistan] General [Stanley] McChrystal has wisely insisted on zerotolerance for civilian deaths in Afghanistan. The use of drones can help us achieve that. What drones cannot do is comply with police rules for the use of lethal force away from the battlefield. In law enforcement it must be possible to warn before using lethal force, in war-fighting this is not necessary, making the use of bombs and missiles lawful. The United Nations Basic Principles for the Use of Force and Firearms by Law Enforcement Officials (*UN Basic Principles*) set out the international legal standard for the use of force by police:

> Law enforcement officials shall not use firearms against persons except in self-defense or defense of others against the imminent threat of death or serious injury, to prevent the perpetration of a particularly serious crime involving grave threat to life, to arrest a person presenting such a danger and resisting their authority, or to prevent his or her escape, and only when less extreme means are insufficient to achieve these objectives. In any event, intentional lethal use of firearms may only be made when strictly unavoidable in order to protect life.

The United States has failed to follow these rules by using combat drones in places where no actual armed conflict was occurring or where the U.S. was not involved in the armed conflict. On November 3, 2002, the CIA used a drone to fire laser-guided Hellfire missiles at a passenger vehicle traveling in a thinly populated region of Yemen. At that time, the Air Force controlled the entire drone fleet, but the Air Force rightly raised concerns about the legality of attacking in a place where there was no armed conflict. CIA agents based in Djibouti carried out the killing. All six passengers in the vehicle were killed, including an American. In January 2003, the United Nations Commission on Human Rights received a report on the Yemen strike from its special rapporteur on extrajudicial, summary, or arbitrary killing. The rapporteur concluded that the strike constituted "a clear case of extrajudicial killing."

Apparently, Yemen gave tacit consent for the strike. States [countries] cannot, however, give consent to a right they do not have. States may not use military force against individuals on their territory when law enforcement measures are appropriate. At the time of the strike, Yemen was not using military force anywhere on its territory. More recently, Yemen has been using military force to suppress militants in two parts of the country. The U.S.'s ongoing drone use, however, has not been part of those campaigns.

U.S. House of Representatives, April 28, 2010.

The United States has also used combat drones in Somalia probably starting in late 2006 during the Ethiopian invasion when the U.S. assisted Ethiopia in its attempt to install a new government in that volatile country. Ethiopia's effort had some support from the UN and the African Union. To the extent that the U.S. was assisting Ethiopia, our actions had some justification. It is clear, however, that the U.S. has used drone strikes independently of the attempt to restore order in Somalia. The U.S. has continued to target and kill individuals in Somalia following Ethiopia's pullout from the country.

The U.S. use of drones in Pakistan has similar problems to the uses in Yemen and Somalia. Where military force *is* warranted to address internal violence, governments have widely resorted to the practice of inviting in another state to assist. This is the legal justification the U.S. cites for its use of military force today in Afghanistan and Iraq. Yet, the U.S. cannot point to invitations from Pakistan for most of its drone attacks. Indeed, for much of the period that the United States has used drones on the territory of Pakistan, there has been no armed conflict. Therefore, even express consent by Pakistan would not justify their use.

The United States has been carrying out drone attacks in Pakistan since 2004. Pakistani authorities only began to use major military force to suppress militancy in May 2009, in Buner Province. Some U.S. drone strikes have been coordinated with Islamabad's efforts, but some have not. Some strikes have apparently even targeted groups allied with Islamabad.

## II. The Battlefield Defined

The Bush administration justified the 2002 Yemen strike and others as justified under the law of armed conflict in the "Global War on Terror." The current State Department Legal Adviser, Harold Koh, has rejected the term "Global War on Terror," preferring to base our actions on the view that the U.S. is in an "armed conflict with al-Qaeda, the Taliban and associated forces." Under the new label, the U.S. is carrying out many of the same actions as the Bush administration under the old one: using lethal force without warning, far from any actual battlefield.

Armed conflict, however, is a real thing. The United States is currently engaged in an armed conflict in Afghanistan. The United States has tens of thousands of highly trained troops fighting a well-organized opponent that is able to hold territory. The situation in Afghanistan today conforms to the definition of armed conflict in international law. The International Law Association's Committee on the Use of Force issued a report in 2008 confirming the basic characteristics of all armed conflict: (1) the presence of organized armed groups that are (2) engaged in intense inter-group fighting. The fighting or hostilities of an armed conflict occur within limited zones, referred to as combat or conflict zones. It is only in such zones that killing enemy combatants or those taking a direct part in hostilities is permissible.

Because armed conflict requires a certain intensity of fighting, the isolated terrorist attack, regardless of how serious the consequences, is not an armed conflict. Terrorism is crime. Members of al Qaeda or other terrorist groups are active in Canada, France, Germany, Indonesia, Morocco, Saudi Arabia, Spain, the United Kingdom, Yemen and elsewhere. Still, these countries do not consider themselves in a war with al Qaeda. In the words of a leading expert on the law of armed conflict, the British Judge on the International Court of Justice, Sir Christopher Greenwood:

> In the language of international law there is no basis for speaking of a war on Al-Qaeda or any other terrorist group, for such a group cannot be a belligerent, it is merely a band of criminals, and to treat it as anything else risks distorting the law while giving that group a status which to some implies a degree of legitimacy.

To label terrorists "enemy combatants" lifts them out of the status of *criminal* to that of *combatant,* the same category as America's own troops on the battlefield. This move to label terrorists combatants is contrary to strong historic trends. From earliest times, governments have struggled to prevent their enemies from approaching a status of equality. Even governments on the verge of collapse due to the pressure of a rebel advance have vehemently denied that the violence inflicted by their enemies was anything but criminal violence. Governments fear the psychological and legal advantages to opponents of calling them "combatants" and their struggle a "war."

President Ronald Reagan strongly opposed labeling terrorists combatants. He said that to "grant combatant status to irregular forces even if they do not satisfy the traditional requirements . . . would endanger civilians among whom terrorists and other irregulars attempt to conceal themselves."

The United Kingdom and other allies take the same position as President Reagan: "It is the understanding of the United Kingdom that the term 'armed conflict' of itself and in its context denotes a situation of a kind which is not constituted by the commission of ordinary crimes including acts of terrorism whether concerted or in isolation."

In the United States and other countries plagued by al Qaeda, institutions are functioning normally. No one has declared martial law. The International Committee of the Red Cross is not active. Criminal trials of suspected terrorists are being held in regular criminal courts. The police use lethal force only in situations of necessity. The U.S.'s actions today are generally consistent with its long-term policy of separating acts of terrorism from armed conflict—except when it comes to drones.

## III. Battlefield Restraints

Even when the U.S. is using drones at the request of Pakistan in battles it is waging, we are failing to follow important battlefield rules. The U.S. must respect the principles of necessity, proportionality and humanity in carrying out drone attacks. "Necessity" refers to military necessity, and the obligation that force is used only if necessary to accomplish a reasonable military objective. "Proportionality" prohibits that "which may be expected to cause incidental loss of civilian life, injury to civilians, damage to civilian objects, or a combination thereof, which would be excessive in relation to concrete and direct military advantage anticipated." These limitations on permissible force extend to both the quantity of force used and the geographic scope of its use.

Far from suppressing militancy in Pakistan, drone attacks are fueling the interest in fighting against the United States. This impact makes the use of drones difficult to justify under the terms of military necessity. Most serious of all, perhaps, is the disproportionate impact of drone attacks. A principle that provides context for all decisions in armed conflict is the principle of humanity. The principle of humanity supports decisions in favor of sparing life and avoiding destruction in close cases under either the principles of necessity or proportionality. According to the International Committee of the Red Cross, the principles of necessity and humanity are particularly important in situations such as Pakistan:

> In classic large-scale confrontations between well-equipped and organized armed forces or groups, the principles of military necessity and of humanity are unlikely to restrict the use of force against legitimate military targets beyond what is already required by specific provisions of IHL [international humanitarian law]. The practical importance of their restraining function will increase with the ability of the conflict to control the circumstances and area in which its military operations are conducted, may become decisive where armed forces operate against selected individuals in situations comparable to peacetime policing. In practice, such considerations are likely to become particularly relevant where a party to the conflict exercises effective territorial control, most notably in occupied territories and non-international armed conflicts.

Another issue in drone use is the fact that strikes are carried out in Pakistan by the CIA and civilian contractors. Only members of the United States armed forces have the combatant's privilege to use lethal force without facing prosecution. CIA operatives are not trained in the law of armed conflict. They are not bound by the Uniform Code of Military Justice to respect the laws and customs of war. They are not subject to the military chain of command. This fact became abundantly clear during the revelation of U.S. use of harsh interrogation tactics. Given the negative impact of that unlawful conduct on America's standing in the world and our ability to promote the rule of law, it is difficult to fathom why the Obama administration is using the CIA to carry out drone attacks, let alone civilian contractors.

## Conclusion

The use of military force in counter-terrorism operations has been counterproductive. Military force is a blunt instrument. Inevitably unintended victims are the result of almost any military action. Drone attacks in Pakistan have resulted in large numbers of deaths and are generally seen as fueling terrorism, not abating it. In congressional testimony in March 2009, counter-terrorism expert, David Kilcullen, said drones in Pakistan are giving "rise to a feeling of anger that coalesces the population around the extremists and leads to spikes of extremism well outside the parts of the country where we are mounting those attacks." Another expert told the *New York Times*, "The more the drone campaign works, the more it fails—as increased attacks only make the Pakistanis angrier at the collateral damage and sustained violation of their sovereignty." A National Public Radio Report on April 26, 2010, pointed out that al Qaeda is losing support in the Muslim world because of its violent, lawless tactics. We can help eliminate the last of that support by distinguishing ourselves through commitment to the rule of law, especially by strict compliance with the rules governing lethal force.

**MARY ELLEN O'CONNELL** is the research professor of international dispute resolution at the Kroc Institute, the University of Notre Dame, and also the Robert and Marion Short professor of law at the university's law school. Among her publications is *The Power and Purpose of International Law* (Ohio State University Press, 2008). She earned her JD from Columbia University.

# NO

Michael W. Lewis

# Examining the Legality of
# Unmanned Targeting

## Introduction

I am a professor of law at Ohio Northern University's Pettit College of Law where I teach International Law and the Law of Armed Conflict. I spent over 7 years in the U.S. Navy as a Naval Flight Officer flying F-14s. I flew missions over the Persian Gulf and Iraq as part of Operations Desert Shield/Desert Storm and I graduated from Top Gun [the U.S. Navy Fighter Weapons School] in 1992. After my military service I attended Harvard Law School and graduated *cum laude* in 1998. Subsequently I have lectured on a variety of aspects of the laws of war, with an emphasis on aerial bombardment, at dozens of institutions including Harvard, NYU, Columbia and the University of Chicago. I have published several articles and co-authored a book on the laws of war relating to the war on terror. My prior experience as a combat pilot and strike planner provides me with a different perspective from most other legal scholars on the interaction between law and combat.

## The Current Laws of War Are Sufficient to Address the Drone Question

There is nothing inherently illegal about using drones to target specific individuals. Nor is there anything legally unique about the use of unmanned drones as a weapons delivery platform that requires the creation of new or different laws to govern their use.

As with any other attack launched against enemy forces during an armed conflict, the use of drones is governed by International Humanitarian Law (IHL). Compliance with current IHL that governs aerial bombardment and requires that all attacks demonstrate military necessity and comply with the principle of proportionality is sufficient to ensure the legality of drone strikes. In circumstances where a strike by a helicopter or an F-16 [a U.S. warplane] would be legal, the use of a drone would be equally legitimate. However, this legal parity does not answer three fundamental questions that have been raised by these hearings. Who may be targeted? Where may they be targeted? And finally who is allowed to pilot the drones and determine which targets are legally appropriate?

## Who May Be Targeted?

In order to understand the rules governing the targeting of individuals, it is necessary to understand the various categories that IHL assigns to individuals. To best understand how they relate to one another it is useful to start from the beginning.

All people are civilians and are not subjected to targeting unless they take affirmative steps to either become combatants or to otherwise lose their civilian immunity. It is important to recognize that a civilian does not become a combatant by merely picking up a weapon. In order to become a combatant an individual must be a member of the "armed forces of a Party to a conflict." This definition is found in Article 43 of Additional Protocol I to the Geneva Conventions. It goes on to define the term "armed forces" as:

> The armed forces of a Party to a conflict consist of all organized armed forces, groups and units which are under a command responsible to that Party for the conduct of its subordinates, even if that Party is represented by a government or an authority not recognized by an adverse Party. Such armed forces shall be subject to an internal disciplinary system which, *inter alia,* shall enforce compliance with the rules of international law applicable in armed conflict.

The status of combatant is important because combatants "have the right to participate directly in hostilities." This "combatants' privilege" allows privileged individuals to participate in an armed conflict without violating domestic laws prohibiting the destruction of property, assault, murder, etc. The combatant's conduct is therefore regulated by IHL rather than [by] domestic law.

U.S. House of Representatives, April 28, 2010.

Combatant status is something of a double-edged sword, however. While it bestows the combatant privilege on the individual, it also subjects that individual to attack at any time by other parties to the conflict. A combatant may be lawfully targeted whether or not they pose a current threat to their opponents, whether or not they are armed, or even awake. The only occasion on which IHL prohibits attacking a combatant is when that combatant has surrendered or been rendered *hors de combat*. Professor Geoff Corn has argued compellingly that this ability to target based upon status, rather than on the threat posed by an individual, is the defining feature of an armed conflict.

After examining the definition of combatant, it becomes apparent that combatant status is based upon group conduct, not individual conduct. Members of al Qaeda are not combatants because as a group they are not "subject to an internal disciplinary system which [enforces] compliance with the rules of international law applicable in armed conflict." It does not matter whether an individual al Qaeda member may have behaved properly; he can never obtain the combatants' privilege because the group he belongs to does not meet IHL's requirements. Professor [David] Glazier's testimony [before this committee] that al Qaeda and the Taliban could possess "the basic right to engage in combat against us" is mistaken. These groups have clearly and unequivocally forfeited any "right" to be treated as combatants by choosing to employ means and methods of warfare that violate the laws of armed conflict, such as deliberately targeting civilians.

If al Qaeda members are not combatants, then what are they? They must be civilians, and civilians as a general rule are immune from targeting. However, civilians lose this immunity "for such time as they take a direct part in hostilities." The question of what constitutes direct participation in hostilities (DPH) has been much debated. While DOD [the U.S. Department of Defense] has yet to offer its definition of DPH, the International Committee of the Red Cross (ICRC) recently completed a six-year study on the matter and has offered interpretive guidance that, while not binding on the United States, provides a useful starting point. The ICRC guidance states that "members of organized armed groups [which do not qualify as combatants] belonging to a party to the conflict lose protection against direct attack for the duration of their membership (i.e., for as long as they assume a continuous combat function)."

The concept of a "continuous combat function" within DPH is a reaction to the "farmer by day, fighter by night" tactic that a number of organized armed terrorist groups have employed to retain their civilian immunity from attack for as long as possible. Because such individuals (be they fighters, bomb makers, planners or leaders) perform a continuous combat function, they may be directly targeted for as long as they remain members of the group. The only way for such individuals to reacquire their civilian immunity is to disavow membership in the group.

So the answer to "Who may be targeted?" is any member of al Qaeda or the Taliban, or any other individuals that have directly participated in hostilities against the United States. This would certainly include individuals that directly or indirectly (e.g. by planting IEDs) [improvised explosive devices] attacked Coalition forces as well as any leadership within these organizations. Significantly, the targeting of these individuals does not involve their elevation to combatant status as Professor O'Connell implied in her testimony [found in the first reading]. These individuals are civilians who have forfeited their civilian immunity by directly participating in hostilities. They are not, and cannot become, combatants until they join an organized armed group that complies with the laws of armed conflict, but they nevertheless remain legitimate targets until they clearly disassociate themselves from al Qaeda or the Taliban.

## Where May Attacks Take Place?

Some witnesses have testified to this subcommittee that the law of armed conflict only applies to our ongoing conflict with al Qaeda in certain defined geographic areas. Professor O'Connell states that the geographic limit of the armed conflict is within the borders of Afghanistan while others include the border areas of Pakistan and Iraq. They take the position that any operations against al Qaeda outside of this defined geography are solely the province of law enforcement, which requires that the target be warned before lethal force is employed. Because drones cannot meet this requirement they conclude that drone strikes outside of this geographical area should be prohibited. The geographical boundaries proposed are based upon the infrequency of armed assaults that take place outside of Afghanistan, Iraq and the border region of Pakistan. Because IHL does not specifically address the geographic scope of armed conflicts, to assess these proposed requirements it is necessary to step back and consider the law of armed conflict as a whole and the realities of warfare as they apply to this conflict.

One of the principal goals of IHL is to protect the civilian population from harm during an armed conflict. To further this goal IHL prohibits direct attacks on civilians and requires that parties to the conflict distinguish themselves from the civilian population. As a result, it would seem anomalous for IHL to be read in such a way as to reward a party that regularly targets civilians, and yet that is what is being proposed. As discussed above, a civilian member of al Qaeda who is performing a continuous combat function may be legitimately targeted with lethal force without any warning. But the proposed geographic limitations on IHL's application offer this individual a renewed immunity from attack. Rather than disavowing an organization that targets civilians, IHL's preferred result, the proposed geographic restrictions allow the individual to obtain the same immunity by crossing an international border and avoiding law enforcement while remaining active in an organization that targets civilians. When law enforcement's logistical limitations are considered, along with the host state's ambivalence for actively pursuing al Qaeda within its borders, it becomes clear that the proposed geographical limitations on IHL are tantamount to the creation of a safe haven for al Qaeda.

More importantly these proposed limitations would hand the initiative in this conflict over to al Qaeda. Militarily the ability to establish and maintain the initiative during a conflict is one of the most important strategic and operational advantages that a party can possess. To the extent that one side's forces are able to decide when, where and how a conflict is conducted, the likelihood of a favorable outcome is greatly increased. If IHL is interpreted to allow al Qaeda's leadership to marshal its forces in Yemen or the Sudan, or any number of other places that are effectively beyond the reach of law enforcement and to then strike at its next target of choice, whether it be New York, Madrid, London, Bali, Washington, DC or Detroit, then IHL is being read to hand the initiative in the conflict to al Qaeda. IHL should not be read to reward a party that consistently violates IHL's core principles and as Professor Glazier points out in his reference to the Cambodian incursion, it was not read that way in the past.

Those opposed to the position that IHL governs the conflict with al Qaeda regardless of geography, and therefore allows strikes like the one conducted in Yemen in 2002, have voiced three main concerns. The first concern is that the United States may be violating the sovereignty of other nations by conducting drone strikes on their territory. It is true that such attacks may only be conducted with the permission of the state on whose territory the attack takes place and questions have been raised about whether Pakistan, Yemen and other states have consented to this use of force. This is a legitimate concern that must be satisfactorily answered while accounting for the obvious sensitivity associated with granting such permission. The fact that Harold Koh, the State Department's Legal Advisor, specifically mentioned [in his testimony] the "sovereignty of the other states involved" in his discussion of drone strikes is evidence that the Administration takes this requirement seriously.

The second concern is that such a geographically unbounded conflict could lead to drone strikes in Paris or London, or to setting the precedent for other nations to employ lethal force in the United States against its enemies that have taken refuge here. These concerns are overstated. The existence of the permission requirement mentioned above means that any strikes conducted in London or Paris could only take place with the approval of the British or French governments. Further, any such strike would have to meet the requirements of military necessity and proportionality and it is difficult to imagine how these requirements could be satisfactorily met in such a congested urban setting.

Lastly, there is a legitimate concern that mistakes could be made. An individual could be inappropriately placed on the list and killed without being given any opportunity to challenge his placement on the list. Again, Mr. Koh's assurances that the procedures for identifying lawful targets "are extremely robust" are in some measure reassuring, particularly given his stature in the international legal community. However, some oversight of these procedures is clearly warranted. While *ex ante* [before the fact/event] review must obviously be balanced against secrecy and national security concerns, *ex post* review can be more thorough. When the Israeli Supreme Court approved the use of targeted killings, one of its requirements was for transparency after the fact coupled with an independent investigation of the precision of the identification and the circumstances of the attack. A similar *ex post* transparency would be appropriate here to ensure that "extremely robust" means something.

## Who May Do the Targeting?

Another question raised in the hearings was the propriety of allowing the CIA to control drone strikes. Professor Glazier opined that CIA drone pilots conducting strikes are civilians directly participating in hostilities and suggested that they might be committing war crimes by engaging in such conduct. Even if these are not considered war crimes, if the CIA members are civilians performing a continuous combat function then they are not entitled to the combatants' privilege and could potentially be liable for domestic law violations.

Therefore, if CIA members are going to continue piloting drones and planning strikes, then they must obtain combatant status. Article 43(3) of Protocol I [to the Geneva Convention of 1949] allows a party to "incorporate a paramilitary or armed law enforcement agency into its armed forces" after notifying other parties to the conflict. For such an incorporation to be effective a clear chain of command would have to be established (if it does not already exist) that enforces compliance with the laws of armed conflict. Without this incorporation or some other measure clearly establishing the CIA's accountability for law of armed conflict violations, the continued use of CIA drone pilots and strike planners will be legally problematic.

## Conclusion

Drones are legitimate weapons platforms whose use is effectively governed by current IHL applicable to aerial bombardment. Like other forms of aircraft they may be used to target enemy forces, whether specifically identifiable individuals or armed formations.

IHL permits the targeting of both combatants and civilians that are directly participating in hostilities. Because of the means and methods of warfare that they employ, al Qaeda and Taliban forces are not combatants and are not entitled to the combatants' privilege. They are instead civilians that have forfeited their immunity because of their participation in hostilities. Members of al Qaeda and the Taliban that perform continuous combat functions may be targeted at any time, subject to the standard requirements of distinction and proportionality.

Placing blanket geographical restrictions on the use of drone strikes turns IHL on its head by allowing individuals an alternative means for reacquiring effective immunity from attack without disavowing al Qaeda and its methods of warfare. It further bolsters al Qaeda by providing them with a safe haven that allows them to regain the initiative in their conflict with the United States. The geographical limitations on drone strikes imposed by sovereignty requirements, along with the ubiquitous requirements of distinction and proportionality, are sufficient to prevent these strikes from violating international law. However, some form of *ex post* [after the fact/event] transparency and oversight is necessary to review the identification criteria and strike circumstances to ensure that they remain "extremely robust."

**MICHAEL W. LEWIS** is a professor of law at Ohio Northern University's Pettit College of Law, where he teaches and writes in the fields of international law and the law of armed conflict. He has served as a U.S. Navy fighter pilot and holds a JD from Harvard University.

# Technology and the Future

Nanotechnology and other scientific developments will continue to produce limitless technological innovations, undoubtedly impacting our individual lives and social systems. The question moving forward is if and how these developments can be used to improve the lives of all. From food to healthcare to defense, what new developments can best serve individual and societal needs on a grand scale? As we have learned, our past decisions regarding technology have served to both help and hinder human lives. We must keep this mind as we think about, evaluate, and make decisions regarding future technology choices. The readings in this section explore the interconnections between society and technology, while also highlighting the need for us to become informed, responsible citizens concerned with protecting our technological future.

## Learning Objectives

1. Define nanotechnology.
2. Critically examine benefits and drawbacks of potential future technologies and technological advances.
3. Recognize the individual and societal responsibility of creating a sustainable technological future.

# Article 43

Fabio Salamanca-Buentello, Deepa L. Persad, Erin B. Court,
Douglas K. Martin, Abdallah S. Daar, and Peter A. Singer*

## Nanotechnology and the Developing World

Nanotechnology can be harnessed to address some of the world's most critical development problems. However, to our knowledge, there has been no systematic prioritization of applications of nanotechnology targeted toward these challenges faced by the 5 billion people living in the developing world.

In this article, we aim to convey three key messages. First, we show that developing countries are already harnessing nanotechnology to address some of their most pressing needs. Second, we identify and rank the ten applications of nanotechnology most likely to benefit developing countries, and demonstrate that these applications can contribute to the attainment of the United Nations Millennium Development Goals (MDGs). Third, we propose a way for the international community to accelerate the use of these top nanotechnologies by less industrialized countries to meet critical sustainable development challenges.

## Developing Countries Innovate in Nanotechnology

Several developing countries have launched nanotechnology initiatives in order to strengthen their capacity and sustain economic growth [1]. India's Department of Science and Technology will invest $20 million over the next five years (2004–2009) for their Nanomaterials Science and Technology Initiative [2]. Panacea Biotec (http://www.panacea-biotec.com/products/products.htm) (New Delhi, India) is conducting novel drug delivery research using mucoadhesive nanoparticles, and Dabur Research Foundation (Ghaziabad, India) is participating in Phase-1 clinical trials of nanoparticle delivery of the anti-cancer drug paclitaxel [3]. The number of nanotechnology patent applications from China ranks third in the world behind the United States and Japan [4]. In Brazil, the projected budget for nanoscience during the 2004–2007 period is about $25 million, and three institutes, four networks, and approximately 300 scientists are working in nanotechnology [5]. The South African Nanotechnology Initiative (http://www.sani.org.za) is a national network of academic researchers involved in areas such as nanophase catalysts, nanofiltration, nanowires, nanotubes, and quantum dots (Figure 1). Other developing countries, such as Thailand, the Philippines, Chile, Argentina, and Mexico, are also pursuing nanotechnology [1].

Science and technology alone are not the answer to sustainable development challenges. Like any other science and technology waves, nanoscience and nanotechnology are not "silver bullets" that will magically solve all the problems of developing countries; the social context of these countries must always be considered. Nevertheless, science and technology are a critical component of development [6]. The 2001 Human Development Report [7] of the UN Development Program clearly illustrates the important roles of science and technology in reducing mortality rates and improving

### A Definition of Nanotechnology

Nanotechnology is the study, design, creation, synthesis, manipulation, and application of functional materials, devices, and systems through control of matter at the nanometer scale (1–100 nanometers, one nanometer being equal to $1 \times 10^{-9}$ of a meter), that is, at the atomic and molecular levels, and the exploitation of novel phenomena and properties of matter at that scale.

The Policy Forum allows health policy makers around the world to discuss challenges and opportunities for improving health care in their societies.

**Citation:** Salamanca-Buentello F, Persad DL, Court EB, Martin DK, Daar AS, et al. (2005) Nanotechnology and the developing world. PLoS Med 2(5): e97.

All authors are at the University of Toronto Joint Centre for Bioethics (Toronto, Canada) and the Canadian Program on Genomics and Global Health (Toronto, Canada). Douglas K. Martin is also at the Department of Health Policy, Management and Evaluation, University of Toronto. Abdallah S. Daar is also at the Department of Public Health Sciences and Surgery, University of Toronto, and the McLaughlin Centre for Molecular Medicine (Toronto, Canada). Peter A. Singer is also at Department of Medicine, University of Toronto and University Health Network.

**Abbreviations:** NIH, National Institutes of Health; MDGs, Millennium Development Goals

*To whom correspondence should be addressed. E-mail: peter.singer@utoronto.ca

**Competing Interests:** Peter A. Singer is on the editorial board of *PLoS Medicine*.

**DOI:** 10.1371/journal.pmed.0020097

life expectancy in the period 1960–1990, but it did not emphasize nanotechnology specifically. In a report released in early 2005 [8], the UN Task Force on Science, Technology and Innovation (part of the process designed to assist UN agencies in achieving the UN MDGs) addresses the potential of nanotechnology for sustainable development.

# Top Ten Nanotechnologies Contributing to the MDGs

In order to provide a systematic approach with which to address sustainable development issues in the developing world, we have identified and ranked the ten applications of nanotechnology most likely to benefit developing countries. We used a modified Delphi Method, as described in our Top Ten Biotechnologies report [9] to identify and prioritize the applications and to achieve consensus among the panelists.

We recruited an international panel of 85 experts in nanotechnology who could provide the informed judgments that this study required, of which 63 completed the project (Table S1). We selected the panelists based on contacts identified in our previous study on nanotechnology in developing countries [1]. A conscious effort was made to balance the panel with respect to gender, specialty areas within nanotechnology, and geographic distribution. Of the panelists, 38 (60%) were from developing countries and 25 (40%) from developed countries; 51 panelists (81%) were male and 12 (19%) were female.

We posed the following open-ended question: "Which do you think are the nanotechnologies most likely to benefit developing countries in the areas of water, agriculture, nutrition, health, energy, and the environment in the next 10 years?" These areas were identified in the 2002 UN Johannesburg Summit on Sustainable Development [10]. We asked the panelists to answer this question using the following criteria derived from our previous Top Ten Biotechnologies study.

**Impact.** How much difference will the technology make in improving water, agriculture, nutrition, health, energy, and the environment in developing countries?

**Burden.** Will it address the most pressing needs?

**Appropriateness.** Will it be affordable, robust, and adjustable to settings in developing countries, and will it be socially, culturally, and politically acceptable?

**Feasibility.** Can it realistically be developed and deployed in a time frame of ten years?

**Knowledge gap.** Does the technology advance quality of life by creating new knowledge?

**Indirect benefits.** Does it address issues such as capacity building and income generation that have indirect, positive effects on developing countries?

Three Delphi rounds were conducted using e-mail messages, faxes, and phone calls. In the first round, the panelists proposed examples of nanotechnologies in response to our study question. We analyzed and organized their answers according to common themes and generated a list of twenty distinct nanotechnology applications. This list was reviewed for face and content validity by two nanotechnologists external to the panel. In the second Delphi round, the panelists ranked their top ten choices from the 20 applications provided and gave reasons for their choices. To analyze the data, we produced a summative point score for each application, ranked the list, and summarized the panelists reasons. Then we redistributed the top 13 applications, instead of the top ten, to generate a greater number of choices for increased accuracy in the last round. Thus, the highest score possible for an application was 819 (63 × 13). The final Delphi round was devoted to consolidating consensus by re-ranking the top ten of the 13 choices obtained in the previous round and to gathering concrete examples of each application from the panelists.

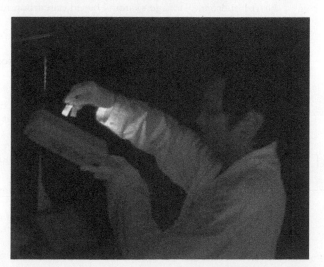

Fig. 1. **Quantum Dots for Disease Diagnostics Quantum dots may be used for cheap, efficient handheld diagnostic devices available at point-of-care institutions in developing countries.**

Our results, shown in Table 1, were compiled from January to July 2004. They display a high degree of consensus with regard to the top four applications: all of the panelists cited at least one of the top four applications in their personal top four rankings, with the majority citing at least three.

To further assess the impact of nanotechnology on sustainable development, we have compared the top ten applications with the UN Millennium Development Goals (Table 1 and Figure 2). The MDGs are eight goals that aim to promote human development and encourage social and economic sustainability [11]. In 2000, all 189 member states of the UN committed to achieve the MDGs by 2015. The MDGs are: (i) Eradicate extreme poverty and hunger; (ii) Achieve universal primary education; (iii) Promote gender equality and empower women; (iv) Reduce child mortality; (v) Improve maternal health; (vi) Combat HIV/AIDS, malaria, and other diseases; (vii) Ensure environmental sustainability; and (viii) Develop a global partnership for development. As shown in Table 1 and Figure 2, the top ten nanotechnology applications can contribute to achieving the UN MDGs.

## Addressing Global Challenges Using Nanotechnology

What can the international community do to support the application of nanotechnology in developing countries? In 2002, the National Institutes of Health (NIH) conceptualized a roadmap for medical research to identify major opportunities and gaps in biomedical investigations. Nanomedicine is one of the areas of implementation that has been outlined to address this concern. Several of the applications of nanotechnology that we have identified in our study can aid the NIH in this process by targeting the areas of research that need to be addressed in order to combat some of the serious medical issues facing the developing world.

To expand on this idea, we propose an initiative, called "Addressing Global Challenges Using Nanotechnology," to accelerate the use of nanotechnology to address critical sustainable development challenges. We model this proposal on the Foundation for the NIH/Bill and Melinda Gates Foundation's Grand Challenges in Global Health [12], which itself was based on Hilbert's Grand Challenges in Mathematics.

A grand challenge is meant to direct investigators to seek a specific scientific or technological breakthrough that would overcome one or more bottlenecks in an imagined path to solving a significant development problem (or preferably, several) [12]. A scientific board similar to the one created for the Grand Challenges in Global Health, with strong representation of developing countries, will need to be established to provide guidance and oversee the program. The top ten nanotechnology applications identified in Table 1 are a good starting point for defining the grand challenges.

**Table 1.** Correlation between the Top Ten Applications of Nanotechnology for Developing Countries and the UN Millennium Development Goals

| Ranking (Score) | Applications of Nanotechnology | Examples | Comparison with the MDGs |
|---|---|---|---|
| 1 (766)[a] | Energy storage, production, and conversion | Novel hydrogen storage systems based on carbon nanotubes and other lightweight nanomaterials<br>Photovoltaic cells and organic light-emitting devices based on quantum dots<br>Carbon nanotubes in composite film coatings for solar cells<br>Nanocatalysts for hydrogen generation<br>Hybrid protein-polymer biomimetic membranes | VII |
| 2 (706) | Agricultural productivity enhancement | Nanoporous zeolites for slow-release and efficient dosage of water and fertilizers for plants, and of nutrients and drugs for livestock<br>Nanocapsules for herbicide delivery<br>Nanosensors for soil quality and for plant health monitoring<br>Nanomagnets for removal of soil contaminants | I, IV, V, VII |
| 3 (682) | Water treatment and remediation | Nanomembranes for water purification, desalination, and detoxification<br>Nanosensors for the detection of contaminants and pathogens<br>Nanoporous zeolites, nanoporous polymers, and attapulgite clays for water purification<br>Magnetic nanoparticles for water treatment and remediation nanoparticles for the catalytic degradation of water pollutants<br>$TiO_2$ | I, IV, V, VII |

| Ranking (Score) | Applications of Nanotechnology | Examples | Comparison with the MDGs |
|---|---|---|---|
| 4 (606) | Disease diagnosis and screening | Nanoliter systems (Lab-on-a-chip) Nanosensor arrays based on carbon nanotubes Quantum dots for disease diagnosis Magnetic nanoparticles as nanosensors Antibody-dendrimer conjugates for diagnosis of HIV-1 and cancer Nanowire and nanobelt nanosensors for disease diagnosis Nanoparticles as medical image enhancers | IV, V, VI |
| 5 (558) | Drug delivery systems | Nanocapsules, liposomes, dendrimers, buckyballs, nanobiomagnets, and attapulgite clays for slow and sustained drug release systems | IV, V, VI |
| 6 (472) | Food processing and storage | Nanocomposites for plastic film coatings used in food packaging Antimicrobial nanoemulsions for applications in decontamination of food equipment, packaging, or food Nanotechnology-based antigen detecting biosensors for identification of pathogen contamination | I, IV, V |
| 7 (410) | Air pollution and remediation | $TiO_2$ nanoparticle-based photocatalytic degradation of air pollutants in self-cleaning systems Nanocatalysts for more efficient, cheaper, and better-controlled catalytic converters Nanosensors for detection of toxic materials and leaks Gas separation nanodevices | IV, V, VII |
| 8 (366) | Construction | Nanomolecular structures to make asphalt and concrete more robust to water seepage Heat-resistant nanomaterials to block ultraviolet and infrared radiation Nanomaterials for cheaper and durable housing, surfaces, coatings, glues, concrete, and heat and light exclusion Self-cleaning surfaces (e.g., windows, mirrors, toilets) with bioactive coatings | VII |
| 9 (321) | Health monitoring | Nanotubes and nanoparticles for glucose, $CO_2$, and cholesterol sensors and for in-situ monitoring of homeostasis | IV, V, VI |
| 10 (258) | Vector and pest detection and control | Nanosensors for pest detection Nanoparticles for new pesticides, insecticides, and insect repellents | IV, V, VI |

[a] The maximum total score an application could receive was 819.

DOI: 10.1371/journal.pmed.0020097.t001

The funding to address global challenges using nanotechnology could come from various sources, including national and international foundations, and from collaboration among nanotechnology initiatives in industrialized and developing countries. These funds could be significantly increased if industrialized nations adopted the target set in February 2004 by Paul Martin, Prime Minister of Canada: that 5% of Canada's research and development investment be used to address developing world challenges [13]. In parallel to the allocation of public funds, policies should provide incentives for the private sector to direct a portion of their research and development toward funding our initiative. The UN Commission on Private Sector and Development report *Unleashing Entrepreneurship: Making Business Work for the Poor* [14] underscores the importance of partnerships with the private sector, especially the domestic private sectors in developing countries, in working to achieve the MDGs.

Perhaps most importantly, our results can provide guidance to the developing countries themselves to help target their growing initiatives in nanotechnology [15]. The goal is to use nanotechnology responsibly [16] to generate real benefits for the 5 billion people in the developing world.

# Acknowledgments

We are grateful to our panelists for providing their expertise, and to W.C.W. Chan and A. Shik for help with our analysis of the nanotechnologies. Grant support was provided by the Canadian Program on Genomics and Global Health (supported by the Ontario Research and Development Challenge Fund, and by Genome Canada through the Ontario Genomics Institute (Toronto, Canada);

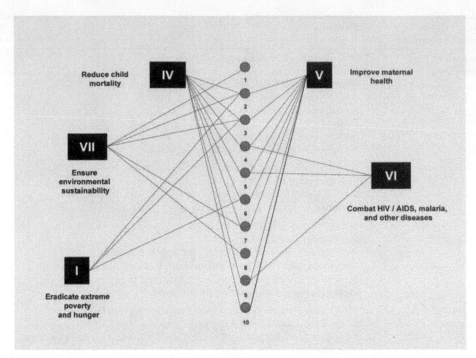

**Fig. 2.** Comparison between the Millennium Development Goals and the Nanotechnologies Most Likely to Benefit Developing Countries in the 2004–2014 Period

matching partners can be found at www.geneticsethics.net). EBC is supported by the Ontario Genomics Institute; DKM is supported by a Career Scientist award from the Ontario Ministry of Health and Long-Term Care; ASD is supported by the McLaughlin Centre for Molecular Medicine; PAS is supported by a Distinguished Investigator award from the Canadian Institutes of Health Research. The University of Toronto Joint Centre for Bioethics (Toronto, Canada) is a PAHO/ WHO Collaborating Center for Bioethics.

## Supporting Information

Table S1. List of Panel Members Found at DOI: 10.1371/journal. pmed.0020097.st001 (43 KB DOC).

## References

1. Court E, Daar AS, Martin E, Acharya T, Singer PA (2004) Will Prince Charles et al diminish the opportunities of developing countries in nanotechnology? Available: http://www. nanotechweb.org/articles/society/3/1/1/1. Accessed 21 February 2005.
2. U.S., Indian high technology will benefit through cooperation (2003) Available: http://newdelhi.usembassy.gov/ wwwhpr0812a.html. Accessed 27 January 2005.
3. Bapsy PP, Raghunadharao D, Majumdar A, Ganguly S, Roy A, et al. (2004) DO/NDR/02 a novel polymeric nanoparticle paclitaxel: Results of a phase I dose escalation study. J Clin Oncol 22, 14S: 2026.
4. [Anonymous] (2003) China's nanotechnology patent applications rank third in world. Available: http://www.investorideas. com/Companies/Nanotechnology/Articles/ China's Nanotechnology1003,03.asp. Accessed 27 January 2005.
5. Meridian Institute (2004) Report of the international dialogue on responsible research and development of nanotechnology. Attachment F. Available: http://www. nanoandthepoor.org/ Attachment_F_Responses_and_Background_Info_040812.pdf. Accessed 21 February 2005.
6. Sachs J (2002) The essential ingredient. New Sci 2356: 175.
7. UN Development Programme (2001) Human development report. Available: http://www. undp.org/hdr2001/completenew.pdf. Accessed 21 February 2005.
8. UN Millennium Project 2005 (2005) Innovation: Applying knowledge in development. Task force on science, technology and innovation. Available: http://unmp.forumone.com/eng_task_force/ScienceEbook.pdf. Accessed 21 February 2005.
9. Daar AS, Thorsteinsdottir H, Martin D, Smith AC, Nast S, et al. (2002) Top ten biotechnologies for improving health in developing countries. Nat Genet 23: 229–232.

10. World Summit on Sustainable Development (2002) Available: http://www. johannesburgsummit.org/html/documents/wehab_papers.html. Accessed 27 January 2005.

11. United Nations (2000) UN millennium development goals, Available: http://www. un.org/millenniumgoals/. Accessed 27 January 2005.

12. Varmus H, Klausner R, Zerhouni E, Acharya T, Daar AS, et al. (2003) Grand challenges in global health. Science 302: 398–399.

13. Government of Canada, Office of the Prime Minister (2004) Complete text and videos of the Prime Minister's reply to the speech from the throne. Available: http://www.pm.gc. ca/eng/news.asp?id=277. Accessed 27 January 2005.

14. UN Development Programme, Commission on the Private Sector and Development (2004) Unleashing entrepreneurship: Making business work for the poor. Available: http://www.undp. org/cpsd/indexF.html. Accessed 21 February 2005.

15. Meridian Institute (2005) Nanotechnology and the poor: Opportunities and risks. Available: http://www.nanoandthepoor.org/gdnp.php. Accessed 21 February 2005.

16. The Royal Society and The Royal Academy of Engineering (2004) Nanoscience and nanotechnologies: Opportunities and uncertainties. Available: http://www.royalsoc. ac.uk/policy. Accessed 27 January 2005.

# Article 44  NOELA INVERNIZZI* and GUILLERMO FOLADORI**

# Nanotechnology and the Developing World: Will Nanotechnology Overcome Poverty or Widen Disparities?

## ABSTRACT

*Nanotechnology proponents expect that it will offer solutions to key problems facing developing countries. In this article, Doctors Noela Invernizzi and Guillermo Foladori argue that this optimistic view overlooks the social factors that shape science and technology development. Invernizzi and Foladori challenge what they see as overly optimistic assessments within recent articles concerning nanotechnology's impact on developing nations. They argue that applications that may benefit poorer nations are only a starting point and that dominant socioeconomic hierarchies may still prevent nanotechnology from benefitting the poor. By recognizing these realities, the nanotechnology community can avoid repeating the mistakes of the pharmaceutical and biotechnology industries and enable nanotechnology to become a tool to alleviate rather than widen disparity.*

## INTRODUCTION

One of the most hotly debated issues, and one of the most difficult to discern in advance in the growing discussion on nanotechnology, is its possible effects on poorer countries and less fortunate segments of the population. There are optimistic stances, wherein nanotechnology is considered to be a panacea, and there are pessimistic viewpoints which suppose that the gap between rich and poor will widen as a result of the diffusion of this kind of technology. The debate on these different stances, supported by theoretical arguments and empirical data, is fundamental for arriving at a balanced viewpoint of the situation.

In early 2005, several influential articles claimed that nanotechnology is a viable alternative for resolving most of the Millennium Development Goals of the United Nations.[1] Some scholars have even attempted to list the top ten nanotechnology applications that will most benefit those in poorer nations. While it is undoubtedly useful to determine which aspects of nanotechnology promise the most to poorer nations in terms of application, the international community needs to question this optimism, placing these new technologies in their social context.

## I. NANOTECHNOLOGIES AS DISRUPTIVE TECHNOLOGIES

Nanotechnology manipulates atoms and molecules to make or build things (or living beings). One may imagine a laboratory which, by combining suitable molecules in quality and quantity, could create electric drills. Although this is theoretically possible, it will take some time, at least until there are nanobots that could do the job by themselves. But this will be at a later stage, if ever. At the moment, what can be made are nanoproducts, in which scientists manipulate matter at the nanoscale to give them special or more efficient uses. Witness the introduction of nanotextiles in recent times.

According to the Nanotech Report, among the first products commercialized in 2004 with nanotechnological content were the following: thermal shoes (Aspem Aerogels); dust and sweat-repelling mattresses (Simmons Bedding Co.); more

---

* Noela Invernizzi is a Ph.D. in Scientific & Technological Policy (UNICAMP, Brazil). Dr. Invernizzi is in the Doctoral Program on Development Studies at the Universidad Autónoma de Zacatecas, México, and is a member of the International Nanotechnology and Society Network.

** Guillermo Foladori is a Ph.D. in Economics (UNAM, México). Dr. Foladori is a professor in the Doctoral Program on Development Studies, Universidad Autónoma de Zacatecas, México. He is also a member of the International Nanotechnology and Society Network. He can be reached via telephone at (52-492) 923-9407 ext. 2778, or by email at fola@estudiosdeldesarrollo.net.

[1] *See, e.g.,* Fabio Salamanca-Buentello et al., *Nanotechnology and the Developing World*, 2 PLOS MED. E97 (2005), *available at* http://www.pubmedcentral. nih.gov/articlerender.fcgi?tool=pubmed&pubmedid=15807631 (last visited June 4, 2005).

[2] *Top 10 Nanotech Products of 2004*, 3 NANOTECH REPORT 1 (2004).

[3] Stephen Baker & Adam Aston, *The Business of Nanotech*, BUS. WK., Feb. 14, 2005, at 64. As a reference, all exports from Latin America and the Caribbean in 2004 totaled $461 billion; foreign debt in Latin America and the Caribbean in 2004 totaled $721 billion. ECON. COMM'N. OF LATIN AM. & CARIBBEAN ("ECLAC"), STATISTICAL YEARBOOK FOR LATIN AMERICA AND THE CARIBBEAN (2004), *available at* http://www.eclac.cl/ publicaciones/Estadisticas/4/LCG2264PB/p1_2.pdf (last visited June 7, 2005).

flexible and resistant golf clubs (Maruman & Co.); personalized cosmetics for different ages, races, genders, types of skin and physical activities (Bionova); dressing for cuts and burns that prevent infections (Westaim Corporation); disinfectants and cleaning products for planes, boats, submarines, etc. (EnviroSystems); spray that repels water and dirt that is used in the building industry (BASF); treatment for glass to repel water, snow, insects etc. (Nanofilm); cream that combats muscular pain (CNBC, Flex-Power, Inc.); and dental adhesives that set the tooth crown better (3M ESPE).[2] Lux Research, a company dedicated to the study of nanotechnology and its business, estimates that the sale of articles with nanoparticles will surpass the mark of $500 billion in 2010.[3]

At least four aspects make nanotechnology a great new development. First, it revolutionizes the manufacturing process. Nanotechnology builds from the smallest number of atoms and molecules to make the biggest final product—the bottom-up process. Nanotechnology can also reverse the process—instead of starting with physical matter as it is found in nature, according to its own structures, by reducing it to the size of the objects to use as has been done until now—the top-down process. Despite this road being familiar in chemical processes, the novelty is that, now, atoms and molecules can be *directly manipulated* to manufacture products.[4] This constitutes a novelty in the history of humanity and a new way of thinking in the world. Its consequences are unlimited. It is even conceivable to think that a process of production that manufactures by summing up molecules will, in theory, generate no waste.

Second, at this nanoscale level, there are few differences between biotic matter and abiotic matter in that it is potentially possible to apply biological procedures to material processes or interfere with materials in living bodies, adapting the latter to certain purposes or offering certain advantages. It may also be possible to manipulate biological matter or procedures to perform specific tasks. One example would be a way of allowing the body to rest without sleep, which would be very useful in war and other activities that are very physically or mentally demanding.

Third, nanoparticles may have physical and chemical properties (conductive, electric, mechanical, optical, etc.) which differ from the same elements on a macroscopic scale. By changing the physical properties of the matter, possibilities arise that surprise and excite scientists who are dedicated to this study. Many nanomaterials that are on sale offer great advantages in this way. Carbon nanotubes, for instance, are harder than diamonds and can be fifty to a hundred times stronger than steel.

Finally, nanotechnology combines several kinds of technologies and sciences such as information technology, biotechnology and materials technology. The latter is not a lesser element if we consider that the true development of nanotechnology will require a totally new professional education which will require rethinking schooling, maybe from the primary level.

The potential benefits of nanotechnology are impossible to calculate. Here we can mention a few of the more probable. In the field of health, it could increase the quality and length of life. Nanosensors, incorporated into the organism, could travel through the bloodstream similar to the way a virus does and detect illnesses before they spread to the rest of the body and combat them efficiently. In the future, drugs may no longer be generic for all people, but may be specifically designed according to the genetic make-up of the individual and his/her gender, age and diet. Ageing mechanisms could be retarded and even reversed, with the human lifespan's being lengthened significantly. With these artificial sensors, a person could become a bionic being, improving her biological capacities and developing others. Some even envision nanotechnology applications that will improve human perception and ability at fundamental levels. The field of prostheses is also among the most promising.

In the materials field, one novelty will be intelligent nanoparticles. Your wardrobe, for example, could be reduced to one single article. The item of clothing you have will react to changes in temperature, rainfall, snow and sun, among other elements, keeping the body always at the programmed temperature. Furthermore, it will repel sweat and dust, which will mean that it will not require washing. As if this were not enough, it would stop bacteria or viruses from penetrating it, protecting it even from possible bioterrorist attacks. In the case of an accident, your clothes would have healing effects, offering first aid. The same that applies to clothing could be adapted to certain dwellings and modes of transport. Another novelty is that carbon nanotubes are stronger than steel and only 1/6 of its weight. This will have a special impact on the aerospace, construction, automobile industries and many others.

The field of computer science will be one of the earliest industries affected and will enjoy the most revolutionary change. Computers can be a hundred times faster and much smaller and lighter, and can be custom built according to the tastes of the buyer in terms of design, size, shape, color, smell and resistance. Prototypes with built-in sensors will speed up designs, adapting to flexible production processes in different parts of the world, overcoming many of the barriers that distance now imposes. The old "just-in-time" production mode will become obsolete and may very well become the "as-you-need" mode of production. The possibilities for monopolistic concentration of production (global business enterprises) will multiply.

The combination of computerized systems, chemical laboratories, miniature sensors and living beings adapted to specific functions will revolutionize medicine (e.g., lab-on-a-chip) and also provide rapid solutions to the historical problems of contamination. Small bacteria with sensors may be able to consume bodies of water that have been contaminated by heavy metals, or decontaminate the atmosphere in record time. Nanocapsules with combined systems of sensors and additives will revolutionize the industries such as lubricants, pharmaceuticals and filters, to make no mention of others.

---

[4] Royal Soc'y & Royal Acad. of Eng'g, Nanoscience and Nanotechnologies: Opportunities and Uncertainties, July 29, 2004, *at* http://www.nanotec.org.uk/finalReport.htm (last visited June 27, 2005).

Nanotechnology may become a disruptive technology that will make obsolete the current competitive technologies, once established and entrenched in economies around the world. The social and economic effects on the international and national levels are difficult to foresee, but an effort must be made at this critical juncture in order to reduce the possible negative or unwanted consequences that have historically accompanied such dramatic transformations.

## II. NANOTECHNOLOGY AS A SOLUTION FOR THE POOR?

Despite the voices that warn of the possible negative consequences or risks of nanotechnology, there are others that suppose that the new technology will be beneficial to everyone, including the poor. In this light, the recent U.N. Millennium Project Report, *Task Force on Science, Technology and Innovation*, puts forward the idea that nanotechnology will be important to the developing world because it harbors the potential to transform minimal work, land and maintenance inputs into highly productive and cheap outputs; and it requires only modest quantities of material and energy to do so.[5] However, these same qualities could be seen as harmful because poor countries have abundant labor, and, in many cases, land and natural resources. In this way, nanotechnology may cause displacements and disruptions in the economies of poorer nations.

Reasoning in a purely technical and linear fashion, any country could theoretically join the nanotechnology wave. An effort for public funding may create the bases to establish specific nanocomponent industries to meet determined needs; or it is possible that businesses with a scientific tradition might justify a technological leap at a relatively low cost. This seems to be the opinion of the authors of at least one article[6] that has received a great deal of attention from the international scientific press.[7] Fabio Salamanca-Buentello and several of his colleagues from the Joint Center for Bioethics at the University of Toronto introduce nanotechnology as the solution to many problems in developing countries.[8] They understand the effort for harnessing nanotechnology in developing countries as a demonstration of the willingness of such countries to overcome poverty: ". . . we show that developing countries are already harnessing nanotechnology to address some of their most pressing needs."[9] After interviewing sixty-three experts in nanotechnology from several developed and developing countries, the authors identified the ten main nanotechnologies that could provide a solution to such problems as water, agriculture, nutrition, health, energy and the environment.[10] The technologies range from energy production and conservation systems, with sensors that will increase agricultural productivity and the treatment of water, to the diagnosis of diseases. In the article, the creation of a Global Fund is proposed for the development of these technologies for all developing countries. Overflowing with good intentions, the proposal reflects the mechanical idea that if a problem can be identified correctly, then all that has to be done is to apply a suitable technology, and it will be solved. Most of the examples used do not take into account the reality that the relationship between science and society is much more complex than identifying a technology and its potential benefits.[11] Let us put some of the examples in their social context.

## 1. The Experience of Poorer Nations with HIV/AIDS Pharmaceuticals

Salamanca-Buentello and colleagues suggest that quantum dots could detect HIV/AIDS molecules in the early stages, thereby facilitating the treatment of AIDS and reducing the number of new cases. While quantum dots may, in fact, provide a useful solution to the HIV/AIDS crisis in developing countries, Salamanca-Buentello's article does little to place this novel technology into the historical experience of poorer nations with advances in the medical field more generally.

---

[5] CALESTOUS JUMA & LEE YEE-CHONG, U.N. MILLENIUM PROJECT TASK FORCE ON SCI., TECH. & INNOVATION, INNOVATION: APPLYING KNOWLEDGE IN DEVELOPMENT (2005), *available at* http://www.unmillenniumproject.org/documents/Science-complete.pdf (last visited June 27, 2005). *See also* David Dickson, *Scientific Advice 'Essential' to Meet Development Goals*, SCIDEV.NET, Jan. 10, 2005, *at* http://www.scidev.net/gateways/index. cfm?fuseaction=readitem&rgwid=4&item=News&itemid=1835&language=1 (last visited June 4, 2005).

[6] Salamanca-Buentello et al, *supra* note 1.

[7] Catherine Brahic, *Developing World 'Needs Nanotech Network'*, SCIDEV.NET (June 4, 2005), *at* http://www.scidev.net/News/index.cfm?fuseaction=printarticle&it emid=1923& language=1 (last visited June 4, 2005); Charles Q. Choi, *Top 10 for Developing World*, UNITED PRESS INT'L (Apr. 18, 2005), *available at* http://www.upi.com/view. cfm?Story ID=20050415-114140-8159r (last visited June 4, 2005); *Taking Nano to the Needy: A* Small Times *Q&A with Fabio Salamanca-Buentello*, SMALL TIMES, June 15, 2005, *at* http://smalltimes.com/print_doc.cfm?doc_id (last visited June 16, 2005).

[8] It must be noted that these authors explicitly recognize that science and technology are not enough: "Like any other science and technology waves, nanoscience and nanotechnology are not 'silver bullets' that will magically solve all the problems of developing countries; the social context of these countries must always be considered." Salamanca-Buentello *et al.*, *supra* note 1, at 2. The authors do, however, visualize science and technology investments and scientists involved in developing countries as an indicator of willingness to overcome poverty. *See id.*

[9] Salamanca-Buentello *et al*, *supra* note 1, at 1.

[10] "In order to provide a systematic approach with which to address sustainable development issues in the developing world, we have identified and ranked the ten applications of nanotechnology most likely to benefit developing countries. We used a modified Delphi Method. . .to identify and prioritize the applications and to achieve consensus among the panelists." Salamanca-Buentello *et al*, *supra* note 1, at 3.

[11] D. Sarewitz et al., *Science Policy in its Social Context*, PHILOSOPHY TODAY, 2004 Supplement, at 67.

The authors seem to forget the story of the last several years, which has been one of seemingly open war between multinational pharmaceutical corporations and the governments of countries that intended to manufacture antiretrovirals against AIDS. In this conflict, the World Trade Organization ("WTO") and the Commercial representative of the United States have systematically played the role of front-line soldier for these corporations. The rigors of the patenting system have used monopolist economics to drive medicine pricing for the last twenty years. This makes it impossible for poor people to buy medicine from companies that hold patents. Experience over the last several years has shown that when an epidemic occurs, some countries cannot afford to cover the cost of remedies very much needed by people within these poorer countries.

One of the most alarming historical cases, illustrating the behavior of the multinational pharmaceutical corporations that tends to undermine public health, was the action brought in 2001 by thirty-nine of the major pharmaceutical corporations against the government of South Africa. In that case, several of the corporations prevented the South African government from producing generic medicine for AIDS treatment. A lawsuit over the matter was soon filed. The lawsuit, which the South African government won, showed total insensibility to human rights on the part of the pharmaceutical corporations. The statements of one of the pharmaceutical company's representatives bore out this insensitivity. According to the reasoning of certain pharmaceutical companies, the court's ruling allowing the government of South Africa to produce affordable generic medicine could have a precedential effect allowing other governments to cheaply develop generic medicines: "while South Africa may represent less than 1% of world drug sales, the precedent of allowing a government to step on drug companies' patent rights would have far-reaching effects, beyond the questions of cost and crises."[12]

Nanotechnology products are already being patented, typically by the most important and largest corporations in the world. A patent in the U.S. costs $30,000 in legal bureaucracy, and a worldwide patent may be as much as a quarter of a million dollars.[13] For an underdeveloped country, it is very difficult to develop any medicine for which there is an important market (as is the case of AIDS) if we take into account the economic and legal medicine market's international "war," as well as the bureaucratic restrictions which drive up costs and reduce availability. This story has a simple moral: technology is produced in a given social context, and the efficiency and implications of its application depend on that social context.

## 2. The Experience of Poorer Nations with Biotechnology

Salamanca-Buentello and his colleagues identify nanotechnology as the solution to five of the eight Millennium Development Goals of the United Nations. Among these supposed solutions are nanosensors and nanocomponents to improve the dosage of water and fertilization of plants. With this technology, it would be possible to reduce poverty and hunger in the world. Simply identifying a potentially useful application, however, overlooks the clear historical experience of poorer countries. Not so long ago, in the 1980s, genetically modified organisms were hailed as the solution that would put an end to hunger and poverty. However, genetically modified organisms ended up being used mainly in developed countries; and three out of four patents are today in the hands of four large multinational companies. There has been no improvement for Third World countries; quite the contrary, transgenics turned up where they were not wanted or expected, as was the case of the contamination of corn in Oaxaca, Mexico. In the case of genetically modified organisms, commercial and technological dependence was increased, not reduced.[14] This historical example could well foreshadow the path that nanotechnology takes in worsening existing gaps between the developed and less developed world unless steps are taken now to avert a repeat of history.

It is far from a foregone conclusion to assume that agricultural nanotechnology will follow the controversial road taken by genetically modified organisms. However, avoiding such a situation requires a healthy debate concerning the possible social, economic and political implications in real time.[15] Michael Mehta highlights three lessons for nanotechnology that should be learned from the experience with biotechnology: (1) to provide legislation on nanotechnology products in such a way that public participation will not be undermined by science-based assessment; (2) to label products with nanocomponents in order to gain acceptance with the corresponding empowerment of the consumer; and (3) to use the precautionary principle in a way that could prevent serious risks without limiting the possible development of these sciences.[16]

One limitation with the above analysis is that nanoproducts are already facing political and economic pressure, in part responsible for building the nanotechnology revolution; and past experience, so far, plays too limited a role in this process. And the difficulty presented by efforts to categorize and regulate nanotechnology frustrates ready-made solutions for the industry to avert the problems encountered by the biotechnology industry with genetically modified organisms. Take the following two statements as an example: nanotechnology products face the paradox that they are (1) elementary particles of known chemical elements;

---

[12] Robert Block, *AIDS Activists Win Legal Skirmish in South Africa*, WALL ST. J., Mar. 17, 2001, at A17.

[13] A. Regalado, *Nanotechnology Patents Surge*, WALL ST. J., June 18, 2004, at A1.

[14] M. SCHAPIRO, BLOWBACK IN GENETIC ENGINEERING in ALAN LIGHTMAN, DANIEL SAREWITZ & CHRISTINA DESSER, LIVING WITH THE GENIE (2003).

[15] David H. Guston & Daniel Sarewitz, *Real-Time Technology Assessment*, 24 TECH. IN SOC'Y 93 (2002).

[16] Michael Mehta, *From Biotechnology to Nanotechnology: What Can We Learn from Earlier Technologies?*, 24 BULL. OF SCI., TECH. & SOC'Y 34 (2004).

and (2) manipulated in a way that is not natural. As for the first statement, nanoproducts do not always need to go through drug trials and registration. Regulations seem not to accompany the speed of technical improvements. A document by the Woodrow Wilson International Center for Scholars is explicit on the contradiction between the reality of nanoparticles and the ambiguity of the American regulatory standards, and it concludes on the need to reform the *Toxic Substance Control Act* ("TSCA").[17] Considering that first statement above, then, nanoproducts are nothing new; rather, they are part of nature.

The clear implication of the second statement is that nanoproducts are being patented as new elements which are not found naturally in that state. The following quote exemplifies this paradox: "[i]t is true that you cannot patent an element in its natural form as found in nature. However, if a purified form of this element is created with industrial uses—for example, [] neon—the new [forms] have a secure patent."[18]

The conclusion at first blush is that it seems as if "business as usual" characterizes the current debate about the implications of nanotechnology and the poor, rather than the old adage that learning from past experience prevents future mistakes.

The moral of the story is that the choice of a technology is not a neutral process. Choosing a technology depends on political and economic forces. It is not necessarily true that the technology which best meets our needs will be the one to survive.

## III. WITHOUT A VOICE? THE POOR AND THEIR INCLUSION IN THE DEBATE ON NANOTECHNOLOGY

Salamanca-Buentello and his colleagues also presuppose that interviewing thirty-eight scientists from developing countries and twenty-five from developed countries permits them to speak of the interests of the developing countries as if they were, in fact, spokespeople for those within developing countries. In a prior article,[19] three of the same authors maintained that the position adopted by Prince Charles[20] (arguing that nanotechnology will widen the gap between rich and poor countries) and by the ETC Group[21] (requesting a moratorium on public funding for nanotechnology) "ignores the voices of the people in developing countries."[22] Surely, Salamanca-Buentello and his colleagues intended to give voice to the people of developing countries on the issue of nanotechnology by conducting research interviews with nanotechnology scientists from the developed and developing world. Their genuine concern for those in the developing world is certainly not doubted here. Unfortunately, the opinion of scientists involved in nanotechnology does not necessarily fall within the most appropriate of pathways for satisfying the needs of the poor. The relationship between scientists and sociopolitical pressures are replete with examples of doubtful practices. In the biomedical arena, for example, we can find cases of independent determination of standards in biomedical trials compromised or auto-censored by the influence of pharmaceutical corporations;[23] and there are examples of funds given by pharmaceutical corporations to universities in order to have influence on decisions pertaining to research and development ("R&D") and to gain the right for subsequent licenses. Even still, there are examples of pharmaceutical companies' bankrolling academic studies that downplay their interests.[24] Some have made claims of fraudulent or doubtful laboratory trials conducted by some large pharmaceutical companies.[25] Still others describe the pharmaceutical corporations' inciting physicians to use governmental forms fraudulently in order to obtain reimbursements for medicine obtained for free from pharmaceutical companies.[26] Pharmaceutical corporations have

---

[17] WOODROW WILSON INT'L CTR. FOR SCHOLARS, NANOTECHNOLOGY & REGULATION: A CASE STUDY USING THE TOXIC SUBSTANCE CONTROL ACT (TSCA), Discussion Paper No. 2003-6 (2003).

[18] Lila Feisee, *Anything under the Sun Made by Man*, Address at Biotechnology Industry Organization (April 11, 2001), *available at* http://www.bio.org/speeches/speeches/041101.asp (last visited June 27, 2005).

[19] E. Court, A.S. Daar, E. Martin, T. Acharya & P.A. Singer, *Will Prince Charles et al Diminish the Opportunities of Developing Countries in Nanotechnology?*, NANOTECHWEB.ORG, Jan. 28, 2004, *at* http://nanotechweb.org/articles/society/3/1/1/1 (last visited June 4, 2005).

[20] *See* Geoffrey Lean, *One Will Not Be Silenced: Charles Rides into Battle to Fight a New Campaign*, INDEPENDENT, July 11, 2004, *available at* http://news.independent.co.uk/uk/this_britain/story.jsp?story=540022 (last visited June 4, 2005) (explaining the position of Prince Charles on nanotechnology).

[21] ETC GROUP, THE BIG DOWN (2003), *available at* http://www.etcgroup.org/documentsTheBigDown.pdf (last visited June 4, 2005).

[22] Court et al., *supra* note 19.

[23] Annabel Ferriman, *WHO Accused of Stifling Debate about Infant Feeding*, 320 BRITISH MED. J. 1362 (2000), *available at* http://bmj.bmjjournals.com/cgi/content/full/320/7246/1362?ijkey=334d739b3ac3456846aa637addf43d5bad31bbf0& keytype2=tf_ipsecsha (last visited June 7, 2005); see also Richard Woodman, Open Letter Disputes WHO *Hypertension Guidelines*, 318 BRITISH MED. J. 893 (1999), *available at* http://bmj.bmjjournals.com/cgi/content/full/318/7188/893/b (last visited June 7, 2005).

[24] Richard Smith, *Medical Journals are an Extension of the Marketing Arm of Pharmaceutical Companies*, 2 PLOS MED. E138 (2005), *available at* http://medicine.plosjournals.org/perlserv/?request=get-document&doi=10.1371/journal.pmed.0020138 (last visited June 7, 2005); J. Montaner, M. O'Shaughnessy & M. Schechter, *Industry-Sponsored Clinical Research: A Double-Edged Sword*, 358 LANCET 1893 (2001); Eyal Press & Jennifer Washburn, *The Kept University*, 285 ATLANTIC MONTHLY 39 (2000).

[25] S. Shah, *Globalization of Clinical Research by the Pharmaceutical Industry*, 33 INT'L J. OF HEALTH SERVS. 29 (2003); T. Bodenheimer, *Uneasy Alliance—Clinical Investigations and the Pharmaceutical Industry*, 342 NEW ENG. J. MED 1539 (2000); CAMPAIGN AGAINST FRAUDULENT MED. RES. ("CAFMR"), THE PHARMACEUTICAL DRUG RACKET—PART ONE (1995), *available at* http://www.pnc.com.au/~cafmr/online/medical/drug1a.html (last visited June 7, 2005); CAFMR, THE PHARMACEUTICAL DRUG RACKET—PART TWO (1995), *available at* http://www.pnc.com.au/~cafmr/online/research/drug2a.html (last visited June 7, 2005); JOHN BRAITHWAITE, CORPORATE CRIME IN THE PHARMACEUTICAL INDUSTRY (1984).

[26] Scott Hensley, *Pharmacia Nears Generics Deal on AIDS Drug for Poor Nations*, Wall St. J., Jan. 24, 2003, at A1.

also been accused of putting pressure on researchers to impede the flow of detrimental information into public forums.[27] And the list can go on and on. Academic opinions, therefore, can hardly be said to represent completely the voices of the poor.[28]

Technology is simply a part of a puzzle. Scholars may concur, for example, that infectious diseases constitute one of the main problems that the developing world is facing, but they may differ radically on how a solution to this problem should be attained. Prevention is not the equivalent of a cure. Nanotechnology is not necessary to reduce malaria radically, for example, as is suggested by Salamanca- Buentello and colleagues. There is no doubt that nanosensors could help to clean water, nor that nanocapsules could make drugs more efficient. Nevertheless, in the Hunan Province of China, malaria was reduced by 99% between 1965 and 1990 as a result of social mobilization backed up by fumigation, the use of mosquito nets and traditional medicine.[29] Vietnam reduced the number of malaria-related deaths by 97% between 1992 and 1997 with similar mechanisms.[30] The moral of this story is twofold: (1) scientists are not always the best spokespeople for the poor, even when they come from poor countries; and (2) there are many means to an end; and technology is not always the solution. Organizing people—which some refer to as *social technology*—can be just as important. In this way, identifying potentially useful scientific technologies for the developing world must become part of a much larger and inclusive social technology if gains are to be actualized in poorer countries.

## IV. OPENING THE DEBATE AND PLACING NANOTECHNOLOGY IN ITS SOCIAL CONTEXT

The history of science and technology is full of examples of technologies that have not always helped the poor. In order to serve the needs of the poor, technology has to be used in a favorable socio-economic context. Furthermore, the building characteristics of the technology, and the technological path, usually impede it from being freely used for the benefit of the masses in developing countries.[31]

Despite the optimistic assessments recently offered, experience suggests that nanotechnology could follow the mainstream economic trends that increase inequality. First, the development of nanotechnology faces many of the same problems faced by prior technological developments because large multinational corporations are patenting the majority of the nanotechnology products. Patents are monopolistic guarantees of earnings for twenty years—something that certainly works against the rapid diffusion of the beneficial potentials of this technology for the poor.[32]

Second, nanotechnology's novel solutions and potentially laudable achievements may never come to fruition in developing countries because the main problem for a developing country is not so much the fixed costs of a laboratory of average sophistication, but the social context that is necessary for really incorporating nanotechnologies into the economy. Without fluid mechanisms of vertical integration between the sectors that produce nanoparticles and the companies that are potential buyers, the nanoparticles will never get out of the laboratory. From many accounts, this seems to be happening, nowadays, in developed countries. Wildson affirms, based on his conducting interviews of individuals with English companies that produce nanoparticles, that "nanoparticles are a solution in search of a problem."[33] Despite their numerous potential applications, the English producers say that they have a shortage of clients. This is confirmed by the cover story in a recent edition of *Business Week*, which, based on information from Lux Research, tells us that despite a promising future, many companies that sell nanotechnology products faced financial difficulties in 2004.[34] The linkages between the science and technology system and the productive sectors are very tenuous in most of the developing countries.

Third, nanotechnology's development in much of the world will do little to help the developing world due to the difficulty in finding qualified workers. A country's ability to foster and support technological careers requires a social context that supplies the necessary equipment and human capital in the long term. It will be difficult for many Third World countries to find

---

[27] J. Collier & I. Ilheanacho, *The Pharmaceutical Industry as an Informant*, 360 LANCET 1405 (2002).

[28] This argument is not meant to dogmatically equate academicians or scientists with pharmaceutical companies. Rather, it is meant to expose the deep and entrenched connections between pharmaceutical corporations and scientific/academic research to illustrate potentially how a new technology or medical application can be manipulated to prevent poorer nations from mechanically applying a useful technology to a problem which is identified by scientists/academicians, even if they come from poorer countries.

[29] SUKHAN JACKSON, ADRIAN C. SLEIGH & XI-LI LIU, ECONOMICS OF MALARIA CONTROL IN CHINA: COST PERFORMANCE AND EFFECTIVENESS OF HUNAN'S CONSOLIDATION PROGRAMME, WLD. HEALTH ORG. ("WHO") SOCIAL, ECON. & BEHAVIORAL RES. REPORT SERIES NO. 1 (2002), *available at* http://www.who.int/tdr/publications/publications/sebrp1.htm (last visited June 27, 2005).

[30] WHO, *Vietnam Reduces Malaria Death Toll by 97% within Five Years*, 2002, *at* http://www.who.int/inf- new/mala1.htm (last visited June 7, 2005).

[31] D. Sarewitz et al., *supra* note 11.

[32] Corporate intellectual property ("IP") departments, which have increasingly sought to turn patents into major revenue streams, are stoking the trend. According to data compiled by the National Science Foundation, IBM won the most nanotech-related patents in 2003. Also among the top ten: computer-memory giant, Micron Technology Inc. of Boise, Idaho; manufacturer, 3M Corp. of St. Paul, Minnesota; the University of California; and Japan's Canon Inc. *See* Regalado, *supra* note 13, at A1.

[33] James Wildson, *The Politics of Small Things: Nanotechnology, Risk, and Uncertainty*, 23 IEEE TECH. & SOC'Y MAGAZINE 16 (2004).

[34] Baker & Aston, *supra* note 3. ("A 2004 study by Lux Research found that many of the 200 global suppliers of basic nanomaterials failed to deliver what they promised.").

the staff necessary to work inter-disciplinarily in nanotechnology. Mexico, for instance, the thirteenth largest exporting power in the world, only has eleven research teams in three universities and two research centers in nanotechnology, with a total of ninety researchers and no official support program for field research.[35] Brazil, which launched a pioneer program for research and development in nanotechnology in Latin America (considering that it was in the same year as the U.S. initiative—2000) had between fifty and one hundred researchers in 2002 and proably around 300 in 2004.[36] Despite these seemingly impressive numbers in Brazil, challenging barriers remain which will continue to plague the ability of nanotechnology scientists in developing countries to produce benefits for the poor. Many nanotechnologists in developing countries may be enticed by higher wages out of poorer countries and into richer ones. The reason that this potentiality must be addressed now is as follows. Some estimate that nanotechnology will mean restructuring all learning to break down the traditional disciplinary frontiers, which, in practice, nanotechnology has already overcome. It is possible that changes in study plans would have to take place starting at primary education.[37] This means that multi-sector efforts are gambled on these changes, and elevated social demands are required. In many instances, poorer nations lack the resources, infrastructure and facilities for such interdisciplinary efforts as nanotechnology—particularly, where transformations must take place at so fundamental a level. Given the higher stakes and more interdisciplinary nature of nanotechnology, therefore, it is possible that the race for qualified scientists will heat up and increase the brain drain from the Third World into more advanced countries. This polarization of the labor market will punish poorer countries with less qualified labor. It is unlikely that the vast majority of developing countries will have the wherewithal, infrastructure and labor force to be able to join the nanotechnology wave and capitalize on its potentials to transform society and industry.

Finally, even if large developing countries that could join the nanotechnology wave (such as China, India and Brazil, for example) can produce nanoproducts that could eventually result in clean and cheap energy options, in clean drinking water or in greater agricultural yields, this does not mean that the poor majority will benefit. For them socio-economic structure is a much more difficult barrier than technological innovation. Nanotechnology, even where fully integrated in developing countries, does nothing to change these socio-economic structures; instead, it could serve to exacerbate existing gaps and further the technological and socio-economic isolation of the poor.

## V. CONCLUSIONS

Nanotechnology is still in its early stages, but the later we choose to address its social and economic implications, the less chance there will be for the technology to help the poor before nanotechnology begins to put down roots within the mainstream hegemonic socioeconomic structure, characterized by worldwide inequality.

[35] Ineke Malsch & Volker Lieffering, *Nanotechnology in Mexico*, Nov. 5, 2004, *at* http://www.voyle.net/Guest%20Writers/Drs.%20Ineke%20Malsch/Malsch%20 2004-0001.htm (last visited June 7, 2005).

[36] Laura Knapp, *Brasil Ganha Centro de Pesquisa de Nanotecnologia*, O Estado de S. Paulo em linea, Jan. 20,2002, *at* http://busca.estadao.com.br/ciencia/noticias/2002/jan/20/138.htm (last visited June 7, 2005).

[37] C.L. Alpert, *Introducing Nanotechnology to Public and School Audiences*, Nanoscience & Tech. Inst., *at* http://www.nsti.org/Nanotech2004/showabstract.html?absno=581 (last visited June 7, 2005) ("The NSF envisions a revolution in science education from elementary school through the post-graduate level; a systemic change that recognizes the convergence of research in physics, chemistry, biology, materials science, and engineering. . .").

# Article 45

Bill Joy

## Why the Future Doesn't Need Us

**Our most powerful 21st-century technologies - robotics, genetic engineering, and nanotech - are threatening to make humans an endangered species**

From the moment I became involved in the creation of new technologies, their ethical dimensions have concerned me, but it was only in the autumn of 1998 that I became anxiously aware of how great are the dangers facing us in the 21st century. I can date the onset of my unease to the day I met Ray Kurzweil, the deservedly famous inventor of the first reading machine for the blind and many other amazing things.

Ray and I were both speakers at George Gilder's Telecosm conference, and I encountered him by chance in the bar of the hotel after both our sessions were over. I was sitting with John Searle, a Berkeley philosopher who studies consciousness. While we were talking, Ray approached and a conversation began, the subject of which haunts me to this day.

I had missed Ray's talk and the subsequent panel that Ray and John had been on, and they now picked right up where they'd left off, with Ray saying that the rate of improvement of technology was going to accelerate and that we were going to become robots or fuse with robots or something like that, and John countering that this couldn't happen, because the robots couldn't be conscious.

While I had heard such talk before, I had always felt sentient robots were in the realm of science fiction. But now, from someone I respected, I was hearing a strong argument that they were a near-term possibility. I was taken aback, especially given Ray's proven ability to imagine and create the future. I already knew that new technologies like genetic engineering and nanotechnology were giving us the power to remake the world, but a realistic and imminent scenario for intelligent robots surprised me.

It's easy to get jaded about such breakthroughs. We hear in the news almost every day of some kind of technological or scientific advance. Yet this was no ordinary prediction. In the hotel bar, Ray gave me a partial preprint of his then-forthcoming book *The Age of Spiritual Machines,* which outlined a utopia he foresaw - one in which humans gained near immortality by becoming one with robotic technology. On reading it, my sense of unease only intensified; I felt sure he had to be understating the dangers, understating the probability of a bad outcome along this path.

I found myself most troubled by a passage detailing a *dystopian scenario:

### THE NEW LUDDITE CHALLENGE

First let us postulate that the computer scientists succeed in developing intelligent machines that can do all things better than human beings can do them. In that case presumably all work will be done by vast, highly organized systems of machines and no human effort will be necessary. Either of two cases might occur. The machines might be permitted to make all of their own decisions without human oversight, or else human control over the machines might be retained.

If the machines are permitted to make all their own decisions, we can't make any conjectures as to the results, because it is impossible to guess how such machines might behave. We only point out that the fate of the human race would be at the mercy of the machines. It might be argued that the human race would never be foolish enough to hand over all the power to the machines. But we are suggesting neither that the human race would voluntarily turn power over to the machines nor that the machines would willfully seize power. What we do suggest is that the human race might easily permit itself to drift into a position of such dependence on the machines that it would have no practical choice but to accept all of the machines' decisions. As society and the problems that face it become more and more complex and machines become more and more intelligent, people will let machines make more of their decisions for them, simply because machine-made decisions will bring better results than man-made ones. Eventually a stage may be reached at which the decisions necessary to keep the system running will be so complex that human beings will be incapable of making them intelligently. At that stage the machines will be in effective control. People won't be able to just turn the machines off, because they will be so dependent on them that turning them off would amount to suicide.

On the other hand it is possible that human control over the machines may be retained. In that case the average man may have control over certain private machines of his own, such as his car or his personal computer, but control over large systems of machines will be in the hands of a tiny elite - just as it is today, but with two differences. Due to improved techniques the elite will have greater control over the masses; and because human work will no longer be necessary the masses will be superfluous, a useless burden on the system. If the elite is ruthless they may simply decide to exterminate the mass of humanity. If they are humane they may use propaganda or other psychological or biological techniques to reduce the birth rate until the mass of humanity becomes extinct, leaving the world to the elite. Or, if the elite consists of soft-hearted liberals, they may decide to play the role of good shepherds to the rest of the human race. They will see to it that everyone's physical needs are satisfied, that all children are raised under psychologically hygienic conditions, that everyone has a wholesome hobby to keep him busy, and that anyone who may become dissatisfied undergoes "treatment" to cure his "problem." Of course, life will be so purposeless that people will have to be biologically or psychologically engineered either to remove their need for the power process or make them "sublimate" their drive for power into some harmless hobby. These engineered human beings may be happy in such a society, but they will most certainly not be free. They will have been reduced to the status of domestic animals.[1]

In the book, you don't discover until you turn the page that the author of this passage is Theodore Kaczynski - the Unabomber. I am no apologist for Kaczynski. His bombs killed three people during a 17-year terror campaign and wounded many others. One of his bombs gravely injured my friend David Gelernter, one of the most brilliant and visionary computer scientists of our time. Like many of my colleagues, I felt that I could easily have been the Unabomber's next target.

Kaczynski's actions were murderous and, in my view, criminally insane. He is clearly a Luddite, but simply saying this does not dismiss his argument; as difficult as it is for me to acknowledge, I saw some merit in the reasoning in this single passage. I felt compelled to confront it.

Kaczynski's dystopian vision describes unintended consequences, a well-known problem with the design and use of technology, and one that is clearly related to Murphy's law - "Anything that can go wrong, will." (Actually, this is Finagle's law, which in itself shows that Finagle was right.) Our overuse of antibiotics has led to what may be the biggest such problem so far: the emergence of antibiotic-resistant and much more dangerous bacteria. Similar things happened when attempts to eliminate malarial mosquitoes using DDT caused them to acquire DDT resistance; malarial parasites likewise acquired multi-drug-resistant genes.[2]

The cause of many such surprises seems clear: The systems involved are complex, involving interaction among and feedback between many parts. Any changes to such a system will cascade in ways that are difficult to predict; this is especially true when human actions are involved.

I started showing friends the Kaczynski quote from *The Age of Spiritual Machines;* I would hand them Kurzweil's book, let them read the quote, and then watch their reaction as they discovered who had written it. At around the same time, I found Hans Moravec's book *Robot: Mere Machine to Transcendent Mind.* Moravec is one of the leaders in robotics research, and was a founder of the world's largest robotics research program, at Carnegie Mellon University. *Robot* gave me more material to try out on my friends - material surprisingly supportive of Kaczynski's argument. For example:

## The Short Run (Early 2000s)

Biological species almost never survive encounters with superior competitors. Ten million years ago, South and North America were separated by a sunken Panama isthmus. South America, like Australia today, was populated by marsupial mammals, including pouched equivalents of rats, deers, and tigers. When the isthmus connecting North and South America rose, it took only a few thousand years for the northern placental species, with slightly more effective metabolisms and reproductive and nervous systems, to displace and eliminate almost all the southern marsupials.

In a completely free marketplace, superior robots would surely affect humans as North American placentals affected South American marsupials (and as humans have affected countless species). Robotic industries would compete vigorously among themselves for matter, energy, and space, incidentally driving their price beyond human reach. Unable to afford the necessities of life, biological humans would be squeezed out of existence.

There is probably some breathing room, because we do not live in a completely free marketplace. Government coerces non-market behavior, especially by collecting taxes. Judiciously applied, governmental coercion could support human populations in high style on the fruits of robot labor, perhaps for a long while.

A textbook dystopia - and Moravec is just getting wound up. He goes on to discuss how our main job in the 21st century will be "ensuring continued cooperation from the robot industries" by passing laws decreeing that they be "nice,"[3] and to describe how seriously dangerous a human can be "once transformed into an unbounded superintelligent robot." Moravec's view is that the robots will eventually succeed us - that humans clearly face extinction.

I decided it was time to talk to my friend Danny Hillis. Danny became famous as the cofounder of Thinking Machines Corporation, which built a very powerful parallel supercomputer. Despite my current job title of Chief Scientist at Sun Microsystems, I am more a computer architect than a scientist, and I respect Danny's knowledge of the information and physical sciences more than that of any other single person I know. Danny is also a highly regarded futurist who thinks long-term - four years ago he started the Long Now Foundation, which is building a clock designed to last 10,000 years, in an attempt to draw attention to the pitifully short attention span of our society. (See "Test of Time," *Wired* 8.03, page 78.)

So I flew to Los Angeles for the express purpose of having dinner with Danny and his wife, Pati. I went through my now-familiar routine, trotting out the ideas and passages that I found so disturbing. Danny's answer - directed specifically at Kurzweil's scenario of humans merging with robots - came swiftly, and quite surprised me. He said, simply, that the changes would come gradually, and that we would get used to them.

But I guess I wasn't totally surprised. I had seen a quote from Danny in Kurzweil's book in which he said, "I'm as fond of my body as anyone, but if I can be 200 with a body of silicon, I'll take it." It seemed that he was at peace with this process and its attendant risks, while I was not.

While talking and thinking about Kurzweil, Kaczynski, and Moravec, I suddenly remembered a novel I had read almost 20 years ago - *The White Plague*, by Frank Herbert - in which a molecular biologist is driven insane by the senseless murder of his family. To seek revenge he constructs and disseminates a new and highly contagious plague that kills widely but selectively. (We're lucky Kaczynski was a mathematician, not a molecular biologist.) I was also reminded of the Borg of *Star Trek*, a hive of partly biological, partly robotic creatures with a strong destructive streak. Borg-like disasters are a staple of science fiction, so why hadn't I been more concerned about such robotic dystopias earlier? Why weren't other people more concerned about these nightmarish scenarios?

Part of the answer certainly lies in our attitude toward the new - in our bias toward instant familiarity and unquestioning acceptance. Accustomed to living with almost routine scientific breakthroughs, we have yet to come to terms with the fact that the most compelling 21st-century technologies - robotics, genetic engineering, and nanotechnology - pose a different threat than the technologies that have come before. Specifically, robots, engineered organisms, and nanobots share a dangerous amplifying factor: They can self-replicate. A bomb is blown up only once - but one bot can become many, and quickly get out of control.

Much of my work over the past 25 years has been on computer networking, where the sending and receiving of messages creates the opportunity for out-of-control replication. But while replication in a computer or a computer network can be a nuisance, at worst it disables a machine or takes down a network or network service. Uncontrolled self-replication in these newer technologies runs a much greater risk: a risk of substantial damage in the physical world.

Each of these technologies also offers untold promise: The vision of near immortality that Kurzweil sees in his robot dreams drives us forward; genetic engineering may soon provide treatments, if not outright cures, for most diseases; and nanotechnology and nanomedicine can address yet more ills. Together they could significantly extend our average life span and improve the quality of our lives. Yet, with each of these technologies, a sequence of small, individually sensible advances leads to an accumulation of great power and, concomitantly, great danger.

What was different in the 20th century? Certainly, the technologies underlying the weapons of mass destruction (WMD) - nuclear, biological, and chemical (NBC) - were powerful, and the weapons an enormous threat. But building nuclear weapons required, at least for a time, access to both rare - indeed, effectively unavailable - raw materials and highly protected information; biological and chemical weapons programs also tended to require large-scale activities.

The 21st-century technologies - genetics, nanotechnology, and robotics (GNR) - are so powerful that they can spawn whole new classes of accidents and abuses. Most dangerously, for the first time, these accidents and abuses are widely within the reach of individuals or small groups. They will not require large facilities or rare raw materials. Knowledge alone will enable the use of them.

Thus we have the possibility not just of weapons of mass destruction but of knowledge-enabled mass destruction (KMD), this destructiveness hugely amplified by the power of self-replication.

I think it is no exaggeration to say we are on the cusp of the further perfection of extreme evil, an evil whose possibility spreads well beyond that which weapons of mass destruction bequeathed to the nation-states, on to a surprising and terrible empowerment of extreme individuals.

Nothing about the way I got involved with computers suggested to me that I was going to be facing these kinds of issues.

My life has been driven by a deep need to ask questions and find answers. When I was 3, I was already reading, so my father took me to the elementary school, where I sat on the principal's lap and read him a story. I started school early, later skipped a grade, and escaped into books - I was incredibly motivated to learn. I asked lots of questions, often driving adults to distraction.

As a teenager I was very interested in science and technology. I wanted to be a ham radio operator but didn't have the money to buy the equipment. Ham radio was the Internet of its time: very addictive, and quite solitary. Money issues aside, my mother put her foot down - I was not to be a ham; I was antisocial enough already.

I may not have had many close friends, but I was awash in ideas. By high school, I had discovered the great science fiction writers. I remember especially Heinlein's *Have Spacesuit Will Travel* and Asimov's *I, Robot*, with its Three Laws of Robotics. I was enchanted by the descriptions of space travel, and wanted to have a telescope to look at the stars; since I had no money to buy or make one, I checked books on telescope-making out of the library and read about making them instead. I soared in my imagination.

Thursday nights my parents went bowling, and we kids stayed home alone. It was the night of Gene Roddenberry's original *Star Trek*, and the program made a big impression on me. I came to accept its notion that humans had a future in space, Western-style, with big heroes and adventures. Roddenberry's vision of the centuries to come was one with strong moral values, embodied in codes like the Prime Directive: to not interfere in the development of less technologically advanced civilizations. This had an incredible appeal to me; ethical humans, not robots, dominated this future, and I took Roddenberry's dream as part of my own.

I excelled in mathematics in high school, and when I went to the University of Michigan as an undergraduate engineering student I took the advanced curriculum of the mathematics majors. Solving math problems was an exciting challenge, but when I discovered computers I found something much more interesting: a machine into which you could put a program that attempted to solve a problem, after which the machine quickly checked the solution. The computer had a clear notion of correct and incorrect, true and false. Were my ideas correct? The machine could tell me. This was very seductive.

I was lucky enough to get a job programming early supercomputers and discovered the amazing power of large machines to numerically simulate advanced designs. When I went to graduate school at UC Berkeley in the mid-1970s, I started staying up late, often all night, inventing new worlds inside the machines. Solving problems. Writing the code that argued so strongly to be written.

In *The Agony and the Ecstasy,* Irving Stone's biographical novel of Michelangelo, Stone described vividly how Michelangelo released the statues from the stone, "breaking the marble spell," carving from the images in his mind.4 In my most ecstatic moments, the software in the computer emerged in the same way. Once I had imagined it in my mind I felt that it was already there in the machine, waiting to be released. Staying up all night seemed a small price to pay to free it - to give the ideas concrete form.

After a few years at Berkeley I started to send out some of the software I had written - an instructional Pascal system, Unix utilities, and a text editor called vi (which is still, to my surprise, widely used more than 20 years later) - to others who had similar small PDP-11 and VAX minicomputers. These adventures in software eventually turned into the Berkeley version of the Unix operating system, which became a personal "success disaster" - so many people wanted it that I never finished my PhD. Instead I got a job working for Darpa putting Berkeley Unix on the Internet and fixing it to be reliable and to run large research applications well. This was all great fun and very rewarding. And, frankly, I saw no robots here, or anywhere near.

Still, by the early 1980s, I was drowning. The Unix releases were very successful, and my little project of one soon had money and some staff, but the problem at Berkeley was always office space rather than money - there wasn't room for the help the project needed, so when the other founders of Sun Microsystems showed up I jumped at the chance to join them. At Sun, the long hours continued into the early days of workstations and personal computers, and I have enjoyed participating in the creation of advanced microprocessor technologies and Internet technologies such as Java and Jini.

From all this, I trust it is clear that I am not a Luddite. I have always, rather, had a strong belief in the value of the scientific search for truth and in the ability of great engineering to bring material progress. The Industrial Revolution has immeasurably improved everyone's life over the last couple hundred years, and I always expected my career to involve the building of worthwhile solutions to real problems, one problem at a time.

I have not been disappointed. My work has had more impact than I had ever hoped for and has been more widely used than I could have reasonably expected. I have spent the last 20 years still trying to figure out how to make computers as reliable as I want them to be (they are not nearly there yet) and how to make them simple to use (a goal that has met with even less relative success). Despite some progress, the problems that remain seem even more daunting.

But while I was aware of the moral dilemmas surrounding technology's consequences in fields like weapons research, I did not expect that I would confront such issues in my own field, or at least not so soon.

Perhaps it is always hard to see the bigger impact while you are in the vortex of a change. Failing to understand the consequences of our inventions while we are in the rapture of discovery and innovation seems to be a common fault of scientists and technologists; we have long been driven by the overarching desire to know that is the nature of science's quest, not stopping to notice that the progress to newer and more powerful technologies can take on a life of its own.

I have long realized that the big advances in information technology come not from the work of computer scientists, computer architects, or electrical engineers, but from that of physical scientists. The physicists Stephen Wolfram and Brosl Hasslacher introduced me, in the early 1980s, to chaos theory and nonlinear systems. In the 1990s, I learned about complex systems from conversations with Danny Hillis, the biologist Stuart Kauffman, the Nobel-laureate physicist Murray Gell-Mann, and others. Most recently, Hasslacher and the electrical engineer and device physicist Mark Reed have been giving me insight into the incredible possibilities of molecular electronics.

In my own work, as codesigner of three microprocessor architectures - SPARC, picoJava, and MAJC - and as the designer of several implementations thereof, I've been afforded a deep and firsthand acquaintance with Moore's law. For decades, Moore's law has correctly predicted the exponential rate of improvement of semiconductor technology. Until last year I believed that the rate of advances predicted by Moore's law might continue only until roughly 2010, when some physical limits would begin to be reached. It was not obvious to me that a new technology would arrive in time to keep performance advancing smoothly.

But because of the recent rapid and radical progress in molecular electronics - where individual atoms and molecules replace lithographically drawn transistors - and related nanoscale technologies, we should be able to meet or exceed the Moore's law rate of progress for another 30 years. By 2030, we are likely to be able to build machines, in quantity, a million times as powerful as the personal computers of today - sufficient to implement the dreams of Kurzweil and Moravec.

As this enormous computing power is combined with the manipulative advances of the physical sciences and the new, deep understandings in genetics, enormous transformative power is being unleashed. These combinations open up the opportunity to completely redesign the world, for better or worse: The replicating and evolving processes that have been confined to the natural world are about to become realms of human endeavor.

In designing software and microprocessors, I have never had the feeling that I was designing an intelligent machine. The software and hardware is so fragile and the capabilities of the machine to "think" so clearly absent that, even as a possibility, this has always seemed very far in the future.

But now, with the prospect of human-level computing power in about 30 years, a new idea suggests itself: that I may be working to create tools which will enable the construction of the technology that may replace our species. How do I feel about this? Very uncomfortable. Having struggled my entire career to build reliable software systems, it seems to me more than likely that this future will not work out as well as some people may imagine. My personal experience suggests we tend to overestimate our design abilities.

Given the incredible power of these new technologies, shouldn't we be asking how we can best coexist with them? And if our own extinction is a likely, or even possible, outcome of our technological development, shouldn't we proceed with great caution?

The dream of robotics is, first, that intelligent machines can do our work for us, allowing us lives of leisure, restoring us to Eden. Yet in his history of such ideas, *Darwin Among the Machines,* George Dyson warns: "In the game of life and evolution there are three players at the table: human beings, nature, and machines. I am firmly on the side of nature. But nature, I suspect, is on the side of the machines." As we have seen, Moravec agrees, believing we may well not survive the encounter with the superior robot species.

How soon could such an intelligent robot be built? The coming advances in computing power seem to make it possible by 2030. And once an intelligent robot exists, it is only a small step to a robot species - to an intelligent robot that can make evolved copies of itself.

A second dream of robotics is that we will gradually replace ourselves with our robotic technology, achieving near immortality by downloading our consciousnesses; it is this process that Danny Hillis thinks we will gradually get used to and that Ray Kurzweil elegantly details in *The Age of Spiritual Machines.* (We are beginning to see intimations of this in the implantation of computer devices into the human body, as illustrated on the cover of *Wired* 8.02.)

But if we are downloaded into our technology, what are the chances that we will thereafter be ourselves or even human? It seems to me far more likely that a robotic existence would not be like a human one in any sense that we understand, that the robots would in no sense be our children, that on this path our humanity may well be lost.

Genetic engineering promises to revolutionize agriculture by increasing crop yields while reducing the use of pesticides; to create tens of thousands of novel species of bacteria, plants, viruses, and animals; to replace reproduction, or supplement it, with cloning; to create cures for many diseases, increasing our life span and our quality of life; and much, much more. We now know with certainty that these profound changes in the biological sciences are imminent and will challenge all our notions of what life is.

Technologies such as human cloning have in particular raised our awareness of the profound ethical and moral issues we face. If, for example, we were to reengineer ourselves into several separate and unequal species using the power of genetic engineering, then we would threaten the notion of equality that is the very cornerstone of our democracy.

Given the incredible power of genetic engineering, it's no surprise that there are significant safety issues in its use. My friend Amory Lovins recently cowrote, along with Hunter Lovins, an editorial that provides an ecological view of some of these dangers. Among their concerns: that "the new botany aligns the development of plants with their economic, not evolutionary, success." (See "A Tale of Two Botanies," page 247.) Amory's long career has been focused on energy and resource efficiency by taking a whole-system view of human-made systems; such a whole-system view often finds simple, smart solutions to otherwise seemingly difficult problems, and is usefully applied here as well.

After reading the Lovins' editorial, I saw an op-ed by Gregg Easterbrook in *The New York Times* (November 19, 1999) about genetically engineered crops, under the headline: "Food for the Future: Someday, rice will have built-in vitamin A. Unless the Luddites win."

Are Amory and Hunter Lovins Luddites? Certainly not. I believe we all would agree that golden rice, with its built-in vitamin A, is probably a good thing, if developed with proper care and respect for the likely dangers in moving genes across species boundaries.

Awareness of the dangers inherent in genetic engineering is beginning to grow, as reflected in the Lovins' editorial. The general public is aware of, and uneasy about, genetically modified foods, and seems to be rejecting the notion that such foods should be permitted to be unlabeled.

But genetic engineering technology is already very far along. As the Lovins note, the USDA has already approved about 50 genetically engineered crops for unlimited release; more than half of the world's soybeans and a third of its corn now contain genes spliced in from other forms of life.

While there are many important issues here, my own major concern with genetic engineering is narrower: that it gives the power - whether militarily, accidentally, or in a deliberate terrorist act - to create a White Plague.

The many wonders of nanotechnology were first imagined by the Nobel-laureate physicist Richard Feynman in a speech he gave in 1959, subsequently published under the title "There's Plenty of Room at the Bottom." The book that made a big impression on me, in the mid-'80s, was Eric Drexler's *Engines of Creation,* in which he described beautifully how manipulation of matter at the atomic level could create a utopian future of abundance, where just about everything could be made cheaply, and almost any imaginable disease or physical problem could be solved using nanotechnology and artificial intelligences.

A subsequent book, *Unbounding the Future: The Nanotechnology Revolution,* which Drexler cowrote, imagines some of the changes that might take place in a world where we had molecular-level "assemblers." Assemblers could make possible incredibly low-cost solar power, cures for cancer and the common cold by augmentation of the human immune system, essentially complete cleanup of the environment, incredibly inexpensive pocket supercomputers - in fact, any product would be manufacturable by assemblers at a cost no greater than that of wood - spaceflight more accessible than transoceanic travel today, and restoration of extinct species.

I remember feeling good about nanotechnology after reading *Engines of Creation.* As a technologist, it gave me a sense of calm - that is, nanotechnology showed us that incredible progress was possible, and indeed perhaps inevitable. If nanotechnology was our future, then I didn't feel pressed to solve so many problems in the present. I would get to Drexler's utopian future in due time; I might as well enjoy life more in the here and now. It didn't make sense, given his vision, to stay up all night, all the time.

Drexler's vision also led to a lot of good fun. I would occasionally get to describe the wonders of nanotechnology to others who had not heard of it. After teasing them with all the things Drexler described I would give a homework assignment of my own: "Use nanotechnology to create a vampire; for extra credit create an antidote."

With these wonders came clear dangers, of which I was acutely aware. As I said at a nanotechnology conference in 1989, "We can't simply do our science and not worry about these ethical issues."5 But my subsequent conversations with physicists convinced me that nanotechnology might not even work - or, at least, it wouldn't work anytime soon. Shortly thereafter I moved to Colorado, to a skunk works I had set up, and the focus of my work shifted to software for the Internet, specifically on ideas that became Java and Jini.

Then, last summer, Brosl Hasslacher told me that nanoscale molecular electronics was now practical. This was *new* news, at least to me, and I think to many people - and it radically changed my opinion about nanotechnology. It sent me back to *Engines of Creation.* Rereading Drexler's work after more than 10 years, I was dismayed to realize how little I had remembered of its lengthy section called "Dangers and Hopes," including a discussion of how nanotechnologies can become "engines of destruction." Indeed, in my rereading of this cautionary material today, I am struck by how naive some of Drexler's safeguard proposals seem, and how much greater I judge the dangers to be now than even he seemed to then. (Having anticipated and described many technical and political problems with nanotechnology, Drexler started the Foresight Institute in the late 1980s "to help prepare society for anticipated advanced technologies" - most important, nanotechnology.)

The enabling breakthrough to assemblers seems quite likely within the next 20 years. Molecular electronics - the new subfield of nanotechnology where individual molecules are circuit elements - should mature quickly and become enormously lucrative within this decade, causing a large incremental investment in all nanotechnologies.

Unfortunately, as with nuclear technology, it is far easier to create destructive uses for nanotechnology than constructive ones. Nanotechnology has clear military and terrorist uses, and you need not be suicidal to release a massively destructive nanotechnological device - such devices can be built to be selectively destructive, affecting, for example, only a certain geographical area or a group of people who are genetically distinct.

An immediate consequence of the Faustian bargain in obtaining the great power of nanotechnology is that we run a grave risk - the risk that we might destroy the biosphere on which all life depends.

As Drexler explained:

"Plants" with "leaves" no more efficient than today's solar cells could out-compete real plants, crowding the biosphere with an inedible foliage. Tough omnivorous "bacteria" could out-compete real bacteria: They could spread like blowing pollen, replicate swiftly, and reduce the biosphere to dust in a matter of days. Dangerous replicators could easily be too tough, small, and rapidly spreading to stop - at least if we make no preparation. We have trouble enough controlling viruses and fruit flies.

Among the cognoscenti of nanotechnology, this threat has become known as the "gray goo problem." Though masses of uncontrolled replicators need not be gray or gooey, the term "gray goo" emphasizes that replicators able to obliterate life might be less inspiring than a single species of crabgrass. They might be superior in an evolutionary sense, but this need not make them valuable.

The gray goo threat makes one thing perfectly clear: We cannot afford certain kinds of accidents with replicating assemblers.

Gray goo would surely be a depressing ending to our human adventure on Earth, far worse than mere fire or ice, and one that could stem from a simple laboratory accident.6 Oops.

It is most of all the power of destructive self-replication in genetics, nanotechnology, and robotics (GNR) that should give us pause. Self-replication is the modus operandi of genetic engineering, which uses the machinery of the cell to replicate its designs, and the prime danger underlying gray goo in nanotechnology. Stories of run-amok robots like the Borg, replicating or mutating to escape from the ethical constraints imposed on them by their creators, are well established in our science fiction books and movies. It is even possible that self-replication may be more fundamental than we thought, and hence harder - or even impossible - to control. A recent article by Stuart Kauffman in *Nature* titled "Self-Replication: Even Peptides Do It" discusses the discovery that a 32-amino-acid peptide can "autocatalyse its own synthesis." We don't know how widespread this ability is, but Kauffman notes that it may hint at "a route to self-reproducing molecular systems on a basis far wider than Watson-Crick base-pairing."7

In truth, we have had in hand for years clear warnings of the dangers inherent in widespread knowledge of GNR technologies - of the possibility of knowledge alone enabling mass destruction. But these warnings haven't been widely publicized; the public discussions have been clearly inadequate. There is no profit in publicizing the dangers.

The nuclear, biological, and chemical (NBC) technologies used in 20th-century weapons of mass destruction were and are largely military, developed in government laboratories. In sharp contrast, the 21st-century GNR technologies have clear commercial uses and are being developed almost exclusively by corporate enterprises. In this age of triumphant commercialism, technology - with science as its handmaiden - is delivering a series of almost magical inventions that are the most phenomenally lucrative ever seen. We are aggressively pursuing the promises of these new technologies within the now-unchallenged system of global capitalism and its manifold financial incentives and competitive pressures.

This is the first moment in the history of our planet when any species, by its own voluntary actions, has become a danger to itself - as well as to vast numbers of others.

It might be a familiar progression, transpiring on many worlds - a planet, newly formed, placidly revolves around its star; life slowly forms; a kaleidoscopic procession of creatures evolves; intelligence emerges which, at least up to a point, confers enormous survival value; and then technology is invented. It dawns on them that there are such things as laws of Nature, that these laws can be revealed by experiment, and that knowledge of these laws can be made both to save and to take lives, both on unprecedented scales. Science, they recognize, grants immense powers. In a flash, they create world-altering contrivances. Some planetary civilizations see their way through, place limits on what may and what must not be done, and safely pass through the time of perils. Others, not so lucky or so prudent, perish.

That is Carl Sagan, writing in 1994, in *Pale Blue Dot,* a book describing his vision of the human future in space. I am only now realizing how deep his insight was, and how sorely I miss, and will miss, his voice. For all its eloquence, Sagan's contribution was not least that of simple common sense - an attribute that, along with humility, many of the leading advocates of the 21st-century technologies seem to lack.

I remember from my childhood that my grandmother was strongly against the overuse of antibiotics. She had worked since before the first World War as a nurse and had a commonsense attitude that taking antibiotics, unless they were absolutely necessary, was bad for you.

It is not that she was an enemy of progress. She saw much progress in an almost 70-year nursing career; my grandfather, a diabetic, benefited greatly from the improved treatments that became available in his lifetime. But she, like many levelheaded people, would probably think it greatly arrogant for us, now, to be designing a robotic "replacement species," when we obviously have so much trouble making relatively simple things work, and so much trouble managing - or even understanding - ourselves.

I realize now that she had an awareness of the nature of the order of life, and of the necessity of living with and respecting that order. With this respect comes a necessary humility that we, with our early-21st-century chutzpah, lack at our peril. The commonsense view, grounded in this respect, is often right, in advance of the scientific evidence. The clear fragility and inefficiencies of the human-made systems we have built should give us all pause; the fragility of the systems I have worked on certainly humbles me.

We should have learned a lesson from the making of the first atomic bomb and the resulting arms race. We didn't do well then, and the parallels to our current situation are troubling.

The effort to build the first atomic bomb was led by the brilliant physicist J. Robert Oppenheimer. Oppenheimer was not naturally interested in politics but became painfully aware of what he perceived as the grave threat to Western civilization from the Third Reich, a threat surely grave because of the possibility that Hitler might obtain nuclear weapons. Energized by this concern, he brought his strong intellect, passion for physics, and charismatic leadership skills to Los Alamos and led a rapid and successful effort by an incredible collection of great minds to quickly invent the bomb.

What is striking is how this effort continued so naturally after the initial impetus was removed. In a meeting shortly after V-E Day with some physicists who felt that perhaps the effort should stop, Oppenheimer argued to continue. His stated reason seems a bit strange: not because of the fear of large casualties from an invasion of Japan, but because the United Nations, which was soon to be formed, should have foreknowledge of atomic weapons. A more likely reason the project continued is the momentum that had built up - the first atomic test, Trinity, was nearly at hand.

We know that in preparing this first atomic test the physicists proceeded despite a large number of possible dangers. They were initially worried, based on a calculation by Edward Teller, that an atomic explosion might set fire to the atmosphere. A revised calculation reduced the danger of destroying the world to a three-in-a-million chance. (Teller says he was later able to dismiss the prospect of atmospheric ignition entirely.) Oppenheimer, though, was sufficiently concerned about the result of Trinity that he arranged for a possible evacuation of the southwest part of the state of New Mexico. And, of course, there was the clear danger of starting a nuclear arms race.

Within a month of that first, successful test, two atomic bombs destroyed Hiroshima and Nagasaki. Some scientists had suggested that the bomb simply be demonstrated, rather than dropped on Japanese cities - saying that this would greatly improve the chances for arms control after the war - but to no avail. With the tragedy of Pearl Harbor still fresh in Americans' minds, it would have been very difficult for President Truman to order a demonstration of the weapons rather than use them as he did - the desire to quickly end the war and save the lives that would have been lost in any invasion of Japan was very strong. Yet the overriding truth was probably very simple: As the physicist Freeman Dyson later said, "The reason that it was dropped was just that nobody had the courage or the foresight to say no."

It's important to realize how shocked the physicists were in the aftermath of the bombing of Hiroshima, on August 6, 1945. They describe a series of waves of emotion: first, a sense of fulfillment that the bomb worked, then horror at all the people that had been killed, and then a convincing feeling that on no account should another bomb be dropped. Yet of course another bomb was dropped, on Nagasaki, only three days after the bombing of Hiroshima.

In November 1945, three months after the atomic bombings, Oppenheimer stood firmly behind the scientific attitude, saying, "It is not possible to be a scientist unless you believe that the knowledge of the world, and the power which this gives, is a thing which is of intrinsic value to humanity, and that you are using it to help in the spread of knowledge and are willing to take the consequences."

Oppenheimer went on to work, with others, on the Acheson-Lilienthal report, which, as Richard Rhodes says in his recent book *Visions of Technology*, "found a way to prevent a clandestine nuclear arms race without resorting to armed world government"; their suggestion was a form of relinquishment of nuclear weapons work by nation-states to an international agency.

This proposal led to the Baruch Plan, which was submitted to the United Nations in June 1946 but never adopted (perhaps because, as Rhodes suggests, Bernard Baruch had "insisted on burdening the plan with conventional sanctions," thereby inevitably dooming it, even though it would "almost certainly have been rejected by Stalinist Russia anyway"). Other efforts to promote sensible steps toward internationalizing nuclear power to prevent an arms race ran afoul either of US politics and internal distrust, or distrust by the Soviets. The opportunity to avoid the arms race was lost, and very quickly.

Two years later, in 1948, Oppenheimer seemed to have reached another stage in his thinking, saying, "In some sort of crude sense which no vulgarity, no humor, no overstatement can quite extinguish, the physicists have known sin; and this is a knowledge they cannot lose."

In 1949, the Soviets exploded an atom bomb. By 1955, both the US and the Soviet Union had tested hydrogen bombs suitable for delivery by aircraft. And so the nuclear arms race began.

Nearly 20 years ago, in the documentary *The Day After Trinity*, Freeman Dyson summarized the scientific attitudes that brought us to the nuclear precipice:

"I have felt it myself. The glitter of nuclear weapons. It is irresistible if you come to them as a scientist. To feel it's there in your hands, to release this energy that fuels the stars, to let it do your bidding. To perform these miracles, to lift a million tons of rock into the sky. It is something that gives people an illusion of illimitable power, and it is, in some ways, responsible for all our troubles - this, what you might call technical arrogance, that overcomes people when they see what they can do with their minds."[8]

Now, as then, we are creators of new technologies and stars of the imagined future, driven - this time by great financial rewards and global competition - despite the clear dangers, hardly evaluating what it may be like to try to live in a world that is the realistic outcome of what we are creating and imagining.

In 1947, *The Bulletin of the Atomic Scientists* began putting a Doomsday Clock on its cover. For more than 50 years, it has shown an estimate of the relative nuclear danger we have faced, reflecting the changing international conditions. The hands on the clock have moved 15 times and today, standing at nine minutes to midnight, reflect continuing and real danger from nuclear weapons. The recent addition of India and Pakistan to the list of nuclear powers has increased the threat of failure of the nonproliferation goal, and this danger was reflected by moving the hands closer to midnight in 1998.

In our time, how much danger do we face, not just from nuclear weapons, but from all of these technologies? How high are the extinction risks?

The philosopher John Leslie has studied this question and concluded that the risk of human extinction is at least 30 percent,[9] while Ray Kurzweil believes we have "a better than even chance of making it through," with the caveat that he has "always been accused of being an optimist." Not only are these estimates not encouraging, but they do not include the probability of many horrid outcomes that lie short of extinction.

Faced with such assessments, some serious people are already suggesting that we simply move beyond Earth as quickly as possible. We would colonize the galaxy using von Neumann probes, which hop from star system to star system, replicating as they go. This step will almost certainly be necessary 5 billion years from now (or sooner if our solar system is disastrously impacted by the impending collision of our galaxy with the Andromeda galaxy within the next 3 billion years), but if we take Kurzweil and Moravec at their word it might be necessary by the middle of this century.

What are the moral implications here? If we must move beyond Earth this quickly in order for the species to survive, who accepts the responsibility for the fate of those (most of us, after all) who are left behind? And even if we scatter to the stars, isn't it likely that we may take our problems with us or find, later, that they have followed us? The fate of our species on Earth and our fate in the galaxy seem inextricably linked.

Another idea is to erect a series of shields to defend against each of the dangerous technologies. The Strategic Defense Initiative, proposed by the Reagan administration, was an attempt to design such a shield against the threat of a nuclear attack from the Soviet Union. But as Arthur C. Clarke, who was privy to discussions about the project, observed: "Though it might be possible, at vast expense, to construct local defense systems that would 'only' let through a few percent of ballistic missiles, the much touted idea of a national umbrella was nonsense. Luis Alvarez, perhaps the greatest experimental physicist of this century, remarked to me that the advocates of such schemes were 'very bright guys with no common sense.'"

Clarke continued: "Looking into my often cloudy crystal ball, I suspect that a total defense might indeed be possible in a century or so. But the technology involved would produce, as a by-product, weapons so terrible that no one would bother with anything as primitive as ballistic missiles." 10

In *Engines of Creation,* Eric Drexler proposed that we build an active nanotechnological shield - a form of immune system for the biosphere - to defend against dangerous replicators of all kinds that might escape from laboratories or otherwise be maliciously created. But the shield he proposed would itself be extremely dangerous - nothing could prevent it from developing autoimmune problems and attacking the biosphere itself. 11

Similar difficulties apply to the construction of shields against robotics and genetic engineering. These technologies are too powerful to be shielded against in the time frame of interest; even if it were possible to implement defensive shields, the side effects of their development would be at least as dangerous as the technologies we are trying to protect against.

These possibilities are all thus either undesirable or unachievable or both. The only realistic alternative I see is relinquishment: to limit development of the technologies that are too dangerous, by limiting our pursuit of certain kinds of knowledge.

Yes, I know, knowledge is good, as is the search for new truths. We have been seeking knowledge since ancient times. Aristotle opened his Metaphysics with the simple statement: "All men by nature desire to know." We have, as a bedrock value in our society, long agreed on the value of open access to information, and recognize the problems that arise with attempts to restrict access to and development of knowledge. In recent times, we have come to revere scientific knowledge.

But despite the strong historical precedents, if open access to and unlimited development of knowledge henceforth puts us all in clear danger of extinction, then common sense demands that we reexamine even these basic, long-held beliefs.

It was Nietzsche who warned us, at the end of the 19th century, not only that God is dead but that "faith in science, which after all exists undeniably, cannot owe its origin to a calculus of utility; it must have originated *in spite of* the fact that the disutility and dangerousness of the 'will to truth,' of 'truth at any price' is proved to it constantly." It is this further danger that we now fully face - the consequences of our truth-seeking. The truth that science seeks can certainly be considered a dangerous substitute for God if it is likely to lead to our extinction.

If we could agree, as a species, what we wanted, where we were headed, and why, then we would make our future much less dangerous - then we might understand what we can and should relinquish. Otherwise, we can easily imagine an arms race developing over GNR technologies, as it did with the NBC technologies in the 20th century. This is perhaps the greatest risk, for once such a race begins, it's very hard to end it. This time - unlike during the Manhattan Project - we aren't in a war, facing an implacable enemy that is threatening our civilization; we are driven, instead, by our habits, our desires, our economic system, and our competitive need to know.

I believe that we all wish our course could be determined by our collective values, ethics, and morals. If we had gained more collective wisdom over the past few thousand years, then a dialogue to this end would be more practical, and the incredible powers we are about to unleash would not be nearly so troubling.

One would think we might be driven to such a dialogue by our instinct for self-preservation. Individuals clearly have this desire, yet as a species our behavior seems to be not in our favor. In dealing with the nuclear threat, we often spoke dishonestly to ourselves and to each other, thereby greatly increasing the risks. Whether this was politically motivated, or because we chose not to think ahead, or because when faced with such grave threats we acted irrationally out of fear, I do not know, but it does not bode well.

The new Pandora's boxes of genetics, nanotechnology, and robotics are almost open, yet we seem hardly to have noticed. Ideas can't be put back in a box; unlike uranium or plutonium, they don't need to be mined and refined, and they can be freely copied. Once they are out, they are out. Churchill remarked, in a famous left-handed compliment, that the American people and their leaders "invariably do the right thing, after they have examined every other alternative." In this case, however, we must act more presciently, as to do the right thing only at last may be to lose the chance to do it at all.

As Thoreau said, "We do not ride on the railroad; it rides upon us"; and this is what we must fight, in our time. The question is, indeed, Which is to be master? Will we survive our technologies?

We are being propelled into this new century with no plan, no control, no brakes. Have we already gone too far down the path to alter course? I don't believe so, but we aren't trying yet, and the last chance to assert control - the fail-safe point - is rapidly approaching. We have our first pet robots, as well as commercially available genetic engineering techniques, and our nanoscale techniques are advancing rapidly. While the development of these technologies proceeds through a number of steps, it isn't necessarily the case - as happened in the Manhattan Project and the Trinity test - that the last step in proving a technology is large and hard. The breakthrough to wild self-replication in robotics, genetic engineering, or nanotechnology could come suddenly, reprising the surprise we felt when we learned of the cloning of a mammal.

And yet I believe we do have a strong and solid basis for hope. Our attempts to deal with weapons of mass destruction in the last century provide a shining example of relinquishment for us to consider: the unilateral US abandonment, without preconditions, of the development of biological weapons. This relinquishment stemmed from the realization that while it would take an enormous effort to create these terrible weapons, they could from then on easily be duplicated and fall into the hands of rogue nations or terrorist groups.

The clear conclusion was that we would create additional threats to ourselves by pursuing these weapons, and that we would be more secure if we did not pursue them. We have embodied our relinquishment of biological and chemical weapons in the 1972 Biological Weapons Convention (BWC) and the 1993 Chemical Weapons Convention (CWC).12

As for the continuing sizable threat from nuclear weapons, which we have lived with now for more than 50 years, the US Senate's recent rejection of the Comprehensive Test Ban Treaty makes it clear relinquishing nuclear weapons will not be politically easy. But we have a unique opportunity, with the end of the Cold War, to avert a multipolar arms race. Building on the BWC and CWC relinquishments, successful abolition of nuclear weapons could help us build toward a habit of relinquishing dangerous technologies. (Actually, by getting rid of all but 100 nuclear weapons worldwide - roughly the total destructive power of World War II and a considerably easier task - we could eliminate this extinction threat.)13

Verifying relinquishment will be a difficult problem, but not an unsolvable one. We are fortunate to have already done a lot of relevant work in the context of the BWC and other treaties. Our major task will be to apply this to technologies that are naturally much more commercial than military. The substantial need here is for transparency, as difficulty of verification is directly proportional to the difficulty of distinguishing relinquished from legitimate activities.

I frankly believe that the situation in 1945 was simpler than the one we now face: The nuclear technologies were reasonably separable into commercial and military uses, and monitoring was aided by the nature of atomic tests and the ease with which radioactivity could be measured. Research on military applications could be performed at national laboratories such as Los Alamos, with the results kept secret as long as possible.

The GNR technologies do not divide clearly into commercial and military uses; given their potential in the market, it's hard to imagine pursuing them only in national laboratories. With their widespread commercial pursuit, enforcing relinquishment will require a verification regime similar to that for biological weapons, but on an unprecedented scale. This, inevitably, will raise tensions between our individual privacy and desire for proprietary information, and the need for verification to protect us all. We will undoubtedly encounter strong resistance to this loss of privacy and freedom of action.

Verifying the relinquishment of certain GNR technologies will have to occur in cyberspace as well as at physical facilities. The critical issue will be to make the necessary transparency acceptable in a world of proprietary information, presumably by providing new forms of protection for intellectual property.

Verifying compliance will also require that scientists and engineers adopt a strong code of ethical conduct, resembling the Hippocratic oath, and that they have the courage to whistleblow as necessary, even at high personal cost. This would answer the call - 50 years after Hiroshima - by the Nobel laureate Hans Bethe, one of the most senior of the surviving members of the Manhattan Project, that all scientists "cease and desist from work creating, developing, improving, and manufacturing nuclear weapons and other weapons of potential mass destruction."14 In the 21st century, this requires vigilance and personal responsibility by those who would work on both NBC and GNR technologies to avoid implementing weapons of mass destruction and knowledge-enabled mass destruction.

Thoreau also said that we will be "rich in proportion to the number of things which we can afford to let alone." We each seek to be happy, but it would seem worthwhile to question whether we need to take such a high risk of total destruction to gain yet more knowledge and yet more things; common sense says that there is a limit to our material needs - and that certain knowledge is too dangerous and is best forgone.

Neither should we pursue near immortality without considering the costs, without considering the commensurate increase in the risk of extinction. Immortality, while perhaps the original, is certainly not the only possible utopian dream.

I recently had the good fortune to meet the distinguished author and scholar Jacques Attali, whose book *Lignes d'horizons* (*Millennium*, in the English translation) helped inspire the Java and Jini approach to the coming age of pervasive computing, as previously described in this magazine. In his new book *Fraternités,* Attali describes how our dreams of utopia have changed over time:

"At the dawn of societies, men saw their passage on Earth as nothing more than a labyrinth of pain, at the end of which stood a door leading, via their death, to the company of gods and to *Eternity*. With the Hebrews and then the Greeks, some men dared free themselves from theological demands and dream of an ideal City where*Liberty* would flourish. Others, noting the evolution of the market society, understood that the liberty of some would entail the alienation of others, and they sought *Equality*."

Jacques helped me understand how these three different utopian goals exist in tension in our society today. He goes on to describe a fourth utopia, *Fraternity,* whose foundation is altruism. Fraternity alone associates individual happiness with the happiness of others, affording the promise of self-sustainment.

This crystallized for me my problem with Kurzweil's dream. A technological approach to Eternity - near immortality through robotics - may not be the most desirable utopia, and its pursuit brings clear dangers. Maybe we should rethink our utopian choices.

Where can we look for a new ethical basis to set our course? I have found the ideas in the book *Ethics for the New Millennium,* by the Dalai Lama, to be very helpful. As is perhaps well known but little heeded, the Dalai Lama argues that the most important thing is for us to conduct our lives with love and compassion for others, and that our societies need to develop a stronger notion of universal responsibility and of our interdependency; he proposes a standard of positive ethical conduct for individuals and societies that seems consonant with Attali's Fraternity utopia.

The Dalai Lama further argues that we must understand what it is that makes people happy, and acknowledge the strong evidence that neither material progress nor the pursuit of the power of knowledge is the key - that there are limits to what science and the scientific pursuit alone can do.

Our Western notion of happiness seems to come from the Greeks, who defined it as "the exercise of vital powers along lines of excellence in a life affording them scope." 15

Clearly, we need to find meaningful challenges and sufficient scope in our lives if we are to be happy in whatever is to come. But I believe we must find alternative outlets for our creative forces, beyond the culture of perpetual economic growth; this growth has largely been a blessing for several hundred years, but it has not brought us unalloyed happiness, and we must now choose between the pursuit of unrestricted and undirected growth through science and technology and the clear accompanying dangers.

It is now more than a year since my first encounter with Ray Kurzweil and John Searle. I see around me cause for hope in the voices for caution and relinquishment and in those people I have discovered who are as concerned as I am about our current predicament. I feel, too, a deepened sense of personal responsibility - not for the work I have already done, but for the work that I might yet do, at the confluence of the sciences.

But many other people who know about the dangers still seem strangely silent. When pressed, they trot out the "this is nothing new" riposte - as if awareness of what could happen is response enough. They tell me, There are universities filled with bioethicists who study this stuff all day long. They say, All this has been written about before, and by experts. They complain, Your worries and your arguments are already old hat.

I don't know where these people hide their fear. As an architect of complex systems I enter this arena as a generalist. But should this diminish my concerns? I am aware of how much has been written about, talked about, and lectured about so authoritatively. But does this mean it has reached people? Does this mean we can discount the dangers before us?

Knowing is not a rationale for not acting. Can we doubt that knowledge has become a weapon we wield against ourselves?

The experiences of the atomic scientists clearly show the need to take personal responsibility, the danger that things will move too fast, and the way in which a process can take on a life of its own. We can, as they did, create insurmountable problems in almost no time flat. We must do more thinking up front if we are not to be similarly surprised and shocked by the consequences of our inventions.

My continuing professional work is on improving the reliability of software. Software is a tool, and as a toolbuilder I must struggle with the uses to which the tools I make are put. I have always believed that making software more reliable, given its many uses, will make the world a safer and better place; if I were to come to believe the opposite, then I would be morally obligated to stop this work. I can now imagine such a day may come.

This all leaves me not angry but at least a bit melancholic. Henceforth, for me, progress will be somewhat bittersweet.

Do you remember the beautiful penultimate scene in Manhattan where Woody Allen is lying on his couch and talking into a tape recorder? He is writing a short story about people who are creating unnecessary, neurotic problems for themselves, because it keeps them from dealing with more unsolvable, terrifying problems about the universe.

He leads himself to the question, "Why is life worth living?" and to consider what makes it worthwhile for him: Groucho Marx, Willie Mays, the second movement of the Jupiter Symphony, Louis Armstrong's recording of "Potato Head Blues," Swedish movies, Flaubert's Sentimental Education, Marlon Brando, Frank Sinatra, the apples and pears by Cézanne, the crabs at Sam Wo's, and, finally, the showstopper: his love Tracy's face.

Each of us has our precious things, and as we care for them we locate the essence of our humanity. In the end, it is because of our great capacity for caring that I remain optimistic we will confront the dangerous issues now before us.

My immediate hope is to participate in a much larger discussion of the issues raised here, with people from many different backgrounds, in settings not predisposed to fear or favor technology for its own sake.

As a start, I have twice raised many of these issues at events sponsored by the Aspen Institute and have separately proposed that the American Academy of Arts and Sciences take them up as an extension of its work with the Pugwash Conferences. (These have been held since 1957 to discuss arms control, especially of nuclear weapons, and to formulate workable policies.)

It's unfortunate that the Pugwash meetings started only well after the nuclear genie was out of the bottle - roughly 15 years too late. We are also getting a belated start on seriously addressing the issues around 21st-century technologies - the prevention of knowledge-enabled mass destruction - and further delay seems unacceptable.

So I'm still searching; there are many more things to learn. Whether we are to succeed or fail, to survive or fall victim to these technologies, is not yet decided. I'm up late again - it's almost 6 am. I'm trying to imagine some better answers, to break the spell and free them from the stone.

1. The passage Kurzweil quotes is from Kaczynski's Unabomber Manifesto, which was published jointly, under duress, by *The New York Times* and *The Washington Post* to attempt to bring his campaign of terror to an end. I agree with David Gelernter, who said about their decision:

   "It was a tough call for the newspapers. To say yes would be giving in to terrorism, and for all they knew he was lying anyway. On the other hand, to say yes might stop the killing. There was also a chance that someone would read the tract and get a hunch about the author; and that is exactly what happened. The suspect's brother read it, and it rang a bell.

   "I would have told them not to publish. I'm glad they didn't ask me. I guess."

   (*Drawing Life: Surviving the Unabomber.* Free Press, 1997: 120.)

2. Garrett, Laurie. *The Coming Plague: Newly Emerging Diseases in a World Out of Balance.* Penguin, 1994: 47-52, 414, 419, 452.

3. Isaac Asimov described what became the most famous view of ethical rules for robot behavior in his book *I, Robot* in 1950, in his Three Laws of Robotics: 1. A robot may not injure a human being, or, through inaction, allow a human being to come to harm. 2. A robot must obey the orders given it by human beings, except where such orders would conflict with the First Law. 3. A robot must protect its own existence, as long as such protection does not conflict with the First or Second Law.

4. Michelangelo wrote a sonnet that begins:

   > *Non ha l' ottimo artista alcun concetto*
   > *Ch' un marmo solo in sè non circonscriva*
   > *Col suo soverchio; e solo a quello arriva*
   > *La man che ubbidisce all' intelleto.*

   Stone translates this as:

   > *The best of artists hath no thought to show*
   > *which the rough stone in its superfluous shell*
   > *doth not include; to break the marble spell*
   > *is all the hand that serves the brain can do.*

   Stone describes the process: "He was not working from his drawings or clay models; they had all been put away. He was carving from the images in his mind. His eyes and hands knew where every line, curve, mass must emerge, and at what depth in the heart of the stone to create the low relief."

   (*The Agony and the Ecstasy.* Doubleday, 1961: 6, 144.)

5. First Foresight Conference on Nanotechnology in October 1989, a talk titled "The Future of Computation." Published in Crandall, B. C. and James Lewis, editors. *Nanotechnology: Research and Perspectives.* MIT Press, 1992: 269. See also www.foresight.org/Conferences/MNT01/Nano1.html.

6. In his 1963 novel *Cat's Cradle,* Kurt Vonnegut imagined a gray-goo-like accident where a form of ice called ice-nine, which becomes solid at a much higher temperature, freezes the oceans.

7. Kauffman, Stuart. "Self-replication: Even Peptides Do It." Nature, 382, August 8, 1996: 496. See www.santafe.edu/sfi/People/kauffman/sak-peptides.html.

8. Else, Jon. *The Day After Trinity: J. Robert Oppenheimer and The Atomic Bomb* (available at www.pyramiddirect.com).

9. This estimate is in Leslie's book *The End of the World: The Science and Ethics of Human Extinction,* where he notes that the probability of extinction is substantially higher if we accept Brandon Carter's Doomsday Argument, which is, briefly, that "we ought to have some reluctance to believe that we are very exceptionally early, for instance in the earliest 0.001 percent, among all humans who will ever have lived. This would be some reason for thinking that humankind will not survive for many more centuries, let alone colonize the galaxy. Carter's doomsday argument doesn't generate any risk estimates just by itself. It is an argument for *revising* the estimates which we generate when we consider various possible dangers." (Routledge, 1996: 1, 3, 145.)

10. Clarke, Arthur C. "Presidents, Experts, and Asteroids." *Science,* June 5, 1998. Reprinted as "Science and Society" in *Greetings, Carbon-Based Bipeds! Collected Essays, 1934-1998.* St. Martin's Press, 1999: 526.

11. And, as David Forrest suggests in his paper "Regulating Nanotechnology Development," available atwww.foresight.org/ NanoRev/Forrest1989.html, "If we used strict liability as an alternative to regulation it would be impossible for any developer to internalize the cost of the risk (destruction of the biosphere), so theoretically the activity of developing nanotechnology should never be undertaken." Forrest's analysis leaves us with only government regulation to protect us - not a comforting thought.

12. Meselson, Matthew. "The Problem of Biological Weapons." Presentation to the 1,818th Stated Meeting of the American Academy of Arts and Sciences, January 13, 1999. (minerva.amacad.org/archive/bulletin4.htm)

13. Doty, Paul. "The Forgotten Menace: Nuclear Weapons Stockpiles Still Represent the Biggest Threat to Civilization."*Nature,* 402, December 9, 1999: 583.

14. See also Hans Bethe's 1997 letter to President Clinton, at www.fas.org/bethecr.htm.

15. Hamilton, Edith.*The Greek Way.* W. W. Norton & Co., 1942: 35.

*Bill Joy, cofounder and Chief Scientist of Sun Microsystems, was cochair of the presidential commission on the future of IT research, and is coauthor of* The Java Language Specification. *His work on the*Jini pervasive computing technology was featured in Wired 6.08.*

# Article 46

Thomas A. Easton

# Should We Reject the "Transhumanist" Goal of the Genetically, Electronically, and Mechanically Enhanced Human Being?

Selected, Edited, and with Issue Framing Material by:
Thomas A. Easton, *Thomas College*

YES: M. J. McNamee and S. D. Edwards, from "Transhumanism, Medical Technology, and Slippery Slopes," *Journal of Medical Ethics* (September 2006)

NO: Maxwell J. Mehlman, from "Biomedical Enhancements: Entering a New Era," *Issues in Science and Technology* (Spring 2009)

## Learning Outcomes

*After studying this issue, students will be able to:*
• Explain what transhumanism is.
• Explain why ethicists worry about "slippery slopes."
• Discuss why some people find the idea of enhancing the human body and mind objectionable.
• Discuss whether government should subsidize technologies that hold the potential to exacerbate differences among people.

## ISSUE SUMMARY

YES: M. J. McNamee and S. D. Edwards argue that the difficulty of showing that the human body *should* (rather than *can*) be enhanced in ways espoused by the transhumanists amounts to an objection to transhumanism.

NO: Maxwell J. Mehlman argues that the era of routine biomedical enhancements is coming. Since the technology cannot be banned, it must be regulated and even subsidized to ensure that it does not create an unfair society.

## Where Do You Stand?

In the early 1970s, scientists first discovered that it was technically possible to move genes—biological material that determines a living organism's physical makeup—from one organism to another and thus (in principle) to give bacteria, plants, and animals new features and to correct genetic defects of the sort that cause many diseases, such as cystic fibrosis. Most researchers in molecular genetics were excited by the potentialities that suddenly seemed within their grasp. However, a few researchers—as well as many people outside the field—were disturbed by the idea. Among other things, they feared that we were on the verge of an era when people would be so modified that they were no longer human. Some critics were also suspicious of the researchers' motives. Andrew Kimbrell, *The Human Body Shop: The Engineering and Marketing of Life* (HarperSanFrancisco, 1993), thought the development of genetic engineering was so marked by scandal, ambition, and moral blindness that society should be deeply suspicious of its purported benefits.

Since then the idea that human beings will one day be enhanced has grown. The idea now encompasses genetic changes to cure or prevent disease and modify height, muscle strength, and cognitive capabilities, the use of chemicals to improve performance in sports, and even the incorporation in the human body of electronic and robotic elements to add senses and enhance memory, thinking abilities, strength, and a great deal more. In fact, the idea has become a movement known as transhumanism that "promotes an interdisciplinary approach to understanding and evaluating the opportunities for enhancing the human condition and the human organism opened up by the advancement of technology" (see the Humanity+ site at http:// humanityplus. org/). The goal is to eliminate aging, disease, and suffering. The transhumanist vision extends to "post-humanism," when what human beings become will make present-day humans look like chimpanzees by comparison. It even includes the possibility of uploading human minds into computers! See George Dvorsky, " Better Living Through Transhumanism," *Journal of Evolution & Technology* ( September 2008).

Some people find this vision frightening. Francis Fukuyama, "Transhumanism," *Foreign Policy* (September/October 2004), has called transhumanism "the world's most dangerous idea." Critics find changing human form and capability objectionable because they believe the result is in some sense unnatural. They believe that making some people more capable will exacerbate social distinctions and put those who can afford the changes in the position of old-fashioned aristocracies. Life will be even more unfair than it is today. Tom Koch, "Enhancing Who? Enhancing What? Ethics, Bioethics, and Transhumanism," *Journal of Medicine & Philosophy* (December 2010), finds transhumanism "a new riff on the old eugenics tune," and the result must be destructive.

Michael Bess, "Icarus 2.0: A Historian's Perspective on Human Biological Enhancement," *Technology and Culture* (January 2008), finds transhumanism in essence dehumanizing: "The technologies of enhancement threaten human dignity precisely because they tempt us to think of a person as an entity that can be 'improved.' To take this step is to break down human personhood into a series of quantifiable traits—resistance to disease, intelligence, and so forth—that are subject to augmentation or alteration. The danger in doing this lies in reducing individuals to the status of products, artifacts to be modified and reshaped according to our own preferences, like any other commodity. In this act, inevitably, we risk losing touch with the quality of intrinsic value that all humans share equally, no matter what their traits may be. In this sense, the well-intentioned effort to enhance a person can result in treating them as a mere *thing*."

Josh Fischman, "A Better Life with Bionics," *National Geographic* (January 2010), describes current work in developing prostheses controlled by nerve signals from nerves that have been surgically rerouted to communicate more effectively with the artificial limb's circuitry, a clear example of "improvement" of the human being. He also discusses electronic cochlear implants and artificial retinas. An accompanying editorial comment says that "Bionics is technology at its most ingenious and humane." Among the most recent developments in this line is an electronic implant that can give the paralyzed robotic arms; see Ian Sample, "Brain Implant Allows Paralysed Woman to Control a Robot with Her Thoughts," *The Guardian* (May 16, 2012) (www.guardian.co.uk/science/2012/may/16/ brain-implant-paralysed-woman-robot-thoughts).

Among those who favor transhumanism, few come through more strongly than James Hughes, executive director of the Institute for Ethics and Emerging Technologies (http://ieet.org/). He has argued vigorously that enhancement technologies such as genetic engineering offer "such good that the risks are dwarfed" and finds "faith in the potential unlimited improvability of human nature and expansion of human powers far more satisfying than a resignation to our current limits." See his "Embracing Change with All Four Arms: A Post-Humanist Defense of Genetic Engineering," *Eubios Journal of Asian and International Bioethics* (June 1996). Nicholas Agar, "Whereto Transhumanism? The Literature Reaches Critical Mass," *Hastings Center Report* (May–June 2007), finds that "transhumanism is a movement brimming with fresh ideas. Transhumanists succeed in making the intuitive appeal of posthumanity obvious even if they don't yet have the arguments to compel everybody else to accept their vision." Julian Savalescu and Nick Bostrom (a prominent founder of the transhumanism movement) provide a very positive overview in *Human Enhancement* (Oxford University Press, 2009). Susan Schneider, "Future Minds: Transhumanism, Cognitive Enhancement and the Nature of Persons," in Vardit Ravitsky, Autumn Fiester, and Arthur L. Caplan, eds., *The Penn Center Guide to Bioethics* (Springer, 2009), considers the question of whether people who have undergone extreme modifications are still the people they were before. Is personhood affected? Is the soul? "There are," she writes, "some serious issues which require working out." James Wilson, "Transhumanism and Moral Equality," *Bioethics* (October, 2007), finds that objections to transhumanism on the grounds that enhanced humans will be considered morally superior to unenhanced humans are groundless, for "once we understand the basis for human equality, it is clear that anyone who now has sufficient capacities to count as a person from the moral point of view will continue to count as one even if others are fundamentally enhanced; and it is [a mistake] to think that a creature which had even far greater capacities than an unenhanced human being should count as more than an equal from the moral point of view." David Gelles, "Immortality 2.0," *The Futurist* (January–February 2009), concludes that "skepticism of transhumanism is, arguably, natural. At the deepest level, living forever interferes with everything we understand about the world. . . . But such concerns may not matter any more." The change is already under way, and we may be underestimating how far it will go. See also Jonathan Weiner, *Long for This World: The Strange Science of Immortality* (Ecco, 2010). However, A. Rajczi, "One Danger of Biomedical Enhancements," *Bioethics* (July 2008), cautions that "By spending too much time, energy, and resources on enhancements, we could set back our pursuit of our deepest goals such as living happily and leading ethical lives." Philippe Verdoux, "Transhumanism, Progress and the Future," *Journal of Evolution & Technology* (July 2009), finds pursuing the transhumanist dream the safest route into the future. Philip Hefner, "The Animal that Aspires to be an Angel: The Challenge of Transhumanism," *Dialog: A Journal of Theology* (Summer 2009), finds that transhumanism "represents a fundamental challenge to our understanding of human nature, and in particular [with] what God has created us to become." Joanna Zylinska, "Playing God, Playing Adam: The Politics and Ethics of Enhancement," *Journal of Bioethical Inquiry* (June 2010), takes a different view of humanity's deepest goals and nature, for humanity coevolves with technology. Maxwell J. Mehlman examines the future implications in *Transhumanist Dreams and Dystopian Nightmares: The Promise and Peril of Genetic Engineering* (Johns Hopkins University Press, 2012).

One way in which the change is already upon us appears in the realm of sports. Steven Kotler, "Juicing 3.0," *Popular Science* (August 2008), notes that the use by athletes of many enhancement techniques—reaction time stimulants, hormones that affect muscle, gene replacement, and even mechanical replacements for missing limbs—are going to become commonplace in the next few years. It may be necessary to accept enhancements as a legitimate part of athletics and other realms of endeavor. See Ivo Van Hilvoorde and Laurens Landeweerd, "Enhancing Disabilities: Transhumanism under the Veil of Inclusion?" *Disability & Rehabilitation* (December 2010), and Brendan Burkett, Mike McNamee, and Wolfgand Potthast, "Shifting Boundaries in Sports Technology and Disability: Equal Rights or Unfair Advantage in the Case of Oscar Pistorius?" *Disability & Society* (August 2011).

In the YES selection, M. J. McNamee and S. D. Edwards discuss the idea that even to start on the transhumanist agenda is to set humanity on a "slippery slope" leading to disaster. They argue that of the several types of slippery slope, the one most threatening to transhumanism is the "arbitrary" slippery slope, meaning that the progression from the first change to the last is not based on any sense of the moral good, but only on subjective preference. They argue that this poses a challenge to transhumanists, to show that the changes they embrace *should* be embraced rather than just *can* be embraced. In the NO selection, Professor of Bioethics Maxwell J. Mehlman argues that the era of routine biomedical enhancements is coming. Since the technology cannot be banned, it must be regulated and even subsidized to ensure that it does not create an unfair society.

# YES

M. J. McNamee and S. D. Edwards

## Transhumanism, Medical Technology, and Slippery Slopes

No less a figure than Francis Fukuyama recently labelled transhumanism as "the world's most dangerous idea." Such an eye-catching condemnation almost certainly denotes an issue worthy of serious consideration, especially given the centrality of biomedical technology to its aims. In this article, we consider transhumanism as an ideology that seeks to evangelise its human-enhancing aims. Given that transhumanism covers a broad range of ideas, we distinguish moderate conceptions from strong ones and find the strong conceptions more problematic than the moderate ones. We also offer a critique of Boström's position published in this journal. We discuss various forms of slippery slope arguments that may be used for and against transhumanism and highlight one particular criticism, moral arbitrariness, which undermines both forms of transhumanism.

## What Is Transhumanism?

At the beginning of the 21st century, we find ourselves in strange times; facts and fantasy find their way together in ethics, medicine and philosophy journals and websites. Key sites of contestation include the very idea of human nature, the place of embodiment within medical ethics and, more specifically, the systematic reflections on the place of medical and other technologies in conceptions of the good life. A reflection of this situation is captured by Dyens who writes,

> What we are witnessing today is the very convergence of environments, systems, bodies, and ontology toward and into the intelligent matter. We can no longer speak of the human condition or even of the posthuman condition. We must now refer to the intelligent condition.

We wish to evaluate the contents of such dialogue and to discuss, if not the death of human nature, then at least its dislocation and derogation in the thinkers who label themselves transhumanists.

One difficulty for critics of transhumanism is that a wide range of views fall under its label. Not merely are there idiosyncrasies of individual academics, but there does not seem to exist an absolutely agreed on definition of transhumanism. One can find not only substantial differences between key authors and the disparate disciplinary nuances of their exhortations, but also subtle variations of its chief representatives in the offerings of people. It is to be expected that any ideology transforms over time and not least of all in response to internal and external criticism. Yet, the transhumanism critic faces a further problem of identifying a robust target that stays still sufficiently long to locate it properly in these webdriven days without constructing a "straw man" to knock over with the slightest philosophical breeze. For the purposes of targeting a sufficiently substantial target, we identify the writings of one of its clearest and intellectually robust proponents, the Oxford philosopher and cofounder of the World Transhumanist Association, Nick Boström, who has written recently in these pages of transhumanism's desire to make good the "half-baked" project that is human nature.

Before specifically evaluating Boström's position, it is best first to offer a global definition for transhumanism and then to locate it among the range of views that fall under the heading. One of the most celebrated advocates of transhumanism is Max More, whose website reads "no more gods, nor more faith, no more timid holding back. The future belongs to posthumanity." We will have a clearer idea then of the kinds of position transhumanism stands in direct opposition to. Specifically, More asserts,

> "Transhumanism" is a blanket term given to the school of thought that refuses to accept traditional human limitations such as death, disease and other biological frailties. Transhumans are typically interested in a variety of futurist topics, including space migration, mind uploading and cryonic suspension. Transhumans are also extremely interested in more immediate subjects such as bio- and nano-technology, computers and neurology. Transhumans deplore the standard paradigms that attempt to render our world comfortable at the sake of human fulfilment.

McNamee, M. J. and Edwards, S.D. From *Journal of Medical Ethics,* volume 32, 2006, pp. 513–518.

Strong transhumanism advocates see themselves engaged in a project, the purpose of which is to overcome the limits of human nature. Whether this is the foundational claim, or merely the central claim, is not clear. These limitations—one may describe them simply as features of human nature, as the idea of labelling them as limitations is itself to take up a negative stance towards them—concern appearance, human sensory capacities, intelligence, lifespan and vulnerability to harm. According to the extreme transhumanism programme, technology can be used to vastly enhance a person's intelligence; to tailor their appearance to what they desire; to lengthen their lifespan, perhaps to immortality; and to reduce vastly their vulnerability to harm. This can be done by exploitation of various kinds of technology, including genetic engineering, cybernetics, computation and nanotechnology. Whether technology will continue to progress sufficiently, and sufficiently predictably, is of course quite another matter.

Advocates of transhumanism argue that recruitment or deployment of these various types of technology can produce people who are intelligent and immortal, but who are not members of the species *Homo sapiens*. Their species type will be ambiguous—for example, if they are cyborgs (part human, part machine)—or, if they are wholly machines, they will lack any common genetic features with human beings. A legion of labels covers this possibility; we find in Dyen's recently translated book a variety of cultural bodies, perhaps the most extreme being cyberpunks:

> . . . a profound misalignment between existence and its manifestation. This misalignment produces bodies so transformed, so dissociated, and so asynchronized, that their only outcome is gross mutation. Cyberpunk bodies are horrible, strange and mysterious (think of *Alien, Robocop, Terminator,* etc.), for they have no real attachment to any biological structure.

Perhaps a reasonable claim is encapsulated in the idea that such entities will be posthuman. The extent to which posthuman might be synonymous with transhumanism is not clear. Extreme transhumanists strongly support such developments.

At the other end of transhumanism is a much less radical project, which is simply the project to use technology to enhance human characteristics—for example, beauty, lifespan and resistance to disease. In this less extreme project, there is no necessary aspiration to shed human nature or human genetic constitution, just to augment it with technology where possible and where desired by the person.

## Who Is for Transhumanism?

At present it seems to be a movement based mostly in North America, although there are some adherents from the UK. Among its most intellectually sophisticated proponents is Nick Boström. Perhaps the most outspoken supporters of transhumanism are people who see it simply as an issue of free choice. It may simply be the case that moderate transhumanists are libertarians at the core. In that case, transhumanism merely supplies an overt technological dimension to libertarianism. If certain technological developments are possible, which they as competent choosers desire, then they should not be prevented from acquiring the technologically driven enhancements they desire. One obvious line of criticism here may be in relation to the inequality that necessarily arises with respect to scarce goods and services distributed by market mechanisms. We will elaborate this point in the Transhumanism and slippery slopes section.

So, one group of people for the transhumanism project sees it simply as a way of improving their own life by their own standards of what counts as an improvement. For example, they may choose to purchase an intervention, which will make them more intelligent or even extend their life by 200 years. (Of course it is not self-evident that everyone would regard this as an improvement.) A less vociferous group sees the transhumanism project as not so much bound to the expansion of autonomy (notwithstanding our criticism that will necessarily be effected only in the sphere of economic consumer choice) as one that has the potential to improve the quality of life for humans in general. For this group, the relationship between transhumanism and the general good is what makes transhumanism worthy of support. For the other group, the worth of transhumanism is in its connection with their own conception of what is good for them, with the extension of their personal life choices.

## What Can Be Said in Its Favour?

Of the many points for transhumanism, we note three. Firstly, transhumanism seems to facilitate two aims that have commanded much support. The use of technology to improve humans is something we pretty much take for granted. Much good has been achieved with low-level technology in the promotion of public health. The construction of sewage systems, clean water supplies, etc, is all work to facilitate this aim and is surely good work, work which aims at, and in this case achieves, a good. Moreover, a large portion of the modern biomedical enterprise is another example of a project that aims at generating this good too.

Secondly, proponents of transhumanism say it presents an opportunity to plan the future development of human beings, the species *Homo sapiens*. Instead of this being left to the evolutionary process and its exploitation of random mutations, transhumanism presents a hitherto unavailable option: tailoring the development of human beings to an ideal blueprint. Precisely whose ideal gets blueprinted is a point that we deal with later.

Thirdly, in the spirit of work in ethics that makes use of a technical idea of personhood, the view that moral status is independent of membership of a particular species (or indeed any biological species), transhumanism presents a way in which moral status can be shown to be bound to intellectual capacity rather than to human embodiment as such or human vulnerability in the capacity of embodiment.

## What Can Be Said Against It?

Critics point to consequences of transhumanism, which they find unpalatable. One possible consequence feared by some commentators is that, in effect, transhumanism will lead to the existence of two distinct types of being, the human and the posthuman. The human may be incapable of breeding with the posthuman and will be seen as having a much lower moral standing. Given that, as Buchanan *et al.* note, much moral progress, in the West at least, is founded on the category of the human in terms of rights claims, if we no longer have a common humanity, what rights, if any, ought to be enjoyed by transhumans? This can be viewed either as a criticism (we poor humans are no longer at the top of the evolutionary tree) or simply as a critical concern that invites further argumentation. We shall return to this idea in the final section, by way of identifying a deeper problem with the open-endedness of transhumanism that builds on this recognition.

In the same vein, critics may argue that transhumanism will increase inequalities between the rich and the poor. The rich can afford to make use of transhumanism, but the poor will not be able to. Indeed, we may come to think of such people as deficient, failing to achieve a new heightened level of normal functioning. In the opposing direction, critical observers may say that transhumanism is, in reality, an irrelevance, as very few will be able to use the technological developments even if they ever manifest themselves. A further possibility is that transhumanism could lead to the extinction of humans and posthumans, for things are just as likely to turn out for the worse as for the better (e.g., those for precautionary principle).

One of the deeper philosophical objections comes from a very traditional source. Like all such utopian visions, transhumanism rests on some conception of good. So just as humanism is founded on the idea that humans are the measure of all things and that their fulfilment is to be found in the powers of reason extolled and extended in culture and education, so too transhumanism has a vision of the good, albeit one loosely shared. For one group of transhumanists, the good is the expansion of personal choice. Given that autonomy is so widely valued, why not remove the barriers to enhanced autonomy by various technological interventions? Theological critics especially, but not exclusively, object to what they see as the imperialising of autonomy. Elshtain lists the three c's: choice, consent and control. These, she asserts, are the dominant motifs of modern American culture. And there is, of course, an army of communitarians ready to provide support in general moral and political matters to this line of criticism. One extension of this line of transhumanism thinking is to align the valorisation of autonomy with economic rationality, for we may as well be motivated by economic concerns as by moral ones where the market is concerned. As noted earlier, only a small minority may be able to access this technology (despite Boström's naive disclaimer for democratic transhumanism), so the technology necessary for transhumanist transformations is unlikely to be prioritised in the context of artificially scarce public health resources. One other population attracted to transhumanism will be the elite sports world, fuelled by the media commercialisation complex—where mere mortals will get no more than a glimpse of the transhuman in competitive physical contexts. There may be something of a double-binding character to this consumerism. The poor, at once removed from the possibility of such augmentation, pay (per view) for the pleasure of their envy.

If we argue against the idea that the good cannot be equated with what people choose simpliciter, it does not follow that we need to reject the requisite medical technology outright. Against the more moderate transhumanists, who see transhumanism as an opportunity to enhance the general quality of life for humans, it is nevertheless true that their position presupposes some conception of the good. What kind of traits is best engineered into humans: disease resistance or parabolic hearing? And unsurprisingly, transhumanists disagree about precisely what "objective goods" to select for installation into humans or posthumans.

Some radical critics of transhumanism see it as a threat to morality itself. This is because they see morality as necessarily connected to the kind of vulnerability that accompanies human nature. Think of the idea of human rights and the power this has had in voicing concern about the plight of especially vulnerable human beings. As noted earlier a transhumanist may be thought to be beyond humanity and as neither enjoying its rights nor its obligations. Why would a transhuman be moved by appeals to human solidarity? Once the prospect of posthumanism emerges, the whole of morality is thus threatened because the existence of human nature itself is under threat.

One further objection voiced by Habermas is that interfering with the process of human conception, and by implication human constitution, deprives humans of the "naturalness which so far has been a part of the taken-for-granted background of our self-understanding as a species" and "Getting used to having human life biotechnologically at the disposal of our contingent preferences cannot help but change our normative self-understanding."

On this account, our self-understanding would include, for example, our essential vulnerability to disease, ageing and death. Suppose the strong trans humanism project is realised. We are no longer thus vulnerable: immortality is a real prospect. Nevertheless, conceptual caution must be exercised here—even transhumanists will be susceptible in the manner that Hobbes noted. Even the strongest are vulnerable in their sleep. But the kind of vulnerability transhumanism seeks to overcome is of the internal kind (not Hobbes's external threats). We are reminded of Woody Allen's famous remark that he wanted to become immortal, not by doing great deeds but simply by not dying. This will result in a radical change in our self-understanding, which has inescapably normative elements to it that need to be challenged. Most radically, this change in self-understanding may take the form of a change in what we view as a good life. Hitherto a human life, this would have been assumed to be finite. Transhumanists suggest that even now this may change with appropriate technology and the "right" motivation.

Do the changes in self-understanding presented by transhumanists (and genetic manipulation) necessarily have to represent a change for the worse? As discussed earlier, it may be that the technology that generates the possibility of transhumanism can be used for the good of humans—for example, to promote immunity to disease or to increase quality of life. Is there really an intrinsic connection between acquisition of the capacity to bring about transhumanism and moral decline? Perhaps Habermas's point is that moral decline is simply more likely to occur once radical enhancement technologies are adopted as a practice that is not intrinsically evil or morally objectionable. But how can this be known in advance? This raises the spectre of slippery slope arguments.

But before we discuss such slopes, let us note that the kind of approach (whether characterised as closed-minded or sceptical) Boström seems to dislike is one he calls speculative. He dismisses as speculative the idea that offspring may think themselves lesser beings, commodifications of their parents' egoistic desires (or some such). None the less, having pointed out the lack of epistemological standing of such speculation, he invites us to his own apparently more congenial position:

> We might speculate, instead, that germ-line enhancements will lead to more love and parental dedication. Some mothers and fathers might find it easier to love a child who, thanks to enhancements, is bright, beautiful, healthy, and happy. The practice of germ-line enhancement might lead to better treatment of people with disabilities, because a general demystification of the genetic contributions to human traits could make it clearer that people with disabilities are not to blame for their disabilities and a decreased incidence of some disabilities could lead to more assistance being available for the remaining affected people to enable them to live full, unrestricted lives through various technological and social supports. Speculating about possible psychological or cultural effects of germ-line engineering can therefore cut both ways. Good consequences no less than bad ones are possible. In the absence of sound arguments for the view that the negative consequences would predominate, such speculations provide no reason against moving forward with the technology. Ruminations over hypothetical side effects may serve to make us aware of things that could go wrong so that we can be on the lookout for untoward developments. By being aware of the perils in advance, we will be in a better position to take preventive countermeasures.

Following Boström's speculation then, what grounds for hope exist? Beyond speculation, what kinds of arguments does Boström offer? Well, most people may think that the burden of proof should fall to the transhumanists. Not so, according to Boström. Assuming the likely enormous benefits, he turns the tables on this intuition—not by argument but by skilful rhetorical speculation. We quote for accuracy of representation (emphasis added):

> Only after a fair comparison of the risks with the likely positive consequences can any conclusion based on a cost-benefit analysis be reached. In the case of germ-line enhancements, the potential gains are enormous. Only rarely, however, are the potential gains discussed, perhaps because they are too obvious to be of much theoretical interest. By contrast, uncovering subtle and non-trivial ways in which manipulating our genome could undermine deep values is philosophically a lot more challenging. But if we think about it, we recognize that the promise of genetic enhancements is anything but insignificant. Being free from severe genetic diseases would be good, as would having a mind that can learn more quickly, or having a more robust immune system. Healthier, wittier, happier people may be able to reach new levels culturally. To achieve a significant enhancement of human capacities would be to embark on the transhuman journey of exploration of some of the modes of being that are not accessible to us as we are currently constituted, possibly to discover and to instantiate important new values. On an even more basic level, genetic engineering holds great potential for alleviating unnecessary human suffering. Every day that the introduction of effective human genetic enhancement is delayed is a day of lost individual and cultural potential, and a day of torment for many unfortunate sufferers of diseases that could have been prevented. Seen in this light, *proponents of a ban or a moratorium on human genetic modification must take on a heavy burden of proof* in order to have the balance of reason tilt in their favor.

Now one way in which such a balance of reason may be had is in the idea of a slippery slope argument. We now turn to that.

## Transhumanism and Slippery Slopes

A proper assessment of transhumanism requires consideration of the objection that acceptance of the main claims of transhumanism will place us on a slippery slope. Yet, paradoxically, both proponents and detractors of transhumanism may exploit slippery slope arguments in support of their position. It is necessary therefore to set out the various arguments that fall under this title so that we can better characterise arguments for and against transhumanism. We shall therefore examine three such attempts but argue that the arbitrary slippery slope may undermine all versions of transhumanists, although not every enhancement proposed by them.

Schauer offers the following essentialist analysis of slippery slope arguments. A "pure" slippery slope is one where a "particular act, seemingly innocuous when taken in isolation, may yet lead to a future host of similar but increasingly pernicious events." Abortion and euthanasia are classic candidates for slippery slope arguments in public discussion and policy making. Against this, however, there is no reason to suppose that the future events (acts or policies) down the slope need to display similarities—indeed we may propose that they will lead to a whole range of different, although equally unwished for, consequences. The vast array of enhancements proposed by transhumanists would not be captured under this conception of a slippery slope because of their heterogeneity. Moreover, as Sternglantz notes, Schauer undermines his case when arguing that greater linguistic precision undermines the slippery slope and that indirect consequences often bolster slippery slope arguments. It is as if the slippery slopes would cease in a world with greater linguistic precision or when applied only to direct consequences. These views do not find support in the later literature. Schauer does, however, identify three non-slippery slope arguments where the advocate's aim is (a) to show that the bottom of a proposed slope has been arrived at; (b) to show that a principle is excessively broad; (c) to highlight how granting authority to X will make it more likely that an undesirable outcome will be achieved. Clearly (a) cannot properly be called a slippery slope argument in itself, while (b) and (c) often have some role in slippery slope arguments.

The excessive breadth principle can be subsumed under Bernard Williams's distinction between slippery slope arguments with (a) horrible results and (b) arbitrary results. According to Williams, the nature of the bottom of the slope allows us to determine which category a particular argument falls under. Clearly, the most common form is the slippery slope to a horrible result argument. Walton goes further in distinguishing three types: (a) thin end of the wedge or precedent arguments; (b) Sorites arguments; and (c) domino-effect arguments. Importantly, these arguments may be used both by antagonists and also by advocates of transhumanism. We shall consider the advocates of transhumanism first.

In the thin end of the wedge slippery slopes, allowing P will set a precedent that will allow further precedents (Pn) taken to an unspecified problematic terminus. Is it necessary that the end point has to be bad? Of course this is the typical linguistic meaning of the phrase "slippery slopes." Nevertheless, we may turn the tables here and argue that [the] slopes may be viewed positively too. Perhaps a new phrase will be required to capture ineluctable slides (ascents?) to such end points. This would be somewhat analogous to the ideas of vicious and virtuous cycles. So transhumanists could argue that, once the artificial generation of life through technologies of in vitro fertilisation was thought permissible, the slope was foreseeable, and transhumanists are doing no more than extending that life-creating and fashioning impulse.

In Sorites arguments, the inability to draw clear distinctions has the effect that allowing P will not allow us to consistently deny Pn. This slope follows the form of the Sorites paradox, where taking a grain of sand from a heap does not prevent our recognising or describing the heap as such, even though it is not identical with its former state. At the heart of the problem with such arguments is the idea of conceptual vagueness. Yet the logical distinctions used by philosophers are often inapplicable in the real world. Transhumanists may well seize on this vagueness and apply a Sorites argument as follows: as therapeutic interventions are currently morally permissible, and there is no clear distinction between treatment and enhancement, enhancement interventions are morally permissible too. They may ask whether we can really distinguish categorically between the added functionality of certain prosthetic devices and sonar senses.

In domino-effect arguments, the domino conception of the slippery slope, we have what others often refer to as a causal slippery slope. Once P is allowed, a causal chain will be effected allowing Pn and so on to follow, which will precipitate increasingly bad consequences.

In what ways can slippery slope arguments be used against transhumanism? What is wrong with transhumanism? Or, better, is there a point at which we can say transhumanism is objectionable? One particular strategy adopted by proponents of transhumanism falls clearly under the aspect of the thin end of the wedge conception of the slippery slope. Although some aspects of their ideology seem aimed at unqualified goods, there seems to be no limit to the aspirations of transhumanism as they cite the powers of other animals and substances as potential modifications for the transhumanist. Although we can admire the sonic capacities of the bat, the elastic strength of lizards' tongues and the endurability of Kevlar in contrast with traditional construction materials used in the body, their transplantation into humans is, to coin Kass's celebrated label, "repugnant."

Although not all transhumanists would support such extreme enhancements (if that is indeed what they are), less radical advocates use justifications that are based on therapeutic lines up front with the more Promethean aims less explicitly advertised. We can find many examples of this manoeuvre. Take, for example, the Cognitive Enhancement Research Institute in California. Prominently displayed on its website front page . . . we read, "Do you know somebody with Alzheimer's disease? Click to see the latest research breakthrough." The mode is simple: treatment by front entrance, enhancement by the back door. Borgmann, in his discussion of the uses of technology in modern society, observed precisely this argumentative strategy more than 20 years ago:

> The main goal of these programs seems to be the domination of nature. But we must be more precise. The desire to dominate does not just spring from a lust of power, from sheer human imperialism. It is from the start connected with the aim of liberating humanity from disease, hunger, and toil and enriching life with learning, art and athletics.

Who would want to deny the powers of viral diseases that can be genetically treated? Would we want to draw the line at the transplantation of non-human capacities (sonar path finding)? Or at in vivo fibre optic communications backbone or anti-degeneration powers? (These would have to be non-human by hypothesis). Or should we consider the scope of technological enhancements that one chief transhumanist, Natasha Vita More, propounds:

> A transhuman is an evolutionary stage from being exclusively biological to becoming post-biological. Post-biological means a continuous shedding of our biology and merging with machines. (. . .) The body, as we transform ourselves over time, will take on different types of appearances and designs and materials. (. . .)
>
> For hiking a mountain, I'd like extended leg strength, stamina, a skin-sheath to protect me from damaging environmental aspects, selfmoisturizing, cool-down capability, extended hearing and augmented vision (Network of sonar sensors depicts data through solid mass and map images onto visual field. Overlay window shifts spectrum frequencies. Visual scratch pad relays mental ideas to visual recognition bots. Global Satellite interface at micro-zoom range).
>
> For a party, I'd like an eclectic look—a glistening bronze skin with emerald green highlights, enhanced height to tower above other people, a sophisticated internal sound system so that I could alter the music to suit my own taste, memory enhance device, emotional-select for feel-good people so I wouldn't get dragged into anyone's inappropriate conversations. And parabolic hearing so that I could listen in on conversations across the room if the one I was currently in started winding down.

Notwithstanding the difficulty of bringing together transhumanism under one movement, the sheer variety of proposals merely contained within Vita More's catalogue means that we cannot determinately point to a precise station at which we can say, "Here, this is the end we said things would naturally progress to." But does this pose a problem? Well, it certainly makes it difficult to specify exactly a "horrible result" that is supposed to be at the bottom of the slope. Equally, it is extremely difficult to say that if we allow precedent X, it will allow practices Y or Z to follow as it is not clear how these practices Y or Z are (if at all) connected with the precedent X. So it is not clear that a form of precedent-setting slippery slope can be strictly used in every case against transhumanism, although it may be applicable in some.

Nevertheless, we contend, in contrast with Boström that the burden of proof would fall to the transhumanist. Consider in this light, a Sorites-type slope. The transhumanist would have to show how the relationship between the therapeutic practices and the enhancements are indeed transitive. We know night from day without being able to specify exactly when this occurs. So simply because we cannot determine a precise distinction between, say, genetic treatments G1, G2 and G3, and transhumanism enhancements T1, T2 and so on, it does not follow that there are no important moral distinctions between G1 and T20. According to Williams, this kind of indeterminacy arises because of the conceptual vagueness of certain terms. Yet, the indeterminacy of so open a predicate "heap" is not equally true of "therapy" or "enhancement." The latitude they permit is nowhere near so wide.

Instead of objecting to Pn on the grounds that Pn is morally objectionable (i.e., to depict a horrible result), we may instead, after Williams, object that the slide from P to Pn is simply morally arbitrary, when it ought not to be. Here, we may say, without specifying a horrible result, that it would be difficult to know what, in principle, can ever be objected to. And this is, quite literally, what is troublesome. It seems to us that this criticism applies to all categories of transhumanism, although not necessarily to all enhancements proposed by them. Clearly, the somewhat loose identity of the movement—and the variations between strong and moderate versions—makes it difficult to sustain this argument unequivocally. Still the transhumanist may be justified in asking, "What is wrong with arbitrariness?" Let us consider one brief example. In aspects of our lives, as a widely shared intuition, we may think that in the absence of good reasons, we ought not to discriminate among people arbitrarily. Healthcare may be considered to be precisely one such case. Given the ever-increasing demand for public healthcare services and products, it may be argued that access to them typically ought to be governed by publicly disputable criteria such as clinical need or potential benefit, as opposed to individual choices of an arbitrary or subjective nature. And nothing in transhumanism seems to allow for such objective dispute, let alone prioritisation. Of course, transhumanists such as More find no such disquietude. His phrase "No more timidity" is a typical token of transhumanist slogans. We applaud advances in therapeutic medical technologies such as those from new genetically based organ regeneration to more familiar prosthetic devices. Here the ends of the interventions are clearly medically defined and the means regulated closely. This is what prevents transhumanists from adopting a Sorites-type slippery slope. But in the absence of a telos, of clearly and substantively specified ends (beyond the mere banner of enhancement), we suggest that the public, medical professionals and bioethicists alike ought to resist the potentially open-ended transformations of human nature. For if all transformations are in principle enhancements, then surely none are. The very application of the word may become redundant. Thus it seems that one strong argument against transhumanism generally—the arbitrary slippery slope—presents a challenge to transhumanism, to show that all of what are described as transhumanist enhancements are imbued with positive normative force and are not merely technological extensions of libertarianism, whose conception of the good is merely an extension of individual choice and consumption.

# Limits of Transhumanist Arguments for Medical Technology and Practice

Already, we have seen the misuse of a host of therapeutically designed drugs used by non-therapeutic populations for enhancements. Consider the non-therapeutic use of human growth hormone in non-clinical populations. Such is the present perception of height as a positional good in society that Cuttler *et al.* report that the proportion of doctors who recommended human growth hormone treatment of short non-growth hormone deficient children ranged from 1% to 74%. This is despite its contrary indication in professional literature, such as that of the Pediatric Endocrine Society, and considerable doubt about its efficacy. Moreover, evidence supports the view that recreational body builders will use the technology, given the evidence of their use or misuse of steroids and other biotechnological products. Finally, in the sphere of elite sport, which so valorises embodied capacities that may be found elsewhere in greater degree, precision and sophistication in the animal kingdom or in the computer laboratory, biomedical enhancers may latch onto the genetically determined capacities and adopt or adapt them for their own commercially driven ends.

The arguments and examples presented here do no more than to warn us of the enhancement ideologies, such as transhumanism, which seek to predicate their futuristic agendas on the bedrock of medical technological progress aimed at therapeutic ends and are secondarily extended to loosely defined enhancement ends. In discussion and in bioethical literatures, the future of genetic engineering is often challenged by slippery slope arguments that lead policy and practice to a horrible result. Instead of pointing to the undesirability of the ends to which transhumanism leads, we have pointed out the failure to specify their telos beyond the slogans of "overcoming timidity" or Boström's exhortation that the passive acceptance of ageing is an example of "reckless and dangerous barriers to urgently needed action in the biomedical sphere."

We propose that greater care be taken to distinguish the slippery slope arguments that are used in the emotionally loaded exhortations of transhumanism to come to a more judicious perspective on the technologically driven agenda for biomedical enhancement. Perhaps we would do better to consider those other all-too-human frailties such as violent aggression, wanton self-harming and so on, before we turn too readily to the richer imaginations of biomedical technologists.

M. J. MCNAMEE is a reader in philosophy at the Centre for Philosophy, Humanities and Law in Healthcare, School of Health Science, University of Wales, Swansea, UK.

S. D. EDWARDS is a researcher at the Centre for Philosophy, Humanities and Law in Healthcare, School of Health Science, University of Wales, Swansea, UK.

# Biomedical Enhancements: Entering a New Era

Recently, the Food and Drug Administration (FDA) approved a drug to lengthen and darken eyelashes. Botox and other wrinkle-reducing injections have joined facelifts, tummy tucks, and vaginal reconstruction to combat the effects of aging. To gain a competitive edge, athletes use everything from steroids and blood transfusions to recombinant-DNA–manufactured hormones, Lasik surgery, and artificial atmospheres. Students supplement caffeine-containing energy drinks with Ritalin and the new alertness drug modafinil. The military spends millions of dollars every year on biological research to increase the warfighting abilities of our soldiers. Parents perform genetic tests on their children to determine whether they have a genetic predisposition to excel at explosive or endurance sports. All of these are examples of biomedical enhancements: interventions that use medical and biological technology to improve performance, appearance, or capability in addition to what is necessary to achieve, sustain, or restore health.

The use of biomedical enhancements, of course, is not new. Amphetamines were doled out to troops during World War II. Athletes at the turn of the 20th century ingested narcotics. The cognitive benefits of caffeine have been known for at least a millennium. Ancient Greek athletes swallowed herbal infusions before competitions. The Egyptians brewed a drink containing a relative of Viagra at least 1,000 years before Christ. But modern drug development and improvements in surgical technique are yielding biomedical enhancements that achieve safer, larger, and more targeted enhancement effects than their predecessors, and more extraordinary technologies are expected to emerge from ongoing discoveries in human genetics. (In addition, there are biomechanical enhancements that involve the use of computer implants and nanotechnology, which are beyond the scope of this article.)

What is also new is that biomedical enhancements have become controversial. Some commentators want to outlaw them altogether. Others are concerned about their use by athletes and children. Still others fret that only the well-off will be able to afford them, thereby exacerbating social inequality.

Banning enhancements, however, is misguided. Still, it is important to try to ensure that they are as safe and effective as possible, that vulnerable populations such as children are not forced into using them, and that they are not available only to the well-off. This will require effective government and private action.

## A Misguided View

Despite the long history of enhancement use, there recently has emerged a view that it is wrong. The first manifestation of this hostility resulted from the use of performance enhancements in sports in the 1950s, especially steroids and amphetamines. European nations began adopting anti-doping laws in the mid-1960s, and the Olympic Games began testing athletes in 1968. In 1980, Congress amended the Federal Food, Drug, and Cosmetic Act (FFDCA) to make it a felony to distribute anabolic steroids for nonmedical purposes. Two years later, Congress made steroids a Schedule III controlled substance and substituted human growth hormone in the steroid provision of the FFDCA. Between 2003 and 2005, Congress held hearings lambasting professional sports for not imposing adequate testing regimens. Drug testing has also been instituted in high-school and collegiate sports.

The antipathy toward biomedical enhancements extends well beyond sports, however. Officially, at least, the National Institutes of Health (NIH) will not fund research to develop genetic technologies for human enhancement purposes, although it has funded studies in animals that the researchers tout as a step toward developing human enhancements. It is a federal crime to use steroids to increase strength even if the user is not an athlete. Human growth hormone is in a unique regulatory category in that it is a felony to prescribe it for any purpose other than a specific use approved by the FDA. (For example, the FDA has not approved it for anti-aging purposes.) There is an ongoing controversy about whether musicians, especially string players, should be allowed to use beta blockers to steady their hands. And who hasn't heard of objections to the use of mood-altering drugs to make "normal" people happier? There's even a campaign against caffeine.

If the critics had their way, the government would ban the use of biomedical enhancements. It might seem that this would merely entail extending the War on Drugs to a larger number of drugs. But remember that enhancements include not just drugs, but cosmetic surgery and information technologies, such as genetic testing to identify nondisease traits. So a War on

Enhancements would have to extend to a broader range of technologies, and because many are delivered within the patient-physician relationship, the government would have to intrude into that relationship in significant new ways. Moreover, the FDA is likely to have approved many enhancement drugs for legitimate medical purposes, with enhancement use taking place on an "off-label" basis. So there would have to be some way for the enhancement police to identify people for whom the drugs had been legally prescribed to treat illness, but who were misusing them for enhancement purposes.

This leads to a far more profound difficulty. The War on Drugs targets only manufacture, distribution, and possession. There is virtually no effort to punish people merely for using an illegal substance. But a successful ban on biomedical enhancement would have to prevent people from obtaining benefits from enhancements that persisted after they no longer possessed the enhancements themselves, such as the muscles built with the aid of steroids or the cognitive improvement that lasts for several weeks after normal people stop taking a certain medicine that treats memory loss in Alzheimer's patients. In short, a ban on enhancements would have to aim at use as well as possession and sale.

To imagine what this would be like, think about the campaign against doping in elite sports, where athletes must notify anti-doping officials of their whereabouts at all times and are subject to unannounced, intrusive, and often indecent drug tests at any hour of the day or night. Even in the improbable event that regular citizens were willing to endure such an unprecedented loss of privacy, the economic cost of maintaining such a regime, given how widespread the use of highly effective biomedical enhancements might be, would be prohibitive.

A ban on biomedical enhancements would be not only unworkable but unjustifiable. Consider the objections to enhancement in sports. Why are enhancements against the rules? Is it because they are unsafe? Not all of them are: Anti-doping rules in sports go after many substances that pose no significant health risks, such as caffeine and Sudafed. (A Romanian gymnast forfeited her Olympic gold medal after she accidentally took a couple of Sudafed to treat a cold.) Even in the case of vilified products such as steroids, safety concerns stem largely from the fact that athletes are forced to use the drugs covertly, without medical supervision. Do enhancements give athletes an "unfair" advantage? They do so only if the enhancements are hard to obtain, so that only a few competitors obtain the edge. But the opposite seems to be true: Enhancements are everywhere. Besides, athletes are also tested for substances that have no known performance-enhancing effects, such as marijuana. Are the rewards from enhancements "unearned"? Not necessarily. Athletes still need to train hard. Indeed, the benefit from steroids comes chiefly from allowing athletes to train harder without injuring themselves. In any event, success in sports comes from factors that athletes have done nothing to deserve, such as natural talent and the good luck to have been born to encouraging parents or to avoid getting hurt. Would the use of enhancements confound recordkeeping? This doesn't seem to have stopped the adoption of new equipment that improves performance, such as carbon-fiber vaulting poles, metal skis, and oversized tennis racquets. If one athlete used enhancements, would every athlete have to, so that the benefit would be nullified? No, there would still be the benefit of improved performance across the board—bigger lifts, faster times, higher jumps. In any case, the same thing happens whenever an advance takes place that improves performance.

The final objection to athletic enhancement, in the words of the international Olympic movement, is that it is against the "spirit of sport." It is hard to know what this means. It certainly can't mean that enhancements destroy an earlier idyll in which sports were enhancement-free; as we saw before, this never was the case. Nor can it stand for the proposition that a physical competition played with the aid of enhancements necessarily is not a "sport." There are many sporting events in which the organizers do not bother to test participants, from certain types of "strong-man" and powerlifting meets to your neighborhood pickup basketball game. There are several interesting historical explanations for why athletic enhancement has gained such a bad rap, but ultimately, the objection about "the spirit of sport" boils down to the fact that some people simply don't like the idea of athletes using enhancements. Well, not exactly. You see, many biomedical enhancements are perfectly permissible, including dietary supplements, sports psychology, carbohydrate loading, electrolyte-containing beverages, and sleeping at altitude (or in artificial environments that simulate it). Despite the labor of innumerable philosophers of sport, no one has ever come up with a rational explanation for why these things are legal and others aren't. In the end, they are just arbitrary distinctions.

But that's perfectly okay. Lots of rules in sports are arbitrary, like how many players are on a team or how far the boundary lines stretch. If you don't like being all alone in the outfield, don't play baseball. If you are bothered by midnight drug tests, don't become an Olympian.

The problem comes when the opponents of enhancement use in sports try to impose their arbitrary dislikes on the wider world. We already have observed how intrusive and expensive this would be. Beyond that, there are strong constitutional objections to using the power of the law to enforce arbitrary rules. But most important, a ban on the use of enhancements outside of sports would sacrifice an enormous amount of societal benefit. Wouldn't we want automobile drivers to use alertness drugs if doing so could prevent accidents? Shouldn't surgeons be allowed to use beta blockers to steady their hands? Why not let medical researchers take cognitive enhancers if it would lead to faster cures, or let workers take them to be more productive? Why stop soldiers from achieving greater combat effectiveness, rescue workers from lifting heavier objects, and men and women from leading better sex lives? Competent adults who want to use enhancements should be permitted to. In some instances, such as in combat or when performing dangerous jobs, they should even be required to.

# Protecting the Vulnerable

Rejecting the idea of banning enhancements doesn't mean that their use should be unregulated. The government has several crucial roles to play in helping to ensure that the benefits from enhancement use outweigh the costs.

In the first place, the government needs to protect people who are incapable of making rational decisions about whether to use enhancements. In the language of biomedical ethics, these are populations that are "vulnerable," and a number of them are well recognized. One such group, of course, is people with severe mental disabilities. The law requires surrogates to make decisions for these individuals based on what is in their best interests.

Another vulnerable population is children. There can be little disagreement that kids should not be allowed to decide on their own to consume powerful, potentially dangerous enhancement substances. Not only do they lack decisionmaking capacity, but they may be much more susceptible than adults to harm. This is clearly the case with steroids, which can interfere with bone growth in children and adolescents.

The more difficult question is whether parents should be free to give enhancements to their children. Parents face powerful social pressures to help their children excel. Some parents may be willing to improve their children's academic or athletic performance even at a substantial risk of injury to the child. There are many stories of parents who allow their adolescent daughters to have cosmetic surgery, including breast augmentation. In general, the law gives parents considerable discretion in determining how to raise their children. The basic legal constraint on parental discretion is the prohibition in state law against abuse or neglect, and this generally is interpreted to defer to parental decisionmaking so long as the child does not suffer serious net harm. There are no reported instances in which parents have been sanctioned for giving their children biomedical enhancements, and the authorities might conclude that the benefits conferred by the use of an enhancement outweighed even a fairly significant risk of injury.

Beyond the actions of parents, there remains the question of whether some biomedical enhancements are so benign that children should be allowed to purchase them themselves. At present, for instance, there is no law in the United States against children purchasing coffee, caffeinated soft drinks, and even high-caffeine–containing energy drinks. (Laws prohibiting children from buying energy drinks have been enacted in some other countries.)

At the same time, it may be a mistake to lump youngsters together with older adolescents into one category of children. Older adolescents, although still under the legal age of majority, have greater cognitive and judgmental capacities than younger children. The law recognizes this by allowing certain adolescents, deemed "mature" or "emancipated" minors, to make legally binding decisions, such as decisions to receive medical treatment. Older adolescents similarly may deserve some degree of latitude in making decisions about using biomedical enhancements.

Children may be vulnerable to pressure to use enhancements not only from their parents, but from their educators. Under programs such as No Child Left Behind, public school teachers and administrators are rewarded and punished based on student performance on standardized tests. Private schools compete with one another in terms of where their graduates are accepted for further education. There is also intense competition in school athletics, especially at the collegiate level. Students in these environments may be bull-dozed into using enhancements to increase their academic and athletic abilities. Numerous anecdotes, for example, tell of parents who are informed by teachers that their children need medication to "help them focus"; the medication class in question typically is the cognition-enhancing amphetamines, and many of these children do not have diagnoses that would warrant the use of these drugs.

Beyond students, athletes in general are vulnerable to pressure from coaches, sponsors, family, and teammates to use hazardous enhancements. For example, at the 2005 congressional hearings on steroid use in baseball, a father testified that his son committed suicide after using steroids, when in fact he killed himself after his family caught him using steroids, which the boy had turned to in an effort to meet his family's athletic aspirations.

Another group that could be vulnerable to coercion is workers. Employers might condition employment or promotion on the use of enhancements that increased productivity. For example, an employer might require its nighttime work force to take the alertness drug modafinil, which is now approved for use by sleep-deprived swingshift workers. Current labor law does not clearly forbid this so long as the drug is relatively safe. From an era in which employees are tested to make sure they aren't taking drugs, we might see a new approach in which employers test them to make sure they are.

Members of the military may also be forced to use enhancements. The military now conducts the largest known biomedical enhancement research project. Under battlefield conditions, superiors may order the use of enhancements, leaving soldiers no lawful option to refuse. A notorious example is the use of amphetamines by combat pilots. Technically, the pilots are required to give their consent to the use of the pep pills, but if they refuse, they are barred from flying the missions.

The ability of government regulation to protect vulnerable groups varies depending on the group. It is important that educators not be allowed to give students dangerous enhancements without parental permission and that parents not be pressured into making unreasonable decisions by fearful, overzealous, or inadequate educators. The law can mandate the former, but not easily prevent the latter. Coaches and trainers who cause injury to athletes by giving them dangerous enhancements or by unduly encouraging their use should be subject to criminal and civil liability. The same goes for employers. But the realities of military life make it extremely difficult to protect soldiers from the orders of their superiors.

Moreover, individuals may feel pressure to use enhancements not only from outside sources, but from within. Students may be driven to do well in order to satisfy parents, gain admittance to more prestigious schools, or establish better careers. Athletes take all sorts of risks to increase their chances of winning. Workers may be desperate to save their jobs or bring in a bigger paycheck, especially in economically uncertain times. Soldiers better able to complete their missions are likely to live longer.

Surprisingly, while acknowledging the need to protect people from outside pressures, bioethicists generally maintain that we do not need to protect them from harmful decisions motivated by internal pressures. This position stems, it seems, from the recognition that, with the exception of decisions that are purely random, everything we decide to do is dictated at least in part by internal pressures, and in many cases, these pressures can be so strong that the decisions may no longer appear to be voluntary. Take, for example, seriously ill cancer patients contemplating whether or not to undergo harsh chemotherapy regimens. Bioethicists worry that, if we focused on the pressures and lack of options created by the patients' dire condition, we might not let the patients receive the treatment, or, in the guise of protecting the patients from harm, might create procedural hurdles that would rob them of their decisionmaking autonomy. Similarly, these bioethicists might object to restricting the ability of workers, say, to use biomedical enhancements merely because their choices are highly constrained by their fear of losing their jobs. But even if we accept this argument, that doesn't mean that we must be indifferent to the dangers posed by overwhelming internal pressure. As we will see, the government still must take steps to minimize the harm that could result.

Individuals may be vulnerable to harm not only from using enhancements, but from participating in experiments to see if an enhancement is safe and effective. Research subjects are protected by a fairly elaborate set of rules, collectively known as the "Common Rule," that are designed to ensure that the risks of the research are outweighed by the potential benefits and that the subjects have given their informed consent to their participation. But there are many weaknesses in this regulatory scheme. For one thing, these rules apply only to experiments conducted by government-funded institutions or that are submitted to the FDA in support of licensing applications, and therefore they do not cover a great deal of research performed by private industry. Moreover, the rules were written with medically oriented research in mind, and it is not clear how they should be interpreted and applied to enhancement research. For example, the rules permit children to be enrolled as experimental subjects in trials that present "more than minimal risk" if, among other things, the research offers the possibility of "direct benefit" to the subject, but the rules do not say whether an enhancement benefit can count as a direct benefit. Specific research protections extend to other vulnerable populations besides children, such as prisoners and pregnant women, but do not explicitly cover students, workers, or athletes. In reports of a project several colleagues and I recently completed for the NIH, we suggest a number of changes to current regulations that would provide better protection for these populations.

## Ensuring Safety and Effectiveness

Beginning with the enactment of the Pure Food and Drug Act in 1906, we have turned to the government to protect us from unsafe, ineffective, and fraudulent biomedical products and services. Regardless of how much freedom individuals should have to decide whether or not to use biomedical enhancements, they cannot make good decisions without accurate information about how well enhancements work. In regard to enhancements in the form of drugs and medical devices, the FDA has the legal responsibility to make sure that this information exists.

The FDA's ability to discharge this responsibility, however, is limited. In the first place, the FDA has tended to rely on information from highly stylized clinical trials that do not reflect the conditions under which enhancements would be used by the general public. Moreover, the deficiencies of clinical trials are becoming more apparent as we learn about pharmacogenetics—the degree to which individual responses to medical interventions vary depending on the individual's genes. The FDA is beginning to revise its rules to require manufacturers to take pharmacogenetics into consideration in studying safety and efficacy, but it will be many years, if ever, before robust pharmacogenetic information is publicly available. The solution is to rely more on data from actual use. Recently the agency has become more adamant about monitoring real-world experience after products reach the market, but this information comes from self-reports by physicians and manufacturers who have little incentive to cooperate. The agency needs to be able to conduct its own surveillance of actual use, with the costs borne by the manufacturers.

Many biomedical enhancements fall outside the scope of FDA authority. They include dietary supplements, many of which are used for enhancement purposes rather than to promote health. You only have to turn on latenight TV to be bombarded with claims for substances to make you stronger or more virile. Occasionally the Federal Trade Commission cracks down on hucksters, but it needs far greater resources to do an effective job. The FDA needs to exert greater authority to regulate dietary supplements, including those used for enhancement.

The FDA also lacks jurisdiction over the "practice of medicine." Consequently, it has no oversight over cosmetic surgery, except when the surgeon employs a new medical device. This limitation also complicates the agency's efforts to exert authority over reproductive and genetic practices. This would include the genetic modification of embryos to improve their traits, which promises to be one of the most effective enhancement techniques. Because organized medicine fiercely protects this limit on the FDA, consumers will have to continue to rely on physicians and other health care professionals to provide them with the information they need to make decisions about these types of enhancements. Medical experts need to stay on top of advances in enhancement technology.

Even with regard to drugs and devices that are clearly within the FDA's jurisdiction, its regulatory oversight only goes so far. Once the agency approves a product for a particular use, physicians are free to use it for any other purpose, subject only to liability for malpractice and, in the case of controlled substances, a requirement that the use must comprise legitimate medical practice. Only a handful of products, such as Botox, have received FDA approval for enhancement use; as noted earlier, enhancements predominantly are unapproved, off-label uses of products approved for health-related purposes. Modafinil, for example, one of the most popular drugs for enhancing cognitive performance, is approved only for the treatment of narcolepsy and sleepiness associated with obstructive sleep apnea/hypopnea syndrome and shift-work sleep disorder. Erythropoietin, which athletes use to improve performance, is approved to treat anemias. The FDA needs to be able to require manufacturers of products such as these to pay for the agency to collect and disseminate data on off-label experience. The agency also has to continue to limit the ability of manufacturers to promote drugs for off-label uses, in order to give them an incentive to obtain FDA approval for enhancement labeling.

An enhancement technology that will increase in use is testing to identify genes that are associated with nondisease characteristics. People can use this information to make lifestyle choices, such as playing sports at which they have the genes to excel, or in reproduction, such as deciding which of a number of embryos fertilized in vitro will be implanted in the uterus. An area of special concern is genetic tests that consumers can use at home without the involvement of physicians or genetic counselors to help them interpret the results. Regulatory authority over genetic testing is widely believed to be inadequate, in part because it is split among the FDA and several other federal agencies, and there are growing calls for revamping this regulatory scheme that need to be heeded.

Any attempt to regulate biomedical enhancement will be undercut by people who obtain enhancements abroad. The best hope for protecting these "enhancement tourists" against unsafe or ineffective products and services lies in international cooperation, but this is costly and subject to varying degrees of compliance.

To make intelligent decisions about enhancement use, consumers need information not only about safety and effectiveness, but about whether they are worth the money. Should they pay for Botox injections, for example, or try to get rid of facial wrinkles with cheaper creams and lotions? When the FDA approved Botox for cosmetic use, it ignored this question of cost-effectiveness because it has no statutory authority to consider it. In the case of medical care, consumers may get some help in making efficient spending decisions from their health insurers, who have an incentive to avoid paying for unnecessarily costly products or services. But insurance does not cover enhancements. The new administration is proposing to create a federal commission to conduct health care cost-effectiveness analyses, among other things, and it is important that such a body pay attention to enhancements as well as other biomedical interventions.

## Subsidizing Enhancement

In these times of economic distress, when we already question whether the nation can afford to increase spending on health care, infrastructure, and other basic necessities, it may seem foolish to consider whether the government has an obligation to make biomedical enhancements available to all. Yet if enhancements enable people to enjoy a significantly better life, this may not be so outlandish, and if universal access avoids a degree of inequality so great that it undermines our democratic way of life, it may be inescapable.

There is no need for everyone to have access to all available enhancements. Some may add little to an individual's abilities. Others may be so hazardous that they offer little net benefit to the user. But imagine that a pill is discovered that substantially improves a person's cognitive facility, not just their memory but abilities such as executive function—the highest form of problem-solving capacity—or creativity. Now imagine if this pill were available only to those who already were well-off and could afford to purchase it with personal funds. If such a pill were sufficiently effective, so that those who took it had a lock on the best schools, careers, and mates, wealth-based access could drive an insurmountable wedge between the haves and have-nots, a gap so wide and deep that we could no longer pretend that there is equality of opportunity in our society. At that point, it is doubtful that a liberal democratic state could survive.

So it may be necessary for the government to regard such a success-determining enhancement as a basic necessity, and, after driving the cost down to the lowest amount possible, subsidize access for those unable to purchase it themselves. Even if this merely maintained preexisting differences in cognitive ability, it would be justified in order to prevent further erosion of equality of opportunity.

The need for effective regulation of biomedical enhancement is only going to increase as we enter an era of increasingly sophisticated technologies. Existing schemes, such as the rules governing human subjects research, must be reviewed to determine whether additions or changes are needed to accommodate this class of interventions. Government agencies and private organizations need to be aware of both the promise and the peril of enhancements and devote an appropriate amount of resources in order to regulate, rather than stop, their use.

**MAXWELL J. MEHLMAN** is the Arthur E. Petersilge Professor of Law, director of the Law-Medicine Center, and professor of bioethics at Case Western Reserve University. His latest books are *The Price of Perfection: The Individual and Society in the Era of Biomedical Enhancement* (Johns Hopkins University Press, 2009) and *Transhumanist Dreams and Dystopian Nightmares: The Promise and Peril of Genetic Engineering* (Johns Hopkins University Press, 2012).